D1593411

THE INTERNATIONAL
HANDBOOK OF
GROUP PSYCHOTHERAPY

THE INTERNATIONAL
HANDBOOK
OF
GROUP PSYCHOTHERAPY

J. L. MORENO, M. D., EDITOR

A. Friedemann, M. D., Associate Editor

R. Battegay, M. D., Assistant Editor

Zerka T. Moreno, Assistant Editor

PHILOSOPHICAL LIBRARY

New York

Copyright, 1966, by

PHILOSOPHICAL LIBRARY Inc.

15 East 40th Street, New York 16, N. Y.

All rights reserved

Library of Congress Catalog Card Number: 65-10661

Manufactured in the United States of America

CONTRIBUTORS

Ackerman, Max, D.O.
Director of Psychodrama
Moreno Institute
New York, N.Y.

Ackerman, Sylvia, M.A.
Director of Psychodrama
Moreno Institute
New York, N.Y.

Altrocchi, John, Ph.D.
Associate Professor of Medical Psychology
Duke University
Durham, North Carolina

Amiel, R., M.D.
Paris, France

Ancelin-Schutzenberger, Anne
Director, Group Francais d'Etudes de
   Sociometrie-Dynamique des Groupes et
   Psychodrame
Paris, France

Andriola, Joseph, Ph.D.
Chief Psychiatric Social Worker
Atascadero State Hospital
California

Arendsen Hein, G.W., M.D.
Consultant in Psychiatry
Ederveen, Holland

Bartoletti, Mario, Ph.D.
Research Psychologist
Toronto Psychiatric Hospital
Canada

Battegay, R., M.D.
Psychiatrische Universitatsklinik
Basel, Switzerland

Benson, Robert R., Ph.D.
Chief of Court Psychological Services
Montgomery County Juvenile Court
Dayton, Ohio

Berger, Milton M., M.D.
Past President, American Group
   Psychotherapy Association
Consultant, Veterans Administration Clinic,
Brooklyn, N.Y.

Beukenkamp, Cornelius, M.D.
Supervisor of Group Psychotherapy
Hillside Hospital, Queens, N.Y.

Bieliauskas, Vytautas J., Ph.D.
Chairman, Dept. of Psychology
Xavier University
Cincinnati, Ohio

Blajan-Marcus, Simone, M.D.
Consultant in Psychiatry
Paris, France

Bobroff, Alvin, B.D.
Rabbi, Island Park
Long Island, New York

Boenheim, Curt, M.D.
Director, Group Psychotherapy
Columbus State Hospital, Ohio

Bolten, Mart P., Ph.D.
Psychosomatic Center
Leyden State University
Oegsteest, Netherlands

Bonzi, A., M.D.
Universitats Nervenklinik
Tubingen, Germany

Borgatta, Edgar F., Ph.D.
Chairman, Dept. of Sociology
University of Wisconsin
Madison, Wisc.

Bour, Pierre, M.D.
Medecin des Hopitaux Psychiatriques
Saint-Venant, Pas de Calais, France

Bross, Rachel B., M.D.
Research Associate Psychiatrist
Neuropsychiatric Institute
University of California Medical Center,
Los Angeles, Calif.

Buckley, Frank M., Ed.D.
Professor of Psychology
Assumption College
Worcester, Massachusetts

Bustamente, Jose, M.D.
Director, Instituto di Investigaciones de la
   Actividad Nervosa Superior
University of Havana, Cuba

Canestrari, R., M.D.
Institut de Psychologie de l'Universite de
   Bologne
France

Capitaine, J., M.D.
Paris, France

Cappon, Daniel, Ph.D.
Assistant Professor
Dept. of Psychiatry
University of Toronto, Canada

Chigier, E., M.D.
Municipal School Health Service
Tel Aviv, Israel

Clarke, Mary G., Ph.D.
Dept. of Psychiatry
University of North Carolina Medical School,
Chapel Hill, N.C.

Collomb, H., M.D.
Senegal, Africa

Cooper, Max, Ph.D.
Community Guidance Service
New York, N.Y.

Cooper, Nathan, Ph.D.
Associate Professor
Los Angeles State College
California

Cortesao, Eduardo Luis, M.D.
Hospital Miguel Bombarda
Lisbon, Portugal

Decobert, Simone, M.D.
Hospital St. Vincent de Paul
Paris, France

de Mare, P.B., M.D.
London, Great Britain

de Perret, E., M.D.
Psychiatric Clinic
University of Lausanne
Switzerland

Derbolowsky, Udo, M.D.
Hamburg, Germany

di Furia, G., M.D.
Senior Clinical Director
Western State Hospital
Ft. Steilacoom, Washington

Dracoulides, N. N., M.D.
President, Psychological-Biological Association
Athens, Greece

Durkin, Helen E., Ph.D.
Postgraduate Center for Mental Health,
New York, N.Y.

Enke, H., M.D.
Psychosomatic Clinic
Freiburg, Germany

Ferchland, E., M.D.
Psychosomatic Clinic
Freiburg, Germany

Fichelet, Raymond, M.D.
Societe d'Etudes et de Recherches en
  Sciences Sociales
Le Kremlin-Bicetre
Seine, France

Fine, Leon, M.A.
Director of Group Processes
St. Louis State Hospital, Missouri

Flegel, Horst, M.D.
Psychiatric Dept.
Dusseldorf Hospital, Germany

Floter, Hans, H., Ph.D.
Heimvolkshochschule
Spring/Deister, Germany

Fontana, Alberto, M.D.
Buenos Aires, Argentina

Foulkes, S.H., M.D.
Founder, Group Analytic Society
London, Great Britain

Friedemann, A., M.D.
Professor of Psychiatry
University of Freiburg,
Biel-Bienne, Switzerland

Fuchs-Kamp, D., M.D.
Aus dem Zentralinstitut fur
  Psychogene Erkrankungen der
  Allgemeinen Ortskrankenkasse
Berlin, Germany

Gantheret, F., Ph.D.
La Verriere, France

Garai, Josef Ernest, Ph.D.
Assistant Professor of Psychology
Pratt Institute, Brooklyn, N.Y.

Garlock, Rose
Alfred Adler Mental Health Clinic
New York, N.Y.

Goldberg, Irving A., Ph.D.
Private Practice
Seattle, Washington

Graham, Thomas, Ph.D.
Chief Psychologist
Massillon State Hospital, Ohio

Hadden, Samuel, M.D.
Professor of Psychiatry
University of Pennsylvania
Philadelphia, Pa.

Hawkins, David R., M.D.
Dept. of Psychiatry
University of North Carolina Medical School,
Chapel Hill, N.C.

Hoff, Hans, M.D.
Professor and Head
Psychiatric Clinic
Vienna University, Austria

Holt, Herbert, M.D.
Private Practice, New York, N.Y.

Horetzky, O., M.D.
Consulting Psychiatrist
Zagreb, Yugoslavia

Houben, A., M.D.
Psychosomatic Clinic
Freiburg, Germany

Hunting, John R., M.A.
American Society of Group Psychotherapy
  and Psychodrama
New York, N.Y.

Ionedes, Nicholas, M.D.
Chief, Legal Psychiatric Services
Washington, D.C.

Jannaccaro, E., M.D.
Assistente, Ospedale Psichiatrico
Provinciale Mombello, Italy

Jean, B., M.D.
Neuropsychiatric Children's Clinic
Salpetriere Hospital
Paris, France

Jones, Maxwell, M.D.
Superintendent, Dingleton Hospital
Roxburghshire, Scotland

Jorgensen, Carl, M.D.
Consultant in Psychiatry
Copenhagen, Denmark

Kadis, Asya L.
Director, Group Therapy Dept.
Postgraduate Center for Mental Health
New York, N.Y.

Kagan, Henry E., Ph.D.
Rabbi, Sinai Temple
Mt. Vernon, N.Y.

Kemper, Werner W., M.D.
President, Society of Analytic
  Group Therapy of Rio de Janeiro
  Brazil

Kestenberg, Jean, M.D.
Private Practice, Paris, France

Kieser, D., M.D.
Universitats Nervenklinik
Tubingen, Germany

Kirstein, Laurette
Coordinator, Foreign Student Affairs
Undergraduate Division
University of Illinois, Chicago, Ill.

Klehr, Harold, Ph.D.
Asst. Director in Charge
Student Counseling Service
Undergraduate Division
University of Illinois, Chicago, Ill.

Knobloch, F., M.D.
Charles University Polyclinic
Prague, Czechoslovakia

Kosemihal, Nurettin Sazi, Ph.D.
Chairman, Dept. of Sociology
Faculty of Letters
University of Istanbul, Turkey

Kotsos, Emanuel D., M.D.
New York, N. Y.

Krasner, Jack D., Ph.D.
Psychologist, Englewood Hospital
Englewood, New Jersey

Krich, Aaron, Ed.D.
Chairman, Admissions Committee
American Association of Marriage Counselors
New York, N.Y.

Kuhnel, G., M.D.
Niedersachsisches Landeskrankenhaus
Tiefenbrunn bei Gottingen, Germany

Lakin, Martin, Ph.D.
Dept. of Psychology
Duke University
Durham, North Carolina

Langen, D., M.D.
Universitats Nervenklinik
Tubingen, Germany

Lassner, Rudolph, Ph.D.
Senior Clinical Psychologist
Colorado State Hospital
Pueblo, Colo.

Leal, Maria Rita Mendes, M.D.
Portugese Society of Neurology and Psychiatry
Lisbon, Portugal

Lebovici, S. M.D.
President, French Society of Group
  Psychotherapy
Paris, France

Lemoine, P., M.D.
Paris, France

Lesse, Stanley, M.D.
Neurological Institute
Presbyterian Hospital of New York, N.Y.

Lewis, Madge K., Ph.D.
Counseling Center
San Francisco State College
California

Locke, Norman, Ph.D.
Mental Health Consultant
New York City Community Mental
  Health Board, N.Y.

Long, Capt. Ralph S., Ph.D.
Chief, Psychology Section
USAF Hospital
Scott Air Force Base, Illinois

Maas, G., M.D.
Psychosomatic Clinic
Freiburg, Germany

MacLennan, Beryce W., Ph.D.
Group Therapy Consultant
Washington, D.C.

Maddedu, A., M.D.
Reparto Alcoolopatie Ospedale Psichiatrico
Prov. le Mobello, Italy

Mann, John, Ph.D.
Asst. Professor
Graduate School of Arts and Sciences
New York University, N.Y.

Mann, Joseph, M.D.
Toledo State Hospital, Ohio

Markowitz, Max, M.D.
Director, Adult Therapy Clinic
Postgraduate Center for Mental Health
New York, N.Y.

Martensen Larsen, O., M.D.
Consultant in Psychiatry
Copenhagen, Denmark

Marti Tusquets, J.L., M.D.
Dept. of Psychiatry
University of Barcelona, Spain

Matsumura, Kohei, Ph.D.
Professor of Psychology
Ochanomizu University
Tokyo, Japan

McCarty, Gerald J., Ph.D.
Private Practice
Seattle, Washington

Meerloo, Joost A.M., M.D.
Attending Psychiatrist
Columbia Presbyterian Medical Center
New York, N.Y.

Mees, H.L., Ph.D.
Clinical Research Psychologist
Western State Hospital
Ft. Steilacoom, Washington

Meier, Liselotte, M.D.
Zurich, Switzerland

Meigniez, Robert, M.D.
Consultant in Psychiatry
Seine, France

Minguzzi, G., M.D.
Institut de Psychologie de l'Universite de
  Bologne
France

Mitchell, Howard E., Ph.D.
Division of Family Study
Dept. of Psychiatry
University of Pennsylvania School of Medicine
Philadelphia, Pa.

Mitscherlich, M., M.D.
Dusseldorf, Germany

Monod, Mireille, M.A.
Institute Claude Bernard
Paris, France

Monroe, John T., M.D.
Dept. of Psychiatry
University of North Carolina Medical School
Chapel Hill, N.C.

Morales, Francisco Perez, M.D.
Buenos Aires, Argentina

Moreno, J.L., M.D.
President, International Council of
  Group Psychotherapy
Beacon, N.Y.
Adjunct Professor
Graduate School of Arts and Sciences
New York University, N.Y.

Moreno, Zerka T., D.R.
Professor of Research
Academy of Psychodrama and
  Group Psychotherapy
Beacon, N.Y.

Northway, Mary L., Ph.D.
Director of Research
Child Study Center
University of Toronto, Canada

Ploeger, A., M.D.
University of Tubingen, Germany

Portugaels, R., M.D.
Centre de Formation pour Educateurs de Liege
Dison, Belgium

Proctor, Miriam
Parents Without Partners
New York, N.Y.

Riemenschneider, Helge, M.D.
Dusseldorf Hospital, Germany

Rotas, P., M.D.
Psychosomatic Clinic Freiburg, Germany

Roumajon, Yves, M.D.
Private Practice, Paris, France

Rouquette, Jacqueline
Groupe Francais d'Etudes de Sociometrie-
Dynamique des Groupes et Psychodrama
Paris, France

Rouslin, Sheila, R.N.
Instructor, Graduate Program
Advanced Psychiatric Nursing
Rutgers University
New Brunswick, New Jersey

Rubes, J., M.D.
Psychiatricka Lecebna V Praze
Prague, Czechoslovakia

Sacchi, C., M.D.
Instituto Psicologia
Universita di Milano, Italy

Sarro-Burbano, Ramon, M.D.
Professor of Psychiatry
University of Barcelona Medical School
Spain

Satir, Virginia M.
Director of Training
Family Project
Mental Research Institute
Palo Alto Medical Research Foundation
California

Schindler, R., M.D.
Specialist in Neurology and Psychiatry
Vienna, Austria

Schwartz, Emanuel K., Ph.D.
Postgraduate Center for Psychotherapy
New York, N.Y.

Senft, Paul, Ph.D.
Marlborough Day Hospital
London, Great Britain

Sivadon, P., M.D.
Professor, University of Brussels, Belgium
Past President
World Federation for Mental Health
Paris, France

Skala, J., M.D.
Psychiatric Clinic, Alcoholic Dept.
Prague, Czechoslovakia

Slipp, Samuel, M.D.
Associate Professor
San Francisco State College
California

Soule, Michel, M.D.
Asst. Physician of Neuropsychiatry
Hospital St. Vincent de Paul
Paris, France

Sow, D., M.D.
Senegal, Africa

Starr, Adaline
Consultant of Psychodrama
Chicago State Hospital, Illinois

Stokvis, Berthold, M.D.
Psychosomatic Center
University of Leiden, Netherlands

Syogo, Inoue, M.D.
Takajiva Mental Hospital
Japan

Tec, Leon, M.D.
Medical Director
Mid Fairfield Child Guidance Clinic
Norwalk, Connecticut

Tedeschi, Gian, M.D.
Rome, Italy

Tellier, Y., Ph.D.
Clinical Psychologist
Notre Dame Hospital
Montreal, Canada

Tenenbaum, Samuel, Ph.D.
Associate Professor
School of Education
Long Island University, N.Y.

Uyeki, Eugene S., Ph.D.
Dept. of Humanities and Social Studies
Case Institute of Technology
Cleveland, Ohio

Van Dalfsen, Gerardina L., M.D.
Lunteren, Netherlands

Van Emde Boas, C., M.D.
Groningen, Netherlands

Vassiliou, George, M.D.
Director, The Athenian Institute of Anthropos
Athens, Greece

Vernon, Charles R., M.D.
Dept of Psychiatry
University of North Carolina Medical School
Chapel Hill, N.C.

Weiner, Hannah B., M.A.
Director of Psychodrama
Moreno Institute
New York, N.Y.

Widlocher, D. M.D.
Clinique de Neuro-Psychiatrie Infantile
Hopital de la Salpetriere
Paris, France

Wittich, G., M.D.
Psychosomatic Clinic
Freiburg, Germany

Wolberg, Arlene, M.S.S.
Englewood Hospital, Englewood, N.J.

Wolf, Alexander, M.D.
Psychoanalytic Training Program
New York Medical College, N.Y.

Wolff, H.H., M.D.
University College Hospital
London, Great Britain

Zacher, Allan N., D.D.
Canon, Christ Church Cathedral
St. Louis, Missouri

Zemplini, A., M.D.
Senegal, Africa

Zimmert, R., M.D.
Zentralinstitut fur Psychogene Erkrankungen
der Allg. Ortskrankenkasse
Berlin Germany

CONTENTS

5

SECTION 4: PSYCHODRAMA

SECTION 5: MENTAL HOSPITALS

SECTION 6: MILIEU THERAPY

SECTION 7: THERAPEUTIC COMMUNITY

SECTION 8: FAMILY THERAPY AND MARRIAGE

SECTION 9: GROUP PROCESSES

9

SECTION 10: CULTURAL CONSTELLATIONS

SECTION 11: TEACHING AND TRAINING METHODS

SECTION 12: SELECTION METHODS AND SOCIOMETRIC GROUP FORMATION

SECTION 13: GROUP PSYCHOTHERAPY WITH ALCOHOLICS AND DRUG ADDICTS

SECTION 14: GROUP PSYCHOTHERAPY AND EXISTENTIALISM

11

SECTION 19: PSYCHOSOMATIC MEDICINE
AND GROUP PSYCHOTHERAPY

SECTION 20: GROUP PSYCHOTHERAPY AND LSD

SECTION 21: INDICATIONS AND CONTRA-
INDICATIONS

PART IV

THE INTERNATIONAL COUNCIL OF GROUP PSYCHOTHERAPY

14

PREFACE

The purpose of this Handbook is to convey to the reader a complete impression of the present status of the group psychotherapy movement and its methods, and, wherever possible, to make known its facts and figures. The book tries particularly to recapture some of the circumstances and ideas of the movement's origins, before they are forgotten and forever lost in the obscurity of the past.

The book is divided into four parts: 1) the origins and history of the group psychotherapy movement; 2) a validation of group psychotherapeutic methods; 3) the Proceedings of the Third International Congress of Group Psychotherapy, Milan, Italy, July 18-21, 1963; 4) the International Council of Group Psychotherapy.

The introductory section, entitled "Evolution and Dynamics of the Group Psychotherapy Movement," and its survey, have been prepared and supervised by Zerka T. Moreno, Director of the Archives of the Sociometric and Group Psychotherapeutic Institutes since 1942. The publications by individuals referred to in the introductory section may be found in the two most comprehensive bibliographies of R. J. Corsini, 1908-1956, and the one covering the last decade, 1956-1964, by B. W. Lubin, both published by Beacon House, Beacon, N. Y.

The validation study was made by Professor John Mann of New York University.

Every contributor to this volume is responsible for his own article and for the accuracy of his data. The Editors wish to thank the contributors for their efforts in making this volume possible.

J. L. Moreno, M.D., Editor,
Beacon, N.Y.

A. Friedemann, M.D., Assoc. Editor,
Biel-Bienne, Switzerland

R. Battegay, M.D., Assistant,
Basel, Switzerland

Zerka T. Moreno, Assistant,
Beacon, N.Y.

15

EDITOR'S FOREWORD

Open Letter to Group Psychotherapists

It is almost twenty years since I wrote the following letter, which appeared in *Sociatry, Journal of Group and Intergroup Therapy,* in March, 1947:

"What is group psychotherapy? This is a question which thousands of therapists working with groups are asking today. Lecturing to a group of individuals on a topic which has some reference to their own problems and discussing their reactions to it afterwards — is this group psychotherapy? Showing a puppet play or motion picture to an audience and watching their reactions — is this group psychotherapy? Presenting a psychodrama of a problem and getting the audience's responses to it afterwards — is this group psychotherapy? Watching a group of people in various activities, eating or working together, and analyzing their behavior with them afterwards — is this group psychotherapy? Witnessing a ball game in the midst of thousands, or going into a social revolution or a popular war with many comrades in arms — is this group psychotherapy? Taking one individual or another in front of a group, letting him present one of his crucial personal problems and permitting the participants to reflect upon experiences of their own — is this group psychotherapy?

"No, these are not, at least not by themselves. If I assume the authority to declare this outright, it is for several reasons: it happens that I introduced the terms 'group therapy' and 'group psychotherapy' in literature, that I connected them with a specific concept, and that I am usually made responsible for the development of sociometry and small group research. Although I believe that I had made myself clear from the beginning, we are all often misquoted as well as misread. Therefore, I will try to recapitulate briefly my original theory on the subject.

17

"The real issue was and is the difference between individual and group psychotherapy. In individual psychotherapy the patient is a single individual. In group psychotherapy the patient is a group of individuals. The premise on which the therapy of an individual is based is a fair knowledge of the structure of the individual psyche, or, as it is often said, of its psychodynamics; on the basis of this knowledge, individual diagnosis and individual therapy can be undertaken. The premise on which the therapy of a group would be based, consequently, would be knowledge of the structure of groups, of the 'sociodynamics' operating within them as the result of the relations between the individual members. At the time that I entered the field, a science of the group was practically non-existent. I made it my business, therefore, by means of carefully organized experiments, to help establish such a science. I was fully aware that without a knowledge of the organization of groups, group therapy is either impossible or else an accident.

"At the time that I started my inquiry there was no science of the group, but there was in the making a psychological science of the individual. Although there were several schools, it revolved more or less around the psychoanalysis of Freud. Freud assumed that the psychological factors operating in an individual also operate in groups and in nations; in fact, in human civilization at large. This view was, at the height of the psychoanalytic movement, perfectly human and understandable, as nobody knew much about the group. The group seemed to be a figment of the individual mind without a reality of its own. Freud might have cautioned himself that certain psychodynamics operating within an individual could become, in the course of inter-individual and inter-group relations, so grossly modified that effects and laws would result which would be inconceivable and unpredictable from the horizon of individual psychoanalysis alone. However, he did not caution himself, at least not sufficiently, his pupils still less; we thus have experienced and are still experiencing interpretations of group phenomena as if they would be crude projections of an individual neurosis. A group, a nation, even mankind was at times examined like an individual patient. The consequence was that psychiatrists, psychiatric social workers, social workers, group workers, psychologists, social psychologists, anthropologists, sociologists, criminologists, all trained or influenced by psychoanalytic doctrines, applied uncritically to the small or large group the terminology and the mechanisms they had learned from psychoanalysis. The results were confusion and chaotic views on the subject, especially when, with the beginning of the Second World War, group psychotherapy (or what went under this label) began to rise to its present popularity. Many non-psychoanalytic workers, however, using their common sense, fared better. Unfortunately, only a few had studied and had been trained in the science of the group, which, as sociometry and related disciplines, had developed in the last twenty years. A considerable body of knowledge was able to give group psychotherapy the beginnings of a scientific foundation.

"Among the ideological barriers to the development of scientific group psychotherapy, besides psychoanalysis, was Alcoholics Anonymous. Alcoholics Anonymous is in itself an offspring of group psychotherapy and has taken over some of its principles. Although it is an excellent example of the therapeutic effects of mirroring technique within homogeneous group membership, no one learned anything about the factors producing it; thus, the advance of scientific knowledge about it was hindered. Psychoanalysis is more difficult to penetrate because of the desire of many psychoanalysts to dominate *every form* of psychological treatment, whether individual, group or mankind. If they cannot claim that the psychoanalytic interview as such is universally applicable, they will try persistently to show that psychoanalytic concepts and theories are; and if the latter is not possible, they will at least stretch the meaning of their terms so that they can apply them to every human situation. Although this is understandable as a grandiose psychoanalytic daydream, it is in disregard of facts and a block to the progress of a science of social pathology and social psychiatry. It is also in utter disregard of Freud's own doctrines. I, an outsider and an opponent of psychoanalytic philosophy, am placed here in the odd position of having to defend the integrity of Freud's work against the abuses it receives from his own students. The only monument which a man of Freud's stature can receive from posterity is that the invention or the instrument which he has developed continues to be useful and is identified by the name he gave to it. What Freud meant by psychoanalysis and psychoanalytic therapy everyone knows who knew him personally and read his books. He never was shaken from his belief that psychoanalysis is *analysis,* that it is not synthesis, not active therapy, not a projective method, not sociometry, not psychodrama, not group psychotherapy, or whatever. I believe he would not have been disturbed by these new inventions if he were alive today. Indeed, the little he knew about them during his lifetime did not shake his faith in his belief that the instrument he had discovered is superior to all others.

"I cannot today formulate better the limits of psychoanalytic theory and the dangers which result from its thoughtless application than I did in 1934 in my book *Who Shall Survive?*, pp. 160-61: 'Individual psychology may aim at an interpretation of group situations through projecting to a group the findings which relate to a single individual, for instance, hysteria, neurosis, etc. But the salient point is to investigate a group of, say, five hundred individuals from the point of view of each individual's contribution and of the socio-emotional product which results in the form of group reactions. Then it becomes evident that projections of hysteria, neurosis, Oedipus complex, etc., from an individual to a group are undue generalizations and symbolizations, and that the actual processes are of a different nature. The investigations of the organization of this group, the position each individual has within it, the psychological currents which pervade it, and the forces of attraction and repulsion which it exerts upon other masses, compel us to formulate new concepts and a special terminology better adapted to the new findings. All up to date findings appeared to indicate that the essential elements of existence are locked within the individual organisms and are recognizable only in respect to the individual. The social impulses also did not seem to present an exception to this rule, however great an influence in shaping them we attributed to the environment; the shape they had attained in the course of their evolution was bound within the individual organism only; nothing which mattered fundamentally existed outside of the individual organism. But there is in the field outside of the organism a special area, the area *between* organisms. Characteristic patterns of interrelation have been found to exist between individuals; definite rules control the development from stage to stage and from place to place; they are of such a regularity of form, and have such a continuous effect upon groups near and distant, that it appears as if social impulses have been shaped not only in respect to the individual organisms but also *between individuals,* and that a remainder of this process is always discoverable whenever social groups are analyzed. Concepts such as reflex, conditioning reflex, instinct, mental syndrome, etc., which may have grown out of the approach of the individual organism, are not explanatory of these findings and have no specific meaning in this area. Fifty individuals who singly are classified as suffering from hysteria may, as a group, reveal a pattern totally different from a mass hysteria, for instance, an extroverted group organization with a high number of incompatible pairs. Or, again, the sexual character of individual members may be male or female, heterosexual or homosexual. And from an individual point of view this is a definable condition. But from a group point of view — the intersexual choices, attractions, repulsions and role relations among such members — a social organization may result which has as a totality different meaning than that of the sexual character of its individual members alone.'

"The science of the group is still in its infancy, although safe foundations have been laid. It seems to develop faster than the science of the individual, perhaps because an individual is more ready to expose his bonds to the group than to himself. It developed late for two reasons; psychiatrists neglected the group because of their professional preoccupation with the single organism; sociologists, although professional students of the group, neglected it because of their preoccupation with social masses and generalities — they rarely gave us more than an abstract, symbolistic, ideological picture of it. But 'small groups' have a realistic and specific organization of their own; they may vary with every sample, and the constant and variable structures characteristic for them can be ascertained by means of a few simple tests and experiments. These can be applied to groups of any size and any type; to a village of a thousand people, a workshop of five hundred, a hospital of two hundred patients, an audience of a hundred spectators, or a family of three individuals.

"The actual beginnings of group psychotherapy as a scientific discipline took place between 1930 and 1935 under the leadership of such disciplines as sociometry, microsociology and role theory. Efforts made before 1930 cannot be called group psychotherapy; it was not until then that full realization grew in the minds of a few that all methods which attempted a therapy of the group without a science of it were inadequate. The new therapeutic thinking culminated in the dictum: One patient can be a therapeutic agent to the other; let us invent devices by which they can help each other, in contrast to the older idea that all the therapeutic power rests with the physician. The new vision did not come from those who have been successful in the development of individual psychology, such as medical psychologists and psychoanalysts; these, rather, were holding back the progress towards an experimental investigation of the group. Its first sponsors were a few physicians, social psychologists and sociologists unbiased by commitment to the rigid individual-centered approach and the rigid group centered approach."

Conclusion

Thanks to the efforts of a number of leaders in both continents — American and European — in the twenty years since I wrote this letter, things have changed for the better.

This volume clearly shows the growing tendency towards convergence between the various schools, however, the interactional trend dominates the field, even in the work of analytic orientation.

Group psychotherapy is striving to attain the status of a vigorous science in its own right. But in the work of many practitioners it is still immature and parasitic, leaning upon other disciplines for its concepts and terminology — psychoanalysis, group dynamics and existentialism, to name a few.

The three mysticisms to be combatted are: 1) psychoanalytic mysticism — the mysticism of the individual psyche as the sole source of group analysis; 2) group mysticism — when the group becomes a self-propelling entity independent of the individuals who comprise it; and 3) existential mysticism — when existential concepts are used instead of those gained through empirical investigation.

J. L. Moreno, M. D.

Beacon, New York

THE INTERNATIONAL

HANDBOOK OF

GROUP PSYCHOTHERAPY

PART I

EVOLUTION AND DYNAMICS OF
THE GROUP PSYCHOTHERAPY MOVEMENT

by Zerka T. Moreno

I. HISTORIC OVERVIEW

Group psychotherapy is a creation of the 20th century. It is an American movement.

Group psychotherapy became an "historic" event through the leadership of a Viennese psychiatrist, J. L. Moreno, who came to the U.S.A. in 1925, and through the efforts of a few American-born pioneers. We are fully aware that scattered efforts in the direction of group therapy have been made under different names in other countries, but they did not crystallize into a movement; this happened only in the United States.

It is comparatively easy to determine the origins and history of the group psychotherapy "movement" as it relates to *events, dates* and *places.* This is the main task of this introduction.

It is far more difficult to trace the origins of various methods and their inventors. We have been only partly successful in this. Further research is necessary to clarify more completely the emergence of one or another method and its influence upon the movement. A method may have loomed important in 1921 but appear overrated in 1935. Methods that emerged in 1935 may appear two decades later as negligible. It is up to future historians of science to explore further.

DEFINING AND NAMING THE FIELD

Looking over the literature of the last thirty years one would get the impression, because of the growing number of modifications, that group psychotherapy is a "leaderless" movement. Actually, there was clear leadership visible in the beginning, of which sight was lost; the situation was like not seeing the forest because of the trees. Whatever changes a movement may undergo in the course of time, it is important to know its *status nascendi.*

The inspiration of a new idea or movement is often expressed in the name by which it becomes known and by which it is identified. "Group therapy" and "group psychotherapy" have become the all-encompassing key phrases representing our field. It is significant that the combination of *group* and *therapy* survived. The combination of the term *group* with *analysis, psychology, treatment* or *guidance* did not last on the global level. It was the emphasis on therapy, rather than on research or analysis, that made history.

The group psychotherapy "movement" must be differentiated from the group "methods" that developed from it. An organized movement is expressed in the creation of institutions, societies, scientific journals, teaching and training centers, and in its tendency to spread among the laity. Examples of organized movements are: Christianity, Marxism, and Psychoanalysis. A distinction is made between the idea and the organizations dedicated to its propagation. Christ was the carrier of the idea, but Paul was the founder of the Church and of Christianity. Marx was the author of *Das Kapital,* an important scientific work, but he and Engels became the founders of the communistic movement when they organized the "First International." Freud developed psycho-analytic methods, but he became the founder of the psychoanalytic movement when he sponsored the First Psychoanalytic Society, the first psychoanalytic journal and psychoanalytic institutes.

There are scientific methods that do not lead to the development of an organized social movement: for instance, the Mendelian Theory of Heredity and the Conditioned Reflex System of Pavlov. They remained laboratory- and university-anchored.

Group psychotherapy belongs to the category of social movements. It has developed institutions, societies, etc., all over the globe.

In the historical account of the group psychotherapy movement we shall present the authors in chronological order. They are recorded one by one as they emerge in history with their ideas or methods in specific publications traceable in literature. The authors are treated as historical phenomena rather than in a summary manner. Because of space limitations we shall apply

28

this principle particularly to the crucial early period (1908-1935), during which the basic and lasting orientations developed. This period may be called the era of the pioneers, an era usually associated with the names of Pratt, Moreno, Lazell, Burrow and Marsh. We trace the work of these men back to the places where they began — Pratt to Boston, Moreno to Vienna, Lazell to Washington, D.C., Burrow to Westport, and Marsh to Long Island.

It has been customary to list the five pioneers in the following order: Pratt, Moreno, Lazell, Marsh and Burrow. Due to facts unearthed in recent years concerning the rank and significance of their contribution, the order has to be revised as indicated: Moreno first, Pratt second, Burrow third, Lazell fourth, Marsh fifth. There are, however, several versions of ranking possible, according to the point of view:

    a) Date of first publication.
    b) Treating problems of mental hygiene, mental disorders, etc.
    c) Concepts still dominating the field.
    d) Continuity of productivity.
    e) Originality of therapeutic philosophy. With these criteria in mind:
    1) According to date of first publication: Pratt and Moreno rank first; Lazell, Burrow and Marsh rank second.
    2) According to treating problems of mental hygiene, mental disorders, etc.: Moreno, Lazell, Burrow and Marsh rank first; Pratt ranks second.
    3) According to concepts still dominating the field: Moreno and Burrow rank first; Pratt, Marsh and Lazell rank second.
    4) According to continuity of productivity: Moreno ranks first; Pratt, Lazell, Marsh and Burrow rank second.
    5) According to originality of therapeutic philosophy: Moreno and Burrow rank first; whereas Pratt, Lazell and Marsh rank second.

AN INTERDISCIPLINARY PROCESS

Group psychotherapy is an interdisciplinary process. It is related to several disciplines: psychiatry, psychology, sociology, anthropology, and education, to mention a few. But it has become a scientific and therapeutic discipline in its own right based on a growing science of the group. It is not an adjunct to any other discipline, such as to psychoanalysis or social psychology. "I am a group psychotherapist" sounds as respectable today as "I am a psychoanalyst." Group psychotherapy means simply to treat people in groups.

The literature of modern group psychotherapy is practically sixty years old (1907-1965), but the movement itself is only thirty-four years old (1931-1965). Sufficient time has elapsed for an objective appraisal of its pioneers, organizers, and methods.

A new revolution in psychiatry is taking place in our century, called by Moreno the "Third Psychiatric Revolution." (The *first*, suggested by Zilboorg, was symbolized by the emancipation of the insane from chains; the *second* by psychodynamics and psychoanalysis.) This Third Psychiatric Revolution has transformed the meaning and practice of psychiatry, largely due to the impact of social forces.

Appraisals have been made from time to time by numerous writers (Giles W. Thomas, Joseph I. Meiers, Raymond Corsini, etc.), but the actual data have come to the fore only gradually.

BEGINNINGS OF AN ORGANIZED MOVEMENT

Group psychotherapy as an "organized" social movement originated in the U.S.A. in 1931. It was in August of that year that the National Committee on Prisons and Prison Labor published the first edition of Moreno's *Plan for the Transforming of Prisons into a Socialized Community.* (It appeared in March, 1932, in a second edition entitled *Application of the Group Method to Classification.*[1]) The book was distributed widely by the National Committee on Prisons and Prison Labor throughout the U.S.A., Great Britain and Europe. The Committee sponsored a research program at Sing Sing Prison and the New York State Training School for Girls at Hudson, N.Y. The objective was the transformation of a prison and a mental hospital into therapeutic communities, and "the therapeutic regrouping" of the occupants of the Hudson reformatory on a sociometric basis (sociometric group psychotherapy based on diagnostic sociograms).

A "Conference on Group Methods" was initiated by Moreno

under the sponsorship of the National Committee of Prisons and Prison Labor. It took place on May 31, 1932, during the annual meeting of the American Psychiatric Association in Philadelphia. The topic of the conference was Moreno's book, which had just appeared in its second edition. More than one hundred psychiatrists, psychologists and sociologists took part in the conference. Its moderator was the late Dr. William Alanson White. The book contained sections on group therapy, describing its application to delinquents, prisoners, children, and mental patients, fields in which the method from then on continued to have its widest application. In this book the term "group therapy" was used for the first time in several places and defined in the meaning that is now universally accepted: "One man the therapeutic agent of the other, one group the therapeutic agent of the other" (p. 103). The definition of group psychotherapy in its current meaning was spelled out two years later in Moreno's *Who Shall Survive?* (page 301): "Group therapy treats not only the individual who is the focus of attention because of maladjustment, but the whole group of individuals who are interrelated." This definition referred to both clinical group therapy and family therapy.

The Application of the Group Method to Classification was not only Moreno's first American book but also *"the" first book on group psychotherapy:* it was the first time that the terms "group therapy" and "group psychotherapy" were put into circulation; and that the subject was studied within the framework of empirical science. It was the beginning of "scientific" group psychotherapy.

Sociometry and group psychotherapy were sponsored by Dr. William Alanson White at St. Elizabeths Hospital, Washington, D.C., in the autumn of 1934. The application of the group method to resettlements was encouraged by President Franklin D. Roosevelt in 1935. These combined activities accomplished the first stage in the group psychotherapy movement.

Summing up, it seems that scientific group psychotherapy is indeed a creation of the 20th century. The field was initiated and named by J. L. Moreno when he introduced the terms "group therapy" and "group psychotherapy" in 1931 and 1932. He has been given credit for fathering the movement. Credit for the "methods", however, should be given to each pioneer according to merit.

THE FIRST BOOK ON GROUP PSYCHOTHERAPY

Early Application of Group Psychotherapy to Prisons,
Hospitals, Schools and Child Guidance

As already pointed out, the first book on group psychotherapy was Moreno's *Application of the Group Method to Classification.* It has been overshadowed by *Who Shall Survive?*, which appeared three years later and developed further its principles. But *Application of the Group Method to Classification* was the first English presentation of the scientific foundations of group psychotherapy, and it introduced several methods of classification. Its main thesis was the study of group formation and its relation to group structure. It started "a study of the inner structures of (small) groups which can be compared with studies concerning the nuclear nature of the atom or the physiological structure of the cell."[2]

In order to accomplish this aim, Moreno introduced a number of methods.

1) The sociometric experiment. "The objectives of these experiments are to add to the knowledge of group structure. In classes with an average of 25 to 35 pupils the children were instructed to choose spontaneously those pupils they would prefer to be associated with" ... "These experiments corroborated the importance of sociometric choice factor in any system of classification which leads to group assignment."[3] These data were then presented in sociometric diagrams and analyzed.[4] They were the first sociometric diagrams published, preceding the sociograms in *Who Shall Survive?*

2) The spontaneity test. "The intelligence tests have been made after the standard of formal interview. But to answer set questions and to meet reality are two different things. We need in addition to what we have, a method of testing which is patterned after a life situation. This is what the spontaneity test attempts."[5] ... "The initial attempt to *warm-up* was crowded in their memory and they experienced resistive conflictive tendencies for the first time."

3) The third method was role playing. "A number of persons were placed opposite one another in a situation whose pattern was unknown to them before the moment of start and in roles and states which were equally unknown to them. The writer's

32

J. L. Moreno, M. D. (U.S.A.), Founder, International Committee of Group Psychotherapy, 1951; President, International Council of Group Psychotherapy

A. Friedemann, M.D. (Switzerland), Secretary and Treasurer, International Council of Group Psychotherapy
Leader of Group Psychotherapy in Switzerland

S. H. Foulkes, M. D. (Great Britain), First Vice-President, International Council of Group Psychotherapy
Leader of Group Psychotherapy in Great Britain

Serge Lebovici, M. D. (France), Second Vice-President, International
Council of Group Psychotherapy
Leader of Group Psychotherapy in France

Joshua Bierer, M.D. (Great Britain), Director, International Council of Group Psychotherapy; Proponent of Therapeutic Social Clubs and the Day Hospital

J. H. Schultz, M.D. (Germany), Director, International Council of
Group Psychotherapy; Founder of "Autogenous Training"

Enzo Spaltro, M. D. (Italy), General Manager and Organizer of the
Third International Congress of Group Psychotherapy, Milan, 1963
Leader of Group Psychotherapy in Italy

R. Battegay, M. D. (Switzerland), Assistant Editor, International
Handbook of Group Psychotherapy

Zerka T. Moreno (U.S.A.), Director, International Council of Group
Psychotherapy; Secretary, World Center of Psychodrama,
Sociometry, and Group Psychotherapy

Wellman J. Warner, Ph. D. (U.S.A.), Former Director, International Council of Group Psychotherapy; Architect of the Election System, International Council of Group Psychotherapy

Berthold Stokvis, M. D. (Netherlands), Late Secretary, International
Council of Group Psychotherapy

W. C. Hulse, M. D. (U. S. A.), Late Prominent Leader of the International Group Psychotherapy Movement

first suggestion to them during the initial phase of experimentation was to let loose unconcerned about involuntary remarks and gestures, faithfully relying upon the spontaneous aptitudes to act and react on the spur of the moment."[6] "The spontaneous responses were recorded in interaction diagrams which were then submitted to measurement and analysis."[7]

4) The fourth method was an objective analysis of interrelation attributes in small groups. "Group formation is to be on the basis of the interrelationship attributes of men. When we observe that the same individual is intolerant and demonstrative in one group, tolerant and abiding in another group, that the same individual takes the attitude of a solitaire in one group but is cooperative and suggestible in another group, we begin to suspect that a great number of these traits are falsely labeled individual and are truly interrelationship products."[8]

In a section entitled "An Illustration of Group Therapeutics", the application of these four methods were demonstrated. "A ten year old girl was sent to us because she used to bite her nails ruthlessly. In the first phase we shifted her from one group of playmates to others, having in mind to acquaint her with a wide range of children. Then we let her *choose* any playmate she liked, as we do not interfere if the patient can shape a remedial situation for himself"... "We laid our emphasis on the *present* because we realized that the products of their interrelations were *new,* constellations resulting from the clash of their individual mechanisms, interrelation effects." . . . "Every situation into which the child was placed was well defined and well prepared, but for the child, each was an impromptu situation. The behavior during each situation was afterwards analyzed, but the analysis and the therapeutic process did not run parallel and were kept apart." ... "Group therapy is thus the result of well calculated spontaneous therapy plus proper social assignment. In other words, psychological treatment is projected away from the clinic into real life situations, and techniques for a proper procedure to be used on the spot are developed. The leader is within the group, not a person outside."[9]

These group methods were similarly applied to a mental hospital and at Sing Sing Prison, breaking up the population into small groups of *seven.* Group therapy was based therefore upon a combination of observations, interviews, discussions, spontaneity tests, sociometric tests, role playing, and objective analysis of interrelations.

Corsini[10] made the following comment: "In 1931 he (Moreno) suggested a new method of prison classification, arguing that if prisoners were grouped sociometrically the interactions would be beneficial. In a monograph on this thesis he used the magic words 'group therapy' for the first time, although, as stated before, in a somewhat different sense from that currently employed. Actually the group therapist did not even have to come into contact with the group members, since groups were to be constituted on paper in terms of analyses of their own strengths and weaknesses."

This comment gives the impression that Moreno introduced a new method of classification exclusively for prisoners. Actually, the method of classification was applied, as quoted above, to numerous social settings, schools, child guidance clinics, and mental hospitals, in addition to the prison situation. It also conveys the impression that Moreno formed groups merely by placing patients together on the basis of their "sociometry", without considering their subjectivities, their confrontation with each other, and their therapist. This, obviously, does not make sense. How could there be any sociometric test without the most intensive interpersonal contact between the group members and their therapist?

This well intended but misleading comment has been repeated by other writers and has spread a false picture of the methods used by Moreno in group formation and of the meaning of group therapy. Actually, the current trend in the forming of small therapy groups increasingly follows the lines Moreno laid out in his first book.

Another significant aspect in Moreno's first book is his early emphasis and reinforcement of the "analytic trend" in group psychotherapy. (He is frequently labeled as anti-analytic.) He was the first to use the term "group analysis" in the current sense. He criticized vigorously "the lack of a group analytical basis."[11] In the following words he opposed the inspirational method: "Spontaneous formation of social groups based on the enthusiasm of the participants or on common interests and aims achieves often miraculous results but cannot be called grouping in our sense, as most of the interrelations remain unanalyzed."[12]

Therapy groups are small groups. They exercised a dominant influence upon small group research. The group therapy movement and small group research developed simultaneously and are closely interlocked.

In the following section we deal with the personalities and contributions of each pioneer of the group methods.

II. PORTRAITS OF THE PIONEERS: 1907-1935

The author met three of the five pioneers whose portraits are sketched in this section. They represent a rich variation of personality, and the portraits can be only partial, at best.

Dr. Pratt was a frequent participant in conventions, group psychotherapy, and psychodrama sessions in New York. He was a warm, outgoing, paternal man, a dedicated practitioner whose feet were enthusiastically planted among those of all humanity. He continued to work and live among people until practically the last moment of his life.

Dr. Lazell was a far more retiring, ascetic, withdrawn person. One gained the impression that he was highly selective in his interpersonal contacts, professional and personal. He completed his life in a seclusive manner, symbolically speaking a mile high — in Denver — above the world, devoting himself to spectral analysis, a far cry from group psychotherapy.

The two other fathers of the movement, Dr. Burrow and Dr. Marsh, emerge from their portraits as quite different from each other. Dr. Marsh, with his talent for the drama, so eloquently described by his wife, might have made a good psychodramatist. Dr. Burrow belongs more in the category of the penetrating searcher for truth.

Dr. Moreno, the only one of the five still in our midst, is a person whom few ever forget. His vigor, enthusiasm, and spontaneity propel all those whom he meets either towards him or away from him onto the periphery, watchful of what his genius might next contrive. His strength and singularity of purpose, his persistent drive towards his goals, never waver. A complex man, he combines both the scholar and the man of action, a combination which is rare and frequently bewildering. Throughout the years the author has met many practitioners of group psychotherapy who declared that they became involved in this work at a time when it was looked at askance by numerous colleagues as something not quite up to snuff, and it was due to Moreno's courage and incentive that they dared to be innovators.

PORTRAIT: J. L. MORENO, M.D.

1907 to 1935

1914, Interpersonal Relations and Role Reversal

"A meeting of two: eye to eye, face to face.
And when you are near I will tear your eyes out
    and place them instead of mine,
    and you will tear my eyes out
    and will place them instead of yours,
    then I will look at you with your eyes ..
    and you will look at me with mine."[13]

1922, The Here and Now, The Moment, Hic et Nunc[14]

"How does a moment emerge? A feeling must be related to the object of the feelings, a thought must be related to the object of thoughts, a perception must be related to the object of the perceptions, a touch must be related to the object of touching. You are the object of my feelings, the object of my thoughts, the object of my perceptions, the object of my touch. Such is an encounter in the *Here and Now.*"

*1923, The Encounter, Interpersonal Relations
and the Therapeutic World Order*[15]

"There are situations for one, there are situations for two, there are situations for more than two, there are situations for all existing beings. When a situation is so structured that its problems are attached to one, then they can be solved by this one to whom they are attached; if a situation is so structured that the problems are not connected only to one but to two, then they can not be solved except through the two of them who are involved. If a situation is so structured that it involves numerous individuals,

36

more than two, then the problems can not be solved except by all these who are involved. Finally, when a situation is so structured that the problems involve *all* beings, then they cannot be resolved but by *all* who are involved in them."

1923, Interaction Diagram[16]

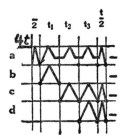

a (husband), b (wife), c (son) and d (daughter) are the roles taken by four individuals. The total diagram represents a process of interaction between these four actors. The plot consists of five scenes, three of equal duration (t1, t2 and t3), two have half the duration of a time unit.

(Duration of Plot)

P=4t, t=5 minutes, p is four times five which equals 20 minutes.

a has the lead in the first scene, b takes the lead over in the second, c and d have the lead in the end scene.

SPACE DIAGRAM

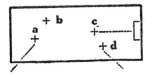

Each cross indicates the position taken on the stage by the four actors, a, b, c, and d, at the beginning of interaction.

1923, Unconscious Processes and Creativity[17]

"The protagonist has to overcome two groups of resistances: a) resistances which block mimic creativity, b) resistances which

37

hinder poetic creativity. Below these barriers stretches the unconscious, the true theater of poetry and creative work.

In order to elevate the sunken treasures, one must determine with a yardstick where and how deep they are located: rapid productivity succeeds the more easily, the nearer the unconscious stages of production are to their end-form (requiring the smallest amount of working through the hindrances).

In contrast, the less formed and the more amorphous the intermediate forms of production are, the greater is the danger that the delivery will be inadequate. The director will be influenced in the assignment of tasks by the creative endowment of an actor, if he has the required symbols in as advanced a form of production as possible.

There are numerous forms of creativity which have the characteristic of providing ready-made symbols: the fairytale, folkplays, harvest, nature and passion plays, and all productions of primitive comedy, wit, caricature, anecdote and humor.

When an hitherto unknown problem is to be presented *hic et nunc,* the ideas must pass through many more layers in order to express the tragic (depressive) rather than the comic (manic). The difference rests in the varying extent of working through the inhibitions. The comic act can come through although the consciousness of the actor is still crowded with inhibitions and blocks. In contrast with it, the condition for the emergence of the tragic act is the most extreme freedom from inhibition."

1923, Illustration of Matrimonial and Family Therapy

"It is a situation of two beings who do not understand one another, because and in spite of fullest clarity and knowledge of one another. It is a situation of two souls whom nothing can help, no transformation of the intellect, the mind, the body, except love. Everything which happens and which is attempted is in vain. They live in eternal recurrence and deepening of the same problems. And even self-destruction would lead here only to the denial and elimination of consciousness, not of the conflict. The conflict is eternal. The conflict is an inner pretext to hide themselves more deeply. The persons play before themselves — as they did once out of necessity in self-conscious deceit, the same life again. The place of the conflict and of its theatre is one and

38

the same. The whole of life is unfolded with all its mutual complications, in the dimension of time, not one moment, not one instance is extinguished from it; each moment of boredom is retained, each question, every fit of anxiety, every moment of inner withdrawal, comes back to life. All their powers, deeds, and thoughts appear on the scene in their original context and sequence, replicas of the phases through which they have once passed."[18]

The author now takes us into the Spontaneity Theater in 1923 to show how a married couple is treated: "I told Barbara how much progress she had made as an actress and asked her whether she would not like to act on the stage with George. They did this and the duettes on the stage, which appeared as a part of our official program, resembled more and more the scenes which they daily had at home. Gradually her family and his, scenes from her childhood, their dreams and plans for the future, were portrayed. After every performance some spectators would come up to me, asking why the Barbara-George scenes touched them so much more deeply than the others (audience therapy). Some months later, Barbara and George sat alone with me in the theater. They had found themselves and each other again, or better, they had found themselves and each other for the first time."[19]

1932, Principle of A-Historical Treatment, the Here and Now

"Both Freud and Jung have studied man as an historical development; the one from the biological, the other from the cultural aspect. On the other hand, our approach has been that of *direct* experiment: man in action, man thrown into action; the moment not a part of history but history a part of the moment — *sub species momenti.*"[20]

1932, Early Application of Group Psychotherapy to a Mental Hospital Setting, Principle of Spontaneous Choice and the Therapeutic Community

"The assignment phase of one patient to another presented here considers first the spontaneous choice factor, as the first reactions indicate the possible development of advantageous relationship.

39

The following reactions were noted. S smiled at R when they met the first time as she was greeted by her in a Jewish American slang with which she was familiar, and in turn R seemed pleased with S as she found in her someone who listened patiently and without stopping her. B ignored M who received her with a cheerful laughter but M expressed pity for S when she saw her break into tears, and began at once to mother her. R appeared refined and clever to M while R took an attitude of satisfaction as though she had found someone she could command.[21]

The method of assignment we have described in this book for the prisoner consists in relating to him the nearest and closest persons, the other prisoners. Similarly, it consists for the insane in an institution in relating to him the nearest and closest persons, the other patients and the personnel. To make this method useful for a mental hospital, complete charts for assignment and interrelation data have to be worked out, rating the prepsychotic factors and the complex of symptoms and interpreting their interconnections. One or two trial groups may lead to various practical rules as to how the treatment can be applied to the whole population of the hospital."[22]

1932, Recording and Playback

"Reactions witnessed by the psychologist and revelations given by any individual during a course of interviews, casual or planned, are, at least from the point of view of cooperative, controllable research, of little value since they are after the event merely memory impressions of the observer. The multiform interpretations offered by the subjectivists in psychology are without proper demonstration and reconsideration as long as they do not conserve the moment. It was suggested frequently therefore that 'a talking machine should photograph the process' and that we should make systematic use of this machinery of personality recording.[23]

Conserves of the test can be repeated, and not only are certain striking symptoms stored for duplication at will but the otherwise unrecordable scale of mimic expressions. Reactions which may have been undervalued in the haste of presentation are available for study. Signs which are preferred by the psychologist and consequently stressed by him are present together with signs which he may have overlooked. A level of 'intelligence' which is

40

indicated in a rich aptitude for mimic expression may then be observed simultaneously with a comparatively poor aptitude for verbal expression, or vice versa, and properly considered in the rating. These inconsistencies of verbal expressions with other expressions of the subject imply that free word-association by itself is frequently a deceptive basis of study. Many gestures and movements, unintentional or intentional, pass unobserved by testers during the test due to the fact that their attention is absorbed by the process. These actions have often a definite bearing on the subject. During the review of the film later, any subtle deviations in behavior may become prominent along with clues to conflicting tendencies within the acting persons."[24]

1933, Analytic Family Dynamics

Finally, I should like to say a word about family patterns. We have studied family organization, but not from the point of view of the psychoanalyst who studies it from the standpoint of the individual, his relationship to the father, to the mother, etc., as these are reflected within the individual. We have studied the interrelations from the standpoint of each member of the family, from all the standpoints. The psychoanalytical approach of the Oedipus drama is correct as long as it considers the Oedipus complex as an individual reaction of Oedipus mirroring all other persons around him. But to represent the real, whole Oedipus drama, an interrelation analysis is necessary. An individual analysis of each of the three persons, Oedipus, his father Laius and his mother Jocaste, has to be made. We will find then, just as Oedipus may have in his complex hate towards father and love towards his mother, that his father has towards him and Jocaste a complex which we may call here briefly "Laius" complex and that his mother Jocaste has toward him and towards Laius a complex which we may call "Jocaste" complex. The interlocking of these three persons, the frictions between them, the clashes between their complexes will produce the actual psychological process of their interrelations, which is different from the manner in which the dramatic process reflects in Oedipus alone, or how it is reflected within his father or mother singly, each apart from the other. In other words, we get a multiplicity of interrelationships which are, so to speak, ambicentric, and through this kind of study we get an insight from within as to how the family group is organized.

1934, From the Foreword to "Who Shall Survive?"

by William Alanson White[25]

"Dr. Moreno develops a technique for a process of classification which is calculated, among other things, to bring individuals together who are capable of harmonious interpersonal relationships, and so creating a social group which can function at a maximum efficiency and with the minimum of disruptive tendencies and processes."

1934, Opening Statement in "Who Shall Survive?"

"A truly therapeutic procedure cannot have less an objective than the whole of mankind. But no adequate therapy can be prescribed as long as mankind is not a unity in some fashion and as long as its organization remains unknown. It helped us in the beginning to think, although we had no definite proof for it, that mankind is a social and organic unity. Once we had chosen this principle as our guide, another idea developed of necessity. If this whole of mankind is a unity, then tendencies must emerge between the different parts of this unity, drawing them at one time apart and drawing them at another time together. These tendencies may be sometimes advantageous for the parts and disadvantageous for the whole or advantageous for some parts and disadvantageous for other parts. These tendencies may become apparent on the surface in the relation of individuals or of groups of individuals as affinities or disaffinities, as attractions and repulsions. These attractions and repulsions must be related to an index of biological, social and psychological facts, and this index must be detectable. These attractions and repulsions, or their derivatives, may have a near or distant effect not only upon the immediate participants in the relation but also upon all other parts of that unity which we call mankind. The relations which exist between the different parts may disclose an order of relationships as highly differentiated as any order found in the rest of the universe."

1934, Religious Mass Psychotherapy

"Christianity can be looked at as the greatest and most ingenious psychotherapeutic procedure man has ever invented, compared with which medical psychotherapy has been of practically negligible effect. It can be said that the goal of Christianity was from its very beginnings the treatment of the whole of mankind and not of this or that individual and not of this or that group of people."[27]

1934, Interpersonal Classification And Measurement

"Classification methods according to type, as Jung's, Kretschmer's and others, have in common with psychometric classification methods which measure an individual's intelligence, aptitudes, and abilities, that their attitude of classification is centered upon *one* individual singly, whereas the individuals and groups around him are only summarily considered. In contrast, we do not deal with an individual separated from the sociodynamic situation in which he lives, within which he appears continuously, attracted to and rejected by other individuals. The crucial point of our classification is to define *an individual in relation to others,* and in the case of groups, always *a group in relation to other groups.* This is sociometric classification."[28]

1934, Concept of "Acting Out"[29]

"Social life has the tendency to attach a definite role to a specific person so that this role becomes the prevailing one into which the individual is folded. Anxiety, fear, resentment, or feelings of difference and distinction are often increased by this condition and the accruing strains and tensions reflect into the group life. They, however, can be reduced through the release and training provided by skillful guidance of the individuals in the performance of play situations. For instance, many things which one girl would not tell to another or to the housemother in life she may 'act out' in a play, and the humor of it may prevent and heal many potential grievances which might otherwise have led to actual conflict.

Everybody is expected to live up to his official role in life, — a teacher is to act as a teacher, a pupil as a pupil, and so forth. But the individual craves to embody far more roles than those he is allowed to 'act out' in life, and even within the same role one or more varieties of it."

43

1934, Role Reversal[30]

"The individuals chose the situation and the roles which they wanted to act and the partners to whom they wanted to act opposite in a certain role, or *they exchanged the roles they had in life,* or they were placed in selected situations. As the acting was pure improvisation, the performance was a yardstick of how they might perform in life situations."

1934, Role Playing and Role Training[31]

"The method has numerous advantages compared with training in adjustment through actual life experiences, particularly for the individual in the formative age. First, in actual life situations an individual often has difficulty in learning from a mistake due to the earnestness of the situation. In his anxiety he may repeat such error when a similar occasion occurs, thus retarding his learning to overcome the error. Second, for many individuals actual life situations encourage an emotional inertia if the performance is successful in a given role, and more is not demanded. Third, in actual life situations, even if these develop an individual for fitting perfectly into a certain role, they make him single-tracked and exclude from his horizon other varieties of situations and vocations.

A series of life situations calling for the embodiment of specific attitudes are constructed. Each of the situation-patterns is constructed through several phases ranging from the simplest possible form of a given situation-pattern through the more complex forms to the most highly differentiated, all carefully graduated according to the requirements of the subject. Hence, the subject is trained through acting in the simplest of roles in any specific situation-pattern through several degrees of differentiation of the same situation-pattern until he can command the pattern adequately.

Another example of how such training is graduated to develop and sustain a specific attitude in a given role in several varieties of the same situation-pattern is as follows: For instance, in the first stage the subject produces the attitude of sympathy towards another individual. In the second stage he has to produce the same attitude in a role in which he has to command a certain function, for instance, the role of a sales person in a dress shop and in relation to certain things, dresses. In the next stage, the subject has to produce the same attitude in the same role as above but in a situation selected by the instructor, as selling dresses to a business-like and ready customer. In a later stage, the task is further differentiated. The subject produces the same attitude and in the same role but the instructor selects a customer who is to act resentful and argumentative. The task of the subject is to sustain the cheerful, sympathetic attitude in the face of such resistance. The differentiation of this pattern can be further elaborated in accord with the ability and progress of the subject."

1945, Family Therapy[32]

"Husband and wife, mother and child, are treated as a combine, often facing one another and not separate (because separate from one another they may not have any tangible mental ailment). However, facing one another deprives them of that elusive thing which is commonly called 'privacy'. What remains 'private' between husband and wife, mother and daughter, is the abode where some of the trouble between them may blossom — secrets, deceit, suspicion and delusion. Therefore, the loss of personal privacy means loss of face and that is why people, intimately bound up in a situation, fear to see one another in the light of face-to-face analysis. (They prefer individual treatment.) It is obvious that once privacy is lifted (as a postulate of individual psyche) for one person involved in the situation, it is a mattter of degree for how many persons the curtain should go up. In a psychodramatic session, therefore, Mr. A, the husband, may permit that besides his wife, his partner in the sickness, the other man (her lover) is present, later his daughter and son, and some day, perhaps, they would not object (in fact they would invite it) that other husbands and wives who have a similar problem sit in the audience and look on as their predicaments are enacted and learn from the latter how to treat or prevent their own. It is clear that the Hippocratic Oath will have to be reformulated to protect a group of subjects involved in the same therapeutic situation. The stigma coming from unpleasant ailment and treatment is far harder to control if a group of persons is treated than if it were only one person."

PORTRAIT: J. H. PRATT, M.D.

"The first meeting of the group was on the morning of April 11, 1930.[33] Since then meetings have been held once a week except during a summer recess. At the start I had the able assistance of Miss Edith Canterbury of the Social Service Department. At the outset, I had no idea how to proceed as I had no precedent. I felt like a mariner travelling uncharted waters. Three women patients from the Medical Clinic were present at that first meeting and the testimony of one of them on her recent relief from pain gave us a successful start. A few days earlier I had interviewed the patient, Mrs. C., in the Medical Clinic. I had already at that time gained her confidence, as some months previously she had come to me complaining of pain in the shoulder and had speedily recovered. This time her condition was much more serious. For three months she had had a pain in the back so severe as to confine her to bed. Finally she had managed to make the trip to the office of a prominent gynecologist. He found some minor pelvic abnormality and to this attributed her disabling backache. He recommended an operation, and as she was a poor woman, had referred her to my clinic at the Boston Dispensary to determine whether her general condition would permit of his undertaking the operation without delay.

Although she complained only of the backache, after listening to her story, I said, 'What is the real trouble? Tell me the whole story.' Without hesitation she replied that it had been fear her husband would lose his job. This had tormented her for months. He looked so tired and wan at night on returning home from work that she was filled with forebodings. It was very difficult to pay the bills with his meagre wages, and what would happen to the children if he became sick and could not work? This state of mental agitation had persisted for some time when the backache developed. Her relief of mind was very great when I assured her no operation was needed and that her backache would disappear when she banished her fears and gained mental serenity. She accepted my statement at once without the least questioning doubt.

At the first class meeting she instilled hope into the minds of the other two patients by telling the story of her dramatic recovery. When she had come to the Dispensary to ascertain

46

whether her condition would warrant the operation, she was so weak that she had to steady herself by keeping her right hand on the brick walls of the buildings as she walked down narrow Bennet Street to the Dispensary. When she left she felt as if she were walking on air. She kept repeating to herself, 'No operation, no operation.' She stopped at the market on her way home and bought provisions. That afternoon she washed the kitchen floor and for the first time in three months prepared her husband's supper. The backache was gone.

A few months later, with health restored after faithfully following the instructions given at the class meetings, she told the following incident; A few days earlier a friend had stopped her on the street and drawing her to one side said in low tones, 'Everyone is talking of your wonderful recovery, Mrs. C., but you tell me the truth for I know it was a miracle. You visited Father Power's grave at Malden and were cured.' 'No,' replied Mrs. C. 'It wasn't Father Power's grave, it was Dr. Pratt's thought control class.' That gave us our name. We had been at a loss to find a suitable name, and here it was supplied by an uneducated member. She had grasped the central teaching that cure was wrought by thought and emotional control. A strong vitalizing emotion had removed her pain but the underlying cause of it had been eradicated by an altered state of mind; in other words by moral re-education as Dejerine termed it.

As I was the physician-in-chief of the Medical Clinic, I was able to make a ruling that all patients whose symptoms were found on thorough examination to be due to a functional nervous disorder were to be referred to the class without delay. As a result over 2,000 patients have been sent to us. Two psychologists, Mr. Winfred Rhoades and Dr. Rose Hilferding, are in daily attendance at the Dispensary and they hold a preliminary interview with all patients before they attend their first meeting. At this interview a psychological history is added to the medical record. A brief explanation is given of the effects of the emotions on the body and mind in an effort to break down the resistance many patients feel to psychological treatment.

The methods used in conducting the meeting have been little changed during the fifteen years of its existence. They were described in some detail in a previous paper. The members are seated in the lecture hall according to the number of sessions they have attended. The four with the highest score sit on a settee placed on the platform to the left of the class leader and facing the other members of the class. This was done at the suggestion of the late Dr. John G. Gehring, the distinguished psychiatrist who supported the class idea from its inception. He wanted the patients who had been members for some time and who had recovered to sit in such a position that the newcomers could see what he termed the radiance in their faces. The newcomers, that is, the candidates for membership, are seated on the front row facing the director. The roll call is made and the class director repeats the name and enters it in a book together with the number of meetings attended by each member beginning with the one with the largest number. This breaks the ice and it serves as an introduction of each member to the others of the group. They come in this way to associate the names and faces of their fellow members. The floor secretary then distributes slips of paper on which each records his progress or lack of progress since the previous meeting. These are collected at once and read by the class director without giving the names signed on the reports. With an average attendance of 20, about 15 will state that they are free from symptoms and feeling 'fine.' The other five, composed chiefly of new members, write that they are no better or only a little improved. Those in the latter group are asked to remain after the class in order that they may be given appointments for personal consultations with our psychologist or with our psychiatrist, Dr. Alfred Hauptmann. All patients who fail to gain after a few treatments are studied by Dr. Hauptmann and when found to be suffering from psychoses, as occasionally happens, are advised regarding other treatment more suitable for them.

Then a relaxation exercise is given. The form I employ is really mild hypnotic suggestion combined with relaxation. For this technique I am indebted to Professor Elton Mayo. This entire procedure lasts only five to seven minutes. As a result, nearly all feel relaxed in muscles and mind, as indicated by raising their hands. As their eyes are closed at the time, they do not know the result, but I always announce how many failed to relax and they are usually only the newcomers. A few may fall asleep and most of the group claim they feel drowsy. This exercise seems to prepare them well for the short address that follows. These talks aim to be inspirational.

I made it a rule not to prepare in advance my little speech. There is much repetition but this is well received by my hearers as many attend the meetings for months or even years after their recovery. I appeal to their hearts rather than their heads; in other words, to their emotions more than to their reason. Dejerine emphasized the truth that action is due to an emotional drive and without action, there is no cure. 'You can't change the world, so change yourself,' is a favorite quotation that the members recite with conviction. Following the talk by the class director, the final ten or fifteen minutes of the hour and a half session are devoted to testimonies from two or three of the members who speak of the progress they have made and the lessons they have learned from their experience.

Patients in the class have usually recovered more quickly than have my private patients. This I attribute to hope of recovery awakened by being in the presence of those who were sick and now are well, and secondly to faith in the class and its methods as well as in the directing physicians.

Other classes have been formed in our clinic and conducted with equal success. Winfred Rhoades, our psychologist, has had an evening class for nearly ten years, established primarily for men who were employed during the day but now attended by both men and women. He published an excellent account of the group method. His book, 'The Self You Have to Live With,' is made up in part of material used in the short addresses prepared for his class and contains also many experiences of class members who had learned to adjust themselves to the conditions of life. This book has proved so helpful that it has been reprinted twelve times. Dr. Herbert I. Harris organized and conducted an afternoon class. His report on the group method is excellent. Dr. Alfred Hauptmann, psychiatrist with large experience in leading German clinics, after a thorough study of our results, published a paper in which he emphasized certain advantages of the group method over individual treatment. He pointed out that it should prove of special value in dealing with the war neuroses among the soldiers. For this reason, the paper was sent for publication to *War Medicine,* but the editor returned it, evidently regarding the subject of group treatment not sufficiently important to deserve publication. Yet within two years General Marshall issued a general order that group therapy should be employed by the psychiatrists of the Army.

So far as I know the first class to be formed along lines similar to ours was that of Dr. Samuel B. Hadden in the outpatient department of the Presbyterian Hospital of Philadelphia early in 1939. A later paper reported the success he had obtained: a statistical analysis of the results of the first three years of the group therapy showed that of those who responded to the questionnaire, 90 percent reported they were benefited, 18 percent as cured, and 50 percent as much improved.

Anyone who has developed a successful psychotherapeutic method of treating individual patients can conduct a class with success, but on the other hand, if he has not achieved an effective technique with individual patients, I doubt if he will succeed with a group."

PORTRAIT: T. BURROW, M. D.

1927, Group Analysis

"In the personal analysis the consummation upon which the analysis depends from the outset is the transference. This must be brought about and preserved at all costs. *Keine Uebertragung, Keine Psychoanalyse.* In our group procedure this condition of a patient's dependence upon his physician is from the outset precluded. We know very well that the essence of the neurosis is the mother-child relationship, that this is the neurotic patient's unconscious impasse, that fixation is his unremitting quest. But, in the group, the mother-child relationship is from the very beginning submitted to consensual observation and study, and no surrogate for this relationship such as obtains in the usual technique of analysis is permitted to creep in unconsciously and defeat the real purpose of a psychoanalysis. I do not mean for a moment that there is not in each patient the tendency toward such a fixation or transference in the group situation. It is constantly present. But under conditions of group association, naturally, there is not the opportunity favorable to its secret lodgement and entertainment, as is the case in the private work involving months of solitary confinement, with the individual analyst. What would be the individual transference in a private analysis becomes neutralized in the social participation of many individuals in their common analysis."[34]

50

1953, Phyloanalysis

"Phyloanalysis: A method developed by the author for investigating disorders in human behavior, originally called group-analysis. Phyloanalysis regards the symptoms of individual and society as but the outer aspect of impaired tensional processes that affect the balance of the organism's internal reaction as a whole. Through the technique of phyloanalysis there is induced in individual and group an awareness of partitive or deviate behavior. This discrimination is made possible by contrasting the internal tensions concomitant to this type of behavior-reaction with the internal pattern of tension concomitant to the organism's motivation as a whole. (Synonym: group analysis. Not to be confused with group-therapy. From *phylum,* race)."

"Unfortunately, in their writing, the group therapists often tend to line up their principles of procedure with what they conceive to be the principles of phylobiology. I do not wish to disparage the work of these students. However non-objective, however devoid of data derived from an acquaintance with the organism's behavioral physiology, their studies will undoubtedly possess academic value from the viewpoint of an interpersonal psychiatry. From this angle they will at least have the merit of indicating what phyloanalysis is *not.* It seems fitting, though, to explain that inasmuch as these psychotherapists have lacked the opportunity to undertake a phyloanalysis of their own ditentive affects and motivations, their accounts can hardly present the method of phyloanalysis as practised by the group of investigators who are the sponsors of it.

A sharp line of distinction should therefore be drawn between the group analysis of my associates and myself and the procedures of more recent adoption among psychiatrists. These group procedures have all the external semblance of our own, but only the external semblance. As regards internal material and method, the gulf between us is an impassable one. For in our approach to disorders of behavior our interest and attention has centered solely in the phenomenon of ditention as a disordered phylic process; while, on the other hand, our colleagues in group therapy, as in individual therapy, have centered their interest and attention

51

upon every manifestation of behavior disorder except ditention —the one disturbance which, in our mind, is responsible for all the rest.

As 'normal' personalities, therefore, these therapists, as was originally the tendency with ourselves, are constantly under the subjective domination of this inadvertent form of attention. They do not bring this deflection of attention under their objective observation as a physiological impediment to the organism's balanced function. Yet this clear line of demarcation between our work and that of our colleagues is one they have persistently failed to recognize. They will in one breath speak of their procedure and that of our laboratory as though their method were susceptible of alignment with the technique of phyloanalysis. This very general misconception of our position is needlessly misleading."

"In order to understand the significance of ditention and our group method of approach to it, it should be recognized very clearly that the term 'group' has never meant for us a conventionally assembled collection of individuals. For us the concept 'group' is not an external connotation, but a biological principle. I have at no time thought of groups as a landscape gardener thinks of an arrangement of trees, or an educator of a class of students. Biologically, such grouping is purely extrinsic and artificial. No inherent principle binds the individuals composing these arbitrary units. Such groups represent but a fortuitous collection of heterogeneous elements. In my use of the term group, I have had in mind from the outset a biological group and biological principle of behavior."

"The sole aim of the phyloanalytic technique is to demarcate between habit-reactions that are ditentive or falsely motivated, and habit-reactions that are biologically integrated and organismic. Our inquiries into behavior have to do with internal physiological processes affecting the organism of man as a species. The major proposition that has been the outcome of our researches is that so-called normal personalities and the so-called neurotic are equally ditentive and are equally victims of a conflict and obstruction in their interrelational life, and that this obstruction and conflict is traceable to internal patterns of behavior that are only internally appreciable by physician, patient, and community alike."[35]

1946, T. Burrow Explained by Hans Syz

"In our laboratory setting the interrelational attitudes and reactions occurring within the group were observed and examined for their underlying content. They were observed not in retrospect but in the actual moment and they specifically included the immediate reactions of the observers themselves. To this end experimental groups met regularly several times a week; they were composed of from four to twenty individuals, both 'normal' and 'neurotic'. In addition, in later years observations which were no less controlled took place in quite informal settings, such as during the meal hour and other routine activities."

"Phylopathology. — The terms *'phylobiology'* and *'phylopathology'* refer to behavior and its disorders and were introduced by Trigant Burrow to describe the researches of himself and his associates into these disorders. These investigations, originated by Dr. Burrow, represent a type of behavior study that is not to be identified with prevailing psychological or psychiatric schools. From the altered frame of phylopathology behavior disorders are regarded as conditions that reflect a biological disturbance within the organism of individual and phylum. This disturbance involved a dislocation of feeling within the system of the self. It involves an *'affecto-symbolic impasse'* that distorts human relations, both personal and social. The investigation is directed specifically toward determining the neurophysiological substrate of the condition and toward developing practical means of readjusting this maladaptation in its extension throughout the species man."[36]

1957, T. Burrow Explained by Hans Syz

"Burrow's group analysis, vigorously opposed in many quarters, was one of the forerunners of the group therapeutic methods. However, it differs from them in that it emphasizes the investigative aspect, the observer is more consistently included as an active component of the adaptive deflection studied, and the goal, as indicated, is not adaptation to a social norm.

In connection with these studies Burrow suggested that an evolutionary miscarriage provided important roots for neurotic disorder and antisocial behavior in individual and community. He proposed that, coincident with the development of language, total feeling and organismic forces became attached to symbolic part-features of the environment, and word and gesture were endowed with artificial power. More important, a separatively conceived image of the self arose, and the isolated self-symbol came to assume an authoritarian position. A world of self-centered individuals was thus created in which each insists on his esoteric right, and each child is trained to respond to right-wrong signals, which are used for personal advantage and distinction. The early omnipotent trend, re-enforced by universal affect-projection, became socially systematized and is enacted in our daily interchanges, in language-usage and customs, and in the prevailing forms of socialization. This *affecto-symbolic* systematization, dominating the individual (Burrow's *I-persona*), embodies an organismic decentering which, with its bent toward hostility and threat of isolation, calls for constant compensatory adjustments. The obsessively defensive cycles thus set in motion in the individual and in social interaction further consolidate the image-dependent trend. A certain equilibration and lessening of anxiety may be effected by these superficial adjustments, but the autistically biased, unstable structuring of the self and of social reality, with its pathogenic implications, remains unaltered.

To present the situation in terms of basic human characteristics, man's ability to objectivate his environment and himself was partly diverted into hostile oppositeness or detachment, into an I-versus-you dichotomy. Constructive self-awareness changed into autistic self-assertion. The urge toward symbolic transformation of experience and its cultural transmission was deflected by the defensive use of the symbolic process. The capacity for responsible relatedness with the world and with others was impeded by image-dependent interaction. That is, man's evolutional innovations of objectivation and symbol-usage were not adequately integrated with his basic organismic forces and with his fundamental need for phylic cohesion.

From the background of field or gestalt concepts, individual and sociocultural processes involved in the adaptive defect are seen as interlinked components within a total configuration which embodies a common denominator. Undue emphasis and dependence upon an autistically distorted self-image and its social projections are expressed in authoritarian and submissive enactments, hostility and guilt, and associated self-defensive maneuvers. We find in this image-fixation a root of disturbed empathy and communication, of inadequate identifications and sexual distortions, of self-affirmative social cluster-formations with their inter-group antagonisms. Thus, important aspects of neurotic phenomena, both individual and social, may be regarded as variations or secondary elaborations of a basic theme. The outcome in any specific situation may become complicated by accidental stresses and conditioning factors. But in spite of the resulting complexity and the tremendous variety of behavior expressions, Burrow emphasized the significance of an underlying dysfunction which is consistent in its structure."[37]

PORTRAIT: E. W. LAZELL, M. D.

"The material and arrangement of the individual lectures which are used in part or in whole with various groups is as follows:[38]

1) Introduction. The fear of the new. Tolerance of other points of view. Geology, the study of the layers of stone on the surface of the earth. The development of the human body through layers. The layers of the mind. The paleontologist and fossils in stone. Repressed experiences, the fossils in the human mind. Self-knowledge is the first step toward recovery. Breakdowns can be prevented and cured. Shame not justified.

2) The primitive instincts. Bisexuality is a normal condition. Death. The fear of death the basis of all fears. Fliess: male and female cycles. Adam and Eve. Urim and Thummin. Yang and Yin.

3) Heredity. Discussion designed to break down the belief in heredity as the cause of nervous and mental disorders. Pointed examples illustrating mental conflict as a cause of physical and mental conditions.

4) The development of primary images of personality: the man-and-woman images. Other images of personality. These

images as symbols for masculinity and femininity. The mother and father as symbols for these images of personality. The mother level. The Oedipus complex, abstract of the drama, illustrating bisexuality.

5) Myths and examples of the Oedipus in other races. Illustrations of the identification of the child with a primary image of personality.

6) Totemism as an example of racial identification with these images. Analysis of totemism. Examples of totemism in the play-activities of children.

7) The myth of the Birth of the Hero and The Family Romance of Neurotics, Otto Rank. Examples from life and among neurotics and the insane, and in the play activities of children.

8) Analysis of Kipling's Jungle Stories showing the Oedipus complex.

9) Analysis of the same showing the hated man-image. Analysis of Taboo. Examples in the life of the neurotic and insane.

10) The myths of Echo and Narcissus and other myths illustrating narcissism or auto-erotism.

11) Physical narcissism. Lecture devised to break down fears and misconceptions as to past experiences. Readings from various authors. The many forms of auto-erotism, exhibitionism, curiosity, etc.

12) Mental and spiritual narcissism.

13) The development of the ego-ideal and conscience.

14) Day-dreaming, its mechanisms and great dangers.

15) Homo-erotism, its development and influence on the individual. Examples in mythology. Types; aggressive and submissive. Fear of the man-and woman-images in etiology.

16) Analysis of the artist and of art. Life of Leonardo de Vinci after Freud's book of the same title. Pictures illustrating conflicts.

17) Abstract of Dr. E. J. Kempf's analysis of the psychology of the Yellow Jacket.

18) The inferiority complex. Reading of a lay magazine story illustrating the feeling of inferiority.

19) The feeling of sexual inferiority. Psychosexual inferiority, after Ferenczi. Other types of sexual complexes.

20) The guilt complex. Origin of the various phobias.
21) The shame complex. Origin of the various phobias.
22) The inadequacy complex. Fear of failure, ridicule, censure, etc.
23) The physical reactions of fear. Causes of fear and anxiety.
24) The training of the child; its transitions and goals.
25) Psychic complexes and mechanisms. Identification, projection, introjection, projection of blame, criticism, elevation and substitution. Displacement and other mechanisms.
26) Overcompensation. Its mechanisms and results on a physical, mental and spiritual level.
27) Sublimation. Adjustment to the Herd. Altruism. The development of ethics, aesthetics, and morality. The social conscience.
28) The causes of failure. The sources of success. Habits and their formation.
29) Thrift of money, energy and time. The minute the most precious of all possessions. The value of work.
30) Emotional control and behavior, including the goals of life. The influence of repressed complexes. Self-study and self-analysis. The effect of rage and fear in anxiety neurosis, hyperthyroidism, and epilepsy.
31) Hygienic living. Alcoholism. Gambling. The responsibility of the individual as a social animal.
32) Summary and review.

Throughout the course inspirational material is used. *A Message to Garcia* is mimeographed and distributed for reading. Other valuable material is Kipling's *If; How to be a Failure* by Industrial Peace; *Opportunity* by Walter Malone; *Fighter or Quitter* by Grantland Rice; *Invictus* by Henley; *Analysis of the Psychology of the 'Yellow Jacket'* by Edward J. Kempf; quotations from many sources.

Finally, the writer wishes to quote from one of his articles[39] published in 1921:

In conclusion, the writer holds the ideal that institutions for the insane now largely devoted to custodial care, hydrotherapy, etc., should be changed into institutions for the instruction of these patients; that such instruction should aim at directing the instinctive demands into normal channels aiming at the heterosexual

57

goal; that defectives not due to organic causes, psychopathic personalities, and the morons should be handled in large numbers by this method; that young men in criminal institutions, reformatories, under the care of the Juvenile Courts, should be given this instruction, believing that society owes it to these patients that they be not allowed to stagnate in mental inactivity, and that large numbers could by this method be raised to a sufficiently high level to be of economic value to the community or return to active life, even if on a lower plane. It is further believed that colonies of these patients should be established looking toward this end. Newspapers should be provided and every method used to assist the patient back to reality."

PORTRAIT: L. CODY MARSH, M. D.

"L. Cody Marsh will be remembered by those who knew him in his young manhood and in his prime as a charming and stimulating companion, a man teeming with ideas, whose chief delight it was to provoke those around him to think along constructive and progressive lines.

Born in Cleveland, Ohio, on September 30, 1883, Dr. Marsh came of Kentucky planters on his father's side and of a Cleveland family — the Codys — on his mother's. The colorful Col. William F. Cody — Buffalo Bill — too well known to need any introduction, was his cousin. But it was not only in Col. Cody that lived the spirit of adventure and the urge to depart from the usual, safe pattern of life. The Cody family seemed never content with things as they were, but must ever try to leave things better than they found them. And so they built churches and became interested in causes, and in an age when the emancipation of women was undreamed of, the Cody women were going to college, sailing away to far countries as missionaries, and even making public speeches on the evils of alcohol. Small wonder that Cody Marsh grew up casting an inquiring eye on existing institutions.

After graduating from a Cleveland High School, Dr. Marsh entered Kenyon College at Gambier, Ohio. He had not distinguished himself scholastically at school, as he had refused, as he later humorously remarked, to let his studies interfere with his educa-

58

tion, and had been too much absorbed in extra-curricular activities to pay due attention to his Latin and Greek. Much more interesting to him was his work in the dramatics club and the various music clubs. An accomplished pianist and organist, he was also possessed of an unusually pleasing baritone voice, and his musical gifts coupled with his marked dramatic ability stood him in good stead all his life. As early as during his high school days Dr. Marsh was drawn by the plights of the mentally ill, and as a youth of seventeen or eighteen secured permission to visit the Cleveland State Hospital — then the Cleveland Insane Asylum — and entertain the patients with his piano playing and singing. His sympathies were always with the oppressed and unfortunate and his life was built around an unquenchable drive to better their lot.

Although Dr. Marsh had from early boyhood planned to enter the field of medicine, he became interested while at Kenyon in entering the Episcopal ministry and graduated from Bexley Theological Seminary in 1907. He was, in many ways, a natural for this field, as in it he found scope for his musical and dramatic talents, his need to serve, and the beauty of the Episcopal service satisfied a yearning in him that would otherwise have been denied.

After fourteen years as an Episcopal minister, twelve of which were spent in historic Queen Anne's Parish in southern Maryland, Dr. Marsh went to Siberia with A.E.F. as Assistant Director in charge of Red Cross work among allied troops and Teutonic prisoners-of-war. Of this expedition, which set forth in October, 1918 and left Siberia on April 1, 1920, little is generally known. An article in the December 1920 issue of the National Geographic Magazine written by Dr. Marsh gives some of the highlights of his year and a half in Siberia.

When he returned to the United States, the country was in the throes of the disillusionment that follows war. He himself was disappointed and discouraged with the role that organized religion had played, feeling it had, through stubborn adherence to old ideologies, failed to meet the challenge of a world at war. And so, no longer a young man, he determined to leave the ministry and enter the field of medicine. Despite the admonitions of almost everyone that only a young man could master the tremendous body of facts required of a medical student, he nevertheless went ahead, graduating in 1928 at the age of forty-five from Albany

59

Medical College, Union University. Incidentally, he won honors in his National Boards, upsetting a good many theories.

The next two years were spent at Kings Park State Hospital, Long Island, and it was there that Dr. Marsh began his work in group therapy. This was done with no help and little tolerance from the rest of the staff, most of whom considered him more or less psychotic himself to want to do anything over and above the daily stint. But to him the phenomenon of mental disease was an exciting challenge and one he felt driven to do something about. He had in his ministerial work seen the tremendous force exerted by the group, and it seemed natural and logical to assume that even among psychotic patients that force would also apply. It did work: the patients enjoyed the group meetings in which they were gently encouraged to take part, and staff and attendants alike had to admit that the effects on the patients were remarkable, those who were withdrawn being stimulated to venture a little into the world of reality and those who were hyperactive becoming calmer. Nurses noted that a definite decrease in sedatives administered at night was possible.

Impressed by Dr. Marsh's work at Kings Park, Dr. William Bryan, superintendent of Worcester State Hospital, Worcester, Massachusetts, a really progressive state hospital superintendent, asked him to come to Worcester for a year with carte blanche to develop his ideas on group therapy. This was an unusual opportunity and it was a year packed full of accomplishment. All the services of the hospital were drawn into the plan to make it a dynamic, living place for the rehabilitation of its patients — occupational therapy, social service, the group of theological students who spent a season there becoming acquainted with types of illness they would later encounter in their parishes, etc. Lectures were given to relatives of patients, to all the different groups working in the hospital, and an enormous amount of work was done in the community through lectures in an effort to remove the stigma from the diagnosis of mental disease. Group meetings for patients were enlarged and elaborated with gratifying results. A great deal was done through the medium of music.

After leaving Worcester State Hospital Dr. Marsh went to Arizona and was thereafter in private practice. He continued his crusade to improve conditions for the mentally ill, particularly in connection with the state hospital. In Tucson, where psychotic patients were, like common felons, placed in the county jail pending court action and removal to the state hospital, he waged a vigorous campaign against the county supervisors until they capitulated and built a ward at the county hospital equipped to handle such patients. He was a fighter who would not acknowledge defeat when he knew he was right, and a formidable opponent, but more of his success was due to his extraordinary personal magnetism, his articulateness, and his expertness in handling people. His genuine love of people gave him a warmth that should be, it would seem, the first qualification of any psychiatrist.

Dr. Marsh died at his home in Tucson, November 4, 1949."[40]

III. EVALUATION OF THE PIONEERS: 1907-1935

R. Corsini:

"The importance of a man in any field depends not only on his insights and operations but also on whether he communicated his ideas. Six men who did the major work from 1906 to 1931 deserve to be called the pioneers of group psychotherapy: Pratt, Lazell, Marsh, Adler, Moreno, and Burrow."[41] For reasons which are given on page 82 Adler is left out from the final evaluation. The list is therefore reduced to five: Pratt, Lazell, Marsh, Moreno and Burrow.

1. Moreno and Pratt entered the field at about the same time, Pratt in 1906-8; Moreno in 1908.

2. Emergence of the interaction method (Moreno, 1908-1825, published in German, and 1928-1934, published in English); emergence of the analytic method (Burrow, 1927).

3. Moreno and Burrow presented a philosophical and psychological system in support of their group methods. Pratt, Marsh and Lazell did not produce any specific philosophy of group therapy.

4. Pratt published between 1908 and 1935 five scientific papers describing his class method. Lazell published two papers; Marsh two; and Burrow two. Moreno published twelve publications in German, seven in English, among them two books. The volume of publications is an indicator of productivity although not necessarily of quality.

5. Burrow, Lazell and Marsh ceased to produce before 1935.

61

Moreno continued to publish numerous papers on the subject of group psychotherapy.

CITATIONS I

PROPOSAL OF J. L. MORENO'S PLAN OF GROUP PSYCHOTHERAPY

Read by WILLIAM ALANSON WHITE

At the annual meeting of the American Psychiatric Association
Philadelphia, Pa., May 31, 1932

"The proposal for the Application of the Group Method to the Classification of Prisoners has grown out of a luncheon conference arranged by the National Committee on Prisons and Prison Labor through the courtesy of the American Psychiatric Association at our meeting in Toronto last year, 1931, at which many of you were present. Dr. J. L. Moreno suggested "group psychotherapy" of prisoners and as a result the authorities of the New York State Department of Correction permitted Dr. Moreno in collaboration with Dr. E. Stagg Witin, Chairman of the Executive Council of the National Committee on Prisons and Prison Labor, to carry on research at Sing Sing Prison."
(From *The First Book of Group Psychotherapy,* Beacon House, 1932)

CITATIONS II

F. LOVELL BIXBY

Consultant on Probation, State of New Jersey, Trenton

"I was at that historic meeting in Philadelphia in 1932 and I was enormously skeptical. I had no hesitation saying this man Moreno is either the greatest thing since Barnum or the greatest thing since Freud, but I thought it was Barnum. Many young people in the correctional world like the late Holsopple and myself resisted that new thing 'group psychotherapy.' Why did we resist it so? Why were we so unwilling to listen? I think we were just at a certain period in the development of correction. Group therapy back in 1932, we sort of equated with mass treatment." (From *Group Psychotherapy,* Vol. 18, No. 1-2, March-June, 1965.)

CITATIONS III

Austin MacCormick

Professor Emeritus in Criminology, University of California at Berkeley, Formerly New York City's Commissioner of Correction Executive Director, Osborne Assn., Inc., New York City

"Dr. J. L. Moreno
Beacon, N. Y.

Dear Friend:
I erred in not giving you full credit for being 'the father of group psychotherapy in prisons.' It has come a long way since 1932, and is now our most useful tool in going beyond the mere imparting of skills to the real task of helping offenders resolve deep-seated problems." (From *Group Psychotherapy,* Vol. 18, No. 1-2, March-June, 1965.)

EVALUATION: J. L. MORENO, M. D.

R. Corsini:

"Anyone looking at these several methods in 1931 would have seen little in common among them. In the way that words have of establishing concepts, it seems that Moreno's term *group therapy,* which he used to indicate a sociometric method of re-classifying prisoners, actually helped to establish the concept of psychotherapy of individuals in groups. This term became the generic name for all methods of therapeutic group work. The modern period of group psychotherapy began with the introduction of the new term: it established a common conceptual frame of reference."

"In 1937 appeared his journal *Sociometry,* and in 1947, *Sociatry,* later to be called *Group Psychotherapy*. He organized the first society of group therapists in 1942 and became its first president. Moreno's major accomplishments are three: first, he introduced a theory to account for group structure and operations; second, he introduced a new method of therapy in groups, which has been accepted by many people in a diversity of forms; and third, he has been the indefatigable exponent of the group therapeutic movement."

"Probably the most important individual in the history of group psychotherapy is J. L. Moreno."[42]

Robert J. Lince:

"The principal new facts elicited from this book are that Jacob Moreno long ago had personal contacts with the great American psychiatrist, William A. White, further, that White, the father of modern American psychiatry, thought well of Moreno's ideas and gave his blessing to further explorations by the new heretic.

It is established by verbatim recordings in this book that Jacob Moreno was the first psychiatrist to see the potentialities of group psychotherapy, and to have a feeling for the use of group dynamic principles in treatment and in research."[43]

Hans Syz:

"I am glad to submit a brief comment on Moreno's *First Book on Group Psychotherapy* from the background of Burrow's phyloanalytic studies. The core of the book, written twenty-five years ago, proposes transforming a prison into a socialized community by selecting individuals through spontaneity tests and various forms of personality recordings, and assigning them to functional units. These interrelationships were to make possible a group therapy in which the problems of individuals would be spontaneously submitted to the regulating influences of the group itself. Authoritative opinions on Moreno's plan expressed at that time, and the discussion of his proposals at the 1932 meeting of the American Psychiatric Association, undoubtedly contributed greatly to promoting the group psychotherapy movement."[44]

Werner W. Kemper:

"There is a question whether it is not possible to develop besides an analytic group therapy one which is entirely different, specifically tied to the group and with greater possibilities — Moreno had first formulated this question and he has always answered it in the affirmative. Already several decades ago he recognized intuitively that the group is different from a stereotype mass. He has also recognized that the physician-patient relation in the therapeutic group, as compared with individual analysis, was radically changed: the patient becomes an important member of the group and eventually an additional assistant 'therapist'. And finally he has built into the framework of group therapy the Stegreiftheater in the form of psychodrama. By this he has created a therapeutic instrument whose manifold and deep-reaching effects are beginning to be appreciated in its full consequences. However, with his thesis of therapeutic acting-out, Moreno has himself involuntarily clouded the true value of his work."[45]

William Alanson White:

"Dr. J. L. Moreno suggested group psychotherapy of prisoners. This relating of the men to one another he calls 'group psychotherapy'."[46]

Winfred Overholser:

"In the development of this form of treatment (group psychotherapy) one thinks especially of the pioneering work of J. L. Moreno. The phrase, 'group psychotherapy' had first been given currency by Moreno."[47]

Wilfred Hulse:

"Moreno has introduced the use of scientific methods in the exploration of intragroup relations. He has tested and charted the intricate forces that unite and divide human beings who live together in natural groupings; he was the first to use the term group psychotherapy and to apply the findings for therapeutic purposes."[48]

Joseph I. Meiers:

"Moreno has been generally recognized as the chief exponent of psychodrama and sociometry. But what has been known to a small group has never been made fully clear to the profession at large: He has been also chief mover in the development of the scientifically based group psychotherapy. Moreno was the first to

65

see the need (1) for knowing the dynamic structure of groups as prerequisite to the therapy of groups; (2) for systematizing such knowledge."[49]

Walter Bromberg:

"In terms of the history of psychiatry, the group therapy movement occupied very few years from the time when it first made its appearance until it spread throughout the clinical psychiatric field. . . . One may point to Moreno's early experimental groups as the beginning of group therapy as we know it today. There seems little historical reason to doubt his pioneership."[50]

A. Friedemann:

"These factors (the interrelationship between psychotherapy and sociology) have been represented particularly by J. L. Moreno, the originator of group psychotherapy."[51]

H. Teirich:

"On the basis of lengthy research in the available literature of group psychotherapy, the reviewer is of the opinion that Moreno may have been the first to systematically build up and apply this method."[52]

EVALUATION: JOSEPH PRATT, M.D.

R. Corsini:

"Pratt's career has two distinct phases. In 1906 he was interested in curing a purely somatic disease, and he called groups together to instruct members in a therapeutic regimen. In 1930, when he established a clinic at the Boston Dispensary, his concern was no longer with frank disease but, on the contrary, with persons who had nothing organically wrong with them but who nevertheless complained of physical symptoms. Now, instead of deprecating the class method, he made it the central therapeutic focus."[54]

"The fact is, as is very clear in Pratt's own writings, that Pratt did not engage in planned psychotherapy in 1905. His sole intention was to prove the validity of his theory that tuberculosis could be treated successfully in the homes of indigent consumptives. For this purpose, he gathered patients into groups for 'time saving' purposes to give them information about the necessity of following a strict hygienic regimen which included rest, fresh air and good food. Pratt explicitly denied the value of the group or of his own personality in his results."[55]

H. Mullan and M. Rosenbaum:

"From Pratt's early writings it is evident that he had little understanding of his own impact upon his patients when they met in the weekly classes."[56]

J. W. Klapman:

"It is probable that what Pratt had in mind principally was to teach the essential rules of hygiene to these patients, and that he found it most expedient to impart such instruction in a group."[57]

Joseph I. Meiers:

"It may seem a sheer coincidence that the earliest and most typical founders of true group psychotherapy were two men who started from entirely different angles. One, a medical doctor in the highly industrialized America of the first decade of this century, was J. H. Pratt of Boston. He, as early as 1906, introduced mass instruction into the treatment of tuberculous patients. This he gradually extended into classes of instruction and encouragement, by many psychological devices, of psychoneurotics and what now might be called sufferers of 'psychosomatic' cases. It was in April, 1930, that the first class of what was subsequently called 'Thought Control' convened. Typical for the importance and specific weight of the group members in Pratt's movement is the fact that the name 'Thought Control' was given not by him, but suggested by one of his first class members.

The other early creation of a methodology that later was to become the fully developed sociometrically and psychodramatically based group psychotherapy, originated in Vienna, a big city which, like Boston, was a centre of industry and a metropolis of learning."[58]

A. S. Luchins:

"Short talks, a feature of the 'Class method' originally used by Pratt (1906, 1907) with tubercular patients, have been used by him and others (Harris, 1939) at the Boston Dispensary for medical patients who had no organic basis for their complaints."[59]

Pratt never treated mental problems before 1930 and he did not do anything resembling modern group psychotherapy before that time. His first publication on thought control appeared in 1934 and presented a lecture-centered technique. He was the only non-psychiatrist of the five. He was not trained in psychiatry and not primarily interested in psychotherapy. The other four pioneers started with contributions to psychiatry or psychotherapy.

EVALUATION: E. LAZELL, M. D., AND L. C. MARSH, M. D.

R. Corsini:

"The proper place of these two psychiatrists in the history of psychotherapy is not easy to assess. The first to publish his views was Lazell, whose earliest paper appeared in 1921, but by far the more important was Marsh, who did not begin to write until 1931." "However, neither Marsh nor Lazell appears to have had any great effect on other therapists; the statistics of the literature indicate that they did not fan the spark into life."[60]

J. W. Klapman:

"Lazell became aware of the need for a therapy for large numbers in hospital wards who are inaccessible to individual psychotherapy. He conceived the idea of delivery of lectures to patients in simple language based on modern psychology. Dr. William Alanson White, Superintendent of St. Elizabeths Hospital, accepted the plan.

Marsh's first experiments at Kings Park State Hospital (1929-30) were not published until 1931; it was also his first publication. He differed from Lazell. Marsh believed that the psychological content of the lectures were immaterial. Any lecture he thought able to capture the interest of the patients would do. He considered more important that the patients were stimulated intellectually and emotionally. He saw the mental hospitals of the future as educational institutions. He proposed an organization of ex-patients on state and national bases. He delivered lectures over the hospital loudspeaker at Worcester State Hospital in 1932."[61]

J. L. Moreno:

"They were 'addressing' the groups instead of working with them; they were using 'class' methods without working through the *interaction* among the members of the group; they were lecturers and teachers."[62]

A. B. Luchins:

"Dementia praecox patients at St. Elizabeths Hospital were given a series of talks by Lazell (1921) on psychopathology and psychosexual development from a Freudian point of view."[63]

EVALUATION: T. BURROW, M.D.

P. Renouvier:

"Burrow was more sophisticated than both Pratt and Lazell and made a definite contribution to group dynamics with his concepts of social neurosis, group analysis and consensual observation. However, his interest in group psychotherapy remained marginal and short lived. By 1931, when the real conceptual, clinical and organizational struggle began, he moved out of group therapy and concentrated on phyloanalysis."[64]

H. Syz:

"Burrow's goal was not adaptation to the social norm but investigation of its noxious aspects. His studies showed that the trend toward autistic focusing upon the self-image is a common pathogenic denominator in the endless variety of personality formations and social structures. It would seem that unless we deal concretely with the social and physiological aspects of this attentional deflection as it is interwoven in patient, therapist and community, we cannot expect our individual and group therapies to meet man's urgent need, and Moreno's 'therapeutic society' must remain a hardly attainable ideal."[65]

69

A. Wolf and E. Schwartz:

"In connection with the group anti-analytic trend in group psychotherapy, of which the group dynamic inclination is merely one facet, it is worth noting how little attention is paid these days to the brilliant contributions made by that pioneer in the field of psychoanalysis in groups (Trigant Burrow). It may be because he was rigorously oriented to the individual in the group."[66]

Burrow was a deep but isolated thinker and deserves recognition because of his bio-social philosophy. However, he did not see the potentialities of group psychotherapy. Were it left to him, there would not be a group psychotherapy movement today.

IV. INTERPERSONAL RELATIONS AND INTERDEPENDENCE OF THE PIONEERS

It has been generally assumed that each of the five pioneers arrived at their approach independently and that they have not been in contact with one another. However, the facts are that between 1934 and 1945, Pratt, Lazell and Marsh became acquainted with Moreno; in their later writings they began to call themselves group psychotherapists. None of them apparently met with Burrow. Pratt and Lazell contributed to the Moreno symposium on group psychotherapy of 1945, each with an article. Both became members of the American Society of Group Psychotherapy and Psychodrama and became contributing editors of *Sociatry, A Journal of Group and Intergroup Therapy,* in 1947. Cody Marsh was in touch with Moreno by correspondence and Mrs. Marsh wrote the obituary of Cody Marsh for *Group Psychotherapy* in 1950.

Pratt, Lazell and Marsh are known as advocates of lecture-centered methods. There is no tangible evidence that they influenced one another, although it is probable that they did. Pratt published four papers on his class method by 1921. One of them appeared in 1907 in the *Journal of the American Medical Association;* another in 1908 in the *British Medical Journal.* It stands to reason that as scientific news travels, Lazell heard of Pratt's work either through these channels or indirectly. Under all circumstances,

Lazell showed his originality by applying the lecture method to psychiatric problems. It is further probable that Marsh heard of Lazell's work via the *Psychoanalytic Review,* which was a very popular psychiatric magazine in the 1920's.

Pratt passed through at least three phases in his development. The first phase, until 1931 or 1934, was identified with the class method for physical ailments. From 1934 to 1945 he moved towards an approach to psychological problems which he called "thought control." From 1945 on he came closer to appreciating the current forms of group psychotherapy and was a frequent speaker at the annual meetings of the American Society of Group Psychotherapy and Psychodrama. Lazell showed interest in sociometric and interaction methods when he was at the Veterans Administration Hospital in Northport, Long Island, and later in Denver, Colorado.

The chain of influence of the lecture-centered method runs, therefore, from Pratt to Lazell to Marsh and from them to Chappell 1936, Schroeder 1936, Buck 1937, Harris 1939, Snowden 1940, Hadden 1941, and Klapman 1946.

The chain of influence of the interactional method was Moreno 1914, Jennings 1929, Bridge 1929, W. A. White 1931, Whitin 1931, Slavson 1931, Branham 1931, Bixby 1932, Stein 1932, Doll 1932, Richmond 1934, Schilder 1934, Lewin 1935, Curran 1938, Solby 1940, Ackerman 1943, Meiers 1945, Dreikurs 1950, Enneis 1950, Luchins 1950, and Corsini 1951.

The chain of influence of the analytic trend was Moreno 1923, Burrow 1927, Syz 1928, Wender 1936, Schilder 1936, Blackman 1940, Ackerman 1943, Foulkes 1948, Wolf 1949, and Ezriel 1950.

CONCLUSIONS

When Moreno arrived in 1925 in the U.S.A., there were only the publications of Pratt on class method and one paper by Lazell describing his lectures to groups of schizophrenics (op. cit.). Both Pratt and Lazell used a lecture method but Lazell had an edge over Pratt because his lectures were at least directed to mental patients. However, they did not add any new concept. Group therapy and group psychotherapy did not yet exist. The era of literature under the heading of group therapy began with Moreno.

71

Pratt's productivity after 1922 was negligible, except for a paper in 1934. There is no record about Marsh's work until 1931. He published three papers and then disappeared from productivity by 1935. Similarly, Burrow ceased to publish on group analysis after 1927, but his contribution was qualitatively superior to that of Lazell, Pratt and Marsh. The productivity of Pratt, Marsh, Lazell and Burrow, was short lived. They stopped producing on the subject of group psychotherapy long before they passed on, whereas Moreno never ceased to produce and organize the movement.

The spread of Moreno's influence among the pioneers is best indicated if we follow the gradual acceptance of his terminology. He introduced the terms group therapy and group psychotherapy in 1931. Until 1935 he was the only writer using these terms. Marsh followed and used the term "group therapy" in the last paper which he published.[67] A. Alpert, M. Schroeder and L. Wender used the term group psychotherapy in their titles in the course of 1936.[68] By 1937 Schilder began to use this term. By 1940 Slavson used it. As it often is with concepts and phrases which become popular, the writers may have been unaware of their sources. Beginning with 1938, both terms group therapy and group psychotherapy began to be used as synonymous with all group methods. In 1939 two papers were listed under this title; in 1940 four; in 1952 one hundred and thirteen papers had the term group psychotherapy in their title, and from then on they appeared in rapidly ascending scale.

The use of the *group* as a participating unit in discussion and action was introduced by Moreno in 1923, and two reports of his audience interaction sessions were reported by H. H. Jennings in 1931.[69] The principle of "therapeutic interaction" was further elaborated by Moreno in 1932. This principle began to penetrate the field very slowly and was met with resistance. Psychoanalysts preferred to treat single individuals within a group setting rather than to treat the interaction of individuals.

Moreno's book *Das Stegreiftheater* was a mixture of interaction analysis and group methods, of spontaneous acting and acting-out procedures, a combination which growingly dominates the current practice of group psychotherapists. The majority of the present practitioners favor interaction among the members, some degree of acting-out, a smattering of knowledge of the group matrix and a modified use of psychoanalytic concepts. *Das Stegreiftheater* contained the following principles: (1) It introduced the concept of group interaction and group participation, p. 12-13. (2) It eliminated the spectator and introduced the concepts of actor and action-catharsis, p. 81. (3) It introduced the concept of the role player versus the self, p. 27. (4) It demonstrated the acting-out of past events, the reliving of the past in action, in contrast to mere verbalization, p. 70. (5) It demonstrated the acting-out of current events, p. 66, in the here and now. (6) It introduced the concept of group catharsis. (7) It introduced the interaction diagram (the notations of spontaneous interactions), forerunner of the sociogram, p. 88-95. (8) It introduced the concept of "medial understanding" ("mediale Verständigung"), initiating the concept of "co-unconscious states," p. 57. (9) It presented the impact of creativity upon unconscious states, p. 35. (10) It explored the dynamics of interpersonal resistance, p. 49. (11) The "empirical" group had emerged, opening the field for concrete group research; thus the principle of therapeutic interaction found its first scientific formulation. (12) It replaced the couch by a flexible social vehicle.[70]

On the basis of the foregoing evaluations, Moreno emerges as the chief organizer of the Group Psychotherapy Movement and as the creator of the scientific foundations of group psychotherapy.

V. SCIENTIFIC FOUNDATION OF GROUP PSYCHOTHERAPY

A. *First Period: 1908-1935*
INTERACTIONAL AND SOCIOMETRIC BASE OF GROUP PSYCHOTHERAPY

The conceptual period between 1908 and 1935 resulted in definite directions of theory and practice of group psychotherapy which in one way or another, whatever their label or modification, have become characteristic of the thoughtways of present day group psychotherapy. At the end of that period, the trend crystallized most eloquently in the interactional method. Many group psychotherapists of the new generation are not adequately acquainted with the history of the early period. For them, group psychotherapy began during World War II.

BASIC CONCEPTS OF SOCIOMETRY
AND GROUP DYNAMICS

The first step beyond Freud was taken by Moreno with the development of a science of the therapeutic group; this science he called sociometry.[71] In order to select and understand the participating patient-members, it was imperative for the physician to gain insight into the structure and arrangements of therapeutic groups by means of tests, observation, interviews and discussions.

Sociometric research prepared the foundation for a diagnostic science of the normal and pathological group. The most important discovery was that each group had a structure of its own, of varying cohesion and depth. Each group differs in composition, and each group from the first meeting possesses a specific structure, which in the course of time develops typical forms. Finally, these group formations indicate the amount of therapeutic success. Moreno's idea was not to start with rigid theories and hypotheses, but to find methods and tests which would enable the researcher and therapist to discover the typical structures of therapeutic groups.

The following are a few sociometric principles important for group therapists:

1) Sociometric status is based on interpersonal relations as they emerge in spontaneous groupings.
2) Every group has an official and an unofficial sociometric basis, the conscious and the unconscious structure of the group.
3) Every group develops according to definite sociogenetic laws.
4) Attractions and repulsions between individuals in groups follow the sociodynamic law.
5) There are three types of leaders: popular leaders, powerful leaders and isolated leaders; accordingly, there are leader-centered, group-centered, and leaderless groups.
6) Every group has a specific cohesion. The task of therapy is to guide a pathological group from a low to a higher degree of cohesion.

The treatment of concrete groups, the real group psychotherapy, consists of therapeutic sessions in which three or more individuals participate in an effort to solve their common problems. In these groups participants are strangers. In another form of group psychotherapy, the so-called family therapy, the participants are members of the same family. Therefore, we differentiated *natural* groupings — *i.e.* the family — from *synthetic* groupings, such as clinical groups. The sessions of natural groups take place where people live and act, in their homes or in their work places — *"in situ."* When the object of therapy is a specific family, the composition of the group is already given, the family members are in their natural milieu. The people know one another intimately, and when the therapist visits their house, they are seated in their customary places. On the other hand, the sessions of synthetic groups consist of unrelated individuals meeting in a medical office, in a hospital or a clinic. The members of the group are strangers; their relations to one another are new and unformed, *"in statu nascendi."* It is particularly in groups of this kind that sociometry can help to select the patients for constant and advantageous group formations.

The formation of synthetic groups has been the earliest problem of the interactional method. The task was to establish a theoretic base for group psychotherapy.

Moreno was keenly aware of the problems presented by psychoanalysis. He started off with an "analysis of psychoanalysis" and arrived at conclusions which took him to a position beyond it. Moreno assembled the new members of the group in the following experiment in 1921; a room was fitted out with a number of couches; every individual was placed on a couch. The fundamental rule of free association was applied to them. The experiment failed — the free associations of one began to mingle with the free associations of the others. This confused them and produced a chaotic situation. The reason for the failure was obvious. Free association works significantly only along individual tracks: free associations which have significance along the track of individual A have no significance on the track of B or of C, and vice versa. They have no "common unconscious." When free association was vigorously applied the result was that a number of individuals were being separately psychoanalyzed. There was no bridge between them. It did not develop into a *group* psychoanalysis but into an individual psychoanalysis of the several individuals within that group. But the objective was *group* production, *group* therapy and *group* analysis, not individual analysis. As the psychoanalytic method of free association for group processes proved unproductive, a new method developed which was based on the observation of the formation of groups *in statu nascendi.* "Individuals who never met before and who from the first meeting on have to be participants in the same group represent a new problem to the therapist; we see them when they enter spontaneously into interrelations which lead them to form a group *sub specie momenti;* we can study their spontaneous reactions in the initial stage of group formation and the activities developing in the course of such organization. We are present when the relationship is born, at the earliest possible stage in the social relation of the individuals who meet, and we can develop, if necessary, the treatment forward instead of backward; we begin with the act, the initial attitude one person has for the other, and follow up to what fate these interrelations lead, what kind of organizations they develop."[72] (Moreno, 1934)

These free, spontaneous actions and interactions between individuals within a group are not identical with "free association" in a psychoanalytic sense unless the true meaning of free association is distorted and stretched to a point at which it loses its scientific meaning and becomes playing with words. These free, spontaneous interaction responses are fundamentally the same in all interaction encounters and psychodramatic operations. Nothing is gained by calling these operations free floating discussions. As operations, these spontaneous interaction responses do not differ from one another except that this initial interaction matrix consisting of words and actions can be used for various kinds of interpretations, psychoanalytic, socioanalytic, psychodramatic, sociometric or otherwise.

In support of the existence of such an initial common matrix, sociometric research has shown that "immediate response between strangers differs significantly from "chance"[73] and that "tele"[74] is already operating between the members of the group from the first meeting. In the therapist-patient relationship two processes can be observed; the one process is transference, the development of fantasies (unconscious) which the patient projects upon the therapist, surrounding him with a certain glamor; but then there is another process still more fundamental, *tele* (derived from the Greek: projection into distance). It radiates from that part of his ego which is not carried away by auto-suggestion. It sizes up the man across the desk and estimates intuitively what kind of person he is. It assesses his immediate behavior, physical, mental or other-

76

wise, and evaluates him as he actually is, consciously or unconsciously, independent of the transference picture the patient may have of him. Simultaneously, just as the patient assesses the immediate behavior of the therapist, the therapist assesses the patient. It is a two-way process, interweaving two or more individuals relating one to another. It is *Zweifühlung* in contrast to *Einfühlung*. It operates from birth on — already in the mother-infant symbiosis (matrix of identity), prior to transference. It is the cement which is destined to hold the group together.

This "primary" cohesiveness can be utilized by the therapist towards the development and sharing of group members' common therapeutic aims. All the interactions between them, abreactions, soliloquies, dialogues, tele, and transference relations to therapist, auxiliary egos and each other in the course of therapy will be influenced by this original structure and will in turn modify it. The multiple couch experiment had failed; it showed that free association is unable to carry from one individual to another. But it led to the discovery that, if "free spontaneous interaction" is permitted, a new operational frame of reference develops, from which one can look at the successive stages of a synthetic group.

The first concern of the group therapist is the *immediate* behavior of the group. When the therapist faces his group for the first session he perceives immediately, with his skilled sense for interpersonal relations, some of the interaction between the members, for example, the distribution of love, hate, and indifference. The group is not just a collection of individuals each living in an ivory tower. He notices one or two sitting all by themselves, physically isolated from the rest; two or three clustered together, smiling and gossiping; one or two engaged in an argument or sitting side by side but giving each other the cold shoulder. In other words, the first contours of a sociometric diagram begin to form in his mind. He does not have to give a formal test in order to obtain this knowledge. He takes notice of this "embryonic matrix." It comes to him through his immediate observations. It becomes his guide for the therapeutic process-in-becoming. The group has, from the first session on, whatever its size, a specific structure of interpersonal relations which, however, does not reveal itself at once on the surface but appears later as an underlying *sociometric or group matrix* and *interpersonal network*. The term sociometric often arouses confusion in the minds of group psychotherapists. They think that sociometry is exclusively metric; actually, the first half of the term socio comes from socius, with emphasis on group process and group structure. It was from the start not only research oriented but also therapy oriented. It is concerned, among other things, with "optimum of satisfaction" for every individual in the group, sociostasis, cohesiveness and therapeutic regrouping.[75]

Natural groupings behave differently from groups of strangers. Mother and child, members of a family, matrimonial partners, two lovers, friends and business partners of long standing, and similar intimate *interpersonal ensembles,* have a common matrix of silent understanding. The members of such groups have a common past, they expect a common future, and they share a life together in their home. When, for instance, husband and wife re-enact in a psychodramatic session an intimate episode in which they have been involved, one appears to know the experience of the other with surprising accuracy; the same clairvoyance is evident in the enactment of present episodes and future projections. It is as if they would have developed in the course of years a long and intricate chain of quasi-unconscious states. If one of the dyad or triad begins to draw from one phase of the common experience, the other one has no difficulty in continuing the same thread, supplementing the other, as if they were one person and "as if" they would have a common unconscious life. They appear to share in what Moreno later called "co-conscious" and "co-unconscious" states.[76] But the insight which one person has about what goes on in the other person's mind is often sketchy. They live simultaneously in different worlds which communicate only at times and even then incompletely. The psyche is not transparent. We see man and wife acting out in an interpersonal therapy session or a psychodrama, side by side, some feelings and thoughts which they never knew in regard to each other. They were themselves taken by surprise upon hearing and seeing what the other party had felt, hitherto fully unnoticed. The checking, reminding and analyzing of each by the other is carried out by the patients themselves. They added parts which one or the other had left out in the particular scene. At times what seemed important to him did not seem important to her. In consequence they placed emphasis upon different points. Indeed, in the interpretation of free associations of a single individual, the psychoanalyst has no control of validity except the assertion of that particular patient that a certain episode has the meaning the therapist ascribes to it. But in the symbiotic responses of co-unconscious states, one acts like a mirror to the other. There are here two subjectivities concurring on the accuracy of an event.[77]

In addition to the subjective dimensions of co-conscious and co-unconscious states, the interactions are accompanied by a system of complementary objective and physical signs. These signs can be operationally explored through psychodramatic methods of enactment. Physical or symbolic signs are guideposts in the process of the mutual recall of crucial episodes. An illustration may be seen, *e. g.* in a trivial psychodramatic episode between a husband and wife. She remembers definitely that he had an outburst of anger towards her but "there was no reason for it." When he reminded her that it happened because she removed the picture of his mother from the piano, and put it on the bookshelf, the incident began to be dimly recalled by her and they began to re-enact it. When she was removing the picture, and she was asked by the director to soliloquize what she was thinking, she said, "Your mother is dead now. It is not necessary that her picture is placed on such a prominent spot in the room." The signs which helped her to recall this mutual interaction and understand its significance were her *walking* towards the piano, *taking* the picture from the piano, *walking* from the piano to the bookshelf and *placing* the picture flat on the bookshelf, then *turning* towards him. His counter-signs were that he suddenly *left* the room but returned when she called him in. Then his outburst took place, and he soliloquized that he had *left* the room in order to *avoid* a scene and when she called out saying she was going for an errand, he felt neglected and retaliated with anger.

Neither the concept of unconscious states (Freud) nor that of the collective unconscious states (Jung) can be easily applied to these problems without stretching the meaning of the terms. The free associations of A may be a path to the unconscious states of A; the free associations of B may be a path to the unconscious states of B; but can the unconscious material of A ever link naturally and directly with the unconscious material of B unless they share in unconscious states? The concept of individual unconscious states becomes unsatisfactory for explaining both movements, from the present situation of A, and in reverse to the present situation of B. We must look for a concept which is so constructed that the objective indication for the existence of this two-way process does not come from a single psyche but from a still deeper reality in which the unconscious states of two or several individuals are interlocked with a system of "co-unconscious" states. Jung postulated that every individual has, besides a personal, a collective unconscious. Although the distinction was useful, it did not help in solving the dilemma described. Jung did not apply the collective unconscious to the concrete collectivities in which people live. There was nothing gained in turning from a personal to a "collective unconscious" if by doing this the anchorage to the *concrete,* whether individual or group, was lost. Had he turned to the group by developing techniques like group psychotherapy or sociodrama, he might have gained a concrete position for this theory of the collective unconscious, but as it is, he underplayed the individual anchorage but did not establish a safe "collective anchorage" as a counterposition. The problem here is not the collective images of a given culture or of mankind, but the *specific* relatedness and cohesiveness of a group of individuals. In the system of co-unconscious states, extended into the interpersonal networks of the group,[78] we have found a rationale for the significance and effectiveness of role reversal, double, and mirror,[79] empty or auxiliary chair,[80] and other psychodramatic techniques. Now we understand that they are the natural instruments for exploring, modifying and retraining co-conscious and co-unconscious states. But this still leaves a question open. Phenomena like hallucinations and dreams require elaborate symbolic systems of interpretation as long as we limit our communications with the patients to language and free association of words. Because they originated in a period of our mental growth when acts have a priority over words in the "no-man's land" of physical signs, act-hunger, and spontaneous role playing,[81] direct operational methods and action techniques like psychodrama are better fitted for their exploration.

The theoretical basis of all varieties of group psychotherapy can be formulated with a greater degree of assurance today than when these experiments were initiated in the early thirties. It has three frames of reference. First, the *common interactional matrix,* which the individuals share, of a changing constellation and cohesiveness expressed in multiple emotional tensions. Second, the common *co-conscious and co-unconscious* experience of the members. The longer a synthetic group endures the more it begins to resemble a natural group, to develop and share an unconscious life, from which its members draw their strength, knowledge and security. This co-unconscious network reflected in sociograms and role diagrams, tying the members together with varying degrees of identity, is the river bed to which the individual histories act as contributories, their "stream" of co-consciousness and co-unconsciousness. Third, the *role reversal of any member with every other member.* The more different and distant the members are, the more urgent it is that they reverse roles with each other in the course of mutual therapy. Psychodrama is an elaborate form of "encounter," and it is the experience of encounter which was the original force in the development of this method.[82] Role reversal puts the cap on the encounter between "you and I." It is the final touch of giving unity, identity and universality to the group.

SOCIOLOGY AND PSYCHOLOGY, THEIR RELATIONS TO GROUP PSYCHOTHERAPY

It has been pointed out[83] that scientific group psychotherapy has three roots, a root in medicine, a root in sociology, and a root in religious existentialism. It is only fair to emphasize the great importance which sociological and psychological principles have had in the formation of group psychotherapy, but the contemporary sociologists and psychologists of the scene between 1925 and 1935 made no *direct* contribution. The attitude of academic psychology and sociology was favourable and greeted warmly the concrete advances made by group psychotherapy practitioners. It is by no means an accident that the same year when Gardner Murphy's first edition of *Experimental Social Psychology* appeared in 1931, a maverick from sociology, psychology and psychiatry entered the scene; this was "sociometry," which established a bridge between the social sciences and group psychotherapy.

THE INDIVIDUAL-CENTERED PSYCHOTHERAPIES

FREUD, ADLER, JUNG

Due to an error in translation, the meaning of Freud's *Massen*

Psychologie und die Analyse des Ich (1922) has been distorted (the German word "Masse" means "crowd" not "group") so that many readers might get the impression that Freud has done something for "group" psychotherapy. Freud never worked with concrete groups. But he has contributed to "Massen Psychologie" by applying psychoanalytic concepts to such social phenomena as the army and the church.

There was, however, around 1920, a great gap between the inarticulate mass and the group. To make the jump from the "mass" to the "group" was exactly the historic job accomplished by sociometry and small group research.

Adler never claimed to be a group psychotherapist but his social philosophy was closer to the spirit of group therapy than that of any other student of Freud. In his child guidance clinics he often presented an individual case in front of adults, but "he himself" was not aware that the group character of the meeting had a therapeutic value for the patient and he did not investigate the group. His position is clearly expressed in an address called *The Individual Criminal and his Cure* published by the National Committee on Prisons and Prison Labor in 1930. It is an apotheosis to *individual* treatment in the strict sense of the word. There is not one word mentioned of groups and group treatment.

Jung was committed to individual analysis exclusively.[84]

As the situation looks at this moment of history, the relationship of Freud, Adler and Jung to group psychotherapy stands out clearly. These three men have never made a "direct" contribution to group psychotherapy. All three of them were individual-centered, although many of their pupils are now practicing group psychotherapy.

THE CONCEPT OF THE ENCOUNTER

BUBER AND MORENO

Among those distinguished non-group psychotherapists mentioned from time to time in connection with the early group psychotherapy movement is Martin Buber. The reason for this reference to him is that in Buber's work the concepts of the "meeting" or "encounter" and of the "I and thou" play a dominant role. It should be brought to the awareness of every group psychotherapist that behind what we call interpersonal relations (or "Zwischenmenschliche Beziehungen" of Moreno) is the concept of the encounter, now considered a cornerstone of existential analysis. Encounter means the fullest sharing of experienced reciprocity. Moreno's concept of the encounter has, therefore, stimulated the development of interpersonal systems which are of great importance in all forms of group psychotherapy. It is interesting to note that the idea of the encounter was formulated by J. L. Moreno, first in his *Einladung zu einer Begegnung,* 1914, and in many other publications between 1914 and 1924 in a series of books published by Gustav Kiepenheuer Verlag in Berlin. Moreno was editor of the *Daimon Magazine* between 1918 and 1921. Buber was one of the contributing editors of the magazine; he became acquainted with Moreno's concept and used it effectively in his famous book *I and Thou (Ich und Du)* published by Insel Verlag in Berlin a few years later (1923). As the concept of the encounter is a foundation stone of the philosophy of interpersonal relations, it is important to claim it as our own. If we do not claim ideas which are our contributions to modern group theory, we are bound to experience that other movements will place them into their own context, with the consequence that the "image" of the group psychotherapy movement will be distorted.

SUMMARY OF DEFINITIONS

Group psychotherapy is a method which attempts consciously, within the framework of empirical science, to treat simultaneously the interpersonal relations *and* the psychological problems of several group members. The following factors are included in the definition:

(a) Group psychotherapy is a conscious systematization of empirical data gained from observing individuals in group interaction.

(b) It consists in treating the psychological and social problems of group participants. Treatment deals with somatic disturbances only if they are caused by psychological conditions.

(c) It undertakes the simultaneous treatment of several individuals in interaction within the group.

(d) It is a method which is founded upon empirical investigations and is carried out within a scientific frame of reference. There are several variations, but the essential operations are the same in all cases. The theoretic framework is group centered, interaction and interpersonal.

The earliest definitions of group psychotherapy (Moreno):

(a) It is a fundamental principle of group psychotherapy that every individual is a therapeutic agent of the other individual, that every group is a therapeutic agent of every other group (1932).

(b) Group psychotherapy is a method of psychotherapy which attempts to find the most satisfactory grouping which will promote the sharing of experiences and increase group cohesiveness. It often initiates a regrouping of its members so as to bring the constellation of the entire group in harmony with the spontaneous motivations and aspirations of the individual members (1932).

(c) Group psychotherapy treats not only the single individual, who is the center of attention because of special difficulties in adaptation to and in coordination in the group, but the entire group and all individuals who are in relation to him (1934).

(d) "A truly therapeutic procedure can not have less an objective than the whole of mankind" (1934). It is a sociatric definition from the viewpoint of medical sociology, which considers all of human society as the real patient.

B. *Second Period: 1935-1938*

INTERACTIONAL GROUP PSYCHOTHERAPY,
THE BEGINNINGS OF THE ANALYTIC TREND
AND SMALL GROUP RESEARCH

By 1935 the early formulations of the group interactional trend were available in a number of publications and began to influence

84

the entire field. The outstanding events which led to this situation were: Moreno started *The Sociometric Review* in 1936, and *Sociometry* in 1937, with Gardner Murphy as Editor; it was the first journal of interpersonal relations, of small group research and group methods. In 1936 Louis Wender[85] and Paul Schilder[86] published their first papers on group psychotherapy, both with a psychoanalytic orientation. Schilder was influenced by reading *Who Shall Survive?;* he used sociometric questionnaires.

The intervention of Burrow as a pioneer of the analytic trend is, as we have seen in the portrait of his work, rather ambivalent. He opposed both the interactional and the current analytic trend. His interests were not directed towards group therapy but towards the study of man's neurosis in a biological framework.

All group psychotherapists of today are openly or implicitly interactional, though many declare allegiance to psychoanalytic concepts and terms. A modern group psychotherapist is an interactional group psychotherapist plus addition of orientation of varying origins, sociometric, psychoanalytic or behavioristic. The majority of schools of group psychotherapy are characterized by three hypotheses: 1) that every individual lives in groups, he must be considered as an individual as well as in his relation to other individuals; 2) that the interaction between members of a group can have therapeutic significance for them; 3) that the total constellation of the group can have a therapeutic effect upon every one of its members. The "explanation" of why these effects take place differ frequently from school to school.

This period, although short, was full of important events: a) the beginnings of diagnostic group psychotherapy with the introduction of the sociogram and of group measurement; b) the establishment of sociometry; c) advances in psychoanalytic group psychotherapy; d) the emergence of psychodrama, role theory and role playing.

The concept of the small group is more inclusive than group psychotherapy. It includes not only therapeutic but also strictly research approaches. Sociometry played an important role in the development of small group research as well as in group psychotherapy. Sociology and social psychology had little *direct* influence upon group psychotherapy; it was largely via sociometry and sociometric methods, through the study of group structure, group cohesiveness and sociogenesis, that they exercised their great influence.

VI. PERSONAL CONTACTS AMONG GROUP-ORIENTED PSYCHOLOGISTS AND EARLY GROUP PSYCHOTHERAPISTS

KURT LEWIN AND J. L. MORENO

Among non-group psychotherapists, two names are indirectly related to this period — Kurt Lewin and Harry Stack Sullivan. Kurt Lewin did not enter the group field until after becoming acquainted with Moreno's work and having personal contact with him in 1935.[87] His non-metric topological diagrams resemble as constructs Moreno's early interaction diagrams and space-time diagrams ("Bewegungsdiagram") published ten years earlier (1923).[88]

Kurt Lewin and J. L. Moreno met in the spring of 1935 in New York City for the purpose of discussing the sociometric studies contained in Moreno's *Who Shall Survive?* and also for discussing various group methods. Prior to the meeting Lewin had seen a motion picture of the activities program at the New York State Training School for Girls in Hudson, New York, in a laboratory of Columbia University.

Lewin announced in the *Sociometric Review* in 1936 (published by the New York State Training School for Girls at Hudson, N.Y.) sociometric studies of young children at the Iowa Welfare Research Station, State University of Iowa, Iowa City, 1936, p. 62. In Volume I of *Sociometry,* 1937-38, he published, in collaboration with R. Lippitt, a study on autocracy and democracy which was based on a preliminary sociometric survey. Lewin became a contributing editor of *Sociometry* in 1942 and continued in this function until his premature death. Lewin and Moreno entertained warm personal relations. Lewin was enrolled in a course on psychodrama and role playing just prior to his death.

H. S. SULLIVAN AND J. L. MORENO

Harry Stack Sullivan is often credited with having introduced psychiatry as a science of interpersonal relations. Actually, Moreno preceded him in *Who Shall Survive?* (1934) and in his monograph *Interpersonal Therapy and the Psychopathology of Inter-*

personal Relations and in the journal *Sociometry* (July, 1937). The journal *Psychiatry* by Sullivan was founded a year later, in 1938. It was Moreno who gave the term interpersonal relations the meaning it has today as a full two-way encounter between two or more individuals.

The phrase "interpersonal relations" had different meanings for Sullivan and Moreno. For Sullivan it was a one-way relation. The therapist is a participant observer rather than a participant actor. This made it difficult for Sullivan to identify himself with group psychotherapy. To Moreno, interpersonal relations meant a sharing of experience, a two-way relationship.

S. R. SLAVSON AND J. L. MORENO

S. R. Slavson visited a session of Moreno's Impromptu Theater in Carnegie Hall, February, 1931, and became interested in Moreno's work, especially in his use of group and action methods for children and adolescents.

Slavson's published work emerged in the third period, between 1937 and 1945. He attracted special attention in the movement not only because of his actual work but also because of his controversy with Moreno. By the time Slavson entered the field, Moreno was already an established figure. Moreno had already named and identified the field and had brought the terms group therapy and group psychotherapy to general recognition. Slavson, influenced by Moreno, started a second society of group therapists and later a second journal.

Slavson repeatedly claimed that the reason for the controversy was a traumatic experience in a session conducted by Moreno at the Impromptu Theater in Carnegie Hall early in 1931.

Such rivalries are not new in scientific movements; it is definitely not worse than the controversy between Freud and Adler, for instance. The question is whether it was productive for the movement at large. We believe that it has harmed the movement, at least in the United States. It encouraged a condition harmful to scientific progress by playing one man against another instead of formulating and validating significant hypotheses. On the other hand, were it not for his obvious concern with Moreno's dominance in the field, Slavson might not have started a second society or a second journal of group psychotherapy. In one point, however, it

87

cannot be compared with the rivalry between Freud and Adler; the enmity between Freud and Adler was far more absurd. They waged a cold war between themselves for almost three decades and never met again, whereas Moreno and Slavson met repeatedly over the years and worked on common objectives.

The time has come to establish and strengthen the tradition of the group psychotherapy movement and reduce the rivalries among the leaders to the inescapable minimum. Now that the movement has reached global proportions, it is important that we try to attain a more precise knowledge as to the conditions under which the movement emerged and of the originators of the movement. Not to know the fathers of a movement is like bringing up children without a parent. The second and third generation of the movement remained ignorant as to the actual origins and were often misled. They grew up without respect for tradition. Confusion about the beginnings of a movement often leads to delusions and unwarranted claims.

C. Third Period: 1938-1945

During this period several developments contributed to the spread of the group psychotherapy movement.

One began in the Jewish Board of Guardians under the direction of S. R. Slavson. His earliest publication on the subject of group psychotherapy was in 1940[89]

Another movement which ignited the spark was Alcoholics Anonymous. It was inspired by the group psychotherapy movement and popularized some of its principles. The title of a book, *Alcoholics Anonymous,* was adopted as the name of the organization. It was started in 1935 in Akron, Ohio, by a physician and broker; they began to treat alcoholics in their own homes, free of charge. They did not publish until much later (1939).[90]

A third development was initiated by Abraham Low of Chicago in 1937, a self-help organization of patients, "Recovery, Inc." (1941).[91]

A fourth development in the direction of group therapy was the self-government of prisoners initiated by Thomas M. Osborne in Sing Sing Prison (1929) and Auburn Prison, both in New York

88

State. The patient governments in mental hospitals followed their model with slight modifications. Patient government[92] is obviously practicable only in institutions of small size. It affords group interaction which simulates, to some extent, the conditions of general society. The large state hospital, with its inherited tradition of custodial care, makes little use of some of its best assets. As the routines and general regimen of large institutions are currently designed, they have the effect of largely eliminating incentive and aspiration in the lives of their patients. Patient government tends to reintroduce some form of motivation in an institution. At the Boston Psychopathic Hospital, "P.G." as it is called, a form of cooperation between the patients and the hospital, has proved itself very instrumental in improvements and recoveries. Patient government is capable of much improvisation to provide roles, status and prestige positions for its participants. Probably the condition most inimical to treatment in the chronic psychotic is his low level of aspiration and motivation. Anything which introduces a motivating element into the hospital atmosphere facilitates psychotherapy proper.

The Sociometric and the Psychodramatic Institutes opened in 1942 in New York City, simultaneously with the organization of the Society of Psychodrama and Group Psychotherapy, with J. L. Moreno as President and Bruno Solby as Secretary. It was the first professional society with the name *Group Psychotherapy* in its title. The first *Bulletin* of the Society of Psychodrama and Group Psychotherapy appeared in 1943, and continued to be published at regular intervals.

In 1943 another Society was organized by S. R. Slavson, called American Group Therapy Association. However, the society changed its name to American "Group Psychotherapy Association" a few years later (1948), following Moreno's model. The formal organization of group psychotherapists in these two societies gave a great impetus to the movement. The growing influence was climaxed by the publication in 1947 of Moreno's *Sociatry, A Journal of Group and Intergroup Therapy,* which was changed in 1949 to *Group Psychotherapy,* the first journal under this name in the fast growing literature. The policy of the journal was electic; it did not only publish Morenian methods but group methods of all variety, including psychoanalytic.

OFFICIAL RECOGNITION OF GROUP PSYCHOTHERAPY
AND PSYCHODRAMA BY THE WAR DEPARTMENT, 1943

War Department Technical Bulletin 103 stated that "group therapy has advantages over individual therapy in dealing with suspicious, hostile and guilt feelings and minimizes personal feelings."

It suggested that "groups be homogeneous, patients be seen individually first and then in groups . . . from 7 to 25 individuals meeting three to six times weekly for about one hour."

War Department Bulletin, TB MED 84 recommended in the section on Treatment Methods:

"Dramatics. To be used in impromptu form (psychodrama of Moreno) as group psychotherapy. If talent is available, the use of short skits, musical numbers, and pantomime."

VII. SPREAD OF THE GROUP PSYCHOTHERAPY
MOVEMENT IN THE U.S.A., 1940-1963

Like a modern St. Paul, Moreno began to travel, between 1940 and 1964, throughout the U.S.A. and the world at large, making public appearances, giving seminars and demonstrations. In contrast with Freud, who rarely left Vienna, Moreno is a world traveller; he carried the message everywhere. His aim was to plant the seed of group psychotherapy, to stimulate research and therapeutic application.

I had the privilege of accompanying him on most of these trips. In spreading the gospel, he emphasized and recommended *all* forms of group psychotherapy — interactional, analytic, and activistic — although he put particular emphasis upon the importance of action methods, especially psychodrama. Moreno differentiated his role as the international leader of the group psychotherapy movement from his role as creator of the special philosophy, theories, and methods which he favored.

Characteristic of this double role was his editing the classic symposium on the entire field of "Group Psychotherapy" in 1945. It contained presentations of all methods then current: For the class method, Pratt, Lazell and Hadden; for the interactional

90

method, F. Braceland, S. Hadden, A. Low, L. Bixby, William A. White, and J. L. Moreno; for the analytic method, J. Sutherland, N. Ackerman, L. Wender, Franz Alexander; for psychodrama and action methods, J. L. Moreno, M. Hagan, Z. Toeman, T. Sarbin, Florence Moreno, and J. Meiers.

During this early period, Moreno spread the movement almost single-handedly to the majority of Veterans Administration and State Mental Hospitals in the U.S.A., to such universities as Columbia, New York University, New School of Social Research, Western Reserve, Denver, Harvard, Yale, Boston, Southern California, Chicago, Emory, Wayne, and Stanford, among others. His seminars consisted of action demonstrations of group psychotherapy and psychodramas, the formation of groups, and training of personnel.

1940 to 1950

During these years a large number of leaders emerged in the U.S.A. without whom the widespread success of the movement would not have been possible. Of this brilliant crop of leaders, the following stand out. Helen Hall Jennings developed the sociometry of leadership. Paul Schilder's work at New York Bellevue Hospital was eclectic; he tried to use all methods, but never gave up the background of psychoanalytic philosophy. He was fearful of involving more than three or four members in a therapeutic group. S. R. Slavson worked with children and adolescents, aiming at an early Morenian activity catharsis. Slavson's laudable efforts were often handicapped by the fact that he had neither a degree in medicine nor in psychology.

Louis Wender used largely the lecture method, sprinkling his lectures with psychoanalytic concepts. Bruno Solby of the U.S. Public Health Service was a brilliant psychodramatist; he aroused, in Washington, D.C., the interest of the late Eleanor Roosevelt. Margaret Hagan, social psychiatric worker and director of the Red Cross, was an excellent director of psychodrama as a training device, as well as the pioneer of the Theater of Psychodrama at St. Elizabeths Hospital. N. W. Blackman was an early exponent of psychoanalytic group psychotherapy. Nathan Ackerman skillfully combined interactional and psychoanalytic ideas. Abraham Low excelled as an organizer of patient groups. Joseph Klapman tried to mediate group psychotherapeutic effects by giving patients

91

specially selected books to read; he advocated a kind of biblio-group psychotherapy. Joseph Meiers was the first comprehensive historian of the movement. A. S. Luchins was a teacher and investigator of group structure. The distinction of Robert B. Haas is that he related group psychotherapy to "learning theory." Ernest Fantel excelled through his application of psychodramatic methods to military settings. Martin Grotjahn was a brilliant psychoanalyst who turned group psychotherapist. James Enneis was a psychodramatist responsible for the growth of the Psychodrama Department at St. Elizabeths Hospital, its definition and establishment in the U.S. Civil Service, and its integration into the professional training program at the hospital. The author, Zerka Toeman Moreno, applied psychodramatic methods to group analysis.

1950 to 1964

Between 1950 and 1964 a large number of productive leaders emerged in the U.S.A. Ray Corsini, a brilliant historian, ranks with Joseph I. Meiers as the most comprehensive analyst of the history of the movement. He also made creative contributions, as the "immediate therapy" technique in psychodrama and a study of role playing in business and industry; Rudolf Dreikurs tried effectively to combine individual psychology with group psychotherapy; Wilfred Hulse was a powerful exponent on the international scene and a practitioner of group psychotherapy in private practice; Paul Torrance was a psychodramatist who made fruitful applications of psychodrama to creativity research in education; Gertrude Harrow Clemens made a classic study of the application of psychodrama to schizophrenia; Adaline Starr, leading exponent of psychodrama therapy in Chicago and the Middle West; Robert Drews, exponent of psychodrama in private practice; Jerome Frank specialized in the study of therapy groups in hospital settings; Lewis Yablonsky specialized in the group psychotherapy and sociometry of juvenile gangs and psychodrama of violent behavior; Rosemary Lippitt, one of the outstanding directors of psychodrama and writers in the area of child development; Edgar F. Borgatta, sociometrist of the small group; Hugh Mullan wrought a subtle combination of analytic and existential group psychotherapy; Theodore R. Sarbin excelled in the theory of role playing; B. J. Speroff, a sociometric investigator of industrial processes; Doris Twitchell Allen, a rare talent in applying broad concepts of social interaction and psychodrama to immediate situations like the family and childhood on the international scene; Walter Bromberg specialized in psychodramatic application in the areas of criminology and sexual pathology; R. W. Hyde made a contribution to the sociometry of the mental hospital; Martin R. Haskell made comprehensive studies of role playing and role training in behavior of juvenile delinquency; Hannah B. Weiner, brilliant director of psychodrama of alcoholics, using especially fantasy techniques; James Sacks, psychodramatist, with an interest in the theater of spontaneity; Neville Murray, forensic psychodramatist with strong ties to psycho-pharmacology; Alexander Wolf developed an extreme form of individual-centered group psychoanalysis; E. W. Semrad, group psychotherapy of psychoses; Carl Whitaker, experiential group psychotherapist with an existential flavor; Asya L. Kadis, talented teacher, organizer and administrator; George R. Bach elaborated theories of group development, leaning towards field theory; Malcolm Shaw gave us insights into the value of spontaneity- and role-training in industry; John Mann gave us a sober evaluation of group psychotherapy, role playing and psychodrama; Robert R. Blake contributed the most comprehensive reliability and validation studies of sociometry and role playing to date. Leon Fine and Rolf Krojanker organized an Institute on psychodrama and group psychotherapy at St. Louis State Hospital. Dean Elefthery of Northeast Florida State Hospital started an elaborate therapeutic program on psychodrama and group psychotherapy. There are many other leading contributors who are not mentioned here (see list of Modifications of Group Psychotherapy).

A symbol for the growing importance of small group research as an anchorage for group psychotherapy and similar adventures in the field of therapy is the fact that *Sociometry* became an official journal of the American Sociological Association in 1956, and is now in its 29th year of publication.

VIII. INTERNATIONAL SPREAD OF THE GROUP
       PSYCHOTHERAPY MOVEMENT, 1947-1965

There is ample evidence that group methods have been proposed by various authors outside of the U.S.A., as in U.S.S.R., in Austria,

93

and in Germany, under various names — collective reflexology, collective therapy, work therapy. But they were scattered and far flung; they did not reach the point of crystallization as an idea and a movement. It is from the U.S.A. that group psychotherapy began to spread since about 1940 and engulf the entire modern world.

If one wants to give an honest account of the international spread, one encounters the name of Moreno again and again. At times I was inclined, as the wife of this man, to tone down his importance. But then I decided that such misplaced modesty is not suitable in an objective account of a movement which may be rated by the year 2000 A.D. as the most important social therapeutic movement of the century. I have collected some of the crucial facts. Perhaps someday an outside historian, less involved than myself, will present a more objective survey. Although Moreno continues to be the prime mover of the movement at large, there is no intention to give him exclusive credit for various methods. Each method has its own history and its own leaders.

It is difficult to separate the influence of sociometry, group psychotherapy and psychodrama; they are parts of an interlocking movement studying group processes, although the tendency towards a split in three sections is marked.

UNITED KINGDOM

The first bridge from the U.S.A. to Europe was naturally the United Kingdom. The developments in small group research and group psychotherapy took place in their country of origin, the U.S.A.; however, the colleagues from the United Kingdom moved slowly but determinedly to catch up with them.

By the end of the 2nd World War, Moreno was invited by the Tavistock Clinic to come to London for a period of several months to introduce the new methods from America. Around this time, Major Fitzpatrick had visited the Sociometric Institute in New York City to exchange information, and one of the results of this visit was a report published in 1945 in the symposium *Group Psychotherapy* entitled, "Some Group Problems in the British Army". It reported the work of J. R. Rees, Hargreaves, Main,

Wilson, Bion, Foulkes, Rickman, Trist, Bridger and Sutherland. In 1947 a British journal on small group research, *Human Relations,* was started, with an editorial board representing both sides of the Atlantic. Moreno accepted Kurt Lewin's invitation to serve as one of its American editors.

I particularly remember one of our trips to Great Britain in 1951. Joshua Bierer was one of our earliest hosts there. He was most generous and showed us around, explaining the significance of his hospital organization and therapeutic social clubs. On a later trip to London, Moreno asked Bierer to call together the leading group psychotherapists in the London area for a meeting. Among the people present then were: J. Bierer, T. P. Rees, H. Ezriel, P. Senft, S. H. Foulkes. Moreno discussed two matters: the plan for a British Society of Group Psychotherapy, and another for a British journal on group psychotherapy. For the journal he suggested the title *International Sociatry.* He planned to publish the new journal jointly with Bierer; the latter suggested *International Journal of Social Psychiatry* as the title, and that is what it became.

We had already met S. H. Foulkes in New York at the Psychodramatic Institute when he visited the U.S.A. He is a prolific writer on group psychotherapy in England; his work shows great skill in combining Moreno's ideas — the here-and-now, the sociogenesis, the social atom, the psychosocial network — with psychoanalytic views and field theory.

Maxwell Jones attended psychodrama and sociodrama sessions at the Psychodramatic Institute in New York and then started a modified form of psychodrama at Belmont Hospital in England. Except perhaps for Foulkes, he did more than any other psychiatrist to spread psychodrama in Great Britain. Jones also became interested in Moreno's idea of therapeutic community and elaborated further on this.

H. Ezriel and J. Sutherland of the Tavistock Clinic came closer to Moreno's position by interpreting every group session as taking place in the here-and-now, and abandoning the reference to traumatic experiences in the past.

The chronological sequence of publications in the United Kingdom were: Bierer (1942), Bion and Rickman (1943), Foulkes (1944), Sutherland (1945), Kraupl-Taylor (1947), Ezriel (1950).

FRANCE

The next step in the international spread took place in France. In 1947 the *Cahiers Internationaux de Sociologie,* edited by Professor Georges Gurvitch, published the first article on "Sociometrie et Microsociologie". Professor Gurvitch wrote this article and was also responsible for the organization, a few years later, of a laboratory of sociometric research within his department, at the Sorbonne, in the same year. This laboratory became the spearhead for numerous investigations into group processes. He inspired also the French translation of *Who Shall Survive?* by the Presses Universitaires (1953), which contained extensive descriptions of group psychotherapy and psychodrama.

A memorable trip to Paris in the spring of 1951 brought about the creation of the First International Committee of Group Psychotherapy, initiated and chaired by Moreno. It included, among others, Dr. J. Favez Boutonier, Dr. S. Lebovici, Dr. S. H. Foulkes, Dr. J. Bierer and Zerka Moreno.

This committee announced the planning of the First International Congress of Group Psychotherapy in 1952, which came to fruition in Toronto, in August, 1954.

I recall vividly a number of meetings with Leon Chertok, Liesel Ostrander, Victor Gachkel, M. Montassut from Villejuif, F. Pasche and J. Delay from Ste. Anne, and G. Heuyer from the Salpetriere. Moreno planned to start an Institute for Group Psychotherapy and Psychodrama in Paris and almost bought a building to house it.

During our trip to Paris in 1954, upon the invitation of the French Institute of Psychoanalysis, Moreno lectured on psychodrama and psychoanalysis in which the late Princess Marie Bonaparte, famous psychoanalyst and descendant of Napoleon, was his discussant. It was an exciting event to see and hear these two giants measuring swords. Demonstrations of psychodrama were also given during this trip at Ste. Anne, upon invitation of J. Delay, and at the Salpetriere, upon invitation of G. Heuyer.

The forerunners of psychodrama and group psychotherapy in France are Monod (1947), Tosquelles (1950), Sivadon (1952), Lebovici (1952), Schutzenberger (1955), and Anzieu (1956). Lebovici tried to combine group psychotherapy with psychoanalytic theory, but leaned far more than the Americans towards orthodox psychoanalysis. Lebovici's distinction is that he gave serious attention to psychodrama.

GERMANY

The earliest link to sociometry and group psychotherapy in Germany was established by Professor Leopold von Wiese in 1948, when he published an article entitled "Soziometrie" in *Kölnischer Zeitung fur Soziologie*. In 1949 Hildebrandt Teirich wrote the first article on group psychotherapy in the *Wiener Medizinische Wochenschrift*, Vol. 99, pp. 617-618. In 1954 the Westdeutscher Verlag in Köln published the first German book dealing with small group research and group therapy. It was a translation of Moreno's book *Who Shall Survive?* under the title *Grundlagen der Soziometrie*. 1954 was also the year in which Moreno returned to Germany for the first time since his arrival in the U.S.A. and gave lecture-demonstrations on psychodrama and group psychotherapy at the Lindauer Psychotherapiewoche.

From Lindau, we covered universities and institutions of higher learning in Hamburg, Bremen, Hannover, Köln, Bonn, Freiburg, Heidelberg, Stuttgart, Frankfurt, Münich, Marburg, Tübingen.

In Germany, Dr. Simon in Gütersloh had employed and encouraged the development of occupational therapy. But group psychotherapy in the modern sense did not develop. It had to be imported from the U.S.A. Sociometry is now flourishing in many public schools; group psychotherapy and psychodrama are beginning to find a foothold in some mental hospitals and clinics. The only development which reminds one of Moreno's early work on the *Begegnung* complex is represented by Hans Trüb. (Hans Trüb, *Heilung aus der Begegnung*, Klett, 1951, Stuttgart, Germany.)

Leaders in group psychotherapy were H. Teirich (1949), J. H. Schultz (1950), and D. Langen (1953).

A leader in psychodrama therapy is Helga Straub, Stuttgart (1963). In sociometry, Elfriede Höhn, Tübingen (1956).

AUSTRIA

According to Teirich (H. Teirich, *Group Psychotherapy*, Vol. 8, 1955), "it was not until after World War II, that Kauders, head of the Vienna University Psychiatric Clinic, roused a new interest in group treatment which had been badly neglected during the days of the Third Reich." Hans Hoff, the present Chief of the Clinic, reintroduced group psychotherapy and built a theater for psychodrama on the premises. However, after the war, "Stransky sometimes was forced, by sheer lack of time, to give up single treatment in favor of group work, and found that he reached his aims much quicker this way." Long before Alcoholics Anonymous became known, Dr. Metzl, physician in the services of the Vienna police, tried to unite his alcoholic patients in groups.

Since then, Dr. R. Schindler became an indefatigable worker in group psychotherapy and introduced the concept of bi-focal group psychotherapy, leaning somewhat upon sociometry of interpersonal relations.

SWITZERLAND

In Switzerland, it was Dr. A. Friedemann who became the most ardent leader of group psychotherapy; he invited Moreno to give a three-day seminar at his Psychohygienisches Institut in 1954; from this man and his work the group psychotherapy movement radiated and involved younger men. Moreno also gave a psychodrama demonstration at famed Burghölzli, with groups of patients. We had been warned by several Swiss citizens that the Swiss have no sense of humor and we should not expect a warm reception of psychodrama there. Nevertheless, the Swiss were moved to loud laughter during the sessions; apparently psychodrama changed the dictum: "In Burghölzli lacht man nicht" ("In Burghölzli no one laughs"). Since then, a young psychiatrist trained by Moreno, Dr. Gretel Leutz, introduced psychodrama with patients at Bellevue Hospital in Kreuzlingen, with the support of Dr. L. Binswanger; she and Dr. H. Teirich also gave a series of lectures on sociometry, group psychotherapy and psychodrama at the Institute for Applied Psychology in Zürich, whence a number of young workers have since emerged and are practicing.

LATIN AMERICA

Leading exponents in group psychotherapy and/or psychodrama are: W. Kemper, Brazil; C. Seguin, Peru; J. Bustamante, Cuba; L. Feder, Mexico; B. Caravedo, Peru; J. J. Morgan, Argentina; J. Rojas Bermudez, Argentina.

SOVIET RUSSIA

A forgotten observation of Marx in *Das Kapital* (1867) is noteworthy: "A dozen persons when working together will, in their collective working day of 144 hours, produce far more than 12 isolated men, each working twelve hours, or than one man who works twelve days in succession." This economic remark has no immediate bearing upon psychotherapy, but it is probably no accident that "work therapy," an important variety of group therapy not to be confused with occupational therapy, rather than clinical group psychotherapy, developed in Soviet Russia more extensively than in other countries.

In 1959, Moreno travelled to Soviet Russia upon the invitation of the Academy of Sciences, and lectured there on sociometry, group psychotherapy and psychodrama, giving several demonstrations with patients in Moscow and Leningrad. A number of sociometric studies were just then to be undertaken in industry and in schools. The Russians were interested in the sociometric aspect of human interaction because of its practical application to increasing production and stimulating worker morale. In Soviet Russia, the leading exponents are V. A. Guilyarovsky and D. D. Fedotov.

The first book on small group research and group therapy published in the U.S.S.R. was a translation into Russian of Moreno's *Sociometry, Experimental Method and the Science of Society* in 1958.

OTHER EUROPEAN COUNTRIES, AND THE NEAR
AND FAR EAST

Seeds of group psychotherapy were also sewn by Moreno during
visits between 1950-1960 to, among others, Spain, Italy, Holland,
Denmark, Norway, Greece, Hungary, Czechoslovakia, Yugoslavia,
Israel and Turkey. The growing activities and literature in these
countries attest to the vigor with which the movement is taking
root there.

Spain, leading exponents, Burbano-Sarro, Marti-Tusquets, Ruiz-
Ogara.
Yugoslavia, leading exponents, Betlheim and Horetzky.
Italy, leading exponents, Spaltro, Meschieri, Viviano and Na-
politani.
Holland, leading exponents, Arendsen-Hein, Van Emde Boas
and Meijering.
East Germany, Szewczyk.
Denmark, leading exponents, Sturup, Martensen-Larsen and
Joergensen.
Norway, leading exponent, Askevold.
Sweden, Harding, Larsson.
Greece, leading exponent, Potamianou.
Hungary, leading exponents, Boszormenyi, Merei and Peto.
Czechoslovakia, leading exponents, Knobloch, Rubes, Siroky,
Buxbaum and Hausner.
Israel, leading exponents, Kreitler and Schossberger.
Turkey, leading exponent, Kösemihal.
Japan, Matsumura.

IX. RANGE OF GROUP PSYCHOTHERAPY
     METHODS, 1945-1965

The rapid growth of the group psychotherapy movement is
dramatically illustrated by the large number of modifications which
are here listed. A growing eclecticism marks this period, indicating
its spread, but also lack of a central core. In the period between

100

1945 and 1955, the analytic orientation was in ascendance; in the last ten years it is in descendance and the movement is once again returning, on a more integrated level, to the earlier inter-action-oriented period.

Forty-seven Modifications of Group Psychotherapy

Although the methods frequently overlap in semantics, concepts and operations, they are living witnesses of the vitality of the movement.

Interactional group psychotherapy — J. L. Moreno
Group analytic psychotherapy — S. H. Foulkes
Family therapy — J. L. Moreno, N. W. Ackerman, D. Jackson, M. Grotjahn, T. Lidz
Recovery group — A. Low
Therapeutic social clubs — J. Bierer
Didactic group psychotherapy — J. W. Klapman
Immediate therapy — R. J. Corsini
Round table group psychotherapy — W. McCann
Music and rhythm therapy — I. Altshuler
Transactional analysis — E. Berne, B. Becker
Synanon — C. Dederich, L. Yablonsky
Therapeutic films — J. L. Moreno
Experiential group psychotherapy — C. Whitaker
LSD Group treatment
Work therapy — U.S.S.R.
Bifocal group psychotherapy — R. Schindler
Intensive group psychotherapy — G. Bach
Violent group psychotherapy — L. Yablonsky
Non-directive group psychotherapy — Carl Rogers
Socioanalysis — J. L. Moreno
Leaderless group psychotherapy — W. R. Bion
Here and Now — J. L. Moreno, H. Ezriel
Analytic group psychotherapy — W. Kemper, S. R. Slavson, G. Kühnel
Institutional group psychotherapy — F. Tosquelles, P. Sivadon
Guided group interaction — L. F. Bixby, J. McCorkle
Group psychoanalysis — A. Wolf
Psychodrama — J. L. Moreno

Symbolic psychodrama — D. Anzieu
Group psychotherapy in private practice — W. Hulse, R. Drews
Analytic psychodrama — J. L. Moreno, S. Lebovici, D. Anzieu
Hypnodrama — J. L. Moreno, J. Enneis
Drama therapy — R. Lassner
Role playing — J. L. Moreno
Role training — J. L. Moreno, Martin R. Haskell
Role therapy — Martin R. Haskell, G. Lawlor
T. group — K. Lewin, L. Bradford
Autogenous training in groups — J. H. Schultz
Sociometric therapy — H. H. Jennings, J. L. Moreno
Drug-induced psychodrama — J. L. Moreno, Jack Ward
Group analysis (phyloanalysis) — T. Burrow
Group remedial reading — J. W. Klapman
Tutorial group psychotherapy —
Silent group psychotherapy — Nina Toll
Drug-induced group psychotherapy
Hypno-group psychotherapy — Calvert Stein
Activity group therapy — S. R. Slavson
Interpersonal therapy, conjoint therapy — J. L. Moreno, Bela
  Mittelman

X. ORGANIZERS OF THE GROUP PSYCHOTHERAPY MOVEMENT

The group psychotherapy movement would not exist were it
not for the sustained efforts of a few individuals, without whom
the various "methods" might have remained limited to a few
mental hygiene clinics and hospitals.

Organizers on the international level: J. L. Moreno, Wellman
Warner, W. Hulse, S. R. Slavson, B. Stokvis, A. Friedemann and
Zerka T. Moreno.

In the United Kingdom: S. H. Foulkes and J. Bierer.

In France: S. Lebovici and Anne Ancelin-Schutzenberger.

In Germany and German-speaking countries: A. Friedemann,
  R. Schindler and H. Teirich.

In Italy: E. Spaltro.

102

J. L. MORENO:

Created the movement by introducing and defining the terms group therapy and group psychotherapy, 1931-1932, and publishing the first book on the subject.

Initiated the first large conference of group psychotherapists in 1932.

Founded the first society which had the term "group psychotherapy" in its name, 1942.

Founded *Sociometry,* the first Journal of Interpersonal Relations, 1936-1937.

Founded *Sociatry, A Journal of Group and Intergroup Therapy* in 1947, the first journal of social psychiatry.

Changed the name to *Group Psychotherapy,* 1949, the first journal bearing the title.

Organized the trial section on group psychotherapy in 1950 and the section on psychotherapy within the American Psychiatric Association in 1952.

Organized the First International Committee on Group Psychotherapy in Paris, 1951.

Organized with W. Hulse, S. R. Slavson and Wellman Warner the First International Congress of Group Psychotherapy in Toronto, 1954.

First President of the Second International Congress of Group Psychotherapy in Zürich, 1957.

Elected President of the International Council of Group Psychotherapy in 1962.

President, the Third International Congress of Group Psychotherapy, Milan 1963.

WELLMAN J. WARNER:

Member of the Executive Committee, 1952, which organized the First International Congress of Group Psychotherapy, 1954, in Toronto.

Chairman of the International Committee of Group Psychotherapy in Zürich, 1957.

Architect of the Election System of the International Council.

Organized in collaboration with Moreno the International Council of Group Psychotherapy, 1961-1962, with membership in 45 countries.

Elected Director of the International Council of Group Psychotherapy, 1962.

A. FRIEDEMANN:

Elected Treasurer of the International Council of Group Psychotherapy, 1962.

Secretary of the Third International Congress of Group Psychotherapy, 1963.

Helped in organizing the Third International Congress of Group Psychotherapy, Milan, Italy, 1963.

B. STOKVIS:

Elected Secretary of the International Council of Group Psychotherapy, 1962.

Helped in organizing the Third International Congress of Group Psychotherapy in Milan, 1963.

S. H. FOULKES:

Member of the First International Committee, 1951.

Director of the International Council of Group Psychotherapy, 1963.

First Vice President of the Third International Congress of Group Psychotherapy, Milan, 1963.

S. LEBOVICI:

Member of the First International Committee, 1951.

Organized the French Society of Group Psychotherapy, 1960.

Program Chairman, Second International Congress of Group Psychotherapy, Zürich, 1957.

Director and Second Vice President of the International Council of Group Psychotherapy, 1963.

J. BIERER:

Member of the First International Committee, 1951.

Organized Institute of Social Psychiatry, United Kingdom.

Published *International Journal of Social Psychiatry,* 1955.

Director of International Council, 1962.

W. HULSE:

Member of the Executive Council, International Committee of Group Psychotherapy.

Assisted in organizing the Congress in Toronto, 1954.

Assisted in organizing the Congress in Zürich, 1957.

J. FAVEZ BOUTONIER:

Member of the First International Committee, 1951.

Director of the International Council of Group Psychotherapy, 1962.

ZERKA T. MORENO:

Member of the First International Committee, 1951.

Director of International Council of Group Psychotherapy, 1962.

Helped to organize all three Congresses of Group Psychotherapy.

S. R. SLAVSON:

Organized the American Association of Group Therapy, 1943. Name changed to Group Psychotherapy, 1947.

Founded the *International Journal of Group Psychotherapy,* 1951.

ANNE ANCELIN-SCHUTZENBERGER:

Organized *Group Francais D'Etudes de Sociometrie, Dynamique des Groupes et Psychodrame.*

H. TEIRICH:

Historian of the group psychotherapy movement in Germany.

R. SCHINDLER:

Organized *Arbeitskreis für Gruppendynamik und Gruppentherapie,* Vienna, Austria.

E. SPALTRO:

General Manager and Organizer of the Third International Congress of Group Psychotherapy, Milan, 1963.

J. H. SCHULTZ:

Director of the International Council of Group Psychotherapy, 1964.

XI. TEACHING AND TRAINING METHODS

HISTORICAL BACKGROUND

The first training Academy was held in Beacon, N.Y. in the spring and summer of 1940. It preceded the foundation of the American Society of Group Psychotherapy and Psychodrama by two years. Among the members of the advisory board of the Academy were Professors John Dewey, William H. Kilpatrick, Gardner Murphy and Nolan D. C. Lewis.

The second Academy took place on June 28, 1941. Among the participants were Professors F. Stuart Chapin, Leonard Cottrell, George Lundberg, Margaret Hagan, Paul Lazarsfeld, Margaret Mead, Helen Jennings, George P. Murdock, Samuel Stouffer, Adolf Meyer, Theodore M. Newcomb, Werner Wolf, S. Bernard Wortis, Eugene Hartley. Since then, the idea of action and group training has spread throughout the U.S.A.

THE TRAINING OF GROUP PSYCHOTHERAPISTS

The group psychotherapist requires special preparation and training before he begins practicing. Psychoanalysts within their own system make personal psychoanalysis a prerequisite before they are permitted to practice. This is perfectly plausible for individual therapy, but the situation is quite different in group psychotherapy. A therapist may be a thoroughly analyzed individual, but still not be qualified to do group psychotherapy. In group psychotherapy he is in the midst of the group, exposed to the love and hate of various individuals. He is confronted with realities in the here and now which an individual analysis could not have prepared him for. He often has to act out himself and become involved. He continuously is analyzed by every member of the group, and he must maintain his equilibrium.

There is a natural predisposition of the trained psychoanalyst to be biased in favor of the psychoanalytic experience and in disfavor of group experience. The prerequisite for a psychoanalyst is to be trained in psychoanalytic theory and skills of interpretation. The group therapist, however, faces a different problem; he needs a different kind of preparation. An individual psychoanalysis may not be indicated for him, in fact, it might prove harmful. Therefore, we propose that group psychotherapists receive their training and evaluation within a group therapeutic and psychodramatic framework. Such a group and psychodramatic analysis of the potential therapists consists of learning how to confront and to work with a group; to develop abilities to absorb aggression from several individuals simultaneously, and to respond to such aggression with equanimity and courage. Many therapists have been exposed to aggression, even hostility, of audiences consisting of hundreds of people, and have had to learn to maintain their equilibrium and presence of mind in such situations.

The group psychotherapist must also learn perseverance in adversity, under circumstances of every conceivable kind of attack. A group psychotherapist must know how to handle tenderness and affection, and to be almost clairvoyant as to events and feelings taking place between members of the group. He must learn to guard himself against being over-analytic, or over-involved with any individual in the group. Such talents can only be learned through training in actual sessions. Furthermore, it is clear that psychodramatic training of a group psychotherapist adds greatly to his perception and maturity of decision. A competent group psychotherapist needs, besides training in group psychotherapy sessions, also to have training in a psychodrama atmosphere. Without it, the final achievement of skillful accommodation to ever-changing life situations of his patients cannot be made. Moreno has been the first to insist that individual psychoanalysis should be left to the students of psychoanalysis, but that group psycho-therapists should be trained in group psychotherapy settings exclusively — in that atmosphere in which they will practice, and not in an atmosphere which is alien to their professional objectives.

If possible, the group psychotherapy atmosphere in which training takes place should not be a synthetic laboratory group, but a grouping of patients and therapists which is constructed similarly to those in which the therapist will eventually practice.

Since February of 1942, training academies and workshops have been held, besides Beacon, N.Y., at the Sociometric and Psycho-dramatic Institutes in New York City. Such training academies and workshops have been models for similar training centers throughout the U.S.A. and abroad. An outstanding training center in the U.S. is St. Elizabeths Hospital in Washington, D.C. But such training can not be carried out without necessarily making distinctions as to the levels of competence. Moreno has therefore been the exponent of recommending and introducing principles of training and the development of professional standards in the field.

TECHNIQUES IN TEACHING

The direct method of teaching has been proposed in successive stages:

a) The resident in a mental hospital may accompany the ward physicians on their rounds to observe the patients and their interaction in their dormitories and occupational rooms.

108

b) He may take part in the group therapy sessions as an observer and a participant.

c) As a part of his training he assists the ward physicians in the making of the sociogram of the groupings of the patients and is asked to suggest changes of placement and regroupings on the basis of the clues in the sociograms. Sociograms are repeated in two to four week intervals so the staff may become aware of changes in interpersonal relations.

d) The student applies the sociometric findings to the group therapy sessions themselves. He interviews the patients before and after the sociograms are made and discusses with them their sociometric status.

e) He may direct verbal group psychotherapy sessions under supervision. There may be discussion and evaluation of his directorial competence in front of the patients and with their help.

f) Such verbal group techniques are gradually combined with action techniques of teaching. A two year training period for future group psychotherapists is recommended.

This direct method has been employed in a large number of mental hospitals. Other methods, like the conference method, the playback method, or replaying a recorded session, may be used in combination with the special procedures described.

CODE OF ETHICS FOR GROUP PSYCHOTHERAPISTS: MORENO'S PROPOSAL[93]

The advent of group and action methods in psychotherapy has brought about a radical change in the relationship of the therapist to the patients and to the general public. An "open discussion" of the new principles and responsibilities for all practitioners in these fields is urgent. The fact that they are put in numerical order from 1 to 10 as follows does not imply that there is any finality about the formulation of these principles, nor that ten is a holy number, nor that this is a rank order as to importance, nor that all aspects of the problem are covered by them.

These principles are addressed to all group psychotherapists.

They are not laws, but standards designed to maintain a high level of ethical conduct.

1) The principal objective of group psychotherapy is to render service to every member of therapeutic groups and to the groups as a whole.

2) A group psychotherapist should practice methods of healing founded on a scientific basis, approved by official professional boards.

3) The designation "group psychotherapist" or "psychodramatist" should be used only by psychotherapists who have obtained training in recognized institutes of learning. As the field is new and expanding, the therapists should continuously improve their knowledge and skill; they should make available to other therapists and their patients the benefits of their attainments.

4) A principal objective of the group psychotherapist is to protect the patient against abuse and to render service to groups of patients with full respect for the dignity of every patient.

5) Therapeutic groups should be so organized that they represent a model of democratic behavior. Regardless of the economic, racial and religious differences of the patients they should be given "equality of status" inside the therapeutic group.

6) Should patients of the same therapeutic group pay the *same* fee or not? Could charging different fees to members of the *same* therapeutic group produce feelings of inequality and thwart the therapeutic aim?

7) The patients should be free to choose the therapeutic groups in which they participate as members. The therapist, in turn, is free to accept or refuse to serve in behalf of a therapeutic group. Indications or contraindications for "coercive" placement in the groups should be carefully weighed in exceptional cases, as in the treatment of deteriorated mental patients.

8) The Hippocratic Oath binds the physician to keep all matters of his professional practice secret. *In group psychotherapy the Hippocratic Oath is extended to all patients and binds each with equal strength not to reveal to outsiders the confidences of other patients entrusted to them.* Like the therapist, every patient is entrusted to protect the welfare of the co-patients.

The link of mass media of communication, like television, to group psychotherapy and psychodrama may produce "leaks" of the confidence pledge difficult to control. Closed circuits in television broadcasting for subscribers is a tolerable but unsafe way out of the dilemma. But the "open" circuits may become a major route for mass psychotherapy. How can we utilize them without taking risks?

9) Every patient is expected to divulge freely whatever he thinks, perceives or feels, to every other in the course of the treatment sessions. He should know that he is protected by the "pledge" and that no disadvantage will come to him because of his honest revelations of crimes committed, of psychological deviations from sexual or social norms, secret plans and activities. The confidences so entrusted may never be violated unless it is imperative to do so by law in order to protect the welfare of the individual or of the community. In extreme cases of improper conduct, therapists and patients may be disqualified from practice or treatment. How can this be brought into harmony with our therapeutic philosophy of taking care of every individual patient?

10) The timing of the "pledge" has to be carefully considered by the therapist responsible for the group. In order that it may not frighten the participants or produce the effect of an unnecessary restraint upon their freedom, it should not be discussed prematurely; the physician or therapeutic leader should wait until the group is ripe and well formed and the meaning of the pledge clear to all members. The critical moment may arise when a patient in the course of the treatment sessions is put on the spot and hesitates to reveal a highly personal event in his life. His hesitancy may be internal, as feelings of guilt, or external, such as fear of gossip, public discomfort or persecution. In such an intense situation the physician can step forward and reassure the patient that all members of the group are bound by a pledge, just as the physician is bound. Thus, an atmosphere of confidence in the proceedings and a feeling of collective security can be established.

GROUP OATH[94]

Group psychotherapists and psychodramatists frequently feel the need to convey to the members of their groups, in the beginning or in the course of the sessions, what responsibility is involved for them during the process of treatment. The following Group Oath is not to be taken as a ritual, word for word, or as a dogma, but tries to convey the spirit of such an Oath which may be expressed or tacitly accepted by all.

"Like the physician who is bound by the Hippocratic Oath, we are bound as participants in this group by the Group Oath not to reveal to outsiders the confidences of other patients.

Like the Physician, each of us is entrusted to protect the welfare of every other patient in the group.

This is the Group Oath to therapeutic science and its disciples. Just as we trust the physician in individual treatment, we should trust each other. Whatever happens in the course of a session of group therapy and psychodrama, we should not keep anything secret. We should divulge freely whatever we think, perceive or feel for each other; we should act out the fears and hopes we have in common and purge ourselves of them."

COMMENTS

Alexander Wolf, M. D.:

"Ideally it would be most desirable in group psychotherapy that the Hippocratic Oath be extended to all patients and bind each with equal strength not to reveal to outsiders the confidences of other patients entrusted to them. But it is difficult to conceive how seriously and consistently some patients would adhere to such a principle in practice, particularly when it is recalled that occasionally human frailty and compulsive protest lead to broken pledges. While one can only appreciate Moreno's zeal in feeling that like the therapist, every patient is entrusted to protect the welfare of the co-patients, it seems to me that a thorough-going analysis of any member's readiness to gossip or otherwise betray another patient is a more practical and at the same time a more basically therapeutic means of resolving this problem in ethics. In a fairly extensive experience of my own, the matter of disclosing intra-group material to outsiders, though an occasional problem, has not been sufficiently seriously recurrent to warrant concern. Almost universally, extra-group revelations have been so nebulous or non-specific with reference to the actual identity of a given

112

member as to preserve his anonymity. If any law is needed to protect the individual undergoing group therapy, I believe legislation that would prevent one group member from revealing in court confidential information about another acquired in the course of group therapy would be more in order."

S. Lebovici, M. D.:

"I quite agree with the Code of Ethics of Group Psychotherapists by Dr. Moreno. In my opinion, the group psychotherapist has to behave as do other psychotherapists under all circumstances. A special problem has to be taken into consideration; I mean the existence of the group and the audience. It is necessary to advise each member of the group to be careful; each of them has to keep in mind that he is the doctor of his colleagues."

Rudolf Dreikurs, M. D.:

"The code of ethics, suggested by Dr. Moreno, is an important step toward the establishment of standards for group psychotherapists. The need to be frank and to talk freely about personal intimacies, normally not discussed with others, is part of the new form of therapy, with its revolutionary social orientation. The ability to accept this outlook and to communicate it to the patients may well be treated in a separate point of standards. Anyone who has reservations or objections to relinquish the heretofore accepted requirements of privacy in psychotherapy would, thereby, violate one of the basic standards of a code for group psychotherapy. The therapy group must be so conducted as to promote an atmosphere of mutual respect and to stimulate complete frankness and willingness to help each other. The therapist must be acquainted with the knowledge and the skill to deal with psychodynamic as well as group dynamic processes."

Paul E. Johnson, Ph. D.:

"Freedom of choice is affirmed for each person in the group, including the leader, at the point of beginning. But what shall we say as to leaving the group? Is anyone free to desert the group whenever he wishes, to absent himself intermittently or finally? What of open and closed membership, and of entering after a group is already well on its way? What shall we do about a terminal date in group therapy for one and all?"

O. Hobart Mowrer, Ph. D.:

"This seems to me an excellent statement of sound propositions and important, thoughtful questions. I wonder if the term, physician, is used advisedly. Might not 'therapist' be preferable, on the assumption that persons other than physicians may do group therapy?"

D. Langen, M. D.:

"Therapeutic groups should be organized in such a manner that they represent a model of a democratic society. The Hippocratic Oath is to be extended to all patients and it should bind everyone with the same responsibility. As every patient is bound and protected by such an oath, he can afford to express himself freely as to what he thinks of the others and how he feels. If one offends or disobeys the basic rule, he should be disqualified from continued treatment. The moment for taking this oath should be carefully chosen. It should depend upon the readiness of the group to appreciate the importance of such a commitment."

Robert R. Blake, Ph. D.:

"Moreno's code for group therapists applies to group training at certain points. There are key differences. Why?

The answer is that fundamentally, therapy starts with illness and focuses on pathology, aiming toward its resolution. Protection and freedom to explore private and subjective aspects of adjustment is indispensable to the objective of gaining health through the resolution or correction of defect. Not so with training. Fundamentally, training *starts* with a healthy individual and aims towards increments in diagnostic sensitivity and social skills of the kind which can increase personal effectiveness in group decision-making situations. Revelation, exposure, and confidences are inconsistent with the objectives of such training. A code suitable for the treatment of defect is given in the Hippocratic Oath; one appropriate for training is no more complicated than love thy neighbor. . . ."

114

Lewis Yablonsky, Ph. D.:

"If we truly believe, as Dr. Moreno has so aptly stated, 'a truly therapeutic method cannot have less of a goal than all of society,' then why should we inhibit or pattern our group approach to some obvious limitations of a secretive individual session which is a microcosm of our over-all societies' ills — *the closing out of one psyche's problems from another.* Group psychotherapists should recognize basic laws of human relations in their codes which are much broader in scope. As group psychotherapists dedicated to broader principles of community therapy we would be eliminating from the therapeutic process by this silence hundreds of others who fit into the small group's networks. The teachers, other parents, children, and many other members of the community would be closed out from participating in the total therapy process. Open discussions of the problems would quickly indicate to others in their networks *(by definition these are the only ones who would hear of their problems)* how close and important the problem was to them. After all, Johnny's problem of delinquency does not rest with his family and school alone; by definition it is a community or social problem. Therefore, this community should have been and was allowed to participate."

Wellman J. Warner, Ph. D.:

"It does not suffice to carry over the traditional stand of the medical profession, with its definition of the relationship between the physician and the patient. A rationale of the ethical code here stems from a new set of conditions. The physician-patient relationship, although it tends to become less clearly so with the emergence of fresh psychological and sociological orientations, derived less from the requirements of the therapy procedure than from an affirmation of civil rights of the individual against public intrusion. In the enlarging scene of group psychotherapy — and in a lesser degree all psychotherapy — the need for definition derives first from the necessities of the therapy procedure itself, and only then can one assess the claim of the individual to protection against the tyrannies of public scrutiny. Dr. Moreno's formulation of standards in order to maintain a high level of ethical conduct is provocative and sensitive. Its value is greater because it does not undertake to be final or complete but to stimulate the kind of probing that is

115

acutely needed during the period when the field is developing and consolidating."

J. L. Moreno, M. D.:

J. L. Moreno agrees with Dr. Mowrer that the term "therapist" is preferable to the term physician, on the assumption that persons other than physicians may do group therapy.

He agrees with Dr. Yablonsky that modifications of the group oath will be required as soon as the mass media of communication will permit broader principles of community therapy. The closed circuit television system is a step in the right direction.

He disagrees with Dr. Blake. Group therapy and group training cannot be strictly separated. They overlap. There is no group therapy without some sensitivity training resulting from it, and there is no group training without some therapeutic involvement. For this reason the same code of ethics applies to both.

XII. COMMON GROUND FOR ALL FORMS OF GROUP PSYCHOTHERAPY

The global spread of the group psychotherapy movement and its rapid growth as a universal therapeutic science has made it urgent to elaborate in greater detail the meaning of the concepts and operations involved in group psychotherapy. Group psychotherapy comprises a multitude of apparently widely differing methods: interpersonal therapy, sociometric therapy, action therapy, milieu therapy, family therapy, work therapy, group analysis, socioanalysis, group psychodrama, role playing, T group, therapeutic community, to mention but a few. If they are to be identified as various forms of group psychotherapy, what do all these methods have in common?

It is particularly important to give an answer to this question which all group psychotherapists can accept. When group psychotherapy began its period of scientific discoveries forty years ago, it was important to point out its essential characteristics, to guard its independence and to develop its own concepts and terms. Our position has still not changed in essence; we are still fighting on two fronts. It is like a young nation trying to ward off enemies from without; applied to our case, it is the struggle to distinguish ourselves from psychoanalysis, existentialism, social psychology,

116

among others. And also like a young nation, the movement is plagued by internal rivalries, the enemy from within. There are problems of formulating common denominators and establishing standards for group psychotherapy.

Because of the controversial nature of many group methods a definite answer is imperative. Freud, in his struggle to identify psychoanalysis in his day, maintained that the cornerstones of psychoanalysis were transference and resistance. This became the rallying point for all psychoanalysts. Do we group psychotherapists have any frame of reference which we can all share?

Yes, we do. Group psychotherapy means 1) "to treat people in groups," and not just living in groups; and 2) every member of the group is given an equal opportunity of getting involved and participating in the therapeutic process; no one is left out, at least not intentionally. One of the models of this operation is the sociometric test, in which every member can express his spontaneous choice or rejection of any member of the group. Everyone gets into the sociogram. The same model in a different form is embodied in the original therapeutic theater, which, as a matter of principle, excludes spectators.

It is secondary to the principle of all-inclusiveness what *methods* are used to get group members to participate with each other in a therapeutic way, whether these methods be dance, music, words, drama, etc. It is the principle of all-inclusiveness and total participation which concerns us.

A lecture method is not group therapy when the spectators are not allowed to interrupt the speaker, where members of the audience are isolated from one another and can not communicate during the lecture. It becomes group therapy if the members of the group discuss the theme and intensive interaction is permitted; then the lecture attains the character of a warming up process and the discussion may become a mild form of group psychotherapy. In this sense, every sociometric test leading to a discussion of the reasons for choice or rejection can turn out to be a genuine group psychotherapy session. By contrast, a psychodrama session in which a protagonist portrays his private world before a group and the group is discouraged from responding, remains an individual therapy session and not a group session. But a group-centered psychodrama in which every individual and his cultural setting is activated is often the most effective type of group therapy.

In certain forms of group analysis, for instance, there may be

117

very intensive analysis of several individuals side by side within a group setting, but some members of the group do not participate or share in the analysis. Such a form of group analysis is not group psychotherapy, or at most, it is a very diluted form of group psychotherapy. Other forms of group analysis, however, which allow, besides individual analysis, the participation and sharing of the entire group in the therapeutic process are better justified in being called group psychotherapy. The degree to which a method places emphasis not only on the psyche of the individual participant but on the interaction and constellation of the group is the degree to which it becomes intensive group psychotherapy. Similarly, in family therapy, the inclusion of all members of the family is of essence. This reaches a particularly intensive form in a "therapeutic community" program which as a matter of principle includes all individuals, not only as patients but as members of that particular society.

I. Any method which denies the principle of all-inclusiveness can not be considered as group psychotherapy. II. Any method which denies the principle of therapeutic interaction cannot be considered as group psychotherapy.

XIII. PAST, PRESENT AND FUTURE OF THE GROUP PSYCHOTHERAPY MOVEMENT

All senior group psychotherapists who have worked, often continents apart, remember that we have gone through 1) a *period of discovery* between 1910-1945 in which concepts, principles and methods were discovered and rediscovered. This period of discovery seems to have substantially come to an end since the Second World War. Then followed 2) *a period of controversy and growth.* It was a difficult time between 1945 and 1957, but the movement has survived its greatest challenge, the rivalries from within. We believe that with the new International Congresses, a new period has been launched, 3) *a period of integration.* It is our hope that within the next period, group psychotherapy and its associated disciplines will prove themselves to be the greatest development in psychotherapy in our century, symbolizing the Third Psychiatric Revolution.

There are several blocks which have interfered with the movement's development and the professional status of its practitioners.

PROPERTY OF WASHINGTON
SCHOOL OF PSYCHIATRY
LIBRARY

We may distinguish among others, three types of blocks: (a) professional blocks, (b) economic blocks, (c) ideological blocks.

(a) Let us begin with the professional blocks, because they are particularly disturbing to workers in the field. The pioneers of modern group psychotherapy were doctors of medicine; but the majority of group psychotherapists today are not doctors of medicine, they are psychologists, sociologists, social workers, nurses, educators, ministers and others. We have calculated approximate figures as to the number of psychologists, sociologists, social workers, nurses, etc., who are practicing group psychotherapy. They number about 50%; the percentage is probably higher, as we know from surveys made in many states and VA hospitals, psychological clinics and therapeutic institutions. Many non-medical group psychotherapists are not members of the official societies now operating, either because of limited economic means or because of difficulties in meeting the standards set by the societies they would like to join. Considering that clinical psychologists and sociologists, social workers, educators and ministers are produced in larger number than medical psychotherapists and show an increasing attraction to group methods, the probability is that in the years to come the non-medical workers will further outnumber the medical ones.

The division of group psychotherapists into groups, the compact group of doctors of medicine versus all other professional groups, has developed meanwhile a strong tendency for a double status of group psychotherapy — medical doctors versus non-medical doctors.

The meaning of the medical vs. the non-medical trends in the countries outside the U.S.A. is difficult to assess because the conditions differ widely from these in our country. Only in a few countries outside the U.S.A. have group psychotherapy societies been formed: in Great Britain, Austria, Israel, Argentina, France and Cuba. In Germany, Denmark, Sweden, Norway, Holland, Switzerland, Turkey, Spain, Italy, Greece, as well as in the Asiatic countries, a great deal of group psychotherapy is practiced but societies in a formal sense are not structured; therapists are scattered, linked to hospitals, clinics and schools. In the U.S.S.R. group psychotherapy is practiced widely but it is not distinctly separated from psychotherapy; the emphasis is on its application "in situ," i. e. *work therapy.*

119

The tension between the two groups is so great that it may come to a splitting up. But global movements cannot afford the splitting up of factions prematurely. Christianity, was at first a single formation before it broke up into several subforms, Catholicism, Calvinism, Lutheranism, Quakerism, etc. Communism, too, was a single formation before it broke up into Stalinism, Trotzkyism, Maoism, etc.

The only thing which can avert a split is the development of *professional standards* which are sufficiently broad in scope to include medical as well as non-medical subjects — anatomy, physiology and chemistry on the one hand, medical sociology, social psychology and sociometry on the other hand. The problem of *standards* is, therefore, in the foreground of consideration. The training standards of doctors of medicine differ greatly from the training standards of psychologists, sociologists, pedagogues and nurses, at least in the U.S.A. A nucleus of common study and training should be designated.

(b) The second block is *economic*. Doctors of medicine, especially psychiatrists, have larger incomes than psychologists, sociologists, social workers, nurses, etc., and are better able to meet membership fees and other expenses. The result is that the latter are stigmatized as the underdogs of the movement.

(c) The *ideological* blocks are even more serious. They are due to the three theoretical roots of group psychotherapy, medicine (psychiatry), sociology and religion. A natural enfoldment of group psychotherapy should include psychiatrists and psychologists because of the psychiatric origin of group psychotherapy, but it should invite also sociologists because of its sociological origin, and finally, it should invite also ministers, educators and counselers of all sort because of its religious origin. Actually, from all these disciplines, individuals have entered the movement and have made contributions in theory and practice.

In the last few years a new ideological factor has entered which may well become the turning point in the global movement. With the re-entrance of the communist countries, particularly the U.S.S.R., into scientific exchange, their attitude towards group psychotherapy is already playing a prominent role and will do so increasingly in the future development of the group psychotherapy movement. The communistic psychiatrists, as far as they are interested in group psychotherapy, are strictly anti-Freudian and represent an increas-

120

ing counterforce against psychoanalytically oriented theory and practice.

Not only the layman, but also scientists and scholars began to think little of the movement which thought so little of itself that it neglected its own pioneers. These professional and ideological controversies may explain why the group psychotherapy movement has not taken an undisputed first place as a therapeutic "Weltanschaung." When it stepped in around 1931 to surpass the psychoanalytic movement, it had all the potentials to take over the leadership and to give the world a new therapeutic social system fitting the needs of our twentieth century. The benefits which come from the group and action methods are universal. One must hope, however, that the group psychotherapy movement would not become the playground in which one or another doctrine will try to dominate the field through political pressure and manipulations, but that it will be open to all varieties of group psychotherapy which are practiced. In a spirit similar to UNO's, it should be a forum for all methods, however large or small their following. Its international congresses should mirror the actualities of the work done. The entire matter will boil down to the question whether we therapists and scientists can do a better job in the matter of coexistence than the politicians.

THE HISTORY OF SCIENCE

History puts the true credits in proper order of justified esteem and corrects false priorities. People who do not get any credit during their lifetime for their achievements may still get it after they are gone. And people who have had their names in the limelight during their lifetime may be erased from memory and forgotten in the annals of science.

A businessman whose business is going well has a lot of money in the bank, but when he fails he must close his account. A politician knows when he fails; if he does not get the votes he is not elected to office. But it is different with a scientist. He does not know where he stands in the hall of fame even if he gets the Nobel prize, until the history of science places him. The history of science is in our world the nearest to a last judgment. If there are any records in the libraries, in the legends of people, the truth will eventually come out.

FOOTNOTES

1. J. L. Moreno, *Application of the Group Method to Classification,* National Committee on Prisons and Prison Labor, Washington, D.C., 1932. Moreno's *Das Stegreiftheater* (*The Theater of Spontaneity*), which contained many of the current concepts, was published in German in 1923; there has been *no* other publication prior to 1923 or 1932 which anticipated the current trends of group and action methods more closely than these two books.
2. *Ibid.,* 1932, p. 84.
3. *Ibid.,* p. 80.
4. *Ibid.,* p. 84.
5. *Ibid.,* p. 13.
6. *Ibid.,* p. 28.
7. *Ibid.,* p. 85.
8. *Ibid.,* p. 73.
9. *Ibid.,* pp. 74-76.
10. R. J. Corsini, *Methods of Group Psychotherapy,* McGraw-Hill, New York, 1957, p. 15.
11. Moreno, *Application of the Group Method,* p. 72.
12. *Ibid.*
13. J. L. Moreno, *Einladung zu einer Begegnung,* 1914, p. 5. All German publications by J. L. Moreno referred to are available at the Library of Congress, Washington, D.C.
14. J. L. Moreno, *Rede über den Augenblick* (*Speech about the Moment*), 1922, p. 22.
15. J. L. Moreno, *Rede über die Begegnung* (*Speech about the Encounter*), 1923, pp. 24-25, Kiepenheuer Verlag, Berlin.
16. J. L. Moreno, *Das Stegreiftheater,* 1923, Gustav Kiepenheuer Verlag, Potsdam, p. 88. In English, *The Theater of Spontaneity,* Beacon House, Beacon, N.Y., 1947, p. 98.
17. *Ibid.,* pp. 30 and 35.
18. *Ibid.,* pp. 90-91.
19. J. L. Moreno, *Psychodrama,* Vol. I, Beacon House, 1946 and 1964, p. 5.
20. Moreno, *Application of the Group Method,* p. 21.
21. *Ibid.,* p. 78.
22. *Ibid.,* p. 79.
23. J. L. Moreno, *The First Book on Group Psychotherapy,* third edition, Beacon House, Beacon, N.Y., p. 16.

24. *Ibid., p.* 18.
25. J. L. Moreno, *Who Shall Survive?*, Nervous and Mental Disease Publishing Co., Washington, D.C., 1934.
26. *Ibid.,* p. 3.
27. *Ibid.,* p. 4.
28. *Ibid.,* p. 80.
29. *Ibid.,* pp. 325-6.
30. *Ibid.,* p. 325.
31. *Ibid.,* pp. 326-7.
32. J. L. Moreno, "Scientific Foundations of Group Psychotherapy", *Group Psychotherapy, A Symposium,* Beacon House, 1945.
33. J. H. Pratt, *op. cit.,* pp. 326-330.
34. T. Burrow, "The Group Method of Analysis", *Psychoanalytic Review,* Vol. 14, 1927.
35. T. Burrow, *Science and Man's Behavior,* Philosophical Library, New York, 1953, p. 531.
36. Hans Syz, "Phylopathology", *The Encyclopedia of Psychology,* edited by Philip Lawrence Harriman, Philosophical Library, New York, 1946, pp. 519-20.
37. Hans Syz, "Trigant Burrow's Thesis in Relation to Psychotherapy", *Progress in Psychotherapy,* Vol. II, Grune & Stratton, New York, 1957, pp. 148-9.
38. E. W. Lazell, "The Group Treatment of Dementia Praecox", *Psychoanalytic Review,* Vol. 8, 1921, pp. 168-79.
39. *Ibid.*
40. Mrs. L. Cody Marsh, "In Memoriam", *Group Psychotherapy,* Vol. III, Beacon House, 1949, pp. 262-65.
41. Corsini, *Methods Of Group Psychotherapy,* McGraw-Hill, New York, 1957, p. 12.
42. *Ibid.*
43. Robert J. Lince, "Review of The First Book on Group Psychotherapy", *Group Psychotherapy,* Vol. X, No. 3, 1957, p. 244.
44. Hans Syz, *op. cit.,* p. 244.
45. Werner W. Kemper, "Zur Heutigen Gruppen-Psychotherapie", *Psyche,* Vol. XI, February, 1958, pp. 707-715. Translated from P. Renouvier, *The Group Psychotherapy Movement,* J. L. Moreno, Its Pioneer and Founder, Psychodrama and Group Psychotherapy Monograph No. 33, Beacon House, 1958.
46. William Alanson White, *The First Book on Group Psychotherapy,* third edition, Beacon House, 1956, pp. 109-10. First edition, 1932.
47. Winfred Overholser, Editorial, *Group Psychotherapy, A Symposium,* Beacon House, 1945, p. 3.
48. Wilfred Hulse, "The Social Meaning of Current Methods in Group Psychotherapy", *Group Psychotherapy,* Vol. III, April, 1950, p. 63.

49. Joseph I. Meiers, *Origins and Development of Group Psychotherapy*, Beacon House, 1945, pp. 267-68.
50. Walter Bromberg, *The First Book on Group Psychotherapy*, p. 3.
51. A. Friedemann, *Progress in Psychotherapy*, Vol. 1, Grune & Stratton, 1956, p. 321.
52. H. Teirich, "Review, *First Book on Group Psychotherapy*", *Group Psychotherapy*, Vol. X, No. 4, 1957, p. 356.
53. S. H. Foulkes and E. J. Anthony, *Group Psychotherapy*, Penguin Books, New York, 1957, p. 41.
54. R. Corsini, *Methods of Group Psychotherapy*, p. 13.
55. R. Corsini, "Historic Background of Group Psychotherapy: A Critique", *Group Psychotherapy*, Vol. 8, 1955, p. 220.
56. H. Mullan and M. Rosenbaum, *Group Psychotherapy, Theory and Practice*, The Free Press, Glencoe, 1962, p. 5.
57. J. W. Klapman, *Group Psychotherapy, Theory and Practice*, second edition, Grune & Stratton, 1959, p. 2.
58. Joseph I. Meiers, "Origins and Development of Group Psychotherapy", *Group Psychotherapy, A Symposium*, Beacon House, 1946.
59. A. S. Luchins, *Group Therapy, A Guide*, Random House, New York, 1964, p. 23.
60. R. Corsini, *Methods of Group Psychotherapy*, pp. 13-14.
61. J. W. Klapman, *Group Psychotherapy, Theory and Practice*, pp. 5-7.
62. J. L. Moreno, *The First Book on Group Psychotherapy*, p. x.
63. A. S. Luchins, *Group Therapy, A Guide*, p. 25.
64. P. Renouvier, "The Group Psychotherapy Movement", *Group Psychotherapy*, Vol. XI, No. 1, 1958, p. 71.
65. Hans Syz, "Review of the First Book on Group Psychotherapy," *Group Psychotherapy*, Vol. X, No. 3, 1957, pp. 244-45.
66. A. Wolf and E. Schwartz, *Psychoanalysis in Groups*, Grune and Stratton, New York, 1963, p. 147.
67. L. C. Marsh, "Group Therapy and the Psychiatric Clinic", *Journal of Nervous and Mental Diseases*, Vol. 82, 1935, pp. 381-93.
68. L. Wender, "The Dynamics of Group Psychotherapy and its Application", *Journal of Nervous and Mental Diseases*, Vol. 84, 1936, pp. 54-60.
69. H. H. Jennings, "Experiments in Impromptu Analysis", *Impromptu Magazine*, Vol. 1, No. 1, Beacon House, 1931; "Psychoanalysis and Dr. Moreno", *Impromptu Magazine*, Vol. 1, No. 2, Beacon House, 1931.
70. P. Renouvier, *The Group Psychotherapy Movement*, Psychodrama and Group Psychotherapy Monograph No. 33, 1958.
71. Leading exponents of Sociometry in the U.S.A., 1925-45, were: Merl E. Bonney, Joan Criswell, H. Infield, Helen Hall Jennings, P. Lazarsfeld, Charles Loomis, George Lundberg, J. L. Moreno, Florence B.

124

Moreno, Zerka Toeman Moreno, T. Newcomb, Mary Northway and Leslie D. Zeleny.

72. J. L. Moreno, *Who Shall Survive?*, pp. 170-71.
73. R. G. Barker, "The Social Interrelations of Strangers and Acquaintances", *Sociometry*, Vol. V, 1942, pp. 169-79.
74. J. L. Moreno, "Interpersonal Therapy and the Psychopathology of Interpersonal Relations", *Sociometry*, Vol. I, 1937.
75. *Sociometric Review*, 1936, p. 27.
76. J. L. Moreno, "Interpersonal Therapy and the Function of the Unconscious", *Psychodrama*, Vol. II, Beacon House, 1954.
77. J. L. Moreno, "Interpersonal Therapy and the Psychopathology of Interpersonal Relations".
78. *Who Shall Survive?*, p. 256.
79. J. L. Moreno, "Psychodramatic Treatment of Psychoses", *Sociometry*, Vol. III, 1940.
80. J. L. Moreno, *Psychodrama*, Vol. I, 1946, p. 1.
81. *Ibid.*
82. J. L. Moreno, *Einladung zu einer Begegnung.*
83. J. L. Moreno, "The Scientific Meaning and the Global Significance of Group Psychotherapy", *Proceedings of the Second International Congress of Group Psychotherapy*, Karger, Zurich, 1958, p. 53.
84. Hans L. Illing, *Human Relations*, Vol. X, No. 1, 1957, pp. 77-83.
85. Louis Wender, "The Dynamics of Group Psychotherapy and its Application".
86. Paul Schilder, "The Analysis of Ideologies as a Psychotherapeutic Method, Especially in Group Treatment", *American Journal of Psychiatry*, 93, 1936, pp. 601-17.
87. Alfred Marrow, "In Memoriam Kurt Lewin", *Sociometry*, Vol. X, No. 2, 1947.
88. A. Paul Hare, *Handbook of Small Group Research*, The Free Press, New York, 1962, pp. 401-2.
89. S. R. Slavson, "Group Psychotherapy", *Mental Hygiene*, Vol. 24, pp. 36-49.
90. *Alcoholics Anonymous*, The Works Company, New York.
91. A. Low, "Group Psychotherapy", *Illinois Psychiatric Journal*, Vol. I, pp. 3-4.
92. J. W. Klapman, *Group Psychotherapy, Theory and Practice.*
93. J. L. Moreno, "Group Oath", *Group Psychotherapy*, Vol. IX, 1955; *Progress in Psychotherapy*, Vol. I, Grune & Stratton, 1958, and *Code of Ethics of Group Psychotherapy and Psychodrama*, Psychodrama and Group Psychotherapy Monograph No. 31, Beacon House, 1962.
94. This Oath and the discussions following it are from *Code of Ethics of Group Psychotherapy and Psychodrama*, Beacon House, 1962.

PART II

PART II

EVALUATION OF GROUP PSYCHOTHERAPY

A REVIEW IN EVIDENCE

by JOHN MANN

Since its inception in the early years of this century, group psychotherapy has been the subject of much excitement and considerable controversy. Its diversity of form and complexity of structure have required a considerable period of time in which to evolve into a mature subject matter. The present volume provides documentation that such an evolution has, in fact, taken place. In this process, one area in group psychotherapy has been largely neglected: namely, the scientific evaluation of group psychotherapy itself.

It is generally supposed by most practitioners that relatively little evidence currently exists relating to the effectiveness of group psychotherapy, beyond the subjective reports of the therapists and their patients. This conclusion is incorrect. A substantial body of evaluative research has accumulated, but it is not for the most part generally accessible. Some of this work is published only in the "Dissertation Abstracts" of microfilm Ph.D. dissertations. The rest of the studies have appeared in a variety of different journals that are not necessarily read by the same audience.

Any re-assessment of the present status of group psychotherapy and any projection of its probable future must be based, at least in part, on a review of the objective attempts to measure change in personality and behavior produced by these methods. It was for this reason that the present review of such research was undertaken. Although it does not constitute an exhaustive review of relevant studies and is not completely up-to-date, it is more complete than any review that is currently available in this area.

In the selection of studies to be included in this paper, two general criteria were employed: 1. The studies themselves had to

129

be methodologically adequate. More specifically, they had to employ a control group design; 2. The changes that were measured in the studies had to be of a fairly fundamental character.

A survey of the literature indicated that there were forty-one studies that met these criteria. The nature and outcome of each of these studies will be briefly described in the body of this paper. For purposes of convenience, they are grouped under three general headings: 1. Studies of single clearly defined methods of group psychotherapy; 2. Studies of single methods of group psychotherapy whose precise nature is not clearly defined; 3. Studies in which more than one method or aspect of group psychotherapy were studied at a single time.

Studies of single specific methods: The first group of studies to be described evaluated psychodramatic group therapy. In the first study by Peters and Jones,[29] 10 experimental and 11 control subjects, all male Negro schizophrenics, were randomly selected. The experimental group received psychodramatic therapy plus group discussion for 1½ hours once a week over a four month period. The control subjects received normal hospital routine for the same period. The effects of the therapy were measured by two performance tests, the Porteus Maze and the Mirror Tracing test. These kinds of change criteria are unusual, but the authors present a rationale for their use. The findings indicated that significant improvement occurred in the experimental group on the qualitative maze score. Other scores were in the same direction but not significant.

In a very similar study, Jones and Peters[21] randomly assigned 24 schizophrenic Negro patients to psychodramatic group therapy and no-treatment control conditions. The therapy group met 1½ hours, once a week, for a four month period, as in the previous study. The effects of the therapy were tested by the Porteus Maze, Mirror Tracing, Gardner Behavior Chart, Rorschach, and the Draw-a-Man Test. The findings indicated differential change in the therapy group over controls on the Mirror Tracing, Gardner Behavior Chart, and the qualitative, but not quantitative, score of the Porteus Maze.

Harrow[19] also used male schizophrenics in a study of psycho-dramatic group therapy. In this case three groups of 10 subjects were matched on unspecified variables. Two of the groups received the experimental treatment and one group acted as a no-treatment control. Two projective tests, the Rorschach and the MAPS, as well as a Situational Role test, were used as change criteria. The Rorschach and the Role test were scored for three identical indices. Of these three, only "realism" showed significant change in the experimental groups. No findings occurred on the MAPS.

Haskell[20] also studied the effects of psychodrama but used a different type of sample. In his study, 66 male inmates of Rikers Island Penitentiary were randomly assigned to experimental conditions. Groups were matched on race, religion, age, amount of education, and degree of drug addiction. The psychodrama consisted of 15 sessions of 1½ hours each. The following instruments were employed to measure change: the Human Relations Inventory, Empathy test, Judgment in Social Situations, Observations of Human Behavior, and a Role test. Only the Role test showed differential improvement favoring the experimental group.

The next group of studies to be described attempted to evaluate non-directive group therapy. An early and inadequate study of this approach was conducted by Fleming and Snyder,[13] who selected a sample of the seven worst children from a children's home. The four boys and three girls who represented the experimental subjects were treated in two separate groups. The remaining 39 children acted as controls. During the experiment 16 of the 39 control children were lost from the sample. It is clear that the so-called control group represented the healthier portion of the population and thus could not be used as a control for the sicker part. For six weeks the experimental subjects met weekly for half hour periods with female therapists. The following three pre-post measures were utilized: the Rogers Personality test, the Guess Who test, and a Sociometric test. The analysis of the data suggested that the girls' group improved on all tests except in sociometric rejection scores. No changes were noted in the boys' groups. However, pre-scores on the change criteria were used to select the experimental subjects so that regression could account for any positive changes observed.

A more satisfactory study of non-directive group therapy was made by Sheldon and Landsman.[36] The subjects for this study were 28 college freshmen in academic difficulties. These subjects were divided into experimental and control and matched on I.Q., adjustment, reading ability, and grade point average. Both groups had three meetings a week devoted to Academic Methods. The control group had two more meetings of a similar nature. The experimental group had two therapy sessions per week. Thus, the amount of exposure was equivalent in both groups. The effects of the experience were measured by three criteria: the California Test of Personality, the Iowa Silent Reading test, and the Grade Point Average. The results indicated that no change occurred in adjustment or reading ability, but that, surprisingly, grades of the experimental subjects improved. Two points should be noted in interpreting the findings. First, the same person conducted both groups, so that the effects of therapy and therapist cannot be separated. Second, it is not non-directive therapy which is being tested, but Academic methods alone vs. Academic methods plus non-directive therapy. It is, therefore, not possible to determine whether the effect of the therapy is additive or interactive.

An additional study, testing eclectic client-centered therapy, was performed by Lassar.[24] In this study 19 mothers, whose pre-school children were afflicted with cerebral palsy, were divided into experimental and control groups that were matched on age, education, income, sex, and number of children. The experimental groups met for 15 weekly discussion groups of 1½ hours' duration. The effect of the experience was measured by a questionnaire and the TAT. The findings indicated that five of the six variables on the questionnaire — overprotection, rejection, discipline, knowledge of child development, and guilt — changed significantly for the experimental group. Three of the five TAT variables — effectiveness, outcome of stories, and recognition of disability — also changed.

Still another study of non-directive group therapy was carefully performed by Lindemann.[25] Thirty male schizophrenic patients, with an average age of 34 and about two years of hospitalization, were divided into experimental and control groups. The experimental group received non-directive group therapy for two one hour sessions a week over a period of 10 weeks. Process analysis confirmed the nature of the therapy used. The effect of the therapy was measured by Hildreth's Battery of Feelings and Attitudes Scales, the Hospital Adjustment Scale, Rotter Incomplete Sentence Blanks, and the F scale from the MMPI. No differential changes were noted on any of the instruments, and there was no relation between the extent of participation and amount of change.

A study of group therapy in quite a different setting was conducted by Newburger.[27] In this study, 60 consecutively institutionalized delinquents, 16-25 years of age, were divided into six groups that were matched sociometrically. Subjects were also matched on economic status, extent of recidivism, age, intelligence, and social background. Three of the groups had interview group therapy for three months, while the other three acted as controls. At the end of that time the design was reversed so that the experimental groups became controls and the controls became experimentals. Three measures of change were used: Discipline Scores, Haggerty-Olson-Wickman Rating Schedule, and Work Marks. The findings indicated that therapy improved discipline scores and the Haggerty ratings. Work marks improved in the groups that received therapy initially but got worse for the group that received group therapy later. The gains of the early therapy group were maintained over the following three months. The special feature of this experiment is, of course, the reversal of the design, enabling not only the experimental-control comparison, but also a follow up and a comparison of late vs. early introduction of therapy.

In a further analysis of the data obtained from this study, Newburger and Schauer[28] examined changes in the sociometric structure as influenced by the administration of group therapy. No tests of statistical significance were presented, but the percentages which are given in this report suggest that the group receiving group therapy increased in number of mutual choices and isolates. This trend continues to develop in the post-experimental control period.

Another study of male juvenile delinquents was performed by Gerstenlauer.[17] In this study, 44 boys in the New York State Training School were divided into groups that were matched on I.Q., age, education, socioeconomic status, and racial and family background. The experimental group was divided into three smaller groups of seven to eight, each of whom received 20 sessions of activity-interview group therapy combining discussion with handicraft activities. The following measures were used to test the effect indicated that significant changes occurred on the Wechsler-Bellevue, Test; Maller's Personality Questionnaire; the Haggerty-Olson-Wickman Ratings completed by teachers, supervisors, cottage parents, and psychiatric social workers; the Rorschach; and an Interaction Analysis of the group meetings themselves. The findings indicated that significant changes occurred on the Wechsler-Bellevue, Stanford and Rorschach, but not on the Maller or the ratings. The Interaction Analysis indicated that the introduction of handicrafts helped the discussion. It is surprising that change was found on measures of intelligence and unconscious aspects of personality, but not on a self-administered personality questionnaire or on ratings by others, which presumably would be the first measures to reflect change.

A very different kind of group therapy was evaluated by Cadman, Misbach and Brown,[5] who call their method Round-Table Psychotherapy. In this method the group is run by the patients. The doctors act before the meeting by focusing the meeting on a particular patient by supplying appropriate material about him to the other group members. The meeting itself takes place in two phases. During the first phase the previous meeting is played back, thus utilizing a formalized feedback approach. During the second phase a leaderless group discussion centers about the target individual. An audience observes the group meeting. For purposes of evaluation, 70 subjects were randomly assigned to experimental and no-treatment control conditions. All subjects were between 17-53 years of age, above moron level of intelligence, and varied in educational level from fifth grade to college. Only feeble minded and organic cases were excluded. Groups were similar in I.Q., level of education, duration of illness, and diagnosis. Each experimental group met for an average of 50 sessions. The following measures were used to evaluate the effect of the method: the Wechsler-Bellevue, Rorschach, MAPS, and Clinical Status. A number of differential changes occurred on Rorschach indices, but these are difficult to interpret. The MAPS indicated increase in normal and decrease in schizophrenic signs in the experimental group. Both I.Q. and Clinical Status improved in the experimental group. Since these findings are given only in terms of difference scores, regression effects may exist. However, the method is clear, and its leaderless nature eliminates the problem of estimating the effect of the therapist as distinct from the therapy.

Finally, Wright[40] has tested the effect of a complex Candidate Employee Program involving a special ward with weekend pass privileges and access to money. The ward was supervised by a counselling psychologist, with additional individual and group counselling, as well as the opportunity for community employment, provided. 34 experimental subjects and 19 controls were used in a pre-post design. Change was measured in terms of Environmental Status, the Curtis Completion Form, an Index of Adjustment and Values, an Ideal-Self and Other Q-Sort, and a Modified Hospital Adjustment Rating filled out by psychiatric aides. The findings indicated that only the ratings of the aides and the Environmental Status measure showed changes favoring the experimental group.

Studies of single general methods: An interesting study of group therapy, formulated as a general approach, rather than as a specific technique, is provided by Wilcox.[39] The sample, 160 institutionalized female defectives, was divided into 97 experimental and 17 control subjects. During the study 46 subjects were lost. The design of the experiment was somewhat unusual. Experimental subjects were assigned to groups on the basis of their passivity or aggressiveness. On this basis, four groups of passive subjects, four groups of aggressive subjects, and four groups containing both passive and aggressive subjects were formed. All experimental subjects participated in 25 group therapy meetings over a nine week period. Four therapists were used, each meeting with the three types of groups. Change was measured by means of a Behavior Rating Scale completed by matrons and attendants. The findings indicated that there were no differences between groups or therapists, but that the variance, as could be expected, was greater in the heterogeneous group.

Another study using a similar change criterion was performed by Sacks and Berger.[32] In this case the criterion was simply the Hospital Status of the patients. 56 schizophrenics were assigned on a random basis to experimental and control groups, with matching demonstrated on age, socioeconomic status, education, and intelligence. Groups of seven met twice weekly for 1½ hours over a year's time with multiple therapists. An examination of the hospital status of the subjects indicated that the therapy groups had improved. This change was confined to patients in the middle range of the Hospital Status measure. Persons on the disturbed ward or nearing discharge did not change. While the study is straightforward, the criterion of change is open to bias since persons responsible for judging the hospital status of patients probably knew which patients were participating in group therapy, and this could have affected their actions with regard to these patients.

Feifel and Schwartz[11] studied the effect of group therapy on hospitalized male World War II veterans. Subjects were shown to

135

be equal in diagnosis, I.Q., age, education, marital status, race, and home location (urban vs. rural). However, the method of assignment to conditions is somewhat uncertain. 68 subjects were divided into two equal groups. The control group participated in the ordinary hospital routine. The experimental group did the same but received, in addition, group therapy sessions of one hour each, twice a week. Two therapists alternated as therapist and observer. The effect of the therapy was evaluated only in terms of Hospital Status after three months. No differences were found, though the trend favored the experimental group.

An unusual sample was studied by Klonoff[22] in his evaluation of group therapy. The subjects were 48 tubercular patients divided into two groups that were matched on social, psychological, and medical variables. The group therapy took place in homogeneous sex groups for 10 one hour sessions that were standardized with respect to theme, therapist and observer. The effects of this therapy were measured by a Situational Attitude Scale that concerned attitudes of importance in TB treatment. The questionnaire results indicated no overall differences; however, the female group changed more than either the male therapy or the control group. No relation was found between attitude change and objective medical improvement, as judged by Roentgen progress.

A very different and equally unusual sample was studied by Abrams.[1] His study utilized 24 male sex offenders assigned to control and experimental groups that were matched on age, I.Q., race, and crime. Experimental subjects received 80 therapy sessions. The effect of the sessions was measured by ratings of Rorschachs on 12 variables in the two general areas of social adaptation and sexual adjustment. Four of the eight variables concerning social adjustment changed for the experimental group, with similar though less marked trends on the sexual adjustment variable. Younger patients changed more than older patients. Furthermore, those who attended the first half of the sessions changed less than those who attended the second half.

The effect of group therapy on a different delinquent sample was investigated by Temmer.[38] In this case 40 white female delinquents were assigned to either control or experimental conditions by an unspecified method. The experimental group received 15 weekly sessions of 45 minutes each. Four change measures were used: the Wechsler-Bellevue, the PAT, the Picture Frustration

136

Test, and an Institutional Rating. The only change in the therapy group was found on the intelligence test; this is surprising in view of the relative stability of the I.Q.

Another study of the effect of group therapy on delinquents was performed by Franklin.[15] In this case 15 delinquent boys were divided into experimental and control groups that were equated on the change criteria. An additional group of five non-delinquent boys was used as a standard of normality. Over a six months' period the experimental boys received 50 bi-weekly therapy sessions of one hour, in five man groups. The effect of this therapy was measured by a Q-Sort made by the subjects on attitudes to self and others, and by Psychiatric Ratings. Some shifts on Q-Sort favoring the therapy group were noted, but the degree of significance was not stated.

A further study of a delinquent sample is provided by Bassin.[2] In this study 30 male adult probationers with average intelligence and education were randomly assigned to experimental and control conditions. Two therapy groups were formed that were racially homogeneous. The groups met with two therapists for 15 weekly meetings of 1½ hours. The following three measures of change were used: TAT, the Bernberg Human Relations Inventory, and the BARO Behavior Rating Scale. Significant improvement was noted on the TAT and the Bernberg, but not on the BARO ratings. Lack of findings on the ratings is surprising, since they are most sensitive to bias and, presumably, also to change; they may have been low in reliability.

An interesting study by Shatter[35] involved a sample of 24 fourth grade boys who were retarded readers, but normal in adjustment. Experimental and control groups were matched on age, intelligence, and extent of reading retardation. The controls, over a period of nine months, met in six man groups for a total of 36 hours at the rate of one hour per week. The experimental boys did likewise but, in addition, the mothers of these boys met in similar group therapy. Five measures of change were utilized: Reading Test, the Rorschach, the Figure Drawing Test, a Parent Attitude Questionnaire, and Teachers' ratings. The findings indicated that changes occurred on all instruments. However, the change on the Parent Attitude Questionnaire did not reach the required level of significance. The implication of this study is that therapy with the child is greatly

137

enhanced if parallel therapy is also carried on with the parent. The general effect of group therapy by itself is not measured.

A final study in this section, by Funk, Shatin, Freed and Rockmore,[16] tested the effects of a complex demonstration program involving group therapy, corrective therapy, occupational therapy, pharmacological therapy, reaction therapy, recreation therapy and electroshock therapy. In order to test this program, 20 schizophrenics with long periods of hospitalization and no recent somatic treatments were divided into experimental and control groups that were matched on age, chronicity and ward adjustment. Change was measured by a Behavioral Rating scale, the Multidimensional Scale for Rating Patients, Weekly Rating Scales, and Psychomotor Efficiency tests. The findings indicated that all ratings showed change favoring the experimental group. The complexity of the treatment makes any findings extremely difficult to interpret. In any case, the findings may reflect only rater bias or the added attention devoted to the subjects who were involved in the program.

Comparison of specific methods: The first study in this series, carried out by Daniels,[8] is not so much a variation in methods as in leader characteristics. A factorial 2x2 design was utilized to test the effect of male and female therapists in four conditions: male therapist, female therapist, both, neither. For this study 24 eighth grade students with behavior problems were assigned randomly to one of the four conditions. The therapy itself consisted of 20 weekly discussions of 45 minutes each. The following indices were used to judge the relative effects of the four conditions: an Intelligence Test, Measures of Overt Behavior, Reading and Arithmetic Achievement Tests, Attitude toward School, Psychological Ratings based on Sacks Sentence Completion, Figure Drawing, and the Tell a Story Test. The findings from the study are unclear, but it appears that mixed leadership under the experimental conditions is less satisfactory than either male or female leadership alone. Whether this is a reflection of heterogeneity of sex in leadership or two leaders vs. one is not indicated in the design.

The next study of Beletsis[3] is not so much a study in comparative methods as a comparison of different intensities of the same method. 30 male schizophrenics were divided into three groups matched on age, length of hospitalization, and severity of illness. Each group was assigned to one of three conditions for a period of six months. The first group received 78 sessions of group therapy, three times a week. The second group received 26 therapy sessions once a week over the same period. The third group received no therapy over the same period. The method used was described as Eclectic Psychoanalytic Group Therapy. Two projective tests, the Rorschach and Human Figure Drawing, as well as the Multidimensional Scale for Rating Psychiatric Patients, were used to measure change. No effects were noted on the projective tests. Both therapy groups improved in the ratings over the controls. The added exposure of the first group, as compared to the second, did not improve the extent of the effect observed in the ratings.

A 2x2 factorial design was used by Harriman[18] in testing the effects of group therapy and films. The four conditions were: non-directive group therapy for 16 sessions, twice a week; films seen with the same frequency, but without any verbal introduction or subsequent discussion; films followed by group therapy; no treatment. The 16 films chosen for use in the study were selected from a total of 49 previewed. The films were selected on the criteria of being non-moral, documentary, and emphasizing the case study approach. The subjects consisted of 87 first offenders with an average age of 31. Subjects were randomly assigned to experimental conditions. The effects of the treatment were measured by the Cattell 15 Factor test (two factors used), the EPPS (three scales used), and the Morris Gripe Scale. No change was found on any of the measures, nor were there any significant interactions.

Another 2x2 factorial study was performed by Peyman.[30] In this case the effects of group therapy, shock, group therapy plus shock, and no treatment, were examined. The group therapy, consisting of discussion and psychodrama, was held over a six month period, twice a week, for one hour. The shock groups received at least 10 electroshocks over the same period. The subjects of the experiments were 32 white female patients, 21-39 years of age, with chronic schizophrenic reaction, hospitalized more than one year, not mentally defective, and able to take psychological tests. They were assigned at random to the four experimental conditions. The Bellevue-Wechsler, Bender-Gestalt, and Rorschach were used to measure change. The findings of the study indicated that no change occurred on the Wechsler. For both the Klopfer Prognostic rating of the Rorschach and Pascal and Suttell's scoring of the Bender, the therapy and the therapy plus shock conditions did better than controls, but were apparently equivalent to each other.

It appears the shock did not add or detract appreciably from the effect of the group therapy.

Another interesting and sophisticated study of multiple group methods was carried out by Knox.[23] In this study group therapy was compared with a social group and a no-treatment control group. The subjects of the study were 22 white male schizophrenics randomly assigned to the conditions. The group therapy, with the aid of two therapists, focused on the discussion of personal problems. The social group met for lunch. The control group had the usual hospital routine. The therapy and social groups met three times a week over a six week period. The effects of the various treatments were assessed by means of Q-Sorts measuring self and ideal self, acceptance of others measured by a photographic sorting task, and conformity measured by determining change in test performance on the picture sort when informed of group norms. No differences were noted on any of these instruments. The measures used were particularly appropriate to the situation. The use of social and therapy groups in the same study represents a potential aid to generalization from clinical fields to social psychology, as well as a control for attention. However, since no change was found in any of the groups, no generalizations can be made.

A somewhat different type of comparison was carried out by Singer and Goldman,[37] who assigned, by means of randomization, 30 male schizophrenics, with a minimum of three years of hospitalization, to one of two experimental conditions. The groups were shown to be matched on duration, type, and severity of illness. The experimental conditions were as follows: a 30 minute lecture plus discussion modeled after Klapman's Didactic Group Therapy; Informal Discussion modeled after Slavson's Interview Group Therapy. Both groups met for 16 weekly sessions. The two therapists alternated in roles of therapist and recorder. The analysis of the interaction served as the measure of change. Specifically, the amount, relevance, and direction of the communication was noted. The data indicated that the authoritarian lecture plus discussion group had high initial proportion of relevant comments, which declined sharply with time; the democratic group showed the reverse trend as well as greater evidence of cohesion and morale.

Semon and Goldstein[34] also compared the effects of a group vs. a leader-centered form of group therapy. 39 hospitalized schizophrenic patients were assigned to either of the experimental condi-

140

tions or to a non-treatment control. Groups were matched on degree of adjustment, interpersonal functioning, length of hospitalization, and age. Both experimental groups had daily one hour meetings, five days a week, for 10 weeks. Two leaders conducted both types of groups with difference in their behavior validated in the two conditions. The Palo Alto Adjustment Scale, completed by hospital attendants, represented the criterion measure. No differences between groups were found on this instrument. The design of the experiment lent itself to an analysis of variance treatment, but unfortunately the latter was not carried out.

A somewhat similar experiment was performed by Clampitt.[6] In this instance, therapy which encouraged interaction among members, the expression of feelings and attitudes, along with clarification and interpretation by the therapist, were compared to a lecture on material concerning adjustment, and to a no-treatment control. In effect the lecture was a control both for attention and for a consideration of mental hygiene material. 69 female freshmen volunteers served as the subjects. They were randomly assigned to conditions. Four therapists were used in both methods, each therapist conducting a group in each method, allowing a test both for the effect of method and of therapist, and of the interaction of the two. The change criteria consisted of Sociometric Rankings derived from dormitory-wide measures, the California Psychological Inventory, and Adjustment Ratings obtained from interviews with dormitory advisors. An analysis of these criteria revealed no differences between the groups. However, persons in all treatments showed a high amount of consistent shifting, significant at the .001 level, on some scales of the California Psychological Inventory. This is surprising, since personality tests are designed to measure fairly stable aspects of personality.

McCann[26] has made a comparison of the effect of nondirective therapy alone with nondirective therapy when combined with systematic feedback. Four groups of open ward neuropsychiatric patients were assigned to two experimental and two control groups. The groups met for 14 sessions. In the therapy plus feedback situation, subgroups listened to recordings of the sessions and discussed them, from the 6th to 11th sessions. Interaction measures were obtained as well as ratings of the subjects on the Multidimensional Scale for Rating Patients. The findings indicated no difference in total responsiveness, but the experimental group

141

increased in numbers of statements indicating acceptance of others and related to personal problems, whereas the therapy alone group had a comparable increase in friendly discussion. No differences existed on the ratings. The effect of the feedback did not appear to be great.

A similar design was used by Roman[31] to study the effects of group therapy and group remedial reading in various combinations. 21 delinquent boys, ages 13 to 16, all retarded readers, were assigned to three groups that were matched on age, intelligence, reading ability, and level of psycho-social adjustment. The treatments were: Tutorial Group Therapy, consisting of remedial reading plus group therapy, Group Remedial Reading, and Interview Group Therapy. A great variety of change criteria were used: the WISC, Gray Oral Reading Paragraphs, Rorschach, Human Figure Drawings, Szondi, Davidson Rorschach Signs, Haggerty-Olson-Wickman Ratings, and Case Histories. The findings indicated that the Tutorial group produced greater change than either of the other methods, on the Rorschach, Human Figure Drawings, Szondi, Davidson Rorschach Signs, and the Haggerty-Olson-Wickman Ratings. No changes occurred on the WISC, Gray Oral Paragraphs, or Case Histories. The greater effectiveness of the two methods combined is clearly indicated.

Francus[14] also compared reading and group therapy. In this study group therapy, preceded by a brief didactic talk, was compared with reading therapy having the same content as the didactic talk. Two groups were formed from 30 hospitalized schizophrenics who were matched on age, I.Q., occupation, and education. Both groups met over a three month span. The effect of the experience was determined by ratings of interviews made by three judges on six variables. The findings indicated that group therapy produced significantly greater improvement in information, control, and guilt, as well as in trends toward improvement in hostility and insight, than the reading group. These findings are in contrast to the previous study in which both group experiences produced equal results.

A further study of group and remedial reading therapy was carried out by Fisher.[12] The experimental conditions consisted of remedial reading plus group therapy, remedial reading, and no treatment control. All methods were used over a seven month period. The WISC, Gates Advanced Primary Reading Tests, the Rorschach, Figure Drawing, Reading Attitudes, and Social Workers'

Rating of Emotional Improvement were used as change criteria. Group therapy and remedial reading combined improved reading twice as much as other approaches; it also resulted in greater gains on all instruments taken together than the other conditions. It is not possible to tell from the design of this study whether the effect of group therapy was additive or interactive.

A rather different comparison was made by Yormak,[41] who studied the relative effects of Patient-Centered Group Discussion similar to nondirective therapy and a General Semantic lecture and discussion. The subjects for the experiment were 20 acute and 20 chronic VA patients. Each group of 20 was divided randomly into experimental and control groups providing a replication of the design with different types of patients. The criteria measures consisted of the General Semantic Information Test, Rotter Level of Aspiration Situation, Mitchell's Intensionality-Extensionality Scale, the Discomfort-Relief Rating Scale, and the I.Q. An analysis of the battery of test data indicated that the semantic training produced differential improvement on the General Semantic Information Test and the Rotter Level of Aspiration Situation.

A more traditional comparison was made by DiGiovanni,[9] who studied the relative effects of Activity group therapy involving shaving, bathing, and playing cards; Orthodox group therapy; and a no-treatment control. The Activity group can be regarded as a control for attention and perhaps also for the patients' faith in the method. All groups met five days a week, for 1½ hours, over a 10 week period, for a total of 74 meetings. The subjects were 36 hospitalized chronic schizophrenics matched on the criteria of age, years of hospitalization and diagnosis. The effect of the various treatments was measured by the Minnesota Social Behavior Scale and the Hospital Adjustment Scale. No difference between the methods was found.

Scire[33] has studied the effect of group therapy used in conjunction with chemotherapy. Three groups of schizophrenic children, sixteen boys and four girls, ranging in age from 6 to 11, were randomly selected from Rockland State Hospital. The first group received group therapy and, at the same time, three months of chemotherapy. The second group received group therapy and chemotherapy beginning two months later. The third group received no special treatment. The group therapy took place over eight months. The change criteria were the WISC, Haggerty-Wickman-

Olson Behavioral Rating Schedule, Discipline Reports, and Socio-metric Choices. The effects were measured before, during, and after the experiment. The only difference on any criterion was in terms of greater peer acceptance in both experimental groups as compared to the no-treatment controls.

An interesting study of the joint effects of group psychotherapy and physiological therapy was carried out by Cowden, Zax and Sproles.[7] In this study, four groups of severely disturbed and agitated schizophrenic patients were divided into groups of eight. In a modified factorial design, groups were assigned to one of four conditions: group psychotherapy plus Reserpine; group psychotherapy and placebo; Reserpine only; no treatment. Group therapy was conducted over six months by two therapists, three times a week in one hour sessions. The change in patients was measured by a large battery of instruments; Lorr Multi-dimensional Scale for Rating Psychiatric Patients, filled out by psychiatrists; a seven point rating scale, filled out by attendants; Bender Gestalt; HTP and HTP chromatic; Self-Concept Drawing; Sentence Completion; Modified TAT; and six behavior indices — wet packs, seclusion rooms, fights, nurse disturbance reports, transfers and discharge. No changes were noted on any of the ratings on projective tests. However, on four of the six behavior indices there was some indication of change favoring group therapy plus Reserpine, group therapy and placebo, Reserpine alone, and control, in descending order of magnitude.

An own-control design was used by Brown[4] in a study of 60 institutionalized delinquent boys divided into three groups. The first group received six weeks of individual library work followed by six weeks of group therapy. The second group received the reverse sequence. The third group received six weeks of no treatment. The latter condition was a control for attention as well as the passage of time. The Haggerty-Olson-Wickman Rating Schedule and a Sociometric Questionnaire were used as change criteria. The data obtained from these instruments indicated that immediate group therapy was more effective than later group therapy; library work also produced effects, but they were lost in the follow-up period; non-permanent changes in sociometric status occurred in group therapy.

Ends and Page[10] have compared three widely used approaches to group therapy — Analytic, Client-Centered, and Learning Theory

— in the treatment of hospitalized alcoholics. They also used a social discussion control group. The study was designed in the form of a pre-post Latin Square Design, with four therapists participating three times a week in each method, for a total of 15 sessions with each method. In the social discussion control the therapist maintained neutrality while participating in discussion. This control is unusual and very helpful in distinguishing the effect of a general group experience from the unique effects of therapy. Two criteria measures were used: the first consisted of various indices obtained from the Butler and Haigh self-ideal Q-Sort. The second was the relapse rate into alcoholism. A number of differences in the ideal-self indices were obtained for the different methods, but direct comparisons between methods are difficult to make and the meaning of the indices is ambiguous. With regard to the rate of improvement and recidivism, both the Analytic and Client-Centered patients improved in status; the Client-Centered patients improved significantly more than the social group on recidivism. A member of questions are not clear about the study. The nature of the subjects is not described. Also, the comparability of the treatments is hard to judge. However, in other respects, the general nature of the study was well conceived.

Discussion and Conclusion: It is difficult to summarize the outcome of forty-one diversely conceived and executed research studies. The only aspects which they have in common are their involvement with some form of group psychotherapy and their use of a control group design.

In order to obtain some general picture of the combined impact of these studies, the relative numbers of positive changes produced by different group methods and measured by different change criteria were determined.

Chi Square analysis of this material indicated that one method seemed to produce change as frequently as another and also one type of change criteria seemed to detect change as frequently as another. More generally, regardless of the group psychotherapeutic method being tested or the instruments used to test it, the results were uniform.

Change was found in approximately 45% of the studies. Thus, the present review clearly substantiates the fact that group psychotherapy does, indeed, produce objectively measurable changes in attitude, personality, and behavior. But this review does not indicate the clear superiority of one method of group psychotherapy over another; nor does it support the notion that group psychotherapy in general tends to produce only certain types of change in the patients who participate in it.

REFERENCES

1. Abrams, A. Effects of group therapy upon certain personality characteristics of a selected group of institutionalized male sex offenders. *Dissert. Ab.* 1953, *13,* 114.
2. Bassin, A. Effect of group therapy upon certain attitudes and perceptions of adult offenders on probation. *Dissert. Ab.* 1958, *18,* 2241-2.
3. Beletsis, J. Jr. Group psychotherapy with chronic male schizophrenics: an evaluation of the frequency of group psychotherapy sessions as a factor affecting the results of the therapy. *Dissert. Ab.* 1956, *16,* 1170-1.
4. Brown, P. M. A comparative study of three therapy techniques used to effect behavioral and social status changes in a group of institutionalized delinquent boys. *Dissert. Ab.* 1957, *17,* 674-5.
5. Cadman, W. H., Misbach, L. & Brown, D. V. An assessment of round-table psychotherapy. *Psychol. Monog.* 1954, *68,* whole 384, 48 pp.
6. Clampitt, R. R. An experimentally controlled investigation of the effects of group therapy. *Rissert. Ab.* 1955, *15,* 2292-2293.
7. Cowden, R. C., Zax, M. & Sproles, J. A. Group psychotherapy in conjunction with a physical treatment. *J. Clin. Psych.* 1956, *12,* 53-56.
8. Daniels, M. The influence of the sex of the therapist and of the co-therapist in group psychotherapy with boys: an investigation of the effectiveness of group psychotherapy with eighth grade behavior-problem boys, comparing results achieved by a male therapist, by a female therapist, and by two therapists in combination. *Dissert. Ab.* 1958, *18,* 1489.
9. DiGiovanni, P. A comparison between orthodox group psychotherapy and activity group therapy in the treatment of chronic hospitalized schizophrenics. *Dissert. Ab.* 1959, *19,* 3361.
10. Ends, E. J. & Page, C. W. Group psychotherapy and concomitant psychological change. *Psychol. Monog.* 1959, *73,* #10, whole no. 480, 31 pp.
11. Feifel, H. & Schwartz, A. D. Group psychotherapy with acutely disturbed psychotic patients. *J. Consult. Psychol.* 1953, *17,* 113-121.
12. Fisher, B. An investigation of the effectiveness of group therapy for the remediation of reading disabilities. *Dissert. Ab.* 1953, *13,* 590-1.

146

13. Fleming, L. & Snyder, W. U. Social & personal changes following non-directive group play therapy. *Am. J. Ortho.* 1947, *17*, 101-116.
14. Francus, J. B. A comparative study of two therapeutic methods of treating the significant relatives of hospitalized schizophrenics. *Dissert. Ab.* 1955, *15*, 1898.
15. Franklin, G. H. The effect of group therapy on the attitudes toward self and others of institutionalized delinquent boys. *Dissert. Ab.* 1958, *18*, 1104-5.
16. Funk, I. G., Shatin, L., Freed, E. X. & Rockmore, L. Somapsychotherapeutic approach to long-term schizophrenic patients. *J. Nerv. Ment. Diseases.* 1955, *121*, 423-437.
17. Gerstenlauer, C. Group therapy with institutionalized male juvenile delinquents. A comparative evaluation of the effects of group therapy on some aspects of behavior and emotional and social adjustment of a selected group of institutionalized male juvenile delinquents. *Dissert. Ab.* 1959, *10*, 101-3.
18. Harriman, B. L. Influence of group-centered therapy and mental health films on attitudes of prisoners. *Dissert. Ab.* 1956, *16*, 1494-1495.
19. Harrow, G. S. The effects of psychodrama group therapy on role behavior of schizophrenic patients. *Group Psychotherapy.* 1951, *3*, 316-320.
20. Haskell, M. R. Psychodramatic role training in preparation for release on parole. *Group Psychotherapy.* 1957, *10*, 57-59.
21. Jones, F. D. & Peters, H. N. An experimental evaluation of group psychotherapy. *J. Abnorm. Soc. Psychol.* 1952, *47*, 345-353.
22. Klonoff, H. An explanatory study of the effect of short-term group psychotherapy on attitudes of tuberculous patients. *Dissert. Ab.* 1955, *15*, 290-291.
23. Knox, W. J. Acceptance of self, other people, and social conformity as a function of group therapeutic experiences. *Unpub. doct. dissert.* Pennsylvania State University, 1958.
24. Lassar, B. T. A study of the effects of group discussion on the attitudes of mothers toward their cerebral palsied children: an investigation of the attitudes of mothers of cerebral palsied children and the effects of group discussion on these attitudes. *Dissert. Ab.* 1957, *17*, 676-7.
25. Lindemann, J. E. The process and efficacy of short-term non-directive group psychotherapy with hospitalized schizophrenic patients. *Ab. Doc. Dissert.* Penn State Coll., 1953, *17*, 690-694.
26. McCann, J. R. A technique to facilitate acceptance and its relationship to interaction during group psychotherapy. *Dissert. Ab.* 1956, *16*, 576.
27. Newburger, H. M. The effect of group therapy upon certain aspects of the behavior and attitudes of institutionalized delinquents: the evaluation of certain aspects of behavior and attitudes toward self,

147

others, and some social institutions following group therapy. *Dissert. Ab.* 1952, *12,* 597-8.

28. Newburger, H. M. & Schauer, G. Sociometric evaluation of group psychotherapy. *Group Psychotherapy.* 1953, *6,* 7-20.

29. Peters, H. N. & Jones, F. D. Evaluation of group psychotherapy by means of performance tests. *J. Consult. Psychol.* 1951, *51,* 363-367.

30. Peyman, D. A. R. An investigation of the effects of group psychotherapy on chronic schizophrenic patients. *Group Psychotherapy.* 1956, *9,* 35-39.

31. Roman, M. Tutorial group therapy: a study of integration of remedial reading and group therapy in the treatment of delinquents. *Dissert. Ab.* 1955, *15,* 1761.

32. Sacks, J. M. & Berger, S. Group therapy techniques with hospitalized chronic schizophrenic patients. *J. Consult. Psychol.* 1954, *18,* 297-302.

33. Scire, H. G. Changes in behavior and personality following use of chlorpromazine and reserpine: adjunct, group therapy: comparison of the immediate administration of a chemotherapeutic program with group therapy administered after delay, i.e., after a period of exposure to group therapy. *Dissert. Ab.* 1959, *19,* 3222.

34. Semon, R. G. & Goldstein, N. The effectiveness of group psychotherapy with chronic patients and an evaluation of different therapeutic methods. *J. Consult. Psychol.* 1957, *21,* 317-322.

35. Shatter, F. An investigation of the effectiveness of a group therapy program, including the child and his mother, for the remediation of reading disability. *Dissert. Ab.* 1957, *17,* 1032.

36. Sheldon, D. & Landsman, T. An investigation of nondirective group therapy with students in academic difficulty. *J. Consult. Psychol.* 1950, *14,* 210-215.

37. Singer, J. L. & Goldman, G. D. Experimentally contrasted social atmospheres in group psychotherapy with chronic schizophrenics. *J. Soc. Psychol.* 1954, *40,* 23-37.

38. Temmer, H. W. An investigation into the effects of psychotherapy upon habitual avoidance and escape patterns displayed by delinquent adolescent girls. *Dissert. Ab.* 1958, *18,* 304.

39. Wilcox, G. T. Changes in adjustment of institutionalized female defectives following group psychotherapy. *Dissert. Ab.* 1957, *17,* 402.

40. Wright, F. H. An evaluation of the candidate employee programs in the rehabilitation of psychiatric patients. *Dissert. Ab.* 1957, *17,* 1604.

41. Yormak, B. B. An investigation of behavior changes following general semantic training of neuropsychiatric patients. *Dissert. Ab.* 1957, *17,* 402-3.

PART III

PROCEEDINGS OF THE THIRD INTERNATIONAL CONGRESS OF GROUP PSYCHOTHERAPY

Milan, Italy, July 18-21, 1963

SECTION 1: GENERAL DIRECTIONS

THE THIRD PSYCHIATRIC REVOLUTION AND THE ACTUAL TRENDS OF GROUP PSYCHOTHERAPY

by J. L. Moreno

I

THE THIRD PSYCHIATRIC REVOLUTION

A. *Introduction*

It is in the atmosphere of the great French Revolution that the First Psychiatric Revolution took place, the emancipation of the insane from chains, symbolized by Philippe Pinel (1793). Many modern recent innovations, like the open door, the day hospital, the night hospital, the halfway-house and the community clinic, can be considered as extensions and reverberations of that original rebellion.

The next important step, the era of the Second Psychiatric Revolution in the course of the nineteenth century, was the development of psychotherapy. It extended from Mesmer to Charcot and Janet, to the leaders of the psychoanalytic movement.

The era of the Third Psychiatric Revolution, with an "elan therapeutique" of its own, is now in progress. While the changes brought about by the First Revolution were institutional, and those by the Second psychodynamic, the changes brought about by the Third Revolution are due to the influence of cosmic and social forces. They are further transforming and enlarging the scope of psychiatry. They made their greatest contribution with group and action methods, especially group psychotherapy and psychodrama. The changes are taking place in many fields, in technology, physiology, pharmacology, communication, mass psychiatry and sociatry. Their ultimate goal is a therapeutic society, a therapeutic world order which I envisioned in the opening sentence of my opus *Who Shall Survive?*, 1943, p. 3: "A truly therapeutic procedure cannot have less an objective than the whole of mankind."

B. *The Third Psychiatric Revolution*

Marx, Kierkegaard, Nietzsche, and Bergson may be considered among the forerunners of the Third Psychiatric Revolution, since their writings were a prelude to group and action methods. Karl Marx, for example, was a forerunner of industrial sociometry. Kierkegaard's religious fantasies, striving toward an heroic existentialism were a prelude to action, to action techniques and psychodrama. Nietzsche, in *Zarathustra* and *Ecce Homo,* desperately tried to move into an heroic life. He was another forerunner of action. Although Kierkegaard and Nietzsche did not attain their hopes and dreams, they triggered a call to action. Another precursor was Henri Bergson, author of *L'evolution creatrice,* who paved the way for the modern concept of spontaneity.

Although these men lived prior to, parallel with, or after Freud, they belong in tempo and spirit to a later era, that of the twentieth century which was the century of many liberations — such as the Russian Revolution of 1917, of the masses of people from the economic fetters of their landlords and the bourgeoisie, the liberation of children from the fetters of their parents, the liberation of adolescents from the authority of their elders, the emancipation of women from their subordination to men, the revolution of sex and birth control, the emancipation of religion, revision of old mythologies, new interpretations of the bible to meet the demands of our age, modernization of the Catholic church and the Ecumenic Council, the wars of liberation in Africa and Asia, and the civil rights struggle of the Negroes in the U.S.A.

During the early years of this century, I formulated the concept of the encounter, which triggered me to a number of existential actions: liberation of the actor from the script — I broke into a theater during a performance and stopped it (1911), demanding that the actors throw away their scripts and begin playing their own selves; liberation of the minister from the bible conserve — I broke into a church during a sermon and stopped the minister, demanding that he practice love and charity in the here and now (1912); liberation of children from their parents — a forerunner of the sociometric test in a gathering of children and parents in which the children were given the privilege of choosing new parents or keeping their own (1909). In addition, I introduced role playing in the gardens of Vienna as a forerunner of psychodrama, group psychotherapy, mass psychiatry, and therapeutic theater. As conductor of psychodramas in the free setting of the Viennese gardens, I triggered a form of mass catharsis, anticipating the therapeutic television for the mass, mass group psychotherapy, and mass psychodrama, which are among the goals and strivings of the Third Psychiatric Revolution.

This revolution has many facets. The one is the psychophysiological revolution, pioneered by Pavlov and Berger — the conditioned reflex and the electro-encephalogram. The second facet is the psycho-pharmacological revolution — pioneered by Sakel, Cerletti, Hoffman, and Delay, among others — with the development of insulin- and electro-shock treatment, the tranquilizers and hallucinogens. The third facet is the psycho-technological revolution, represented by space travel, automation, cybernetics, and the methods of birth control. The fourth facet is the mass media of communication — radio, motion pictures, television and their impact upon the behavior of individuals and masses. However, the final and most important facet is the development of group and action methods, because they facilitated and integrated the benefits of all the revolutionary methods enumerated above — the physiological, pharmacological, technological, and sociological — into a single package, so that they could reach and aid the masses of the people towards a mass psychiatry.

One of the greatest achievements of this era is the discovery of methods of measurement through calculated experimental methods — the measurement of small groups, the measurement of the brain, and the measurement of human relations. Social measurement, with sociometry as its exponent, established the first solid bridge beyond psychiatry into sociology. It proposed "sociatry," a concept of healing which transcends psychiatry. Sociatry aims at a science of the normality and pathology of large masses of individuals, of entire communities and nations, and perhaps, someday in the future, of the entire mankind. Psychiatric concepts such as neurosis and psychosis are not applicable to group and mass processes. A group of individuals may become "normotic" or "sociotic" and the syndromes producing this condition have been called "normosis" or "sociosis."

II

EARLY VISIONS OF GROUP AND ACTION METHODS

A. *Background of Psychodrama*

As I was walking through the streets and beautiful gardens of Vienna, now more than half a century ago (1908-1914), a very anonymous and intensive young man, observing and playing with children, I had a vision which triggered my entire lifework and which gave me a precocious anticipation of the great changes which have since taken place in our world.

I meditated about the meaning of the universe and about my place in it. According to legend, Buddha, when he was reborn, did not return as Buddha but as Bodhisattva. Buddha, instead of fleeing from the world, moved into it to live in it and, if necessary, to change it. I remembered the efforts of Freud, whom I met in the Vienna Psychiatric Clinic (1912), to analyze himself and the world to its very depth and, like a modern Buddha, to find a way out of his misery. But if Freud would be reborn, would he continue to analyze himself, or would he take a new turn, as Buddha did, and become a psychoanalytic Bodhisattva? I asked myself: If an "analysis" is successfully terminated, what is the next step? One has to live! The technique of psychoanalysis may be good for an analysis on the couch, but what does it offer the cosmos into which we enter as modern Bodhisattvas? We need techniques of living. There must be methods of living which satisfy the deepest needs of

154

personality, of our society and of the world. Psychodrama offers such methods. They are applied and are effective *hic et nunc*, "in the midst of life." We call these methods *psychodrama in situ*, that is, not applied within a therapeutic setting but in the "kairos of living," in the daily challenges and transactions within oneself between husband and wife, parents and children, around the dining table, in the bedroom, in the workshop, wherever life is lived productively (soliloquy techniques and monologues), assisted by role reversal, mirror, double, future techniques, etc. Illustrations for psychodrama in situ I have given repeatedly in my recent publications, *The Discovery of the Spontaneous Man*, 1956, *The First Psychodramatic Family*, 1964, and in my earliest writings (1911-1925), such as my dialogues in a church setting, in a library setting, in a theater, in actu and in situ; the earlier period included a psychodrama in situ between a husband and wife, in a family setting in *Das Stegreiftheater*, 1923, pp. 74-78.

Two questions bewildered me and I could not rest until I found an answer: (1) How can I communicate with the entire world, with all people, and how can all people communicate with me? (2) How can this be done in the here and now? How can I emancipate myself from the past and create in the moment and for the future, with the people I encounter? Then and there the miracle happened, at least in my fertile imagination; the "encounter" took place: I met all the people and the people met me. I spoke to the people in India, in China and in America, in Africa, to the people in Russia and to the people in France. And they spoke back to me. I saw them and heard them and felt them.

As I see it now what happened to me was not exactly what we call delusion and hallucination; it was a healthy, goal-directed experience. It was rather an anticipation of the future which fifty years later has become feasible. I just saw the future and I was experiencing it, without telegraph and radio, without tape recordings and without computers, without mass two-way television, without any of the miracles of the machine being at my disposal. Because I had that vision, I began to work so as to make that vision come true. I began to work on electro-magnetic fields and developed the radio-film (radio-telephone tape recording). I worked with small groups and developed inter-actional and co-actional group psychotherapy. I began to work on the invisible underground of mankind and developed sociometry. Then came psychodrama, as a climax.

155

B. Background of Group Psychotherapy

After freeing the children from their parents' rigid views of life I knew intuitively every next step I should make in order to bring the new world to realization. I looked after the weakest links in the chain of our social existence and found the most vulnerable and helpless victims — in the streets of Vienna — the prostitutes. I followed them into their sexual ghetto, Am Spittelberg (1913), in which they lived in small groups in individual houses. The question was: what can be done to free them from their chains and to give their life true meaning? They wanted to appeal to the sexual appetites of men and sell their body to them. The answer was simple: as the body is their property, give them the privilege to do whatever they wish to do with their body, give them freedom of sex. But I found out rapidly that to establish sex as a commodity met with enormous resistance and the barriers were practically unsurmountable. The logical step seemed to be to follow the spirit of our time and to put the problem on an economic basis. We established a "union of prostitutes," just as there are other labor unions. But the revolution of complete sexual freedom appeared to be a greater revolution still than the revolution of the proletariat. The labor unions of the communist and socialist parties did not recognize them as equals; the religions and their charity organizations did not accept them unless they were willing to give up their identity and look for respectable occupations. We had meetings from time to time in their houses during which economic and legal problems were first discussed. Gradually their personal sufferings became the most important aspect of the meetings. Their emotional needs pushed the idea of a labor union into the background and group psychotherapy "in situ" took over. It is interesting that what was an absurdity and a paradox in the Vienna of 1913 has taken a novel appearance in our time. What is the meaning otherwise of the "sexual explosion" of today except a further move towards the freedom of the body?

Modern group psychotherapy started in the sexual ghetto of Vienna, in a natural setting, in situ (1913), and not in clinical settings, as it developed in the U.S.A. in the nineteen thirties, where professional experts — psychiatrists, psychologists, social workers, etc., took over therapeutic leadership.

The forerunners of the modern group psychotherapy movement of professional groups took different forms in various cultures. In early Christianity it grew out of the monasteries in which comparatively small groups of monks or nuns lived in intimate ensembles. Although the value systems and aims were religious, the results were often unconsciously therapeutic. It was to save the soul and not to heal the sick. The idea of mental illness is a modern concept. One monk helped another within the religious ritual of the monastic hierarchy (see J. L. Moreno, *Application of the Group Method to Classification,* 1932, and *Who Shall Survive?,* 1934).

It is interesting to compare the autonomous group movements of lay people in our time, the movement among the prostitutes in Austria, 1913, with the Alcoholics Anonymous Movement (A. A.) in the U.S.A., 1934, and the Synanon Movement among drug addicts, 1960. The movement among the prostitutes started with the principle of "affirmation" and "acceptance" of the body as an indisputable property of every woman, so to speak as the first natural law. They did not want to give up sex as a commodity, but to be recognized as having the professional and legal right to practice prostitution. The tendency in the autonomous movements in the U.S.A. are quite different. Similar to the early Christian movements to heal the soul from impurities, also the modern movements in the U.S.A. express themselves in *denial* rather than *affirmation.* This trend expresses itself in diet; do not eat what you like and as much as you like, but follow dietetic rules. Do not drink alcoholic beverages because they make you sick. Do not take drugs because they make you pathological. Do not indulge in sex, because it's immoral unless it is sanctioned by marriage. We see here the old value conflict betweeen upholding the natural law and the natural rights of the body and mind, the sanctity of food, of sleep, of love, of creativity, versus the tendency to control them and restrain them by principles which are unnatural or at least unproven as to their validity.

C. Background of Sociometry

When the first World War broke out in 1914, I was employed by the Department of the Interior of the Austro-Hungarian monarchy as an Officer of Health in a camp, a community of refugees near Vienna. My determination to find new solutions to difficult social problems found here a fascinating and unexplored target. I recognized that just as the prostitutes lived in two worlds, the community of Mitterndorf had an official and an invisible part. In order to resolve the tensions between these two aspects of this sick community I began to make graphs of the structure of every house, "sociometric diagrams," and gradually developed the system of sociometry which has become a basic science of sociology.

D. *The Triadic System, Sociometry-Group Psychotherapy-Psychodrama*

I merged group psychotherapy, sociometry and psychodrama into a single system: the Triadic System.

The triadic system is the integration of three theories: the science of the group, the science of sociometry and the science of action. These are interrelated and indispensable to one another.

1. The first discovery was that interaction of individuals in groups has a therapeutic potential. Social interaction can lead to indifference, to violence and destruction, but also to integration and catharsis. The result was the concept of "therapeutic interaction" (one man a therapeutic agent of the other) and interactional, co-actional group psychotherapy, which has become the foundation of all forms of group psychotherapy.

2. Therapeutic interaction found a solid scientific basis in the science of sociometry.

3. The greatest benefits accrue to group psychotherapy and sociometry through the action methods, therapeutic psychodrama, psychodrama in situ, and behavior training.

The experimental methods of group and action therapy did not prosper in university laboratories; they require the open communities as fields of testing and research. One can distinguish between two directions of experimental methods: (a) in the atmosphere of a university laboratory, for instance, Pavlov's experiment, and (b) in the atmosphere of the open community, as sociodrama, group psychotherapy, sociometry, family therapy, etc.

Conditions of the open experiment are: the visible body in space, in the here and now, real life, on the spot, in situ, the group, action and interaction, acting out, action and social catharsis.

III

THE SCIENTIFIC METHOD AND GROUP PSYCHOTHERAPY

A. *Philosophy of Group Psychotherapy*

The first question which can be raised is: why group psychotherapy? Adjustment may make human relations sterile. Maladjustment may make them more spontaneous. A sane world may be stereotype, an insane world may be creative. The question: Why group psychotherapy? falls into the same category as the question: Is eating, sleeping and reproduction necessary? They are a matter of survival. Living in groups is also a matter of survival. There is no alternative, to live in groups or not to live in groups, we are existentially stuck. Group therapy is a process which goes on regardless of whether it is done by means of scientific methods or not. The answer is that ongoing, unorganized group psychotherapy can be improved by scientific methods.

The second question is: if the individual is only a fragment or a part of reality, what is real and more comprehensive? Our answer was that however real the individual is, the group is a greater reality and includes it. Mankind is a greater reality still than the groups and the universe at large includes all individuals, all groups, and all possible mankind. In my philosophy the essence of the universe was its creativity-spontaneity. The development of physical and cultural conserves, with the latter getting the upper hand more and more, led to the pathology of man, who became deficient as a spontaneous and creative agent. The objective of group psychotherapy became, therefore, to stimulate and train man's spontaneity and creativity, in the vehicles in which he naturally exists, that is, in groups.

With different connotations, Burrow asked the same question. His answer was: the individual is an illusion, the race — phylum — is the real reality. We have to analyze the group through phyloanalysis and return the I into the phylum. Burrow's query was how to integrate individual man into the bio-racial groups from which he has separated himself.

The neurosis of man has been visualized by the theoretical forerunners of group psychotherapy in various ways. It can be best expressed in terms of the fundamental process of alienation from reality. For Marx, for instance, who can be considered as a forerunner of theoretical group psychotherapy, the cause of the neurosis is the *economic* alienation of man, the fragmentation of man's productivity in the work process. For Burrow the cause of the neurosis is *biological* and *phyloanalytic* alienation of man, the separation of his I from the total phylum. According to my system the cause of neurosis is the *cosmic* alienation of man, his alienation

159

from the essential meaning of the universe, its primary creative processes. It stands to reason that the philosophy envisioned by these early leaders would determine to a large extent the type of method which they sponsored and the kind of operations they considered significant. Marx found it indispensable to solve the economic alienation of man by a social revolution in which the working man becomes the top figure in the hierarchy of values. Burrow turned from verbal group therapy to the study of the distortions of the physiological condition of the individual produced by his separateness. He engaged, therefore, in physiological experiments and abandoned the group vehicle. I saw a remedy in developing methods which would train and re-train the behavior of individuals and groups in terms of their spontaneity and creativity. I claimed that the economic and the biological neurosis of behavior are interlocked and related to the more primary neurosis of spontaneity and creativity.

B. *The Scientific Method and the Therapeutic Group*

The trends which dominated the group psychotherapy movement from its inception are: a) the interactional trend; b) the analytic trend; and c) the activistic trend, psychodrama, sociodrama, role playing and allied forms.

All group psychotherapists have come to agree that a *science of the therapeutic group* is basic to "scientific" foundations of group psychotherapy.

But how is a science of the "therapeutic" group possible? It is often considered in conflict with the demands of pure basic science. The advent of sociometry and group psychotherapy has had a revolutionary impact upon the orthodox, customary meaning of the scientific method which John Stuart Mill developed after the model of the physical sciences. Mill had come to the exasperating conclusion that the experimental method can not be applied to the social sciences, their subject matter being too complex; eo ipso, it could not be applied to a science of the group, thus making group psychotherapy an anecdotal, second-class science. My argument was (see my *Sociometry, Experimental Method and the Science of Society,* 1951) contrary to the model postulated by physical science that group research, whether under laboratory or in situ

160

conditions, *must* appear of *consequence* to the subject. The subjects must be motivated, they must expect to be helped, or potentially helped, by the process. If the subjects are cold themselves, uninvolved in the outcome of the research, it has no tangible validity. The very fact that the methods of group psychotherapy are so constructed that the patients are subjectively participating, involved in the process and expecting beneficial results from it, has given the patients the "status of research actors" and the experimental method in social science a new slant. Every group psychotherapy session (analytic, discussional or psychodrama) is an experiment. Cold laboratory experiments carried out by academic social psychologists with subjects who are unmotivated and uninvolved from within their own depth, are of questionable value. In this context, indeed, we are in full accord with Mill, only that we replaced the skeptical conclusion of Mill by positive conclusions and by carrying out experiments in natural and laboratory settings.

The earliest task of sociometry and of sociometric group therapy was to construct a group psychotherapy experiment and a comparable control group which permitted rational evaluation and measurement. All schools of group psychotherapy have explicitly or implicitly followed this thought, trying whenever possible, to go beyond the anecdotal evaluation of the group process and to set up experimental situations.

C. *The Small Group vs. the Large Group*

The majority of studies to date have been made with small groups of from three to ten persons. The earliest conscious, analytic determination of the size of a small group was made in my Sing Sing Prison study in 1931. The number of participants was *seven*. "Forty-seven prisoners, inmates of Sing Sing Prison have been charted. From them, seven men have been selected and assigned to a possible group, 'Group I.' A double analysis is that of two analyzed together; a triple analysis, that of three persons analyzed together, and a group analysis is that of more than three analyzed together but of no more than such number of persons as can know one another intimately." But seven is by no means final; any number between three and ten or more has been recommended. The number changes with the criterion of the group.

161

In the context of family therapy, for instance, when an entire family is treated, we must accept the number of members in the family, whether it is three, ten or whatever. Here the number of participants is determined by the specific family and changes from case to case.

Another barrier to the rigid number of participants has arisen in groupings which represent "intimate ensembles." It is often therapeutically indicated to permit participation of a larger number because they share, for instance, the same hospital ward. The same is true in collective forms of psychodrama where social problems are treated. In St. Elizabeths Hospital, for example, as many as fifty to sixty patients are treated simultaneously. In the course of such sessions every patient of the group can be reached.

But the greatest need for innovation and extension has come from the more recent efforts of the author to combine group psychotherapy and psychodrama with the mass media of communication like motion pictures and television and to give the benefit of therapy to the largest possible number of individuals. It is obvious that we have to pursue the goal of mass psychotherapy with the greatest possible caution; the therapeutic and ethical responsibilities are far greater than in small group psychotherapy. We are aware of the first revolutionary step beyond individual-centered therapy, made now more than fifty years ago and which has proven so fruitful. We have been able to overcome, to some extent, the resistance of the individual-centered schools. The approach to the large group is, of course, a new challenge to our inventiveness and courage. It is a second revolutionary step to extend the size of the group so that any number of individuals can be included without being limited by size. In order to accomplish this, an objective "reanalysis" of the therapeutic situation has to be made and new methods have to be invented. The question is how to move within a rational therapeutic framework from small group psychotherapy to mass psychotherapy and mass psychiatry. There is no reason why we should fear that forms of individual psychotherapy will be neglected and become unnecessary. On the contrary, there is good reason to assume that the three dimensions of psychotherapy, individual psychotherapy, group psychotherapy and mass psychiatry, will parallel and stimulate each other.

IV

When the need for mass psychiatry emerged in our time, there were two questions: (1) Why is the need for mass treatment greater and more urgent *now* than perhaps at any other time in history? (2) By what methods can we reach the masses effectively?

Let us first answer question one: The development of mass media of transportation and communication have projected and filtered into every home innumerable ideas, perceptions and persuasions which have reduced the influence of the immediate family and the primary group (Cooley). It is not an accident that the sociometrists have introduced the term "tele" which means "influence at a distance" as the basic concept of communication. Of course, mass media such as television and motion pictures are influences at a distance, but they are notoriously one-way relationships. Therefore, it is implied in the tele concept that two-way relationships be established between two individuals, however far distant from one another, so as to restore the intimacy which exists in the dyads of the family group.

But what instructions should we give the technologist as to the minimum requirements the television instrument must fulfill in order to be useful for some form of group psychodramatic therapy? The television production would have to be so arranged that every viewer could communicate with the therapist and the protagonist in the broadcasting station. In other words, the present one-way has to be transformed into a "two-way" television system. Just as in a typical psychodramatic session in which every member communicates with every other, or with the therapist, a psychotherapeutic television system must permit every viewer to see every other viewer in action as if they were in the same social space. Even if other requirements are not met, this is a minimum.

Question two has been answered in two ways: (a) By the known methods which have proven effective with small groups; (b) By methods which can reach large masses of people, in the literal sense, the entire living community.

163

Among the methods which are being developed in our time to reach large masses of people is the therapeutic theater, which is increasingly following the psychodramatic group model.

In Paris, in collaboration with the Italian producer, Roberto Rossellini, I made a few years ago (1956) a psychodramatic motion picture sponsored by the French Government Radio and Television. In the French Cinema, the producer, Rouch, has approached psychodramatic rules many times in his productions. In the U.S.A. an increasing number of television productions apply psychodramatic techniques. These are all signs of the time, indicating how mass media of communication are used for therapeutic aims.

The television-psychodrama is at present the future method *par excellence*. But other, better methods may emerge in the future. The commandment is that all beings be included in the therapy, all mankind.

In the psychodrama of small action groups, in the synthetic group formations in clinics, in natural groupings like families and community settlements in forms of psychodrama in situ, on the spot, in the here and now, the small group approach has spread all over the world and is practiced in many varieties. The treatment of large masses, consciously or unconsciously, is already in full swing in many places or waiting to be organized in an overall system of operations. The treatment of the entire living humanity, which was at the time of *Who Shall Survive?* an utopian dream, is moving now towards becoming a practical reality.

Every group psychotherapy session can be viewed as a modified Stegreiftheater, a modified theater of spontaneity. The original dictum of the psychodramatic process was that there are "no" spectators permitted in the theater of psychodrama. All participants are to play their own roles and to switch roles with every member in the group, each acting out his perception of the other fellow. The idea of psychodrama, reaching back to the dimmest memories of earliest civilizations, presents the first modern model of mass psychiatry. Although the "public" sessions of psychodrama are limited in the numbers of people who could participate in person, they contain the seed which could be taken up by the mass media of communication, especially by television, to be developed further into the televised psychodrama.

164

V

We must face realistically all the fronts in the group psychotherapy movement; scientific, clinical, cultural, political, its growth as well as its spread. The movement has become easily the most popular and influential among the psychotherapies of our time. But in the rapid spread there is danger that the movement may go out of hand. The many trends and sub-forms, although a sign of productivity and progress, threaten to break it up from within into fragments.

SOME BASIC CONCEPTS IN GROUP PSYCHOTHERAPY

by S. H. FOULKES

Human living has always been done in groups. These are always in a state of change, according to geographical, economical, historical, technical, and cultural conditions. Correspondingly, the ideas that the human individual has of himself and his group, and of the relation between the two, are ever-changing also.

In recent times, in fact since the end of the Renaissance, and in a society that stresses individual property and competition, a configuration has arisen that has brought about the idea of the individual existing in isolation. The individual is then confronted with the community and the world as if they were outside of him. The philosophy of Descartes starts from this premise, and its strict subject/object juxtaposition is still responsible for many pseudo problems of our time. Yet one of the surest observations one can make is that the individual is pre-conditioned to the core by his community, even before he is born, and his personality and character are imprinted vitally by the group in which he is raised. This concerns his psychology even more than his genetic inheritance, inasmuch as the former is developed in the interaction between him, objects and persons.

Nature itself speaks in a clear language. It is abundantly clear that throughout all species the individual specimen is entirely unimportant and that the only thing which matters is the survival of the group and community. Modern circumstances also speak of and treat the individual as expendable. Plans are made that literally discount millions of human lives without hesitation. No wonder the modern individual is afraid of the group, of losing his very existence, of his identity being submerged and submitted to the group. The individual, while helplessly compressed into a mere particle of social groups and masses, is at the same time left without any true companionship in regard to his inner mental life. The relative isolation and alienation of the individual is thus a very real problem of our time. Whereas all sickness is liable to

166

register in this way, mental sickness has a disturbance of integration within the community as its very roots — a disturbance of communication. This modern sickness, so often displayed in deep doubts and fears about integrity and identity, is also reflected in our theoretical terms. Any mention of "group dynamics" gives rise to passionate objections on the part of our theoreticians. They behave as if the individual was in mortal danger, awaiting only their chivalrous rescue. To look upon any natural group as if it was the result of a confluence of isolated individuals is untenable. Paradoxically, our own particular groups are really constructed of isolated, unacquainted individuals meeting for the purpose of treatment. Yet behind this disparateness are certain pre-conditioned ideas often silently formed, of which the most general ones are as follows:

1. That the biological species is the same.
2. That the cultural background is similar, which means among other things that there is agreement as to what is desirable normal behavior, what is sick, good, bad and so forth.
3. That the patient and therapist speak the same language literally as well as metaphorically. Otherwise there cannot be an efficient communication between them.
4. That the patient has reasons to lay himself open to the therapeutic process (his motivation by suffering).
5. That we have a method of access to unconscious processes.

The last two points, 4 and 5, indicate why there is a premium on psychopathology: because it does appear that without disturbance, without pathology, these conditions are not fulfilled.

6. That the relationship which develops on the basis of strong emotions is accepted and responded to in a particular fashion, and expressed in a particular attitude and situation (the therapeutic situation).
7. That the doctor at least takes the whole patient in the whole situation into account, although as a background. In the foreground are individual details as they are presented to the patient.

For the purposes of this paper, I am concerned only with groups in their psychological aspects, or with psyche groups, to use Helen

Jennings' term. I am further leaving out of account the psychological relationship between groups or between any particular group and the community of which it is part, *i.e.* group dynamics.

What I am concerned with are internal psychological processes, particularly as they are observable in groups under conditions such as I have just indicated. Let me repeat this, that I am concerned with internal psychological processes, endo-psychic reality, and intra-psychic mechanisms or dynamics. It is at this point that one is up against a prejudice deeply ingrained, erroneous as it is.

We have become used to thinking of intra-psychic processes *ipso facto* as inside the same individual person; inside the same skull as it were. If we make such an assumption, however, we beg one of the most important questions that arises. The fact that these mental processes take place physically in each individual brain is undoubted. If we hear an orchestra playing a piece of music, all the individual noises are produced each on one particular individual instrument only; yet what we hear is the orchestra playing music, the conductor's interpretation, etc. We do not even, in terms of pure sound, hear a simple summary, a summation of all the individual waves which reach our ears; rather, these are significantly modified, being part and parcel of a total sound. In truth, what we hear is the orchestra. In the same way, mental processes going on in a group under observation reach us in the first place as a concerted whole. Those familiar with *Gestalt* psychology will find no difficulty in understanding that the whole is more elementary than the parts. With this insight we have arrived at one of the basic concepts in group psychotherapy, without which all other observations are misinterpreted or insufficiently described, namely, that which we experience in the first place is the *group as a whole.*

The network of all individual mental processes — the psychological medium in which they meet, communicate and interact — can be called the *Matrix.* This is of course a construct — in the same way as is for example the concept of traffic, or for that matter, of mind. In a further formulation of my observations I have come to conceive these processes not merely as interpersonal but as transpersonal. In short, we have a concert of interactions which is our primary basis for orientation, interpretation and confrontation. This orientation shows on which level our interventions are most useful, but the whole process takes place solely for the benefit of the individual member. There can be no question

168

of a problem of group versus individual or individual versus group. These are two aspects, two sides of the same coin.

Psychoanalysis has shown that neuroses are based on conflict, conflict that arose early in life with respect to parents or their equivalents. This conflict at bottom is one between the individual's instinctive impulses and his group's cultural taboos. This becomes internalized — unconscious in the dynamic and the systematic sense; that is to say, subject to the operation of the primary process: primitive pre-logical mentality. As soon as the therapist enters into the situation, this endo-psychic material becomes capable of involving two persons. Simply to call this "interpersonal" is not enough. It is an endo-psychic common union between two people. The analyst can afford to enter into the patient's primary world without having to respond from his own primary world. This is his particular contribution. Out of this common ground arises a relationship which becomes the battle field for the solution of the patient's neurosis — the so-called transference neurosis. There is no need for us, nor do we wish, to abandon these foundations. Concepts like the Oedipus complex, patriarchal and matriarchal, assume a conflict based on the primary family group. Infantile sexuality and incest barriers are all based on the species and its cultural development. Even fathers and mothers are archetypes, the personal father and mother only representing them. The culture and values of a community are inescapably transferred to the growing infant by its individual fathers and mothers, as determined by the particular nation, class, religion, region. They are transmitted verbally or non-verbally, instinctively and emotionally, twenty-four hours a day. Even objects, movements, gestures and accents are determined in this way by these representatives of the cultural group. On top of this, all but permeating it, is the particular personal stamp of the individual father and mother. Individual psychotherapy is thus a form of group psychotherapy, without being aware of it.

Group psychotherapy simply brings back the problems to where they belong. The community is represented in the treatment room. Valuations and norms are restated and modified by comparison, contrast and analysis. Communication leading to a shared experience and understanding is in terms of the group.

Turning now to group psychotherapy, this can be practiced with or without an analytical orientation. In both cases it operates in a group situation, which it must take into account. I will first say a few words on group psychotherapy in general and then concentrate on an analytic approach. For the latter I will take the group-analytic situation as a model. Concepts used here and throughout have arisen from this particular method of group analysis. The relation is a dialectic one. New insights lead to the development of a new method of group analysis which in turn leads to new concepts. The task was to find a method and theory which would do away with such pseudo problems as biological versus cultural, somatogenic versus psychogenic, individual versus group and reality versus phantasy. Instead we must endeavour to use concepts which from the beginning do justice to an integrated view.

The first and foremost aspect with which group psychotherapists are usually concerned, and according to which they form their concepts, is that of belonging, of participation. Being a respected and effective member of the group, being accepted, being able to share and to participate, belongs to the basic constructive experiences of human life. No health is conceivable without this. This happens throughout life, but the need for psychotherapy arises when this participation and sharing are disturbed. This is important because we have now to deal with the restoration of this disturbed communication. Resistances displayed in the group's interactions usually reflect the unconscious defenses in the individual. At this juncture I might point out that what is dynamically unconscious is also at the same time subject to the primary process. Which is to say that it is cast in a primitive, symbolic language. This language is understood unconsciously, and its transmission, or communication, does take place without consciousness. The group, through processes of progressive communication, works its way from this primary, symbolic level of expression into a conscious, articulate language. This *work in communication* is the operational basis of all therapy in group. This leads us to the interpretative, psychoanalytic part of our work, which is the analytic part, superimposed on the constructive part of group participation, going hand in hand.

Group analysis, as I understand it, works on the group model. It finds many of its processes, we know, in a two-personal situation, but with the additional feature that they can be seen in full in interaction between two, three and more persons. They can be seen as what they are, as interactional processes, not as processes in the isolated individual. In addition to this we can make observations that are concealed in the one or two personal situation and thus discover *group specific factors* in operation.

As far as the therapist is concerned his most important contribution can be summed up as follows:

1. To be the representative of the analytic attitude in the group.
2. To understand and maintain the group analytic situation. As a psychoanalyst he is familiar with transference processes. As always, the analyst orientates himself on the basis of the total situation in which he works. In the individual situation, he will refer part processes to the individual as a whole. From the two-personal situation to the transference situation, from the group situation to the group as a whole, he uses this orientation to the total situation as a background for the perspective that he needs; even more so in his analytic activity, which could in a certain way be said to be a destructive one. He breaks this whole down into parts in order to do justice to them.

What about access to the unconscious? This, as we know, in the two-personal situation in psychoanalysis, is based on so-called free association. It has not always been understood that by replacing this free association in the group by "group association" — which, I believe, I was the first to have done — we make a decisive step not only in method but also in theory. The concept of associations in the individual mind was originally based on the assumption that these were acquired by the individual in his experience and firmly held down in his brain. In the two-personal situation this process became already modified by the presence of the second person and the second person's response. The group minds of strangers, with totally different individual conditioning, react and respond to each other. If we find as we do that their responses, verbal or non-verbal, conscious or unconscious, to each other's productions can be used as quasi-associations to a common context, we can make a totally new assumption. We now treat associations as based on the common ground of the unconscious instinctive understanding of each other. We no longer take as our basis of operation the conditioning by old experiences based on traces in

171

the brain. Instead, we accept the notion that ideas and comments expressed by different members have the value of unconscious interpretations. As an observation this had already been understood clearly by Freud and other analysts working within the individual situation. Besides, it would be quite impossible, for obvious reasons, for the group therapist to base his procedure in a group situation on free association as understood in the individual sense. The relationship which now develops is that of a complex and mutual interaction between members. Only the therapist maintains the proper analytic attitude and detachment, and can see the inner mechanism of this interaction — the unconscious dynamics of it. It would be quite impossible for him to follow each individual separately. He focuses on the total interactional field, on the matrix in which these unconscious reactions meet. His background is always, and should consciously be, the group as a whole. Conflicts are now dynamically displayed in the group, and yet are — as I have pointed out — not less intrapsychic for that reason.

I cannot here go further into the consequences, for all psychotherapy and theory, of seeing the total situation in the psychotherapeutic small group as one inter-connected whole. I have given at least some indication for this. Our particular contribution as group psychotherapists thus rests on the fact that we study human beings and their problems in their full social context, and that this study is enriched by the laying open of the otherwise concealed aspects through psychopathology, which in studying we also restore at the same time.

All psychopathology, psychology and psychotherapy would thus be social, based on intrapsychic processes in their interaction. To conclude, may I once more say that greater freedom, whether looked upon from the group's or from the individual's point of view, is the result of our successful operations. The individual gains in independence and strength by his experience of an effective interaction between himself and the group — a two way process and on many levels. Thus, individuality, which we so rightly estimate highly, emerges in greater spontaneity in the group in both patient and therapist alike.

LE DEVELOPPEMENT DU PSYCHODRAME

par S. Lebovici

Mon propos n'est pas de présenter ici un bilan géographique de la remarquable extension de l'abord psychodramatique en psychothérapie de groupe. La gratitude que nous devons à MORENO, qui nous a donné ce moyen d'expression, s'exprimera mieux à travers le bilan plus théorique que je veux présenter ici brièvement.

D'une part, je montrerai qu'à côté des psychodramatistes qui restent fidèles aux pratiques recommandées par MORENO et à la théorie qui les sous-tend, les psychanalystes utilisent également ce moyen, en l'orientant sans doute dans un sens différent, afin d'en faire une technique qui reste dans le cadre des psychothérapies psychanalytiques.

D'autre part, j'aimerais aborder le problème de certaines utilisations du psychodrame qu'on pourrait appeler didactiques, qui se situent, dans le cadre d'une perspective formative, aux limites de l'action psychothérapique.

I. *L'Aire de Diffusion de la Technique Psychodramatique*

Le psychodrame a acquis indiscutablement droit de cité, parmi les psychothérapies de groupe, dans de nombreux pays. Je ne prétends pas en dresser ici un catalogue qui serait éloquent. Ce qui est sans doute le plus remarquable, c'est qu'en dehors des psychothérapies de soutien ou rationnelles, le psychodrame est la seule forme d'action psychothérapique qui soit, à mon avis, l'objet d'applications systématiques dans les pays de l'est. Pour ma part, j'ai eu l'occasion de le voir mis en oeuvre au cours d'une brève mission pour le Bureau Européen de l'Organisation Mondiale de la Santé à Prague: à la clinique de névrosés de Lobec, les malades sont fréquemment réunis pour les discussions de groupe où leurs problèmes conflictuels font l'objet d'une mise en forme dramatique. Le renversement des rôles y est constamment utilisé. Je ne donne cet exemple qu'à titre de témoignage. Il me paraît d'ailleurs important de signaler que les psychothérapeutes de la clinique psychiatrique de la faculté de Médecine de Prague, se réfèrent dans leur étude pathogénique des états névrotiques à l'étude des conflits actuels à l'intérieur des petits groupes dont la famille n'est pour eux qu'un exemple. Par là, ils se situent dans une perspective très proche de celle de MORENO, récusant la valeur de l'histoire dramatique vécue et reproduite dans le cadre de la relation transférentielle.

II. *Le Développement des Théories et des Techniques Pyschodramatiques*

L'exemple que je viens de mentionner montre d'une façon extrêmement claire que la théorie Morénienne est plus facilement acceptée que celle des psychanalystes qui utilisent le psychodrame.

Il m'est néanmoins difficile de tenir la balance égale entre ceux qui restent fidèles à la doctrine de MORENO et ceux qui, comme moi, parceque psychanalyste, font du psychodrame un moyen d'action privilégié dans le cadre des psychothérapies psychanalytiques de groupe. La justice exige pourtant qu'on reconnaisse d'emblée que même dans les pays où le psychanalyse connaît un grand développement, certains practiciens restent fidèles à l'abord technique et théorique que préconise MORENO: c'est le cas évidemment aux Etats Unis, mais des psychodramatistes Moréniens pratiquent leur art en Angleterre, en France, et dans d'autres pays occidentaux.

Je crois nécessaire de m'expliquer clairement sur la position des psychanalystes qui consacrent une partie importante de leur temps à l'abord psychodramatique en psychothérapie de groupe. Pour la commodité de l'exposé, je présenterai leurs vues à propos de deux aspects de l'abord psychodramatique:

—le psychodrame comme moyen d'expression, d'abord.

—le psychodrame comme technique de manipulation transférentielle, ensuite.

Il était tout naturel que des psychanalystes d'enfants songent à utiliser l'activité dramatique spontanée de leurs patients. Mais nous devons dire d'emblée que nous nous situons dans une perspective très différente de celle de MORENO, selon lequel l'expérience psychodramatique transcende en quelque sorte la réalité. Bien que nous ne le suivons nullement sur ce terrain, nous ne sommes pas pour autant d'accord avec SLAVSON qui assimile l'activité psychodramatique à un perpétuel passage à l'acte, ce qui impliquerait une déformation du réel par la constante projection des images. L'expérience concrète montre que ceci ne se produit pas chez les psychotiques même pas chez les schizophrènes.

MORENO a affirmé que l'intérêt de l'expression dramatique est de permettre au malade de retrouver sa spontanéité. Nous avons fait des constatations un peu différentes: la faculté qu'ont les malades de se livrer au jeu psychodramatique montre que la spontanéité dépasse parfois celle du sujet réputé sain. Mais leur comportement nous a paru déterminé par une série de facteurs dans lesquels nous pouvons retrouver ce qui précisément régit, non seulement le discours, mais aussi le comportement de nos patients au cours des cures psychanalytiques. Aussi bien deux opinions nous paraissent aussi erronées l'une que l'autre: celle des thérapeutes qui croient que c'est un signe de guérison prochaine pour les malades de pouvoir jouer grâce à une spontanéité retrouvée; celle des malades qui croient que jouer un rôle c'est apprendre à vivre.

Le psychodrame n'est pas seulement un moyen d'expression sur le plan verbal, en raison des facilités qu'il procure aux malades, de l'importance des facteurs émotionnels qu'il induit, de ses effets sur le groupe thérapeutique et sur l'audience, mais il engage tous les moyens d'expression de l'individu en action dans le groupe. René DIATKINE a employé au deuxième Congrès International de Psychothérapie de Groupe une expression que je désire reprendre: il a parlé du psychodrame comme un moyen d'expression sociometrice.

De là résulte une utilisation du psychodrame que nous considérons comme très importante, celle de l'exploration diagnostique, en particulier chez les adolescents et les jeunes adultes: les patients révèlent alors très rapidement certains aspects de leur vie intime, mais en mettant en jeu des mécanismes de défense spécifique qu'il faut étudier.

Sans doute pourrait-on théoriser la situation en se référant à la notion de rôle assumé: le psychodrame permettrait aux patients l'apprentissage de leur rôle et conduirait à l'assouplissement des identifications. Il est peut-être des situations privilégiées où des malades se trouvent très améliorés par le fait d'assumer un rôle, dans des conditions généralement très régressives. Mais l'étude économique des névroses et des psychoses nous fait comprendre que le rôle assumé par l'individu dans un groupe est lié dans une large mesure, non seulement à la structure du groupe, mais aussi à l'équilibre entre les satisfactions que l'individu trouve dans son existence et les expériences frustrantes dont il a souffert. Cette remarque montre combien nous sommes sensibles dans notre expérience aux données de la dynamique de groupe. Ce serait retourner à la proto-histoire de la psychanalyse que de considérer comme seuls valables les effets cathartiques de la spontanéité psychodramatique, même si l'on tient compte de la spécificité du psychodrame qui fait appel à des moyens d'expression bien au-delà du langage.

On peut peut-être considérer le psychodrame comme un moyen d'expression d'autant plus réel qu'il fait appel à la surréalité ne serait-ce que parce qu'il se déroule en dehors de toutes les conventions théâtrales, sans presqu'aucun décor. Il apporte même dans bien des cas une gratification réelle pour les patients, par exemple lors du processus de mise en train où ne font pas défaut les contacts corporels.

L'hédonisme particulier à cet abord technique a des effets indéniables aussi bien du côté des patients, que du côté des thérapeutes d'où l'interêt de leur psychanalyse personelle. Mais si l'on songe que de nombreux patients ne peuvent pas agir dans le sens de leurs pulsions et de leurs désirs, même à l'abri de la fiction dramatique, on peut proposer à titre d'hypothèse l'aphorisme suivant: l'intrication de la dénégation et de l'expérience vécue du jeu dramatique est un des caractères spécifiques du psychodrame. Ainsi l'équilibre doit-il être maintenu entre les satisfactions et les frustrations. Pour les thérapeutes, la règle d'or serait de jouer, sans jouer le jeu des malades chez qui l'expression, aussi riche soit-elle, est tempérée par son aspect partiellement involontaire, par les mécanismes de dénégation, tandis que les bénéfices sont compensés par la frustration qu'impose la fiction.

Ces quelques réflexions conduisent à examiner la situation transférentielle qui se développe au cours du psychodrame.

Un exemple concret illustrera une thèse que je n'ai pas le loisir de développer longuement: José est un adolescent très déséquilibré dont la conduite le situe au bord de la délinquance. Au lieu d'aller à l'école d'art où il est inscrit, il traîne des journées entières dans le métro sans oser rentrer chez lui.

On joue une scène où sa mère et sa jeune amie le croyant à l'école se félicitent de le voir travailler. On lui demande ensuite de jouer une scène où il prend le rôle de sa mère: il y montre combien il ressent douloureusement les exigences maternelles et le désir que cette dernière a de le voir travailler.

Ainsi cette dramatisation montre que José n'ose pas affronter la colère de sa mère et qu'il ressent terriblement ses exigences. Le constater, c'est déjà dépasser le sens que José donne généralement à sa peur pour toucher à ses racines historiques que se situent dans le cadre de conséquences lointaines des expériences relationnelles précoces.

Au moment où la scène s'arrête, José regarde un plat qu'il a déjà observé et qu'il a fait parler de mandragore, la plante qui, dit-il, se nourrit du sperme des pendus.

On pourrait se féliciter de ce processus associatif qui, à la grande satisfaction contre-transférentielle du groupe des thérapeutes, pourrait faire penser que José a saisi le sens le plus profond de ce qu'il craint des exigences maternelles, c'est à dire, sa destruction.

Mais nous craignons qu'à la clarté remarquable de ce matériel s'oppose la perpétuation de l'équilibre économique de l'organisation du Moi de ce patient. La situation est dangereuse à cause même de la richesse des identifications dans la relation thérapeutique.

Il nous paraît donc nécessaire que le psychodrame comporte une manipulation de la situation transférentielle à travers les résistances qu'elle détermine et qui sont en partie propres à cet abord technique.

Rappelons seulement qu'on peut étudier le transfert sur le directeur de scène: il est coloré par l'évocation des relations entre lui et le groupe des thérapeutes. Mais le transfert sur les psychothérapeutes auxiliaires est très particulier, parcequ'il est déterminé non seulement par l'attitude des patients mais aussi par les réponses des psychothérapeutes.

D'ailleurs la situation de groupe intervient pour modifier la situation transférentielle dont les émois sont plus aisément exprimés, qu'ils soient libidinaux ou aggresifs, vis à vis des autres patients, que des thérapeutes.

Aussi bien sommes nous amenés à utiliser l'interprétation de transfert au travers de la résistance: celle-ci comme dans toute relation psychothérapique s'appuie essentiellement sur la perception des phénomènes transférentiels et peut mettre à son service la technique même du psychodrame. Mais on se trouve ici dans une situation privilégiée, car on peut élucider plus facilement les mécanismes de défenses spécifiques qui l'alimentent. C'est ainsi que les sujets qui ont peur de leur propre agressivité peuvent saisir, au moment où ils renoncent à assumer le rôle d'un personnage agressif, l'inefficacité de leurs défenses les plus élaborées.

La situation psychodramatique comporte des dangers contre-transférentiels qui lui sont particuliers. Ils sont d'abord faits de relations transférentielles à l'intérieur du groupe des thérapeutes. C'est pour cette raison que nous pensons que les thérapeutes auxiliaires doivent avoir une formation psychanalytique. Elle leur permet de s'approcher de l'attitude idéale qui peut-être définie de la manière suivante:

1. Sur le plan technique, être capable de jouer divers rôles avec le maximum de véracité.
2. Etre en même temps capable de fournir aux patients une base d'identification aux divers imagos que peut recouvrir un même personnage de façon à permettre la mise à jour de leurs fantasmes et de leurs mécanismes défensifs.

Ces brèves remarques veulent seulement montrer dans quelles perspectives les psychanalystes peuvent parler de psychodrame analytique: il s'agit d'une psychothérapie de groupe qui sans aucun doute fait appel à la spontanéité, mais qui alimente sa résistance par le mécanisme du jeu. Pour ne pas faciliter les resistances par ce qui deviendrait simple passage à l'acte, on ne peut donc pas se contenter de la remarquable intensité émotionnelle qui se fait jour dans la fiction dramatique.

L'áttendue des indications du psychodrame chez les enfants et les adultes, ses remarquables possibilités d'application chez les sujets psychotiques, rendent compte du développement de cette technique, aussi bien pour ceux qui restent fidèles à la technique de MORENO, que pour ceux qui la considèrent comme une psychothérapie analytique de groupe.

III. *Le Psychodrame Didactique*

Les profonds effets d'audience déclanchés par le psychodrame ont conduit de nombreux psychiatres à utiliser ce moyen aux limites mêmes de l'action psychothérapique dans un objectif, formatif ou didactique. Là encore MORENO nous a proposé un instrument de première importance avec la technique du jeu de rôle ou "rôle-playing". Pour les psychiatres et les psychothérapeutes, le psychodrame est une démonstration vivante des organisations confictuelles et défensives de la personnalité. Il peut être utilisé pour approfondir la formation de nombreuses catégories professionnelles, par exemple de ceux qu'on à appelé les "personnes clefs" dans le domaine de la santé mentale. La représentation psychodramatique des difficultés de la vie émotionelle des équipes psychiatriques permet de diminuer les tensions dans l'organisation hiérarchique et fonctionelle, d'en atténuer les effets néfastes.

Mais il est nécessaire de rappeler que le psychodrame ne doit pas se contenter d'obtenir l'émotion et l'identification par la démonstration des conflits. Les assistants doivent aussi comprendre l'organisation des inter-relations pathogènes.

Nous ne croyons pas que le "rôle-playing" puisse avoir une influence décisive dans l'apprentissage d'une profession. De toutes façons la transformation d'habitudes professionnelles qu'experiment les défenses caractérielles ne saurait être assurée par quelques séances de psychodrame. Mais dans les professions qui touchent au domaine de la santé mentale et de ses troubles, les relations inter-individuelles et inter-professionnelles jouent un rôle essentiel. Grâce à la dramatisation, chacun peut s'identifier à l'autre et ressentir les effets transférentiels et contre-transférentiels qui jouent un rôle dans la vie professionnelle. La participation à l'audience psychodramatique peut être à elle seule féconde par les mécanismes de l'identification et de l'empathie. A la limite certains groupes professionnels et même certains groupes d'étude peuvent bénéficier de la participation émotionnelle déclanchée par certaines expériences psychodramatiques.

Il nous paraissait impossible de ne pas évoquer ici les possibilités d'utilisation qu'offre le psychodrame non seulement pour la formation des psychothérapeutes, mais aussi pour l'information qui ne saurait éviter d'être formative ou didactique dans de ce qui touche de près ou de loin au domaine de la santé mentale. Ainsi, en dépit du fait que la specificité du psychodrame en tant que moyen d'expression, n'exclue pas selon nous l'étude et le maniement de cet outil dans le cadre des données des relations inter-personnelles dont la psychanalyse nous fournit l'explication la plus cohérente, nous croyons que son développement s'explique par la gamme très large de ses possibilités et de ses indications. On ne peut reprocher aux psychanalystes de l'avoir utilisé dans le cadre de leur action psychothérapique, et de la base théorique qui la sous-tend nécessairement. L'essentiel est, en constatant son développement, la gamme de ses indications, en étudiant ses résultants, d'en approfondir le sens pour donner à ce moyen d'expression spécifique sa place de choix dans la psychothérapie de groupe.

AN OPERATIONAL APPROACH TO THE
FORMATION OF GROUPS

by Berthold Stokvis and Mart P. Bolten

I. *Introduction*

Everyone interested in group psychotherapy will sooner or later meet the lack of reliable criteria with regard to the composition of therapeutic groups and to the assessment and evaluation of what happens in the group. During our experiences with therapeutic groups we arrived at the conclusion that there exists a real need for these kinds of criteria, or parameters. Neither psychodiagnostic data, nor data about the focal conflicts, nor factual data such as age, sex, social economic level, etc., can be fully trusted in this respect.

The subject of this paper is our search for exact, preferably quantitative, data that can inform us about the processes which play a role in the constitution of groups. It goes without saying that the sociogram, as founded by Moreno and used by him and others, such as Lebovici, Friedemann and Schindler, gives us a clear insight into the interpersonal relations in the group. However, clear and unambiguous parameters based on the *protocol*— that is to say, the literal record of the verbal production of the group— are not yet available. We think that objective, empirical and reliable indications with regard to the attitude and mood of a group are lacking so far. There exists nevertheless a great need of such indicators.

In plain words: how can one evaluate the group processes in such a way that this evaluation is not largely dependent on the evaluating person? We think that it is about time we start looking for other objective methods in addition to the sociometric methods in order to obtain reliable and valid estimations of the group sessions.

181

In our investigation we have tried to compare the results of objective methods of assessment with the results obtained by subjective methods. If both are valid, the results must be the same; if this is not the case, new hypotheses about the validity of both methods will be needed.

So, we intend to find criteria which, as objectively as possible, will provide us with an insight into what happens in the group. Secondly — these criteria must be easy to use. In that way an objective diagnosis of the group must be possible. When one reads the literature on group psychotherapy one finds how difficult it is to inform colleagues about the course of a group session. For instance, it is rather improbable that the reports made by a certain group leader about a certain group session will be the same as the reports made by another therapist. The therapist with an Adlerian training will report quite other features of the group than a disciple of Rogers. The danger exists that the impressions about a group session will depend as much on the person who reports as on what really happened.

The above considerations have impelled us to investigate the question of whether it is possible to find objective criteria that can serve as reliable indications about the processes in a therapeutic group.

II. *The Experiment*

To be able to answer this question, a therapeutic group was formed which consisted of a group leader and 5 patients; these patients were suffering from psychoneurotic and/or psychosomatic complaints. Each week, two group sessions took place at a fixed place and time. Furthermore, an observer was present in the room; this observer was sitting apart. We took care that before the session started the group leader and observer had taken their fixed places in the room. Obviously the observer abstained from participation in the group. Except for the beginning of the first group session, the group leader did not show any social initiative. When the members of the group addressed the group leader, he reflected their questions or statements to the whole group; but he did not give any interpretation. Of course, his presence meant, from the psychological point of view, a participation in the group.

In order to provide the opportunity of studying group processes, the composition of each group was changed after 10 sessions. After every 10 sessions two group members were replaced by two others. Together, 40 sessions took place. Intentionally, one patient was a member of all 4 groups.

After each session a report of the impressions obtained during the group session was made by the group leader and the observer. We used the same list every time. This list contained the following topics: 1. Subjects of the discussion; 2. Sociogram; 3. Silences; 4. Participation of the patient who took part in all the groups; 5. Sub-groups and tendency for splitting up; 6. Nucleus of the group, "scape-goat"; 7. Problems about dependency; 8. Focal conflict; 9. Resistance, frankness, introspection; 10. Mood.

All these data were considered as the most immediate and most subjective estimations of each session. The objective evaluation of the group sessions was obtained on the basis of the protocol. In order to prevent a contamination of criteria, this objective evaluation was realized by persons who had no knowledge of the subjective evaluations concerning the same group sessions. This twofold approach enabled us to become acquainted with the processes during the formation and transformation of the groups. Our original problem was worked out in a number of concrete questions: in how far can each of the 4 groups be considered as a closed entity? That is to say: Were those 4x10 sessions really different from each other? This question was tackled by means of an analysis of variance.

Comparison of the 4 groups was based on the following objective data: 1. How many questions are expressed during one session; 2. How many adjectives with a positive appreciating content were used; 3. How many adjectives with a negative disqualifying content were used?

As stated before, these criteria were scored by independent judges, who neither were present at the group sessions nor were acquainted with the subjective qualification of the group sessions by the group leaders.

III. *Results*

1. THE EFFECT OF ABSENTEEISM:

A. The Objective Approach — We first of all investigated the question: how far is the group affected by absenteeism? We can safely assume that the members of the group experience their group as a unit; the absence of one of its members is experienced by those present as threatening. We found that in the case of absence the group produces more emotional expressions. Statistically it was found that in those group sessions which were complete, the number of emotional expressions was reduced to 50% in comparison to the group with one or more members absent. Furthermore, it was found that when the incidences of absenteeism in the sessions increased, the emotional expressions had a more positive content. When the incidences of absenteeism decreased, the patients felt more at ease and the number of negative disqualifying adjectives decreased.

So we see that absenteeism is correlated with more emotion in the group; these emotional attitudes can be described as mutual appreciation, affection and a drawing together. This is understandable, as in this situation the group members lost their anonymity.

Furthermore, we supposed a relation to exist between absenteeism and the number of times that members of the group asked each other questions. This asking of questions might be a good indicator with regard to inner insecurity and dependency. The expected relation was found indeed: when absenteeism increases, the number of questions increases too.

Summarizing, the objective data confirm the theoretical assumptions that a therapeutic group reacts in an emotional sense when one or more members of the group are not present. Those who are present feel more threatened, and they react with a more intensive way of interacting.

B. The Subjective Approach — When one tries to find the same relations by means of the subjective approach, the results are disappointing. In the first place, departing from the sociogram, the number of hostile and affectionate relations was obtained for each group session. Contrary to our expectations, the hostility was more pronounced in the case of incomplete group sessions. In our objective approach quite the reverse was found. In the second place, we tried to find in how far a relation exists between absenteeism and the inclination towards splitting up of the group. Our hypothesis was that the incomplete groups would show more internal cohesion. This trend was found in fact, yet the results

184

were not significant. In the third place, the relation between dependence, interdependence, counterdependence and absenteeism was investigated. We did not find a definite relation; the differences that manifested themselves militate against the theory that interdependence should prevail in the incomplete group sessions. With regard to introspection, resistance and frankness, no relation to absenteeism was found.

Summarizing the results of the objective, formal approach and those obtained by the subjective method, we see that the effects of absenteeism can be traced by means of the objective method. Both the character and intensity of the group processes correlate with absenteeism; it's remarkable that the same objective events can be assessed by the simple means of counting adjectives and questions, but that they cannot be found by means of the subjective impressions of group leaders concerning the group sessions.

It is clear that the intensity and quality of the affective resonance can better be ascertained when departing from formal characteristics of the protocol than from subjective impressions of group leader and observer.

2. THE REPLACING OF GROUP MEMBERS:

We just discussed the effect of absenteeism. Now we will discuss the effect of the replacement of group members.

A. The Objective Approach — In the first two sessions immediately following the replacement of group members, significantly more aggressive and hostile adjectives were used than during the group sessions more distant from this change in group composition.

B. The Subjective Approach — As subjective criteria of the group sessions, immediately following replacement of members, were chosen: resistance, decreased frankness and decreased inclination towards interpersonal relations. Once more, the subjective approach did not seem to correlate with replacement of members.

3. THE BEHAVIOR OF THE PATIENT *L:*

It will be remembered that one patient was a member of all 4 consecutive groups. We supposed that when patient *L* is a member of the first group he will be subjected to different "forces" than

185

when taking part in the other groups. So we reasoned that his behavior should differ in the 4 consecutive groups. Again this hypothesis was tested by means of the subjective method and the objective method.

A. *The Objective Approach* — Of the different objective indicators, only the number of negative disqualifying adjectives was statistically significant.

B. *The Subjective Approach* — This time the subjective approach provided us with quite interesting results: significant differences in the patient's behavior between his participation in each of the four groups were found by studying the various sociograms, as well as by tracing the participation of patient *L* in each session. Summarizing, it can be said that the subjective approach enabled us to evaluate the behavior of the patient who took part in all 4 groups. Or, in other words: if in fact this same patient behaves differently within the dynamic field of forces of each group, we are able to trace such differences by means of our subjective approach. In this case the objective approach had little result. This leads us to the conclusion that the objective approach is satisfying in case we want to study the behavior of the group as a whole, whereas when we want to study one single member of the group, the subjective method is preferable.

4. INDIVIDUAL CHARACTERISTICS AND GROUP PROCESSES:

A consideration of this aspect calls forth the actual question of what exactly is a therapeutic group; does the group as such constitute a unity — an entity — or is it a collection of separate individuals? This question goes hand in hand with the problem of group selection. During the last few years many selection-criteria, such as complaints, nuclear conflict and personality structure, have been investigated. In our investigation we purposely have chosen, as a measure of the personality, extroversion, because many investigators agree with the importance of this characteristic (as, for instance, followers of C. G. Jung and H. J. Eysenck). We assessed extroversion from the diagnosis of the individual psychiatrist. In order to avoid misunderstanding, it should be mentioned that Eysenck considers hysterical and psychopathical patients as extroverts, and those undergoing anxiety neuroses and compulsive obsessional neuroses as introverts.

186

According to this division of the group members into introverts and extroverts, the number of emotional expressions and the number of questions asked proved to be significantly higher for the extroverts. So, one is tempted to infer that the individual differences were — in this case — reflected in the group processes. However, it was not possible to reduce the differences in emotional output — as measured by the number of adjectives used — between the 4 groups to the number of extroverts in each of these groups. It was even found that the smallest number of emotional expressions occurred in the group with the highest number of extroverts (group 3), and that the group with the most introverts (group 1) showed the highest number of emotional expressions! Therefore, an extrovert group is not the same as a group of extroverts. Our most extrovert group contained the highest percentage of introvert members!

IV. *Summary*

We now come to a summary of our experiences. The best method by which to study the behavior of a group is the objective elaboration of certain factual characteristics of the protocol. In our case we used as characteristics the number of adjectives, subdivided into positive and negative ones, and the number of questions, or the number of times the group members addressed themselves towards each other in an interrogative way. By means of these criteria it was possible to differentiate groups. The same differentiation was not possible by means of the subjective approach, according to which the group leader and observer assessed the degree of frankness, resistance, introspection, hostility and so on. The objective method proved to be the most favorable one with regard to the behavior of the group. This method constitutes a way of evaluation which leads to the same conclusions, independently, from the person who uses the method.

On the other hand, as has already been pointed out, the objective method has its disadvantages as well; in case we want to study the behavior of one single person in the 4 groups, the differences cannot be detected by the objective method. In that case it is the subjective method that yields the best results. The profit of our investigation may be seen in that we succeeded in arriving at a simple method which enabled us to get some insight into the behavior of a group. However, the investigation of the individual behavior of single group members requires different means.

This discrepancy, between the behavior of a group as a unit and the behavior of one of its members, was met again in the relation between the characteristics of the individuals that compose the group and the characteristics of the group as a unit. A group which consists mainly of extroverted individuals is not necessarily an extroverted group. There is no reason to presume that this should only be the case with extroversion; a compulsive obsessional group could as well consist of hysterical members. In other words: what happens in the group is not necessarily a magnified reproduction of what happens in the individuals.

We shall conclude by referring once more to the actual need for an easy, applicable method that will enable the practical worker to arrive at a reliable judgment concerning groups. We are of the opinion that the method described by us here indicates criteria that can be used in daily practice. We ourselves have been conscious, during the many years in which we have applied group psychotherapy, of the necessity to arrive at simple methods. These methods tell us in a reliable and easy way something about the group processes which have unrolled themselves before our eyes and ears. We hope that we may have contributed, with this presentation, to a solution of this problem.

THERAPEUTIC COMMUNITIES
AND SOCIAL PSYCHIATRY

by MAXWELL JONES

Britain and America, as well as other countries, seem to be moving into a field of what might widely be called Social Psychiatry, where there is a much greater preoccupation with minor degrees of ill health and deviant behavior than was previously the case. Moreover, the psychiatrist is now vying with the social worker for the treatment role in the community. Nurses, too, are beginning to clamor for a place in the work outside the hospital, not only in out patient clinics but in performing home visits and following through on patients previously in their wards. It is interesting to note that in Scotland there is no equivalent of the English Ten Year Plan, and that they are much more circumspect about the relative disappearance of the mental hospital and its replacement by psychiatric units in general hospitals. Moreover, the Scots have not adopted that part of the Mental Health Bill which applies to the commitment of psychopaths to mental hospitals. The fact is that psychiatry is in a stage of transition and must await much more research information before any certainty about current planning can be justified.

I would like to give one other example of the state of transition that characterizes current psychiatric thinking, especially the extent to which it must inevitably become more critically evaluative and linked with the social sciences if we are to increase our effective contribution to mental health problems. The views on the effects of maternal deprivation on young children expounded by Bowlby and others have been generally accepted as an important factor in the development of mental health problems.

It has also been generally supposed that the Kibbutz in Israel has to a large extent counteracted this effect of maternal deprivation. From the day of their birth, children spend all but three or four of the 24 hours in the care of a nurse in the Children's House. They do not sleep at their parents' homes but see them a few hours a day and all day on the Sabbath. During a recent visit to a Kibbutz, Bowlby questioned the oversimplified claims that the Kibbutz adequately offsets the effects of maternal deprivation seen in ordinary homes. The fact is that the whole ideology of the Kibbutz is in favor of mothers being freed from the ties of domestic work and permitted to compete with men in the open employment field. Moreover, the expectation is that children looked after by nurses who are trained for the job will, in many cases, be more adequate contacts for children than many unstable mothers. Bowlby feels that, despite the mother's relative freedom from child rearing responsibilities through the practices of the Kibbutz, she still remains the most important person in the development of the child's personality. In other words, he questions the basic assumption that the Kibbutz can in fact offset the effects of maternal deprivation. This whole problem still awaits careful research evaluation before any final conclusions can be drawn, but it does demonstrate the limits of the most careful social planning when it is unaccompanied by adequate research.

How can we begin to train people for work in a field where there are so many unknown factors? I would like to put forward the thesis that if we envisage the psychiatric hospital as a microcosm of society and if we study, analyze and treat behavior within that small society, utilizing all the skills available from the field of psychiatry and the social sciences, we will be preparing staff personnel for work in the outside community as well as for hospital work. Ideally, one would like to think of the personnel who have therapeutic roles to play in relation to the patient — doctors, nurses, social workers, occupational therapists, etc. — as all having had a good grounding in the social science field while they were doing their undergraduate training. However, such a possibility is a long way off, and the most we can hope for at the present time is an in-service training which will develop an awareness of the social forces operating within the environment and teach us how to utilize these in treatment.

I would like to take as an example a typical admission ward of, say, 30 beds, where the patient's stay is limited to a period of between a few weeks to a few months. Ideally, one would like to have as the leader a psychiatrist who has had training and experience in analytic psychotherapy and in group work, and a long exposure to the social sciences as applied to hospital work. Such a psychiatrist would be in a good position to organize and carry out a daily ward meeting of all patients and staff personnel. Frequently, however, the social worker or psychologist may have had a more appropriate training for such a group task. A daily ward meeting, lasting, say, 50 minutes, followed by a 30 minute discussion with the staff, should, I think, form the basis of training in social psychiatry at the present time. It may be that as our experience grows we will think of some better way of sensitizing the staff to the social forces in the environment, but in the meantime I feel that we cannot dispense with the daily ward meeting. In this setting all staff members are exposed to a sample of the patient interaction and the ward climate at any one time. Tension caused by the admission of a disturbed patient the previous night will be manifested in both verbal and non-verbal communications from the patient population. The immediate response of various staff members to this situation can be observed by their fellows and by the patients. The skill with which the situation is handled by both staff and patients can be analyzed in the staff seminar afterwards. In this seminar we are in a position to examine not only the formal skills in a psychotherapeutic sense of supportive and analytic therapy, but are also in a position to examine the roles and role relationships between the patients and the various categories of the staff. Inevitably, some of the personality problems of staff members as well as the tensions and misunderstandings within the staff group come up for discussion and may form the basis for "living learning" situations. The patients may clamor to have the new patient transferred to another ward. The nurses may want to use isolation with some physical form of treatment. The psychiatrist may want to understand the meaning of the disturbed behavior before deciding on a course of action. And the social worker may feel that the domestic situation must be attended to immediately if the patient is going to be able to settle.

In the staff discussion it may be suggested that the patients can be helped to a much more supportive and therapeutic role towards their peer if they are given more understanding of the background to the development of the acute psychotic episode. The nurse may be reassured by the psychiatrist's statement that he will see the patient immediately; and if he cannot get through to the patient and quiet his fears he will utilize temporarily some physical aid to treatment. The psychiatrist may have already decided that the anxiety in the patients and nurses is at such a level that they cannot yet relate to the patient in a truly therapeutic way, and it will take time before the patient is accepted in the ward as someone who can be understood and helped. It may even be that at this point the staff can accept the fact that the physical treatment is as much a treatment of their own anxiety as it is of the patient's condition.

The point I want to make is that if a ward meeting is held daily, and if sufficient time is set aside by the staff to analyze the interaction occurring during that meeting, as well as to get the feedback from the night staff and from the auxiliary departments, such as the workshops, O.T., home visits, etc., then day in and day out the staff will be forced to examine what they are doing and why they are doing it, in the presence of their colleagues. This represents a rich learning experience for all concerned, but calls for a considerable degree of skill from the leader, whether he be a psychiatrist, social worker, psychologist or nurse. Given such a setting, good leadership, and daily meetings for at least a year, average individuals in one of the four disciplines mentioned should be able to develop ward meetings of a similar kind in a new ward setting. During this training year they will have been in a position to see for themselves how the patient's conception of his or her role is modified by the different staff expectations. The patients usually arrive at a hospital expecting to be looked after and having things done for them by the doctor and hospital staff. To learn that they can only be helped if they themselves do much of the work, and communicate freely, is very upsetting for many patients. However, whenever they begin to realize that there is something in this approach for themselves, they begin to participate more willingly.

This leads us to the concept of a therapeutic culture which develops in a ward of this kind in a most interesting way. As behavior is studied day in and day out in the ward meetings, a culture develops that has many characteristics which are different from the world outside.

Many married couples have never really learned to discuss their problems with each other, and in group life many people cling

192

to the childhood concept that informing is a bad thing and implies malicious intent. In a group setting it may become clear that informing is done in order to help the patient to look at his deviant behavior and learn more appropriate ways of dealing with problems which overwhelm him. It is, I think, one of the basic tenets of what might be called social psychiatry that patients can be helped to deal with everyday problems in ways which are much more effective than anything they had previously understood. It is notoriously true that patients who are in greatest need of help from their social environment are frequently the people who have the least knowledge of how to use it or where to find it. The daily discussion of problems in the living situation in the ward inevitably throws up many problems which are familiar to most, if not all, the patients; by attempting to resolve these with all the psychiatric skills available, the whole community of patients and staff are put through frequent living learning situations.

By focusing on the ward meeting as an illustration of a training setting, I wish in no way to minimize the importance of the more fundamental types of training, which are familiar to us all. The formal training of the psychiatrist, nurse, social worker, etc., must continue to form the core of any adequate training for the future demands of community psychiatry. I am simply focusing on the additional training which will be required if we are to develop skills for psychiatric practice in the community. My own experience in ward meetings held over the last 22 years suggests that not all, perhaps in fact a minority, of psychiatrists are suited to the kind of role that has been described here. Many, if not most, psychiatrists are much more comfortable in individual treatment sessions with their patients, in the seclusion of their offices.

It is not clear to me *how* these psychiatrists can best be utilized in the practice of psychiatry in the community. President Kennedy recommended in a report to Congress that private psychiatrists may well supply a significant proportion of psychiatric endeavor that will be needed for the new mental health clinics. It remains to be seen how relevant analytically oriented psychotherapy will be in this community setting. It would still seem to be true that the best way of learning psychotherapeutic skills is through an initial exposure to individual treatment under supervision of a trained analyst. The next step would desirably be to act as a co-therapist with an experienced group worker in a small therapeutic group. Such a training would be highly desirable before undertaking the large ward meetings which we have been discussing. However, it is my experience that psychiatrists, nurses, social workers, psychologists, occupational therapists, work supervisors in industrial therapy programs and other categories of staff coming in contact with patients, can *all* be trained to make intelligent use of the social forces in the environment, a development which has sometimes been given the term "sociotherapy."

I have given only the briefest outline of the possibilities of this approach to therapy and how it can apply to the new role for which psychiatry is being cast in the community. For a much more advanced treatise on the methodology which is beginning to evolve I would refer you to John and Elaine Cummings' new book *Ego and Milieu*.

GRUPPENPSYCHOTHERAPIE MIT ÄRZTEN

von A. Friedemann

Unsere Gruppenpsychotherapie mit Ärzten ist aus zwei Wurzeln erwachsen. Einmal aus der psychotherapeutischen Einzelbetreuung unter besonderer Berücksichtigung unserer psychoanalytischen Erfahrung, dann aber auch aus der Erfahrung in der Gruppenarbeit, die wir 1925 unter dem Einfluss des Stegreifspieles von J. L. Moreno in der psychiatrischen Klinik begonnen haben, um sie später extra muros fortzusetzen.

In mehr als 35 Jahren hat sich die Erfahrung gefestigt, dass Psychotherapie im allgemeinen und Gruppenpsychotherapie im besonderen als Technik umso besser beherrscht werden könne, je tiefer die Erfahrung im Selbsterlebnis durchgearbeitet wird. Die Entdeckung des Stegreifspieles in seiner therapeutischen Bedeutung durch Moreno schliesst sich mit den klassischen Ausführungen Heinrich von Kleists in seinem Marionettentheater in der Erfahrung der freien Assoziation. Immer wieder gelingt es, auf diese Art Konflikte so zu erledigen, dass sie "jenseits von Gut und Böse" im Spiel oder in der liebevoll verständnisvollen Umgebung erledigt werden können.

So dienen unsere Ärztegruppen der Vermittlung gruppenpsychotherapeutischer Möglichkeiten im Rahmen der Selbsterfahrung, die von der Gruppe durchgearbeitet wird. Hier zeigt sich vor allem die Tatsache, wie stark nicht nur der "unanalysierte," sondern auch der "ananalysierte" und oft auch der "durchanalysierte" Arzt gefährdet ist. Es zeigt sich, wie häufig gerade die sogenannten Abwehrmechanismen noch weiter durchgearbeitet werden müssen. Im Vordergrunde stehen ferner die Konflikte, die sich aus dem persönlichen "Familiendrama" ergeben, die sich im Ehedrama wiederholen. Sie kehren schliesslich auch in den Schwierigkeiten mit Patienten und Kollegen wieder.

Wir versuchen, das Gruppenerlebnis, so weit es irgendwie

möglich ist, im Rahmen einer freien, nicht dirigierten Gruppe zu verwirklichen. Im Gegensatz zur Annahme von *Kurt Lewin* verfäll eine solche freie Gruppe nicht der Anarchie, so lange das Gruppenbewusstsein als solches erhalten bleibt. Gefährdet ist eine solche freie Gruppe vor allem dann, wenn es nicht rechtzeitig gelingt, die schwachen Gruppenmitglieder zu stützen. Fehler geschehen hier am häufigsten dadurch, dass die Ich-Kontrolle des vermeintlichen Gruppenleiters versagt. Dieses Versagen zeigt sich in der Unfähigkeit zum Schweigen. Es zeigt sich vor allem im Durchbruch des Narzismus, der Eigenliebe, der Selbstbespiegelung und nicht genügend gesteuerter Aggressionen.

Das Gruppenbewusstsein muss ebenso gepflegt werden, wie die Kontrolle der Übertragungsreaktionen bei analysierten Gruppenmitgliedern. Übertragung und Gegenübertragung werden in der freien Gruppe von unbefangenen Mitgliedern leichter korrigiert, als von Gruppengliedern, die mit der Analyse vertraut sind, bei denen aber das Problem des Narzismus, der Übertragung und der Tragfähigkeit ungenügend durchgearbeitet worden sind. Ähnlich der Grundregel in der Psychoanalyse müssen gewisse Grundregeln in der Gruppenarbeit angenommen werden, die das Gruppenbewusstsein und das Gruppengewissen stützen. Das Gruppenbewusstsein wird durch die Aufgabe, um die es geht, wach gehalten. Das wäre in unserem Falle "das Selbsterlebnis in der Gruppe." Das Gruppengewissen wird durch Annahme von Verpflichtungen stimuliert, wie etwa im hippokratischen Eid oder im Gruppeneide Morenos oder auch bei entsprechend gestimmten Gruppen durch Übernahme religiöser Verpflichtungen. Mit der Übernahme dieser Verpflichtungen erhält die Gruppe den Wert einer Suchgruppe, die in gemeinsamer Arbeit bestimmt, wie weit die Überich-Funktionen, die aus der Gruppenverpflichtung erwachsen, in das Selbsterlebnis eingebaut werden können.

Dieses Gruppengewissen entsteht also: 1. in der Gruppenmitteilung *(Kommunikation)*, 2. in der Annahmebereitschaft *(Akzeptation)*, 3. Entwicklung des inneren Unabhängigkeitsbedürfnisses in Harmonisierung mit der Gruppenrealität. Das heisst Disziplinierung der inneren Freiheit aus der Erkenntnis der Rechte und Pflichten, die aus der Betätigung dieser Freiheit erwachsen *(Personale Evolution)*.

Die Bearbeitung persönlicher Probleme in der Gruppe geschieht im freien Agieren, im freien Gespräch und im Psychodrama.

196

Im Psychodrama haben wir neben den bereits bekannten Methoden insbesondere die Methode des *"Echo aus dem Schatten"* entwickelt. Bei dieser Methodik wird der erste Teil des Psychodramas abgelöst durch die gleiche Anzahl von Spielern, die nun genau das Gegenteil der Handlungen ausspielen, die von den Figuren des ursprünglichen Psychodramas übernommen worden waren (etwa der unterwürfige Ehemann gegenüber dem herrschsüchtigen oder die böse Schwiegermutter gegenüber der allzu guten). Es hat sich ferner bewährt, in diesem "Echo aus dem Schatten" auch die Frauenrollen von Männern, die Männerrollen von Frauen spielen zu lassen. In dieser Weise gelingt eine vertiefte Katharsis, an der die ganze Gruppe beteiligt ist.

Als besondere Probleme haben sich in Ärztegruppen folgende Nöte herausgestellt: der Kranke als der geliebte Feind; das Eheproblem; das Familiendrama (Eltern, Geschwister), die soziale Geltung; Erledigung von Machtansprüchen und Machtüberansprüchen; Bedrohung aus der Psychose; Kontrolle neurotischer Fehlhaltungen.

GRUPPENTHERAPIE BEI PSYCHOSOMATISCHEN ERKRANKUNGEN

von Hans Hoff

I. Was ist Psychosomatik?

Wir haben auf unserer Klinik seit 10 Jahren eine psychosomatische Modellstation errichtet. Bevor wir unsere Arbeit im einzelnen schildern, müssen wir auf den Begriff der Psychosomatik näher eingehen. Ist Psychosomatik wirklich nur Ganzheitsmedizin? Ist sie nichts anderes als die Erfassung der gesamten Persönlichkeit und beschäftigt sie sich nur mit dem Studium der gegenseitigen Beeinflussung von Körper und Geist, worauf bereits Hippokrates seine Aufmerksamkeit gerichtet hat? Nein, Psychosomatik im modernen Sinn ist etwas ganz anderes: Sie ist die Aufdeckung des psychogenen Anteils an der Pathogenese bestimmter Erkrankungen. Sie berücksichtigt alle Faktoren, welche zu einer Erkrankung führen, denkt also multikonditional und beleuchtet die psychischen Determinanten nicht nur nach Art einer Momentaufnahme der unmittelbar vor der Erkrankung gegebenen aktuellen Situationen, sondern erfasst die ganze psychodynamische Entwicklung seit der frühesten Kindheit mit ihrem Zusammenspiel zwischen Psyche und Soma.

Nach Mitscherlich sagt die Psychosomatik aus "wie seelisches Geschehen körperliche Abläufe krankmachend beeinflusst." Eine strenge Einschränkung auf die spezifisch psychosomatischen Erkrankungen wie z.B. Asthma, Ulcus ventriculi et duodeni, Colitis, Hypertonie usw. wurde von uns angestrebt. Keinesfalls soll es zu dem von Haseloff kritisierten Ausdehnungsbestreben kommen, von dem dieser sagt: "In der wirklichkeitsfremden Überdehnung der biographischen Interpretation sämtlicher pathologischer Vorgänge werden die organischen Krankheiten mit Hilfe einer oft anfechtbaren intuitiven Symboldeutung so verständlich gemacht, als seien sie insgesamt konversionshysterische Phänomene und als stellten Entzündungen oder Tumoren Leistungen des Subjektes dar. Beweisführung und Forschungslogik gahen dabei über die Erzeugung subjektiver Evidenzgefühle nicht hinaus."

Wir wollen kurz unsere Auffassung über die Entstehung psychosomatischer Erkrankungen zusammenfassen.

Durch einen neurotischen Konflikt in der Kindheit infolge einer chronisch traumatisierenden Situation entsteht ein erstes psychosomatisches Reaktionsmuster (am häufigsten anamnestisch bei Hauterkrankungen und bei Magen-Darm-Erkrankungen zu erfassen). In der frühen Kindheit konnte dass Kind Empfindungen am besten körperlich, eben im Bereich der Haut usw. ausdrücken. Es hatte sozusagen nur die Organsprache zur Verfügung.

Als weiterer Faktor ist das konstitutionelle Moment zu berücksichtigen, wobei es infolge der Minderwertigkeit eines Organs zu einem Entgegenkommen des Körpers kommen kann. Eine weitere wichtige Rolle spielt die Entwicklung eines psychodynamisch bedingten Lebensstiles, welcher immer wieder ein bestimmtes Organ in den Mittelpunkt chronischer Belastung stellt. Der Patient ist sehr geneigt, diesen Lebensstil als etwas aufzufassen, was ihm von aussen her aufgezwungen wird, z.B. verteidigt er seine Gewohnheit Mahlzeiten in übersteigertem Tempo hastig und sorglos hinunterzuschlingen damit, dass sein Beruf ihm keine Zeit lasse usw. In Wirklichkeit ist er es selbst, der sich hetzt und es ist also die Schadigung seines Magens nicht als äusserlich, sondern als psychodynamisch bedingt anzusehen.

Auch auslösende traumatisierende Situationen führen dazu, dass das frühkindliche psychosomatische Reaktionsmuster wieder anklingt, was zum Ausbruch der Erkrankung führt.

Freilich kann es auch Fälle geben, in denen die gesamte Vorentwicklung nicht überblickbar ist und bloss ein aktueller Konflikt zu einer Reaktion geführt hat. Doch sind diese Fälle selten gegenüber jenen, bei denen die chronische Entwicklung seit der Kindheit aufzeigbar ist.

Zusammenfassend sehen wir also bei psychosomatischen Erkrankungen, dass ein neurotischer Konflikt zu einer Somatisierung geführt hat. Es erscheint uns sehr wichtig, den Unterschied zwischen der Konversionsneurose und der psychosomatischen Erkrankung zu verdeutlichen, da ja auch die Konversionsneurose zu einer Organfunktionsstörung führen kann.

199

Nach Alexander stellt ein hysterisches Konversionsphänomen seiner Natur nach ähnlich jeder beliebigen willkürlichen Innervation eine Ausdrucksbewegung dar. Wir glauben, dass es nicht die Art des Konfliktes (jeder Konflikt kann sowohl zur Konversionsneurose wie zur psychosomatischen Erkrankung führen), sondern der Zeitpunkt seiner Entstehung ist, der für die Somatisierung der Neurose verantwortlich ist.

Buchner stellte folgende Entwicklungskette auf: Seelische Störung — organische Funktionsstörung — irreversible organische Strukturstörung.

Es sind vor allem die Störungen in der oralen und analen Phase, die zur Bildung psychosomatischer Reaktionsmuster führen, während in der genitalen Phase eine Entlastung erfolgt und zwar dadurch, dass die Konflikte bereits auf andere emotionale Weise ausgedrückt werden können. Da in den ersten Kindheitsjahren, die ja der oralen und analen Phase entsprechen, die Mutter die einzige oder erste Beziehungsperson ist, sehen wir die psychosomatischen Erkrankungen demnach als "Mutterneurosen" an. Dieser Wechsel innerhalb der neurotischen Symptomatik ist sehr interessant, wenn man auch hier einen Vergleich mit der Jahrhundertwende zieht: Es schwinden die Neurosen, die durch den Vater bedingt sind und es nehmen jene zu, die auf die ersten Lebensabschnitte zurückgehen, in denen die Mutter die entscheidende Rolle spielt; so spiegelt sich das Ende des Patriachats auch im Neurosengeschehen wider. Nach dieser Darstellung unserer Auffassung von der psychosomatischen Erkrankung wenden wir uns nun der Frage zu, was die Gruppentherapie in unserem Behandlungsplan zu leisten vermag.

II. *Was kann die Gruppentherapie?*

Unter analytischer Gruppentherapie verstehen wir eine, in der vorwiegend die Reaktionen der Gruppe gedeutet werden, die aber nicht die Summe der Einzelanalysen der Teilnehmer darstellt. Es wird im hic et nunc gedeutet und die Prognose ist umso günstiger zu stellen, je mehr die Positionen der Gruppenmitglieder in ihrer Beziehung zueinander wechseln können. Als Ergänzung der Einzelanalyse ist die Gruppe deshalb so wertvoll, weil in der ersteren der Patient sich oft dem Therapeuten gegenüber unterlegen fühlt als einer, dessen Fehlverhaltensweisen und Schwächen aufgedeckt werden, während die Gruppe entlastend wirkt. Der Patient kann seine eigenen emotionalen Regungen und deren Spiegelungen in den anderen Teilnehmern erleben und kommt so zu einer unmittelbaren Einsicht in seine Konflikte mit der Umwelt. Zugleich wird durch die Deutung des geheimen Sinnes hinter dem, was der einzelne Teilnehmer aussagt, die Entwicklung zur Einsicht gefördert und die gemeinsame unbewusste Phantasie der Gruppe erfasst. Durch das Mitschwingen der eigenen unbewussten Inhalte mit den Ausserungen der übrigen Teilnehmer wird eine Heilung auch dann bewirkt, wenn die eigenen Probleme nicht klargelegt wurden.

Während in der Einzeltherapie innerhalb der Übertragung die eigenen Empfindungen, die bisherigen Einstellungen zur Umwelt auf den Therapeuten projiziert werden, führt in der Gruppe die Tatsache, dass man nicht mit diesem allein ist, dazu, dass der Patient sein Erleben in die anderen Mitglieder der Gruppe projiziert, in ihnen aber auch einen Rückhalt findet und dem Therapeuten gegenüber sowohl weniger abhängig, als weniger benachteiligt erscheint, wodurch die erlebte Gefährdung abnimmt. Obwohl die analytische Therapie sowohl in der Einzel- wie in der Gruppentherapie auf Deutungen beschränken soll, wird doch in der Einzeltherapie die Gefahr der suggestiven Beeinflussung und von seiten des Patienten die passive und unterschiedslose Annahme der Suggestionen oft nicht vermieden, wodurch es zwar zu einem Verschwinden der Symptomatik kommen kann, wobei jedoch die Persönlichkeit selbst unverändert bleibt. Innerhalb der Gruppe kann durch den ständigen Wechsel von Projektion und Introjektion, der gedeutet werden muss und die hiedurch bedingte Veränderung innerhalb der Gruppenstruktur eine Persönlichkeitsänderung erreicht werden.

Gerade in der wesentlichen Veränderung der Grundstruktur besteht die bedeutsame Möglichkeit der Gruppentherapie: Es können Hassgefühle offen geäussert und zugleich ihre Auswirkungen als nicht so verhängnisvoll wie gefürchtet erlebt werden. Der Schaden, der angerichtet worden ist, kann wieder gut gemacht werden, sodass es infolge wiederholter Wandlungen zu einer Veränderung der früher fixierten Grundeinstellung kommt, wodurch die Teilnehmer ihrer Heilung entgegensehen.

Foulkes hat deshalb von einer "Spiegelreaktion" gesprochen: Jeder Patient sieht sich selbst im anderen gespiegelt. Durch die Deutungsarbeit des Therapeuten wird die Reaktion des Partners nicht mehr als etwas — dem anderen zugehörigen beurteilt, sondern in der Deutung der Partnerreaktion findet der einzelne Patient sich selbst gedeutet. Während in der Einzelanalyse, der Therapeut zufolge der Übertragung hintereinander als Vater, Mutter, Partner erlebt wird, kann in der Gruppe die Relation zu den bisherigen Beziehungspersonen wieder erlebt und agiert werden. Da die neurotische Konstellation immer wieder zu einer Schicksalswiederholung führt, wird innerhalb kurzer Zeit in der Gruppe die Mutter-oder Vaterproblematik durchagiert, und zugleich von den anderen Teilnehmern mit Hilfe der deutenden Analyse verstanden, wobei es zum "Mitspielen" und damit zum tieferen Selbstverständnis der übrigen Teilnehmer kommt.

Die Deutung selbst bezieht sich immer auf die Aktion der ganzen Gruppe, es wird also gedeutet: Die Ausserungen während der Gruppensitzung, der Widerstand und die Abwehrmassnahmen. Was in der Gruppe vorgeht, versteht der Therapeut auf Grund seiner Gegenübertragung, wobei unter dieser nach der Definition von Kemper verstanden wird die Gesamtheit aller bewussten und unbewussten Haltungen und Gefühlsreaktionen, die der Therapeut dem Patienten gegenüber erlebt.

Der Therapeut fungiert also einerseits nach Beranger wie eine Leinwand, auf der sich zweierlei projiziert. Er gibt ein zutreffendes Bild der Aussenwelt und ermöglicht es dem Patienten eine Korrektur und Vervollständigung seiner Innenwelt zu erreichen und er ermöglicht die therapeutische Wirkung durch eine ständige Gegenüberstellung der Innen- und Aussenwelt. Es ist hier sehr der Bemerkung von Grinberg und Langer beizupflichten dass "der Abstand zwischen der Innen- und Aussenwelt, für die Gruppe viel kleiner ist als für das Individuum". Durch projizierende Mechanismen werden die Konflikte in die Aussenwelt verlegt und das erleichtert das Erkennen bis dahin unbewusster Innenvorgänge. Ihre Bedeutung wird intellektuell und emotional leichter erfasst, wenn man sie im Verhalten der anderen gespiegelt sieht. Gerade die Möglichkeit, innere Gegebenheiten in anschaulicher sinnfälliger Weise in der Aussenwelt zu verkörpern und ihnen dort gegenüberzutreten (was mit Hilfe der besprochenen Identifizierungsvorgänge geschieht) begünstigt die Entwicklung und Verfestigung der Einsicht.

In der Gruppe können also viele psychodynamische Prozesse, die in der Einzeltherapie nur im zeitlichen Nacheinander durchgearbeitet werden könen, im Nebeneinander auftreten. So kann z.B. das

Verständnis der Ambivalenz, die innerhalb der neurotischen Störungen von besonderer Bedeutung ist, in der Gruppe dadurch erreicht werden, dass z.b. die mit Aggression verbundene Ablehnung des Therapeuten und die idealisierende Zuwendung zu ihm, die in der Einzeltherapie nur in der zeitlichen Abfolge erlebt werden können, hier von verschiedenen Gruppenmitglieder ihm gleichzeitig entgegengebracht und dadurch der Gruppe als Projektionen gedeutet werden.

III. *Analyse des Widerstandes gegen die psychosomatische Forschungsrichtung in Ärzten, Laien- und Patienten-kreisen*

Wir glauben, dass wir noch auf eine erstaunliche Tatsache hinweisen müssen, nämlich, dass wir uns auch nach 10 jähriger Tätigkeit im Rahmen unserer psychosomatischen Station immer noch im Vorfeld unserer Pioniertätigkeit befinden. Dies ist umso überraschender, als — wie sie alle wissen — die Zahl der psychosomatischen Erkrankungen ständig zunimmt.

Wenn Kafka gemeint hat, es gebe vielleicht nur *eine* Krankheit, die von der Medizin gejagt werde wie ein Tier durch die Wälder, so fühlen wir uns an diese Auffassung manchmal erinnert, wenn wir die Verwandlungsfähigkeit beobachten, mit der einzelne Krankheitsphänomene verschwinden, dafür andere in verstärkten Masse auftreten: Dass die grosse Hysterie, das klassische Studienobjekt der Psychiater der Jahrhundertwende, fast vollkommen verschwunden ist, wissen sie alle. Bei uns in Österreich, ist es interessant zu beobachten, dass die wenigen Fälle, die noch zu uns zur Einweisung kommen, fast alle aus dem Burgenland stammen, dass sowohl durch seine späte Eingliederung in unser Staatsgebilde sowie durch die Schichtung seiner Bevölkerungsgruppen ein Reservoir archaischer Phänomene und primitiver Mechanismen darstellt. Dass im übrigen die klassischen Hysterieformen dem Patienten scheinbar kaum mehr zu Gebote stehen, ist darauf zurückzuführen, dass die Erkenntnis der tiefen-psychologischen Schulen durch populär — medizinische Vortrags — und publizistische Tätigkeit insofern bis in Laienkreise vorgedrungen ist, dass diese sie als seelische Fehlleistungen verstehen oder zumindest den Zusammenhang mit seelischen Konfliktsituationen anerkennen. Es scheint, als wäre dadurch, dass diese Tatsachen weitgehend ins allgemeine Bewusstsein gehoben wurden, den unbewussten Triebpotentialen gleichsam der Weg nach aussen — in die Ausdrucksformen der klassischen Hysterien vesperrt worden.

Weizsäcker, der sich, von der inneren Medizin herkommend, als einer der ersten mit psychosomatischen Erkrankungen beschäftigt hat, hat immer wieder darauf hingewiesen, wie sehr die Patientin die Ich-Ferne ihrer Erkrankung brauchen, d.h., dass sie es ablehnen, seelische Komponenten im Entstehen ihrer körperlichen Leiden anzusehen. Er war immer wieder überrascht von dem heftigen Widerstand, den die Patienten seinen Deutungsversuchen, die ja Heilungsversuche waren, entgegensetzten. Da der Widerstand nicht auf die Kranken allein beschränkt bleibt, wollen wir zunächst nun auf diese Widerstandshaltung eingehen. Nach der analytischen Grundregel, dass das Ausweichen eines Kranken vor einer tiefergehenden Analyse seiner Beschwerden als Widerstand aufzufassen ist und selbst einer Analyse bedarf.

Wir können nämlich Weizsäckers Beobachtungen nicht nur bestätigen, sondern noch insofern erweitern, als wir es nicht nur mit dem Widerstand der Patienten, sondern auch mit dem unserer medizinischen Kollegen, vor allem der Internisten und der praktischen Ärzte zu tun haben: Die seelische Genese oder die seelische Mitdetermination derjenigen Krankheiten, die Jores die menschlichen Krankheiten deshalb genannt hat, weil sie beim Tier nicht vorkommen, ist nicht nur dem Patienten selbst verborgen, sondern auch vielen Ärzten. Mit der vollständigen Analyse dieses Problems können wir uns leider nicht beschäftigen, obwohl sie ausserordentlich wichtig wäre:

Einerseits steckt dahinter der Widerstand gegen die Psychiatrie, die in den meisten Fällen ein Widerstand gegen eigene unbewusste Ängste und Gefährdungen ist. Andererseits beruht er auf einem Phänomen der Gegenübertragung: Da der Patient von der Aufdeckung seiner Konfliktsituationen und damit vor der psychiatrischen Behandlung zurückschreckt, fürchtet der Arzt ihn zu verletzen, ihn schliesslich zu verlieren, wenn er ihm eine psychische Behandlung vorschlägt. Schliesslich aber beruht der Widerstand in Kollegen-und auch Laienkreisen gegen diese Art der Problembewältigung darin, dass von den einzelnen mehr oder weniger deutlich so formuliert wird: Wenn gewisse Erkrankungen auf seelische Fehlhaltung zurückgehen oder überhaupt mit psychischem Geschehen eng verknüpft sind, dann wird die Krankheit aus einem schicksalhaft Auferlegten plötzlich zu einem im weitesten Sinn selbst auferlegten, oder zumindest unter eigener Mitwirkung entstandenen Geschehen, also einem, an dem der Einzelne im gewissen Sinne selbst verantwortlich ist.

Diese Auffassung nun erregt den höchsten Widerstand aller Beteiligten. Es wird damit nämlich letztlich die Schuldfrage anvisiert und somit fühlt sich das bedrängte Ich eingeengt zwischen den strafenden Instanzen des Über-Ich und den anflutenden Aggressionen des Unbewussten Es, die bereits zur Somatisierung, nämlich zu organischen Läsionen geführt haben. Es kommt dadurch in eine höchst bedrohte Lage und wehrt sich mit heftiger Ablehnung. Es sei als Beispiel für diesen Mechanismus eine Beobachtung gebracht, die jeder aus seinem eigenen Leben kennt: Ein Kind in einem aktuellen schulischen Konflikt erkrankt an heftiger Gastroenteritis. Solange diese als rein somatische Krankheit von Eltern und Hausarzt akzeptiert wird, geht alles gut: Die Eltern, die bisher als fordernde Repträsentanten der Schulmoral aufgetreten sind, verwandeln sich in besorgte und zärtliche Helfer, die Bettruhe befreit von allen dringenden Verpflichtungen; die gefürchtete Schularbeit geht inzwischen vorüber—; kurz und gut Krankheitstendenz und Krankheitsgewinn überwiegen bei weitem körperliche Schmerzen und Übelbefinden. Es ist gelungen, die somatische Erkrankung als Exkulpierung von dem strengen Zensor des Über-Ichs einzusetzen. Es wird auf somatischer Ebene bewältigt, was auf seelischer nicht bewältigt worden ist, und Betroffene und Umgebung sind — zumindestens dann, wenn die Krankheit nur eine kurzdauernde Episode bleibt — mit dieser Lösung zufrieden. Dieses Beispiel ist ausserordentlich vereinfacht und daher wie alles Schematische auch irgendwie verfälscht, aber es eignet sich, glaube ich, doch zur Illustration dessen, was gesagt werden soll. Ähnlich geht es dem Menschen, dessen Zärtlichkeitsbedürfnis seit der Kindheit immer wieder enttäuscht worden ist und dem der Asthmaanfall endlich erlaubt, umsorgt und betreut zu werden, dem Aggressiven, dessen Zerstörungswünsche niemals im offenen Kampf ausgetragen worden sind, sondern nur ihn selbst in ständige Anspannung versetzt und schliesslich seinen Blutdruck in die Höhe getrieben haben — aber es besteht bei den lentztgenannten Fällen ein grosser Unterschied gegenuber unserem ersten Beispiel: Die Patienten sind mit diesem Lösungsversuch nicht mehr zufrieden. Wenn er vielleicht auch einigen Krankheitsgewinn mit sich bringt, so ist er doch weit über das Ziel hinausgeschossen und hat letzten Endes mehr Schaden als Nutzen gestiftet. Der Patient wünscht also von diesem Übel befreit zu werden, aber er wünscht, dass diese Befreiung gemäss den Vorstellungen erfolge, die er sich selbst über seine Krankheit gemacht hat. Er wünscht also die medikamentöse Behandlung, den Kuraufenthalt, die Rücksichtnahme seiner Umgebung — alles Massnahmen, die seine eigene Passivität weiter ermöglichen. Wie er die Krankheit als etwas auffassen will, das an ihm geschieht, so wünscht er auch eine Therapie, die an ihm, aber nicht mit ihm oder durch ihn geschieht.

Wenn wir aufrichtig sind, können wir dieselbe Haltung sehr oft auch an uns selbst beobachten. Hier ist das grösste Spannungsfeld im Rahmen der medizinischen Therapie: Auf der einen Seite als Extrem die Operation in Narkose, bei der der Patient als Mittäter völlig ausgeschaltet ist und auf der anderen Seite die aktive Introspektion oder Einsicht, die der Analysand "erarbeitet".

Während chirurgische Patienten auf der einen Seite der rein somatischen Therapie überantwortet bleiben (obwohl wir auch hier seit der Erforschung z.B. der Unfallspersönlichkeiten manche interessante Beobachtungen gesammelt haben) und auf der anderen Seite die "reinen Neurosen" der Psychotherapie anvertraut werden, bewegt sich die Front zwischen diesen beiden Kampffeldern gerade mitten durch das Kerngebiet der Medizin, nämlich durch die interne Klinik. Man könnte also im gedachten Kraftfeld den psychosomatischen Krankheiten den Platz an der Wasserscheide zwischen den Gebieten der rein somatischen und der rein psychischen Krankheiten zuweisen. Ob man die erkrankten Patienten selbst einer Klinik für innere Medizin oder wie bei uns einer Nervenklinik zuweist, ist zwar nach all dem bisher Gesagten nicht gleichgültig, da der Einrichtung einer psychosomatischen Station auf einer inneren Klinik weniger Widerstand entgegengesetzt würde, ist aber nicht von entscheidendem Interesse.

IV. *Spezifische Möglichkeiten der Gruppentherapie bei psychosomatischen Erkrankungen*

Wen wir nun die Erfahrungstatsachen, die wir aus der Führung analytischer Gruppen gelernt haben, speziell auf unsere psychosomatischen Patienten anweden, können wir an das bereits Gesagte anknüpfen. Was der bewussten Verarbeitung entzogen blieb, suchte

sich bei ihnen durch die Übersetzung in die Köerpersprache sinnge-
mäss auszudrücken. So bringt der Hypertoniker z.B. verdrängte
Gefühle von Feindseligkeit in seiner Körpersprache zum Ausdruck,
der Asthmatiker aber hat die Gefühle von Abhängigkeit und
Zärtlichkeitsbedürfnis verdrängt. Die Wortsprache der gleichen
Patienten wird also in dem einen Fall vielleicht respektvolle Höf-
lichkeit, im anderen Falle Kälte und Gleichgültigkeit zum Ausdruck bringen. In der Gruppensituation aber wird an einem hinge-
worfenen Wort des Partners die Aggression sich entzünden und
zur Entladung kommen — was jetzt die Deutung ermöglicht. Damit
wird letztenendes schliesslich ein Gefühl der Verantwortung für
die eigene Krankheit erreicht. Bisher hatte der Patient nach Kemper "das Übel" nur in einen Teil seiner selbst verlegt, entweder in
den Geist, oder aber, wie es bei unseren Erkrankten geschieht, eben
in den Körper, um sich auf diese Weise wenigstens den anderen
Teil heil zu bewahren. Wenn er sich nun aber seiner Aggresionen
durch den Kampf innerhalb der Gruppe bewusst wird, schwindet
die Überzeugung vom seelischen oder geistigen Heilsein, was zur
Erschütterung, zugleich aber zur Freigabe eines Ausweichgeleises
führt: Erregungen müssen nun nicht mehr über das Vegetativum
als Tonuserhöhung der glatten Muskulatur oder als Spannung-
swiderstand in den Gefässen abgeführt werden, sondern fliessen
über verbale Aggressionen ab, die dann bewusst erlebt, gedeutet
und verstanden werden können.

Es ist für die angestrebte Heilung nicht nötig, homogene
Gruppen, d.h. solche mit gleicher Problematik oder gleicher Er-
krankungsart der Patienten zusammenzustellen, z.B. Gruppen von
Asthmatikern oder Magenerkrankungen, obwohl auch diese Gruppen Vorteile haben. Da wir je nach den Zuweisungen von den
internen Stationen Patienten mit verschiedenen Leiden aufnehmen,
sind die stationären Gruppen heterogen. Wir haben aber Patienten
aus der psychosomatischen Ambulanz auch in ausgewählten homogenen Gruppen therapeutisch behandelt, so z.B. eine Gruppe von
vegetativen Dystonien.

Die Tatsache, das innerhalb der homogenen Gruppe alle
Patienten an der gleichen Krankheit leiden, ermöglicht schneller
eine grössere Vertraulichkeit der Gruppenmitglieder untereinander
und eine grössere Bereitschaft, Einsicht in die Psychosomatik zu
erlangen und das Abgespaltene wieder in die Persönlichkeit zu
integrieren. So haben wir auf der Klinik z.B. mit Gruppen von

Fettsüchtigen gute Erfahrungen gemacht, da innerhalb der Gemeinsamkeit sehr schnell — zunächst am anderen und erst dann an sich selbst — verstanden wurde, wie häufig larvierte Depressionen auf Grund emotionaler Frustrationen zum Vielessen geführt hatten. Vielfach war die depressive Symptomatik eine Aggressionshemmung und mit dem Freisetzen der aggresiven Impulse, die sich sowohl gegen den Therapeuten wie gegen die anderen Gruppenmitglieder richteten und gedeutet wurden, verschwand der süchtige Esszwang. Aber auch in einer inhomogenen stationären Gruppe haben wir bei einer adipösen Patientin im letzten Jahr ohne jede medikamentöse Beihilfe und ohne autoritäre Massnahmen bei der Speisenausteilung eine Gewichtsabnahme von 19 kg erreicht, nachdem sie erkannt hatte, dass sie, die noch bei der Einweisung ihre Ehe als überaus glücklich gepriesen hatte, heftige aggressive Gefühle gegen ihren Mann in sich unterdrückt hatte. Nachdem die Problematik in der Gruppe ausagiert worden war, kam es dann zu einer Aussprachen zwischen der Patientin und ihrem Ehemann und daraufhin nicht, wie sie gefürchtet hatte, zu einer Lösung, sondern zu einer Vertiefung der gegenseitigen Beziehungen. Die Katamnese zeigte, dass die Gewichtsabnahme auch nach der Entlassung unter vollen Aufnahme der bisherigen Tätigkeit eingehalten werden konnte und dass auch die vor der Einweisung aufgetretenen Zyklusstörungen nicht mehr bestanden, was Propter oder Post der wiedererlangten Orgasmusfähigkeit erreicht worden war.

Innerhalb der heterogenen Gruppen, die ja zugleich die praeformierten Gruppen des Krankenzimmers sind, kann nun sehr gut das beobachtet werden, was Bion als Grundeinstellung der Gruppen beschrieben hat: Die Abhängigkeit, das Ausleben der Antriebe zu Kampf und Flucht und die Paarbildung. So zentrierte sich die Gruppe eines Krankenzimmers um eine asthmakranke Patientin, die infolge schwerer Anfälle eines hohen Masses an Rücksichtnahme und Hilfe bei der Pflege durch die Mitpatienten bedurfte. Gleichzeitig projizierten die anderen ihre eigenen Ängste in die als schwerer krank erlebte Patientin und eine Verschlechterung bei ihr löste in allen Schuldgefühle aus, weil die Zimmergefährtinnen ihr Leiden als stellvertretend erlebten, so als hätten sie gewünscht, dass sie sterben könne, damit die übrigen weiterleben könnten. Mit der langsamen Besserung der Erkrankten rückte diese immer mehr aus dem Zentrum als passive Leiterin der

Gruppe heraus und die Mehrzahl der Projektionen der anderen wurde auf neue Gruppenmitglieder übertragen.

In einem Diapositiv haben wir die spezifischen Besonderheiten der psychosomatischen Gruppentherapie zusammengefasst.

Sie haben daraus ersehen, dass wir auf der Station eine Kombination von Organotherapie und Psychotherapie durchführen, d.h., dass ein Internist ebenso wie ein Psychotherapeut die Patienten betreut, dass wir eine Kombination von Gruppen- und Einzeltherapie durchführen und dass wir als Hilfsmethoden zur Korrektur des physiologischen Unterbaus der Erkrankung das autogene Training, die Atem- und Heilgymnastik und Sportgruppen anwenden.

Unser IV. und letztes Diapositiv soll Ihnen deutlich nachen, warum wir uns dafür entschieden haben, unsere Patienten sowohl in Einzeltherapie wie in Gruppentherapie zu behandeln. Die Gruppentherapie ist uns abgesehen von ihren speziellen, oben ausführlich dargelegten Funktionen, also auch als Wegbereitung und Unterstützung der Einzeltherapie nötig. Da die psychosomatischen Reaktionsmuster sich in frühester Kindheit geprägt haben, kommen wir ohne Einzeltherapie, d.h. ohne Analyse der individuellen Kindheitssituation und der Träume nicht aus. Die Gruppentherapie aber ist uns ein wertvolles therapeutisches Hilfsmittel dadurch, dass sie die Konfrontation von Innen- und Aussenwelt, die Introspektion mit Hilfe des Spiegelbildes und das Ausleben emotioneller Konflikte in der Partnerschaft ermöglicht. Durch das Bewusstmachen der bisher verdrängten seelischen Spannungen wird deren Somatisierung entgegengewirkt. Während die neurotische infantil gebliebene Persönlichkeit keine andere Möglichkeit hatte, ihre inneren Spannungen auszudrücken und sich ihrer zu entledigen als den Umsatz in körperliche Vorgänge, soll der geheilte und gereifte Patient zu einer bewussten Auseinandersetzung geführt werden.

THE IMPACT OF SOCIAL PSYCHOLOGY
ON GROUP PSYCHOTHERAPY

by Edgar F. Borgatta

It is reasonable to assert that the relationship between social psychology and group psychotherapy has been close, but it is difficult to trace the exact ways in which each may have influenced the other. Social psychology generally refers to the scientific discipline that focuses on the interaction nexus, the meeting point of the study of the individual and the group phenomena. Group psychotherapy, on the other hand, is a field of practice that attempts to use scientific and practice theory for the betterment of the individual and the group within the same focus of attention, the interaction nexus. Social psychology was named a century ago, and it has been a flourishing area of specialization in sociology and psychology for well over half a century. Group psychotherapy, however, as a recognizable field of specialization in the practicing professions, has existed only a little over three decades. Thus, in the historical sequence, it might well be expected that the practicing profession would draw heavily from the science. We may examine the case by paying some attention to the actual developments.

First, the general setting of the social and psychological sciences at the turn of the century should be considered. In sociology, there were many strong points of view rather than an accumulation of well-organized knowledge. The positivistic bias influenced many presentations, and this was not unrelated to a commitment to evolutionary historical analyses. While in looking back we give great credit to some of the simpler and more empirical analytic presentations, the dominance at that time of the rationalization of social forms from assumptions of historical development should not be ignored. In addition, the great synthesis of the social sciences, following the work of Comte, took over in many places, and in France and Italy, for example, much attention went into the exposition of why sociology was the queen of the social sciences — to the detraction of work in sociology, and possibly ultimately to a depreciation of sociology when it could not deliver its presumptuous promises. Still, there were many strongly scientific investments. As general sociologists in America, for instance, there were L. Ward, A. Small, F. Giddings and others who set the scene for a science with fewer assumptions. These were followed by C. Cooley, who essentially wrote the first modern organization of a book in social psychology in 1902 under the title of *Human Nature and the Social Order,* a book relatively devoid of evolutionary, racist, synthetic, moralistic, and other biases that marked the major theses on human nature and social behavior until that time. This was followed shortly by the books of E. Ross, *Foundations of Sociology* (1905) and *Social Psychology* (1908), the latter being the first volume in America to appear with that title. The former book was actually more important for social psychology than the latter, since his essays on the elements of social structure were more related to the interaction frame of reference than his concern with crowd behavior.

While it is not fair to other contributors to sociology in America at the turn of the century to stop with Ross, he provides an appropriate point to examine contributions in other nations. Ross's work in the *Foundations* was meant to be an organizing set of essays taking advantage of the best work available, and thus his references and predecessors warrant some explicit mention. The frame of reference of the analysis of the elements of social structure thus may be seen as related to the pioneering work of G. Simmel in the analytic approach that came to be known as "formal sociology," the emphasis on the extraction of the underlying form from the observation of broad scope of relevant phenomena. As applied to the analysis of coalitions, of formation of groups, of the consequences of amount of knowledge of the other and of the ordering of relationships, the contribution of Simmel must be viewed as of gigantic proportions. On another score the impact of Emil Durkheim was important, although the reading of historical documents suggests that this may be more of an attribution of recent decades than of actual fact at the turn of the century. Nevertheless, the emphasis associated with Durkheim in the analysis of the division of labor, in the partialing of effects in the analysis of processes, and in the seeking of underlying forces of a social order for impact on individual behavior, has been important. Historically, it needs to be recalled that Durkheim's analysis proceeds, at least partially, as a criticism and extension of the work of E. Morselli, whose book on *Suicide,* except for the concluding chapter on positivistic relevance, is essentially a good representation of the Italian statistical school and embodies the best methodological principles for social science. (Unfortunately, when Morselli's book was originally translated into English, the long methodological essay introducing it and the interpretive analytic comments were omitted; thus, possibly, the major reading of his work outside Italy was in ignorance of the developments of the statistical school. Subsequently, the Comtian influence in Italy appears to have become stronger on entering the 20th century.) The scientific vigor in the early Italian statistical sociologists may be seen in their close identification with the work of J. S. Mill.

In psychology, an island existed in the work on national character by W. Wundt, but aside from this most of the social psychological concern was with personality and the development of the self. The work of J. Baldwin centered on this topic, but the subject was covered as well in the writings of W. James and others, and in related disciplines notable analyses and discourses occurred in the work of J. Dewey and J. Royce. An important development that appears not to have caught the fancy of the profession was the work on suggestibility in the absence of hypnosis, by G. Binet, some of which was repeated in an isolated work by L. Terman in America.

In short, at the turn of the century, social psychology was beginning to show signs of shifting from an area of speculation to one of empirically based generalizations, even though the range of observation or experimentation was often very limited. The concern was rather central in sociology but more peripheral in psychology with its individualistic orientation.

It is not possible to move from this point to a complete inventory of developments in the 20th century in social psychology, but we will note some of the more relevant developments. It should be noted that much of the investment in the development of social psychology during this period occurred in America, although the developments certainly cannot be identified with native Americans in any way. In the first quarter of the 20th century, the developments were relatively few. On the empirical side, the work of F. Allport is notable, along with the entire concern with together-and-apart experimentation on the influence of presence of others on the individual. This led to some consideration of the "realness" of group phenomena, a question that in some ways still plagues the science. G. Mead contributed, largely through his influence on a generation of students, to the development of a more sophisticated view of the socialization process, to the learning of social behavior in the developmental process and to the relationship of this to such fundamental concepts as social perception and principles of learning in psychological terms. J. Piaget's work with children, while having impact later, is associated with the end of the first quarter century.

This brings us to the beginning of the era of group psychotherapy, and it must be noted that the greatly accelerated growth of social psychology actually barely leads the development of the practicing profession. The appearance of the volume *Experimental Social Psychology* (G. Murphy, L. Murphy, and T. Newcomb) is justified as a revision of the earlier book by the Murphys on the grounds that such outstanding and impressive work as that of J. Moreno, K. Lewin, M. Sherif, and others, has appeared.

When one considers the work of Moreno, it is necessary to see academic social psychological concerns fused with the problems of a practicing profession. In social psychology, the development of the sociometric test has been impressive if not revolutionary. It blended in with problems in the description of persons through ratings, and it made the transition of relating assessments of a person to the structure within which the characteristic of the person is seen. A leader is not only a person said to lead; the recognition of the property attributed to the person is charted in the recognition of the contemporaries of the status of the person. This avenue of development was extended by H. Jennings and many others in social psychology, and has led, for example, to the mathematical analysis of group structures now carried out by elaborate programs in the large computers.

At the level of impact in the field of social psychology, Moreno's concern with role-playing and the more formal procedures of Psychodrama and Sociodrama has led to such avenues of endeavor

213

as the attempts at direct assessment, such as are described in the volume *Assessment of Men*. More important, a merger of interests occurred here with important consequences for group psychotherapy.

K. Lewin and a number of his students made important contributions which were augmented by the availability of techniques for analysis, and thus power was added to the more abstract and theoretical work of Lewin in the study of group processes. But here the merging of interests and influences becomes nebulous, and Lewin's influence is seen going in two directions. One is in the educational processes and action orientation of the group dynamics movement; the other is in the more academic work of R. Lippitt, L. Festinger, S. Schachter, and a large group of other distinguished social psychologists. Again, the action-oriented section developed human relations training procedures embodying practice theory that was drawn loosely from Lewin's work, and also from that of Dewey (as they happened in education), even if misread. Practice techniques and the development of the programs, however, involved heavy borrowing from educational sources as well as from Moreno's formalization of role-playing techniques. This development is worth stressing, because in many ways it appears to embody the eclectic (possibly agnostic) form of group psychotherapy that is practiced broadly today.

It is not possible to outline either the development or the inclusive set of approaches to group psychotherapy, but since several major emphases have been mentioned, it is necessary to pass on to others. Influences of H. Sullivan in psychiatry, along with other interactionist splinters, have had great impact on the practical orientation to psychotherapy, and thus have fit well the development of group psychotherapy. The Adlerian influence may be viewed, similarly, as a pragmatically oriented one, directive, and much concerned with the interaction processes. In social work (with its frequent commitment to classical Freudian theory), S. Slavson joined forces with psychoanalytically oriented therapists. There are early roots, of course, in the work of others, and there have been many, many persons with their own brands of group psychotherapy. What group psychotherapy is today, however, is at best an eclectic cousin to the pragmatically oriented sources, however rationalized in theory. On this score, it is difficult for someone not brought up in the quasi-mystical belief in Freud to

214

see the relationship of current procedures to his writing. In fact, there appears to be something quite inconsistent between the common pragmatism of group discussion, training and psychotherapy approaches, and elaborate superstructures of theories.

In this setting of a development of a generalized, eclectic orientation to group psychotherapy, social psychology has entered in several ways. First, we have noted that people like Moreno have been important contributors in both areas. Second, as techniques developed, the analogy to social and psychological processes has permitted borrowing of concepts from social psychology and relieved a press for comprehensive theories (in opposition to pressures of professionalism). Additional methods for description, such as that of R. Bales's *Interaction Process Analysis,* have led to an objectification of social processes. Such direct observation procedures have permitted the comparison of different types of groups, and the objectification of developmental sequences and the direct analysis of structures, permitting at times the direct testing of theoretical assertions both in social psychology and in the theory of practicing professions. Here it needs to be noted that much of the contribution has been negative, in the sense that assertions and assumptions have been unsupported more often than principles and well-ordered regularities of behavior have been uncovered.

The third way that social psychology has entered in the development of group psychotherapy has been in the issue of whether the therapies as a whole have impact. In the second quarter of the 20th century, it can be asserted, much social and psychological science departed from the scientific method in appearing to give belief to theories *until disproved,* which is certainly contrary to the notion that the burden of proof belongs to the one who makes the assertion. From the social psychologist has come the question of demonstration of the effects of therapies, and this has been phrased in many ways. The most drastic assessment of group psychotherapy that can be made is the one that asks for scientific proof of effectiveness. There are scientific standards that can be applied, and there are methods for test, yes, and possibly even for isolating the most effective techniques of induced change, but from the point of view of a rigorous science they have not yet been applied. From this point of view, group psychotherapy is operating largely on good intentions, belief and self-confidence.

Pragmatic and eclectic utilization of the tools available is necessary in the absence of firm knowledge, but this neither guarantees results nor suggests that flight into speculative theories is an improvement. With the number of persons concerned with psychotherapy, both group and individual, and the time that has passed since the questions have been raised, study of effectiveness warrants the kind of systematic study that has been given to some vaccines in recent years, rather than sporadic attention.

In conclusion, it would seem that social psychology has made its impact on group psychotherapy in providing some descriptive knowledge, in assisting in the discarding of unnecessary and erroneous assertions and assumptions, and in providing a mandate for evidence that should be the goal of any scientifically based, practicing profession.

FAMILIENTHERAPIE IN OFFENER GRUPPE IM RAHMEN EINER ANGEHÖRIGENBERATUNGSSTELLE

von R. Schindler

Die Ära der Tranquilizer und Neuroplegica hat uns zwar bis heute dem Problem der echten Heilung der grossen Psychosen nicht wirklich näher gebracht, aber sie hat die psychiatrische Therapie ungeheuer in Bewegung gebracht. Dauerinternierungen gehören heute zu den Ausnahmen, die stationäre Behandlung nimmt die Gestalt einer abgesteckten Kur an, nach deren Absolvierung der Patient wieder in den Rahmen seiner Familie zurückkehrt. Betratchtet man die psychotische Krise als eine Ich-verändernde Abwehr Ich-bedrohender Kräfte des Seelenlebens, so lassen sich in ihrem Ablauf 2 Phasen ziemlich deutlich auseinanderhalten: 1. Die Phase *akuter Abwehr,* im wesentlichen getragen durch die Ersch einung von Erregung, Hemmung und wahnhafter Projektion; und 2. Die Phase der *Persönlichkeitsabwandlung* und *Konfliktverarbeitung.*

Die stationäre Behandlung reicht heute ziemlich genau bis zur Bewältigung der akuten Abwehr; die wesentlich langwierigere 2. Phase wird unter dem Schutz neuroplegischer Medikation bereits ausserhalb der Anstalt durchlebt. Während die akute Abwehr sich früher oder später auch so erschöpfen würde, hängt vom Verlauf der 2. Phase das Ergebnis der Stabilisierung hinsichtlich sozialer Angepasstheit und Remissionsfestigkeit ab, wie ich, z.T. zusammen mit H. Gastager, an einem grossen Material schizophrener Psychosen nachweisen konnte.

Es gehört zu den Paradoxien der modernen Psychiatrie, dass sie, offenbar fasziniert vom Aspekt der Gefährlichkeit, ihr therapeutisches Schwergewicht der akuten Abwehrphase zuwendet und den Patienten in der für das Endergebnis ungleich bedeutenderen, langen Stabilisierungsphase der Betreuung des unspezialisierten Hausarztes, der Familie oder gar sich selbst überlässt. Die hohe

Rückfallsquote, die der modernen Psychiatrie das zynische wort vom "Drehtür-prinzip" eingetragen hat, zeigt, dass der Patient in der langen Zeit der Stabilisierung erst recht spezialisierter Hilfe bedarf. Will man nicht wieder zu jahrelangen Spitalszeiten zurückkehren, so bedeutet das die Notwendigkeit des Aufbaus einer spezialisierten, psychiatrisch geleiteten Nachbetreuung. Dieser Aufbau ist auch in eigentlich allen Kulturländern bereits im Gang, zum Teil schon seit langem.

Dabei zeichnen sich 3 Medien ab, durch die wir indirekt modifizierenden Einfluss auf den Stabilisierungsprozess nehmen können, nämlich: 1. Die Familiengruppe; 2. Die Arbeitsgruppe; 3. Die Freizeitgruppe. Es ist natürlich kein Zufall, dass es sich hier um lauter Gruppenmedien handelt, sondern ein Hinweis auf die Ichwirksamkeit der Gruppensituation, auf die bereits a.a.O. eingegangen worden ist. Es sind ja auch die gleichen 3 Medien, in denen sich präpsychotisch die Konflikte, die zur Auslösung der Krise führen.

Während Arbeitsgruppe und Freizeitgruppe relativ leicht gewechselt werden können, ist dies bei der Familiengruppe nicht möglich. Sie ist auch gleichzeitig die älteste, die an die frühesten Bindungen heranführt und damit sowohl in gutem wie schlechtem Sinne über Brücken zum Patienten verfügt, auch wenn dieser sonst die Welt hinter sich zu lassen sucht. Sie steht daher im Zentrum des wissenschaftlichen und therapeutischen Interesses. Ich denke da sowohl an die interessanten Forschungen von Lidz und Mitarb., die zeigen konnten, dass eigentlich jede Familie um einen schizophrenen Patienten bei genauer Untersuchung Störungen ihres Gleichgewichtes in z.T. typischer Form zeigt, an die Bemühung um die Typisierung pathogener Elterngestalten, wie sie besonders in der amerik. Literatur nicht abreisst, als auch an die zunehmenden Versuche die Familie zu Therapie mit heranzuziehen, etwa in der Methodik der Familientherapie von Jackson u. Mitarb., bei der Patient und Familie in gemeinsamer Gruppe behandelt werden, der mehr erzieherisch ausgerichteten Arbeit des Ehepaares Knobloch, oder der von uns entwickelten "bifokalen Gruppentherapie", bei der Patienten und ihre Angehörigen jeweils eigene Gruppen bilden, die in gewisser Abstimmung, aber doch getrennt voneinander arbeiten.

Als vor etwa 2 Jahren der *psychiatrische Rehabilitationsdienst* als spezialisierte Nachbetreungsorganisation des Gesundheitsamtes der Stadt Wien geschaffen wurde, konnte bereits auf den von H. Gastager, gegründeten "Therapeutischen Club" als überleitende Freizeitgruppe nach den Anregungen der Bierer'-schen Clubs in London zurückgegriffen werden. Auch einzelne Arbeitsgruppen standen zur Verfügung, andre wurden angefügt, so dass ein Oganisationsnetz gebildet werden konnte, über das bereits a.O. berichtet worden ist. Zur Betreuung der Angehörigen wurde eine *"Pflegeberatung"* geschaffen, die, basierend auf den fast 16-jährigen Erfahrungen mit der bifokalen Gruppentherapie, ebenfalls auf Gruppenbasis organisiert wurde. Über die Erfahrungen des ersten Arbeitsjahres dieser Pflegeberatungsstelle soll im weiteren berichtet werden.

Die am 14.2.1962 eröffnete Pflegeberatung arbeitet nach Art einer offenen Gruppe unter der Leitung eines Psychiaters und einer psychiatrischen Fürsorgerin. Sie acceptiert nur Angehörige von Patienten; Patienten selbst werden nicht zugelassen und auf die vormittägliche Beratung verwiesen. Die Angehörigen kommen zumeist spontan, sei es über Hinweis der Spitalsabteilung von der der Pat. entlassen wurde, sei es aufmerksam gemacht durch eine fragebogenartige Erkundigung, die jeder ehemalige Anstaltspatient 6 Monate nach seiner Entlassung zugesendet bekommt und in der die verschiedenen Beratungsmöglichkeiten des psychiatrischen Rehabilitationsdienstes angeführt sind. Ein kleiner Teil kommt über direkte Einladung. Die Pflegeberatung findet 1x pro Woche abends nach der allgemeinen Arbeitszeit statt und dauert 90 Minuten. Es kamen durchschnittlich 6 — 15 Angehörige pro Abend, insgesamt wurden im Laufe des einen Jahres, 104 Familien solcherart erfasst und betreut.

Die eintreffenden Angehörigen nennen nur der anwesenden Fürsorgerin ihren Namen und werden sodann um einen länglichen Tisch zusammengesetzt. Es hat sich alsbald als günstig herausgestellt, wenn der leitende Psychiater erst eine Viertelstunde später eintrifft, denn inzwischen entsteht ein spontanes Gespräch unter den Angehörigen, man beginnt sich kennenzulernen und seine Sorgen auszutauschen; Einzelne bleiben abgekapselt schweigsam; Sie wollen nur mit dem Psychiater reden und empfinden die Anwesenheit der andern unangenehm. Andre wieder tun sich leicht, weil sie schon einmal oder öfter dagewesen sind und gewinnen führende Gruppenposition (Alpha).

Der eintreffende Psychiater hat bereits durch seine Abwesenheit gewirkt: In der Erwartung auf ihn hat sich eine Gruppensituation gebildet und die Wiedergekommenen wurden in eine gehobene Gruppenposition manipuliert. Während er seine Überkleider ablegt, kann er die Gruppe beobachten und sich ein erstes Bild über ihre Dynamik machen. Nun setzt er sich auch an den Tisch, die Fürsorgerin reicht ihm einen inzwischen entworfenen Sitzplan und die von den zugehörigen Patienten aufliegenden Unterlagen. Er weiss nun mit wem er spricht, es braucht aber kein Name zu fallen, die Anonymität bleibt gewahrt.

Nach ihrem Gruppenverhalten lassen sich unschwer 3 Hauptformen unterscheiden: 1. Die spontanen Wortführer; 2. Schweiger, die sich von der Gruppe distanzieren, aber sich des Psychiaters zu bemächtigen versuchen; 3. Schweiger, aus Vorsicht und Angst vor dem Psychiater und der ihm zugeordneten Institution.

Ad 1) Die spontanen Wortführer — soweit sie nicht aus Situationskenntnis durch frühere Teilnahme an Beratungen in diese Rolle geraten — erwiesen sich in hohem Grade als stabile schizophrene Defektzustände (7 von 18). Sie meinen über die Krankheit ihres Angehörigen wohl Bescheid zu wissen und machen sich damit, oft in belehrendem Unterton, wichtig vor den andern. Dieses Wissen um die Krankheit hat jedoch bei näherem Hinhören, meist nur den Charakter einer magischen Formel, manchmal beschränkt es sich auf das mit gewichtigem Ton ausgesprochene Fremdwort "Schizophrenie", manchmal werden mehr oder weniger fantastische Theoreme darum gebildet, vielfach mit Bezug auf gestörte Verdauungstätigkeit, von der sich wiederum oft komplizierte Diätforderungen ableiten. Die Krankheit erscheint diesen Angehörigen als Ausdruck eines magischen Schicksals, durchaus analog der Besessenheit von Dämonen und Geistern. Sie belastet nicht, sie macht interessant. Der Angehörige fühlt sich von diesem Schicksal nicht selbst berührt, sondern eher als Besitzer eines mystischen Gegenstandes. Er ist nicht so selten stolz darauf, weil er meint als einziger mit dem Patienten richtig umzugehen, bisweilen schliessen sich ganze weltverbesserungsvorschläge daran.

Ad 2) Eine grössere Zahl von Angehörigen (27) verhält sich schweigend und distanziert von der übrigen Gruppe der Angehörigen bis zum Eintreffen des Psychiaters. Diesen versuchen sie jedoch dann mit Beschlag zu belegen, wodurch sie rasch die Aggression der übrigen Gruppe hervorrufen. Die übertragen eine deutliche Aggressivität auf die Gruppe. Sie erweisen sich auch im Leben gesellschaftlich isoliert, weichen der gesunden Welt aus

220

und verkriechen sich mit dem Kranken, den sie oft ängstlich verstecken, bisweilen aber auch unangepasst rücksichtslos ihren verbleibenden Bekannten aufzwingen. Sie genieren sich des Kranken und fühlen sich von ihm in der gesunden Gesellschaft desavouiert, übertragen diese Erfahrung auf die Gruppe und erhalten sie prompt auch scheinbar bestätigt. Sie sind alle brennend an den wissenschaftlichen Erbvorstellungen interessiert, das Votum des Psychiaters macht sie daher mehr oder weniger am makel des Kranken in der Form eines latenten Genschadens teilhaftig, sie verlangen danach, wie nach einem Urteil. Gerade ihnen sind aber nicht irgendwelche Erklarungen hilfreich, sondern der Anschluss an die Gruppe selbst, das Erkennen des ähnlichen Schicksals der anderen, das Überwinden der Introversion.

Ad 3) Die grösste Zahl der Angehörigen (37) schweigt aber aus Vorsicht und Angst vor dem Psychiater und der ihm zugehörigen Institution. Sie warten auch nach seinem Eintreffen ab, sie testen ihn und eventuell auch schon vor ihm die Fürsorgerin durch vorsichtige Scheineingeständnisse von Verhaltensfehlern, oder sie eröffnen unverhüllt ihre Aggression durch Kritik an behandelnden Ärzten oder sie versuchen ein scheinbar auswegloses Verhaltensproblem vorzulegen. Sie gehen von der Vorstellung einer höflich versteckten Gegnerschaft aus, erwarten Vorwürfe und Kritik, oder aber eine Führung, die eigene Überlegung, Wille und Verantwortung ersetzt. Diese Angehörigen sind zu den Patienten entweder aggressiv — vorwurfsvoll oder massiv overprotektiv eingestellt, übertragen und projizieren diese Haltung nun auf den Psychiater. Sie verstehen die Krankheit als einen Erziehungsschaden und tragen schwer an dem damit zusammenhängenden Schuldgefühl, das zu entlasten ihr wesentliches Interessebleibt. Diese Angehörigen suchen daher in der Gruppe Führung, Schuldentlastung und Erklärung, sie zeigen die lebendigste Widerstandsdynamik, erweisen sich aber auch am dankbarsten und interessiertesten am Fortgang der Beratung.

Ausserdem fanden sich noch 5 deutlich wahninduzierte Angehörige, 17 andere verfolgten reale Interessen, wie etwa Wohnungssuche, Scheidungsanliegen, Minderung der Behandlungskosten oder stellen Sonderfälle dar, die sich einer allgemeinen Einordnung entziehen.

Die sich so auseinandersondernden 3 Hauptteilnehmerformen lassen unschwer erkennen, dass sie den in unserer Gesellschaft vorliegenden 3 Bewältigungsformen des Wahnphänomens entsprechen: 1. Der magischen Erklärung, die den Wahn als Ausdruck fremder Mächte vom eigenen Schicksal abhebt und zu einem kosmischen Problem macht; 2. Der Erbtheorie, die den Wahn als Ausdruck einer Krankheit zum belastenden Schicksal der im gleichen Erbgut verbundenen Familie macht; 3. Der psychologischen Theorie, die den Wahn als Ausdruck einer durch einen schädigenden Einfluss bedingten Krankheit auffasst und den Blick auf diese Schädigung hinwendet, somit im allgemeinen gegen den schuldigen Einfluss der erziehenden Familie.

Es ist interessant zu sehen, wie unterschiedlich die Angst—bewältigung im Rahmen dieser 3 Theoreme erfolgt: Offenbar am geglücktesten durch die magische Verlagerung des Problems aus dem persönlichen in den kollektiven Raum. Diese Angehörigen fühlen sich daher sofort wohl in der Gruppe, sie zeigen aber die geringste affektive Verbindung zu den Kranken, die sie nur als Objekt und Material ihrer eigenen Geltungsbedürfnisse verwerten. Bemerkenswert die hohe Zahl schizophrener Defektzustände in dieser Angehörigengruppe. Das therapeutische Anliegen der Pflegeberatung zielt hier auf die menschliche Befreiung des Patienten aus einem auf irrationalen Vorstellungen beruhenden, oft sehr grausamen Ritual, das zumeist aus Diäteinschränkungen, Waschzeremonien und bisweilen auch sektiererhaften religiösen Praktiken besteht. Die geltenden Entmündigungsformen und verschiedenen Reverse, die dem Angehörigen bei der Spitalsentlassung des Kranken eine schwer abgrenzbare Verantwortung über diesen übertragen, kommen natürlich dieser unbeabsichtigten Freiheitseinschränkung sehr entgegen. Durch das Hereinnehmen des kosmologischen Anliegens dieser Angehörigen in die Aufmerksamkeit und Diskussion der Pflegeberatungsgruppe gelingt eine faktische Entlastung des Patienten, die auf juristischem Wege nie zu erreichen wäre. Es wird dadurch möglich für solche Patienten zum Beispiel die gesellschaftliche Bereichserweiterung des therapeutischen Klubs und späterhin einer Arbeitsaufnahme und damit einer sehr weitgehenden Versel beständigung zu erwirken.

Dem gegenüber bedeutet die Erbtheorie eine beängstigende Einschliessung des Angehörigen mit dem Kranken, die sich durch ein, dem Verhalten des Kranken durchaus analoges, Zurückziehen aus der Gesellschaft und Vereinsamen geltend macht. Diese Angehörigen genieren sich des Kranken, der einen auch ihnen anhaftenden Erbmakel sichtbar macht. Ziel der Pflegeberatung liegt hier darin dem Angehörigen den verlorengegangenen sozialen Anschluss wieder zu ermöglichen, was bereits durch den Einbau in die Pflegeberazungsgruppe gelingt. Der Psychiater muss gerade hier sorgfältig darauf achten nicht in ein Einzelgespräch mit diesen Angehörigen verstrickt zu werden, sondern ihre Fragen, Nöte und Thesen an die Gruppe weiterzugeben, sowie Gemeinsamkeiten hervorzuheben. Gelingt es den Angehörigen in dieser Weise zu entängstigen und wieder and die Soziëtät anzuschliessen, so erwirkt dies auch indirekt einen gleichartigen Anstoss für den Patienten. Er, der bisher verschämt vor den Menschen versteckt gehalten wurde, darf sich allmählich wieder zeigen und letzlich sogar in die Öffentlichkeit eines Arbeitsverhältnisses vermittelt werden.

Am geängstigten zeigen sich die psychologisch "Aufgeklärten". Sie bedürfen eines Schuldigen zur Erklärung der Krankheit, machen sich daher als Eltern gegenseitig Vorwürfe über Erziehungsfehler und erleben den Kranken als eine lebendige Anklage. Sie sind im Grunde böse auf ihn wegen dieser Anklage und versuchen sich davon zu befreien, indem sie ihm seine Krankheit vorwerfen, wie einen Verhaltensfehler, eine Unart oder gegen sie gerichtete Böshaftigkeit. Tatsächlich besteht zwischen diesen Eltern und ihren kranken Kindern ein Verhältnis voll unbewusstsymbolhafter Aggressionen und Kränkungen, sie wissen sich gegenseitig am wunden Punkt zu treffen und aufzuregen. Die Pflegeberatung diesen Personenkreises verlangt die klärende Auseinandersetzung mit z.T. symbolhaften Vorstellungsinhalten und Voreingenommenheiten, deren Schwierigkeit in den Übertrangungsverhältnissen liegt. Die autoritäre Haltung gegenüber der "Behörde" veranlasst diese Angehörigen meist zur aggressiven Auseinandersetzung mit dem Psychiater oder seiner Fürsorgerin, indem hier Ratschläge provoziert und dann als undurchführbar hingestellt werden oder eine Beurteilung verlangt und sodann bekämpft wird. Zankapfel kann hier z.B. schon der Rat eines Medikaments oder die Beurteilung einer Arbeitsfähigkeit werden. Obwohl hier zunächst eine Entlastung der aggressiven Auseinandersetzung mit dem Patienten resultiert, kann eine solche Entwicklung doch nicht gutgeheissen werden, weil der Patient hier zumeist zum Ausdrucksorgan des Unbewussten seiner Eltern wird: Das umstrittene Medikament muss er zwar nehmen, aber es wird ihm nicht gut tun, die umstrittene Arbeit wird zwar versucht, aber der Pat. scheitert. Die Gruppenform der Beratung lässt nun eine Technik zu, bei der sich die aggresive Auseinandersetzung in die Gruppe ablenken lässt. Von dort kommt Rat und Urteil, während sich der Psychiater strengster Passivität befleissigt. Erst in die sich entwickelnde Auseinandersetzung greift er dann insoweit ein, als er die mitgemeinten unbewussten Gehalte aufzeigt und sich mit seinem Verstehen schützend vor den bedrohten Angehörigen stellt. Er erreicht damit eine Schuldentlastung und eine Bereitschaft zum Verstehen, die sich wiederum für den Patienten auswirkt, ihn ermutigt und Möglichkeiten des Verständnisses erschliesst.

Diese Therapieführung ist natürlich die interessanteste und komplizierteste, deren genaue Darstellung jedoch die heute verfügbare Zeit überschreiten wurde.

THE PASSING OF THE CONCEPTION OF CLASSIC TRANSFERENCE IN THE WORK OF MORENO

by Ramon Sarro-Burbano

(Editor's note: Unfortunately, the original of Dr. Sarro's improvised address was not available. The Editors are aware that this short summary by a Congress participant does not do justice to Dr. Sarro's comprehensive presentation).

1. Psychoanalysis suffers from a monomania for retrospect and sexuality.
2. Projected phenomena are given first place in the therapeutic situation. The real phenomena are given second place.
3. Psychoanalysis has a tendency towards oversimplification. The adult is viewed too much as a child.
4. The "here and now" and the future are neglected; the present is seen in retrospect.
5. The psychoanalyst, even more than the hypno-therapist, exercises an extreme suggestive influence upon the patient. This influence is particularly strong because the psychoanalyst claims that the world can be changed through questionable interpretations.
6. Summing up: man is more than his past, and psychoanalysis has no means to adjust him to the on-going reality.

ANALYTISCHE GRUPPENPSYCHOTHERAPIE

von G. KUEHNEL

Ich möchte über 10 Jahre Erfahrungen in einer Klinik mit analytischer Gruppenpsychotherapie berichten. Zunächst einige Angaben über die Klinik:

Tiefenbrunn ist eine staatliche, offene Klinik, speziell für psychotherapeutische Behandlung bei Kassenpatienten eingerichtet. Die 180 Betten sind aufgeteilt in eine Kinderabteilung mit 14 Betten, eine Abteilung für Jugendliche mit 24 Betten, und 7 Abteilungen für Erwachsene mit je 18 bis 24 Betten.

Auf diese 180 Betten kommen im Jahre 1400 Aufnahmen, d.h. pro Bett 7 bis 8 Aufnahmen im Jahr; oder anders ausgedrückt, die durchschnittliche Aufenthaltsdauer ist 6 Wochen. Wie jeder Durchschnitt ergibt auch dieser ein falsches Bild: Wir haben Pat. für 3 Tage, bei Fehleinweisungen, bis zu 3 Jahren bei schwersten chronifizierten Erkrankungen.

Diesem Patientenstrom stehen 17 ausgebildete analytische Psychotherapeuten gegenüber, also wieder im groben Überschlag: für 11 Patienten *ein* Psychotherapeut.

Diese Relation — 180 Betten; 1400 Aufnahmen; 17 Therapeuten — stellte uns vor die unerbittliche Realität des ökonomischen Einsatzes des therapeutischen Leistungsquantums.

Zunächst aber erlebten wir noch eine Erschütterung. Es zeigte sich, dass wir die Einweisungsdiagnosen nur sehr bedingt übernehmen konnten. Die Beurteilung einer Psychogenie ist noch in keiner Weise, zumindest in Deutschland, ein sicherer Bestand ärztlicher Ausbildung. So mussten wir uns zunächst einen eigenen differenzierten diagnostischen Apparat aufbauen. — Jeder Pat. durchläuft bei uns als erstes eine körperliche, vorwiegend internistisch-neurologische Untersuchung.

Wir sind dankbar für diesen äusseren Zwang, er erhält uns die feste Verwurzelung in medizinisch-klinischer Arbeit.

Viel schwerer war die Durcharbeitung der 1400 Aufnahmen mit dem Ziel der tiefenpsychologischen Erfassung.

Wir erheben nach der körperlichen Untersuchung eine sog, erweiterte Anamnese in 3 bis 6 Stunden individuellem Interview. Dann erfolgt in Supervision die Festlegung des Behandlungsplanes.

Die praktische Organisation unserer klinischen Arbeit steht und fällt mit Diagnose und Prognose, besonders auch im psychischen Bereich. Dies ist für Psychotherapeuten ein wenig beschrittenes Gebiet. Wir haben gelernt, uns den erforderlichen Einblick in die psychischen Zusammenhänge zu verschaffen, ohne den Pat. im Unterbewussten zu beunruhigen und wir haben Kriterien entwickelt, die uns eine ausreichend sichere Prognostik ermöglichen.

In diesem Rahmen nun steht die Frage der geeigneten psychotherapeutischen Versorgung unserer Patienten.

Es mag aus unserer ausgesprochen analytischen Einstellung entspringen, dass wir nur analytische Gruppenpsychotherapie durchführen. Hier ist zu einem Punkt gesondert Stellung zu nehmen. Freud ging es nicht um die Therapie, sie war für ihn sekundär. Er suchte wissenschaftliche Erkenntnis. Dies ist in den Briefen an Pfister erneut klar zum Ausdruck gekommen. Für othodoxe Psychoanalytiker ist tiefenpsychologische Erkenntnis und die Durchführung der Therapie ein einheitliches Arbeitsbereich. Diese Bereiche sind jedoch — besonders im Interesse der Therapie zu trennen.

Die Therapie bedarf der eigenen Theoriebildung. Das zeigt sich deutlich bei der Einführung der Gruppenpsychotherapie. Gegenüber der Individual-Analyse hat die Gruppenpsychotherapie wesentliche Sonderheiten, dis wir immer mehr als eine grundsätzliche Bereicherung unseres therapeutischen Repertoires empfinden. Es ist ein erheblicher Vorteil, die Übertragung auf dem sozialen Boden der Gruppe weitgehend gemeinschaftsgerecht ausspielen zu lassen. In der Gruppe tritt das Realitätsprinzip sofort und unerbittlich in der Zuwendung oder Ablehnung der Gruppe auf. Therapeutische Gruppendynamik ist ein neues eigenständiges Erkenntnisbereich.

Andererseits aber sehen wir — und dies erscheint mir sehr wesentlich — dass ohne überlegene tiefenpsychologische Sicherheit gerade der Gruppenpsychotherapeut verloren ist und schwimmt. Hier hilft nach unseren Erfahrungen die soziometrische Orientierung allein nicht. Der Gruppenpsychotherapeut muss sofort jede Aeusserung eines Mitglieds der Gruppe dynamisch einordnen und den dahinterstehenden, sich meldenden Antrieb für seine persönliche Orientierung als Gruppenleiter erfassen können. Unsere Gruppenpsychotherapeuten verhalten sich nach der alten analytischen Grundregel vorwiegend passiv. Das wird oft, aber sehr irreführend, mit "non directive" bezeichnet. Die Passivität des Gruppenführers, bringt die Gruppe zu eigener Dynamik und ist direkt und aktivierend. Unsere Gruppen verlaufen oft höchst dramatisch. Zur Führung einer Gruppe sind nur sehr erfahrene Psychotherapeuten befähigt, die ausserdem die Bereitschaft mitbringen, im Spiel der oftgeballten Auseinandersetzung ihr Teil zu übernehmen; eine Rolle, die anders ist, als im Stuhl hinter der Couch. Für Anfänger ist nach unserer Erfahrung Gruppenpsychotherapie kein Feld.

Diese Einstellung auf tiefenpsychologischer Grundlage halten wir für das Charakteristikum der analytischen Gruppenpsychotherapie.

Wir müssen nun noch einmal zurüchschalten und uns die Verteilung der 1400 Aufnahmen auf die verschiedenen Psychotherapie-Formen, worunter die Gruppenpsychotherapie ja nur eine ist, ansehen. Damit kommen wir ins Bereich der Statistik.

Einige Angaben über die Art unserer Gruppen: Wir führen nach vielen Versuchen nur noch gemischte, geschlossene Gruppen mit 8 Patienten. Die Gruppen laufen 3 x wöchentlich je 2 Stunden. In *einer* Stunde is die Dynamik nicht zu voller Entwicklung zu bringen. Wir haben ein einziges Trennungsprinzip — nach Altersstufen —: Kinder, Jugendliche, Erwachsene und neuerdings auch Gruppen alter Menschen mit ihrer gesonderten Lebensproblematik. Die Gruppen laufen 8 Wochen. Diese Grenze wird uns durch die finanzielle Leistungsbreite der Kostenträger gesetzt. Bei einzelnen Patienten wird sofort eine 2. Gruppe angeschlossen, oder es erfolgt Wiedereinberufung nach einer gewissen Zwischenzeit.

Wir können jetzt gleichzeitig 12 Gruppen besetzen und laufen lassen. Im grossen Durchschnitt stehen von den 180 Patienten 35 in einer langlaufenden Individual-Analyse. Hierüber habe ich hier nicht zu berichten; 96 Patienten sind in Gruppenpsychotherapie. Das ist ein sehr hoher %-Satz und Sie können ermessen, welche Hilfe uns die Gruppenpsychotherapie bedeutet. Ungefähr 24 Patienten sind in gezielter analytischer Beratung und in Eizelbesprechungen, sog. Counseling. Der Rest, ungefähr 25 Pat., entfällt

228

auf die Neuaufnahmen mit ihren diagnostisch-prognostischen An-
fangeklärungen, Gutachten und sonstige Sonderfälle, auch rein
symptomatische Behandlungen. Eine Gruppe also, bei der kein
direkter analytisch-psychotherapeutischer Einsatz erfolgt.

Zur Indikationsstellung für Gruppenpsychotherapie eine Feststellung: Bei geeigneter Zusammenstellung und Führung der Gruppe
sehen wir immer wieder mit Erstaunen, wie tragfähig Gruppen
auch für schwerste Einzelfälle sein können. Trotzdem is für uns
schwerer Autismus, ausgeprägte Paranoia und perverse, besonders
kriminelle Symptomatik, immer noch eine Gegenindikation und
zwar mehr zum Schutz der Gruppe. Wir machen jetzt Versuche
bei schweren Erkrankungsformen, Gruppenbehandlung gleichzeitig
mit Einzelanalyse zu kombinieren, ein Sakrileg für eingeschworene
Gruppenpsychotherapeuten. Aber bei Einverständnis der Gruppen
finden wir die Gruppen selbst für solche Sondermassnahmen tragfähig.

Die Erfolgsstatistik, auf die ich jetzt eingehen will, ist für jede
Klinik ein schwieriges Problem. Hier wäre ein fruchtbares Gebiet
— z.B. für die Welt-Gesundheits-Organisation durch Einsatz eines
Forschungs-Teams exakte Zahlen zu erarbeiten.

Der vorgennante Entlassungserfolg ist ein ärztlicher Schät-
zungswert. Wir enthalten uns der Kategorie "geheilt" und sprechen bei der Entlassung nur von "befriedigend" und "unbefriedi-
gend", etwa im Sinne der sozialen Rehabilitation. Dann ergibt
in unserer Klinik die Gruppenpsychotherapie einen befriedigenden
Entlassungserfolg von durchschnittlich 60%. Das ist für klinische
Arbeit-ganz allgemein gesehen — ein sehr hoher Satz, und wir
führen ihn auf unsere genaue prognostische Auswahl zurück und
sehen auch in den 40% unbefriedigenden Ergebnissen eine Bestätigung unserer vorherigen, wenig günstigen prognostischen Beurteilung.

In Jahre 1961 wurden uns 89 Pat. zugewiesen, die bereits für
"dauernd arbeitsunfähig" erklärt worden waren, die also invali-
disiert und berentet waren. Von diesen hielten wir nach unserem
prognostischen Urteil nur 18 für noch therapiefähig, von diesen
18 nahmen 14 nach Gruppenpsychotherapie ihre alte Arbeit wieder
auf. Katamnesen, also die Beurteilungen des Dauererfolges,
erfordern einen grossen Arbeitseinsatz, der bei unserer ärztlichen
Besetzung — neben der klinischen Arbeit — kaum darzustellen ist.
Wir haben versucht, uns zu orientieren und sind 230 Gruppen-

Patienten, 2 Jahre nach der Entlassung, katamnestisch nachgegangen. Wir konnten das nur mit schriftlichen Anfragen, also Fragebögen, tun. Wir erhielten 160 Antworten. 70 Ausfälle, also Pat., die keine Antwort gaben, machen eine grundsätzliche prozentuale Answertung unmöglich. Trotzdem ermöglicht dieser katamnestische Versuch einen gewissen Einblick. 55, also 1/3 der 160 antwortenden Pat., hatten sich in ambulante psychotherapeutische Behandlung begeben. Dadurch wird die Bewertung der Wirkung unserer klinischen Gruppenpsychotherapie allein erschwert. Den aktiven Einsatz dieser Pat. für ihre Gesundung verbuchen wir aber als gutes Ergebnis unserer Gruppenpsychotherapie. 16, dies waren 10% von 160, berichten Erfolglosigkeit. In der Beurteilung der Einzelfälle — und das war das Ergiebigste dieser Katammesen — zeigte sich, daß unsere Entlassungs-Beurteilungen mit 40% unbefriedigendem Entlassungsergebnis zu ungünstig war. Ein Teil der von uns mit "unbefriedigt" Entlassenen hatte teils mit Nachbehandlungen, teil durch persönlichen Einsatz, eine positive Entwicklung erreicht.

Nehmen wir die 70 Patienten ohne Antwort einfach als Misserfolge — was sicher zu ungünstig bewertet ist — so ergeben sich mit den 16 Misserfolgen die geantwortet haben, 86 Misserfolge bei 230 Behandlungen. Das wäre noch immer eine Bestätigung unserer Entlassungs-Beurteilungen mit 60% erfolgreichen Gruppenbehandlungen. Dadurch stellt unser katamnestischer Versuch auf jeden Fall den hohen Wirkungswert der Gruppenpsychotherapie, wie wir sie in der Klinik handhaben, sicher.

Damit bin ich am Ende meines kurzen Überblickes über unsere Erfahrungen. Ich habe das dankbare Gefühl, zu Recht auf diesem Kongress berichten zu dürfen. Wir können uns nicht vorstellen, wie wir ohne Gruppenpsychotherapie versuchen sollten, unseren klinischen Aufgaben in dem uns gegebenen Rahmen gerecht zu werden.

SOCIOGENESIS OF INDIVIDUALS AND GROUPS

by ZERKA T. MORENO

The sociodynamically oriented group psychotherapist views the development of the individual and of the group according to certain "sociogenetic laws." One of the first of these is that the group has a structure of its own which can be studied and measured, and another, that group organization develops from early, simple forms into more complex and higher forms. The group, like the individual, has a skeleton which can be made visible by sociometric and psychodramatic microscopic intervention. A description of the sociometric skeleton of the group includes the following findings which have been discovered and verified to exist in all groups so studied: individuals who form no relationship, they do not choose and are not chosen, these are called isolates; individuals who choose but are not chosen in turn, these are called unchosen or neglected; individuals who are rejected, rejectees; individuals who form mutual pairs or dyads; individuals who form incongruous pairs, one choosing the other who rejects him in turn; individuals who form chains and clusters of mutual choice or of mutual rejection; individuals who form "interpersonal networks" of mutual relations though not necessarily on a face-to-face basis, but through links of key individuals who act as junctures for numerous sets of mutual relationships.

The instrument used to bring to light these skeletal structures is the sociometrict test, and the findings are always in relationship to a criterion on which the choices are based, and only relate to a particular group at a specific time and place and in reference to a shared function within the group.

Groups develop from a non-specific, horizontal type of structure without a top or bottom to highly differentiated substructures which propel the individuals within the group towards choice, isolation or rejection, and with leaders on top of the pyramid. Various types

231

of leadership have been uncovered as well as various types of isolation. These findings are being confirmed by researchers all over the globe and in varying cultures.

The psychodramatist extends the sociometric test. He views man as an improvising actor, living in roles. Some of these roles may be productive and integrative, others deficient or weakly developed, and some actually destructive to himself and to others. The actor emerges slowly from a non-specific mold into an individual with his own particular, private set of roles; but even these private roles partake of and are shaped by collective elements within the culture in which he shares. The child from birth until about the twenty-sixth week of life lives in what is called in sociometry "a stage of organic isolation"; he does not recognize his peers and is not recognized by them in turn. In psychodramatic terms he lives in what Moreno has called the "matrix of all-identity"; he experiences his universe as a totality of himself; only gradually does he become aware that he is not the entire universe, that his being has limits and that other beings move to and fro in this universe.

Once he begins to be aware of separation between himself and other beings and objects, his psychodramatic and social role repertoire starts to form. What is usually described as the ego grows out of the roles enacted by the human actor. The psychodramatic view of man states that the neonate is not given an ego or an identity from the start, but that he works on it, slowly, painfully; it is molded, assisted or distorted by the world around him, his co-actors. He starts with the physical organism which has been endowed to him, using it as the interaction of his spontaneity with his environment allows. His ego emerges from the roles, and not, as is usually claimed, the other way around.

Roles are divided into three major categories: (1) psychosomatic roles — which are active from birth on — such as the eater, the sleeper, the walker, etc.; (2) psychodramatic or phantasy roles, as God, the angels, devils, gremlins, etc.; and (3) social roles, as the policeman, the judge, the soldier, the teacher, and so on. Every culture can be studied from the framework of these roles and each culture produces the roles that are relevant for it. The role of the astronaut, for instance, now so important in our technologically advancing era, certainly has no place as yet in the heart of the Congo.

232

The family, too, has been investigated from both the sociometric and psychodramatic viewpoints. The same dynamics operate within the hierarchy of the family that operate in groups at large. There are the highly chosen, the medium-range, and the underchosen or rejected individuals. The sociometric hierarchy does not necessarily parallel the official, authority-based structure and may at times run completely counter to it; such families tend to fall apart as family units or to congeal into substructures which are anathema to good parent-child relations. They may, for example, show close sibling to sibling relations or warm parent-parent relations, the other generation being left out of the socioemotional contact so necessary for family cohesion.

The factor responsible for mutuality of relationships, the cement which binds individuals in a group together, is called "tele." Tele is defined as the mutual feeling into one another and assessment of each other. The existence of tele, its effect upon group structure as deviating from chance, has been experimentally validated. Without tele, groups can not cohere and will fall apart. Transference, in this orientation, is the dissociative factor and the pathological branch of tele. A group can not survive on transference alone. The so-called "counter-transference" is a misnomer; transference is never "counter" for it is always a one-way process of projection from one to the other; transferences can not meet, since they are totally subjective. At best, there can be two parallel transferences between two individuals. Tele, however, is the reality-based feelings which individuals have for one another in relationship to their interaction in roles and situations they share together here and now.

The sociometrist speaks of another law: "the sociodynamic law," which is basic to our understanding of the sociogenesis of groups and of individuals. In a given group, a percentage of individuals will be overchosen, obtaining more love than they can give or consummate (the sociometrically rich, sometimes referred to as the sociometric capitalists); another, larger percentage will represent the sociometric middle class, giving and receiving approximately an equal amount of choices, about as much as they can use productively; another percentage will represent the sociometric proletariat, the unwanted, unchosen or rejected individuals, who obtain and give far less love than they need for emotional growth and integration. It may shock this audience to know that

233

in many groups studied so far, especially in groups of school-children, the percentage of unchosen individuals runs between twelve and fourteen percent. Think of it, more than one tenth of the entire population of our globe may be found to fall within this category, and these are only the extremes on the scale! A far larger percentage will have to be included if we think of those who hover on the edges of isolation in our societies.

To highlight the implications of this kind of finding, I would like to refer to the following. Studies of groups of children in school and of adults in industry have shown repeatedly that those individuals most frequently involved in bodily injury or accidents, are those who are found to be isolated or rejected in the sociometric group evaluation. Children involved in repeated accidents on playgrounds, and workers in a steelmill "hot strip", tend to drag innocent bystanders into their vortex of suffering, and to cause bodily harm to them also (misery loves company). In contrast, whenever highly chosen individuals become involved in accidents, their liability is more likely to be a rare incident, the injury is to themselves alone and, in addition, it is usually neither as severe nor as incapacitating. The repeaters mentioned above, the accident or injury prone, fall into the sociometric category of isolated, un-wanted or rejected individuals. Recently, in New York State, an intensive campaign was waged against repeaters in driver-caused accidents. Their frequent involvement in such accidents made them poor insurance risks. The only satisfactory approach to them — and many were tried including individual psychotherapy — was group psychotherapy. A report by the Governor of New York State quite emphatically pointed out that the follow up on these individuals made this mode of psychotherapy the treatment of choice in their case.

Just as we have little control over the time or place of our birth, so we have little control over the sociometric family structure into which we are born. These sociometric family structures pre-exist us; every child has to find his place within it. The sociometric structure in the family is different for every child; hence we are able to observe how some children thrive and others do not, within one and the same family. There are good sociometric reasons for these differences. Some of the variables which influence our sociometric situation are: culture, race, sex, religion, economic status, position in the family ranking, and, as we grow older, age.

234

An individual who is born male, for instance, when the sociometric choice of the mother is for a female child, immediately is confronted with a major setback with which it may well take him his entire lifetime to learn to deal. How does one cope with the existential fact that one is not of the desired sex, race, religion, culture, age, etc.? We know the impact of these problems and their compounded effects only two well. The sociometrist sees the seeds of these conflicts within every family, in every group and in every culture, though their outward expressions may differ.

What can the sociometrist contribute to the amelioration of these existential conditions? Is he only a diagnostician or can he effectively engage in sociodynamic therapy? Yes, he can. After the diagnosis has been made, he can use the choices of the individuals for one another to restructure the groups more along the lines of their spontaneous inclinations. For example, in a group of institutionalized cerebral palsy children, the sociometrist entered into an investigation of their sitting order around the dining-room table. The children had been assigned to these seats arbitrarily by the administration. There was considerable resistance to change, the teachers arguing that they had made the best possible choices for the children, an argument which, parenthetically, the majority of parents use against giving their children greater freedom of action. Besides, they remonstrated, many of these brain damaged children were hardly able to express their choices, so how could we possibly suggest a sociometric choice for seating partners? Undeterred, we informed them that nothing would be lost, so why not chance it? Grumblingly, they acquiesced. The children were collected in the playroom and the sociometric choice process explained to them in simple terms. We suggested that those children who were unable to write or speak each should be given the choice: "With whom do you want to sit at the table in the dining-room at mealtimes?" verbally, and allowed to motion in the direction of the two children of his choice, in any way he was able, by a nod of the head, pointing of his big toe, pinky or whatever. Those who could, recorded their choices on paper; the others were assisted by the teachers who recorded their choices for them. After sorting out the choices, the seating order was rearranged according to the optimum of satisfaction, that is, in such a manner as to give each child at least one partner whom he had chosen to be near. Here, physical proximity was a determining factor in children whose motor control was either disturbed or much lower than that of their normal peers. The following observations were recorded by the staff members: accidents, spillages and breakages of dishes at dinnertable were dramatically reduced, way beyond chance. The noise and arguments began to subside tremendously. (By the way, how does one measure differences in silence?) Temper tantrums became noticeably rarer. But, after one month of this sociometrically fertilized emotional soil, the most startling finding was made by the nursing and medical staff: a general, over-all improvement in the physical condition of the entire school population showed up on the health charts, an improvement which was several times larger than the previous curve for this particular item.

Similar findings have been uncovered, for instance, in the seating order around table in the so-called "normal family." In most families, in our western culture, the baby sits nearest to Mama, so she can supervise his prowess. However, sociometrized families have taught us that this typical seating order is often the worst arrangement possible for baby, whose first choice for table partner is frequently Daddy and not Mummy, this being the one time of day he can get close to Papa. Disorderly, rebellious behavior in the family, with the concomitant disturbed atmosphere so bad for digestion and emotional health — and what can be a more devastating situation than one which recurs with such deadly certainty in all families at times more than once daily? — has been rectified by the simple maneuvering of the seating arrangement, in accord with all the choices of all the partners involved. Even in a democracy — a much abused term — how often is the baby's choice as heavily weighted as that of his authority figures? Sociometry is pure democracy in action; but it is more that that. We are by now used to the idea of transplanting our vegetation in accord with its needs. We analyze carefully the elements that make up the soil in which our crops will thrive. We build special hothouses, artificially regulated as to light, temperature, moisture, etc. The same general approach is used for our livestock. By comparison, our manipulation of humans is, to say the least, exceedingly crude. Sociometry finds the suitable group soil and then proceeds to so transplant individuals that their growth, integration and equal participation in group life is insured, by scientific means.

In the philosophy of spontaneity-creativity, every man is viewed

236

as a potential genius; one whose spontaneity and creativity, if permitted to grow closer to its potential, will produce levels of integration which are rarely achieved, at least in our western culture. This is not to say that more primitive cultures are likely to produce more spontaneous individuals. Rather, that a culture based on spontaneity-creativity will produce a different type of personality development than is now possible. Most known cultures regard highly such qualities as intelligence, memory, mechanical skills, motor coordination, etc. But spontaneity-creativity for their own sakes are not considered of equal importance. It has taken the psychodramatists a long time to make the spontaneity-creativity axis acceptable and we are still struggling with having its essential features understood and appreciated.

Spontaneity is defined varyingly as: an adequate response to a new situation, or a new response to an old situation, or further qualified, a response of varying degrees of adequacy to a situation of varying degrees of novelty. The only truly spontaneous individual is the neonate at the moment of birth. He is entering for the very first time into a situation which is entirely novel and his adequacy of performance in it will determine whether he will live or die. He will go through numerous kinds of learning from that point on, but this response makes all the others possible. We may, therefore, think of the neonate as the true genius of mankind. Psychodramatic therapy revolves around restoring some of the neonate's spontaneity to persons whose later learnings have cramped, distorted, submerged or denied it. But spontaneity in one person meets or fails to meet counter-spontaneity in the other. Therefore, spontaneity training has to deal with all the persons involved in a relationship; it was Moreno who first stated that, for instance, a marital couple represents not two, but three entities, the husband, the wife, *and* the relationship between them. This third entity, the relationship between them, is the particular expression of their interaction in numerous roles, the arena in which they meet as actors, co-actors and inter-actors.

Actors do not act alone, but with others, in concert or disharmony. The disharmony may start very early in the development of the infant. The neonate, for example, is entirely dependent, in the first months of life, upon auxiliary egos, helpers who do for him what he is unable to do, and who assist him in gradually doing those things he can begin to achieve alone. We have assumed

237

too long that parents are born, not made. We know now that the mere biological production of a child not yet a mother makes. The role of the mother is exceedingly taxing and one in which we could all stand training.

Psychodramatic training of motherhood proceeds from the basis that every mother carries within her collective experiences of babies in general, besides the individual experiences and images which she has of her own baby. She has also private experiences of her specific mother, and collective experiences of the mother role besides those of her own role as a mother. Learning takes place in psychodrama through enacting these collective experiences but with the special reference to her own baby as embodied by a trained auxiliary ego. These action images and feelings may differ from culture to culture. The psychodrama teaches mothers in a simple, direct way how to accept life as it is, in whatever environment, to become more relaxed in relation to their infants, to learn to help themselves and their children by becoming more effective auxiliary ego mothers and to achieve more harmonious interaction.

The psychodramatist views the child as the chief protagonist in the mother-child drama, because it is he who needs most help. The mother is tested in action and assessed in terms of her spontaneity, adequacy of performance and ability to serve the child's needs. Because the child is incapable of giving full expression to his experiences, a trained auxiliary ego who has had a chance to observe the mother in action with her own child will step in when training commences, taking the "role" of the baby, warming up as intensively as possible to the perceptions she feels the mother has of her child. The auxiliary ego will "speak" for the baby, even if it is a neonate, trying to come close to the mother's action perception; she will think and express and do things which the mother may feel about the baby, even though the baby is not capable of doing so. It is the mother's perception of the child which may be weak, totally or partially distorted, incomplete or negative, which the auxiliary ego attempts to arouse and confront, in order that change may take place. It is action learning in a non-threatening situation which, though molded after life, is more plastic. The auxiliary ego child will not be damaged by the mother's mistakes, and in turn, the auxiliary ego is objective enough to assist the mother's attempts to change. The auxiliary

238

ego is a go-between; he operates between the chief therapist and the protagonists, an actor, interpreter and guide all in one.

There is another, subtler aspect to the need for motherhood training which psychodrama has uncovered. Every female bears within her, from early infancy on, an imaginary, or psychodramatic, fantasy baby. In some this fantasy baby is weaker, in others stronger. This baby exists within her and continues to do so, in varying stages of dormancy or development, whether she actually bears children or not. The "psychodramatic baby" is an universal phenomenon, occurring in different cultures, as sociogenetic studies indicate. In some women this idealized baby is such an intensive experience that it may interfere with and overlie the actuality of her live child. The psychodramatic baby is then "real," the live child but a phantom to her.

Therapy lies in helping the mother to bring the perception of the psychodramatic baby and that of the real baby closer together, first by permitting the psychodramatic baby to live in the retraining situation. Once it has been "born" and is outside of her, finished like a real child, she can begin the separation from it; we can not let go of those precious things with which we have not yet finished. Therapy consists for all our patients, in whatever category, in learning to complete unfinished business and then settling down to the tasks at hand which require their attention, here and now. Once she has been able to deliver herself of the fantasy baby, she will be readier to become available as the mother to her live baby.

To illustrate psychodramatic training of mothers, I would like to describe the following. In a well-baby clinic conducted by a university medical school, mothers bring their four-week-old infants for a routine checkup; because they are numerous the mothers are seen in groups of ten by teams of staff members, each of whom spends about one half hour with a group. The physician conducting the session combines psychiatry and pediatrics. I am there as a group member to serve in whatever capacity may become necessary. We are seated in a circle; the babies are stripped and lie on their mothers' laps. The group psychotherapist walks around, examines the children, then sits down among us and explains that he and I will be glad to answer any questions concerning their babies' care. The warm-up commences typically, in direct space-relationship to the chief therapist, the mother on his

239

right speaking first, the one on his left second, and so on, around the circle until every group member is involved. There is some discussion of skin rashes, taken up by several, then a lull. The physician examines the babies whose mothers complain about their skin, makes suitable recommendations for care and sits down again. He addresses the group.

Therapist: "Do you have any feeding problems?"

There is a general headshaking: "No."

The therapist throws a challenging remark at them: "What remarkable children, or maybe you are all remarkably fine mothers!"

This dart reaches its mark, for again the mother seated at his right speaks first:

"Well, I have had some trouble with her. She was spoon-fed some vegetables this week and she spit them out."

At this point the chief therapist looks inquiringly and challengingly at me as if to ask:

"What does a psychodramatist do in such a situation?"

I fall into line and take the part of the baby. In a very soft, rather weak and appealing voice I say: "Well, those vegetables don't taste good after the milk. I'm not used to them yet. They're kind of rough and hurt my sensitive mouth. I don't like them so I spit them out. I don't know what else to do with them, it hurts me to swallow them. After all, I'm only a month-old baby!"

The mothers look at me, surprised at my entry into the situation and startled by this turn of events. Slowly, I notice one after another beginning to smile, especially the mother who had brought up this problem.

The therapist asks her: "Do you think your baby could be thinking and feeling something like that?"

"Yes, she could."

"Do you think she might resent it if you continue to do this?"

"Yes, she might."

"What made you start her on vegetables?"

"*I* didn't start, it was my mother."

"Was it her own idea or was it someone else's, a friend of your mother, who urged her to give your baby vegetables so soon?"

"I don't know. I work and my mother takes care of the baby."

"Perhaps the baby is not ready for such food yet. Maybe you

240

had better wait a while until we tell you about solid food and what to give her."

The mothers generally approve of this and the protagonist-mother agrees. By the end of the half hour, during which I repeatedly become their baby's spokesman, the mothers beam at me as if I really were their baby. Incidentally, these were Negro mothers and I had been warned by the chief therapist that they might have difficulty accepting me in the group because of my clipped speech, as we were in the deep south of the United States. Furthermore, I'm obviously neither a baby nor Negro, and yet here I was becoming identified with their infant. It was their spontaneity, which meshed and clicked with mine, that produced the tele effect.

Lest we psychodramatists be accused of favoritism towards the child in all parent-child conflicts, allow me now to present a situation in which psychodrama is used, not as a method of *expression*, but as a method of *restraint*. It is our contention that where restraint is indicated, it should be so presented as to come from within the child, rather than having it imposed from without. Imposition of restraint from without may lead to still greater rebellion or may increase the barriers between mother and child, rather than reduce them. Psychodrama presents opportunities for built-in spontaneous restraint, via the use of the role and role reversal.

In role reversal, the parent takes the role of the child, while the child takes the role of the parent, thus borrowing the status, dignity, authority, actions and feelings which the child experiences in his parent. Psychodrama, like charity, should begin at home. The following illustration deals with a role reversal which took place between my own son, Jonathan, at two and a half years of age, and myself. He had become very adept at using role reversal to strengthen his own ego several times, and it looked at times as if the role playing and role reversal game might deteriorate into an "I-can-do-everything-I-want with this role reversal business" on his part. However, the psychotherapist in me would not permit abuse of either a method or a person. One day, when he was just getting ready to go upstairs for his afternoon nap, he waited at the bottom of the steps to be carried to the second floor of our house. In his most precious-baby tones he stated with much conviction: "I'm a little baby. You're Mummy

241

now," like a psychodramatic director who doles out the roles at the beginning of a new scene. He looked at me with his great big beautiful shiny orbs and commanded: "Carry me, Mummy." "Oh," I replied in my most charming manner, "You be Mummy and I'll be Johathan." We reversed roles and changed places in space. Now I, in the role of Jonathan, stretched out my arms to him and commanded: "Carry me upstairs, Mummy!" Jonathan, as Mummy, replied with more dignity than subtlety: "You are a big boy now and very heavy. Walk up the steps by yourself." We reversed roles again and he walked proudly upstairs, without assistance or complaint.

Role reversal is based on a very ordinary, diurnal idea; how often have we not said in the midst of an heated argument with another person: "But what do you want from me? Just put yourself in *my* position!" Psychodrama is scientific, for it is organized common sense personified. Instead of merely talking about this, we actually do it, by means of role reversal. There is an old American Indian saying which states: "Let me not judge another man until I have walked two weeks in his moccasins." Role reversal is what parents must learn to do with their children, what marital partners must learn to do with their mates, what every person should learn to do, in order to become the well balanced, well rounded, properly integrated, satisfactorily interacting, spontaneous being for which he has the potential. We may well start with our children because their spontaneity and wisdom is closer to the truth than our own.

In the sociometrically organized world of the future we will live by the commandment: Be Spontaneous!

SECTION 2: INTERACTIONAL GROUP PSYCHOTHERAPY

SOCIO-PSYCHOTHERAPY IN SOCIOLOGY, GROUP PSYCHOTHERAPY AND SOCIOMETRY

by Nurettin Sazi Koesemihal

Since very ancient times men, while using medicines to cure their ills, could not keep themselves from praying to and asking help from spiritual and mystical powers. Briefly, from the early periods of history, the physiochemical therapy of individuals always went along with psychotherapy, so that medicines often showed their effects only by means of incantation.

Societies, just as individuals, have gotten ill since the very early periods of history and have undergone great crises and troubles time and time again. We see that in each period there appeared a magician, a prophet, a hero, a sage, a philosopher, a governor, who tried to prevent these social troubles by some empirical precautions based on intuition. As it is known, socio-therapy had the character of a mixture of material-spiritual, real-mystic. These precautions and advices that tried to remedy the troubles of societies for thousands of years constitute the source of sociology.

Briefly, just as practical medicine was founded with the purpose of curing individuals, empirical sociology has been established with the purpose of curing societies. Magicians, prophets and sages who tried to apply the half-real and half-mystical principles of this science always came forth to cure the societies and to put them in order. Therefore the purpose of empirical sociology, before all, is sociotherapy.

The methodical and systematic knowledge called science is rather new as compared with the history of mankind. It was born in Greece about 2300 years ago. But unfortunately it was hindered by the world view of mediaeval times, which idealized the other world. Therefore, it was not able to recover for a thousand years and only pulled itself together at the time of the Renaissance.

After empirical geometry and mathematics, which already had gained a scientific value in the Hellenistic period, astrology gave way to astronomy in the sixteenth century, empirical physics to scientific physics in the seventeenth, alchemy to chemistry in the eighteenth, and empirical biology to scientific biology in the nineteenth. After a while, empirical psychology and sociology gained a scientific character.

From this point of view it is possible to divide human thought into two great periods: a) pre-scientific period of empirical knowledge; b) scientific period.

Though the first has a past of more than a hundred thousand years, the latter, if the shuffling period in Greece is not considered, has a life of only a few hundred years. Especially, the lives of the new sciences, like biology, sociology and psychology, are not even 150 years long.

Sociology, or social science, is a new science for the whole world. It was born in France about 130 years ago. After the French Revolution, in 1789, learned men and thinkers directed their attention to social problems. Sociology developed in the hands of Le Play and A. Comte during the period 1830-1850. Later it spread to other Europian societies and to the whole world.

The study of socio-therapy, using a scientific method, became possible only by means of sociometry and of various sociometrical techniques, which were founded thirty years ago and spread quickly all over the world.

J. L. Moreno's book *Who Shall Survive* has shown very clearly the world view of sociometry, its philosophy, fundamental theories and various methods, and the application of these methods to small groups. In fact, it would have been better to name the book *The Foundations of Sociometry*.

I will now briefly point out the most peculiar characteristics existing between the sociological current which was founded in France a hundred thirty years ago and Moreno's sociometry founded in the U.S.A.

a) Sociology and its schools always considered the global society in the first plan. Even Le Play. Though he started studying small groups, such as workers' families, before making a deep research of family groups, he at once started to look for the necessary precautions for the reform of French society.

On the other hand, sociometry began its studies not from the global society point of view but by focusing attention on small groups, which were more convenient for experimentation. Small groups contain the most considerable characteristics of global societies. For instance, today sociometry divides the social world into three dimensions: external society, sociometric matrix and social reality. These three dimensions are called "Trichotomy". When we say external society we mean concrete, visible, small or large, official groups that constitute the human society. Sociometrical matrix is that part of the society which is not convenient for macroscopic observation but can be understood by sociometrical analysis. And social reality is the synthesis made of the conflict between these two. By means of this conflict between external society and matrices, groups which are formed of networks of emotional attachments, wishes, loves, hates, sympathies, antipathies, friendships and enmities, become stronger. The tension in social reality strengthens too.

b) Sociology, as we mentioned above, uses a traditional method called observation. But it is rather half observative and half speculative, the speculative side usually being heavier.

245

On the other side, sociometry, in order to study group dynamics, has used a complete scientific method called experimentation and its techniques. These techniques study groups not as inanimate but as animate; they take subjects not as guineapigs or organisms but as men, as actors joining in the social experiment; they prevent the investigator from being only a passive observer and cause him to join the experimentation actively. This is a kind of technique which may be considered qualitative-quantitative.

On this occasion I would like to point out the important difference between sociometrists and those who use the method of experimentation outside the sociometrical point of view. Both ground their studies on a theory of actions. But as Moreno mentioned, it would be better to devote the theory of actions to sociometry and to call the theory of actions used by the experimenters outside of the sociometrical field: Theory of organisms-behavior. According to this separation we must consider all experimentors who observe social groups from outside, thinking of them as a group of organisms, appliers of the theory of organism-behavior; and all sociometrists who study the social group from inside, taking it as a group of actors, appliers of the theory of actions.

c) Like scientific sociology, having a past of 130 years, and empirical sociology, buried in the shades of history, sociometry was born with the purpose of therapy. The only difference is: empirical sociologists used an empirical-mystical method and sociologists of the scientific period used a speculative-observative method for the socio-psychotherapy of global societies. But sociometrists deal with the therapy of millions of small groups within the global societies; that is, they study group psychotherapy by means of an experimental method based on the theory of "actor in situ".

The purpose in both is the therapy of global society. Only sociometry tries to reach this goal by means of studying small groups and from there going to global societies and mankind gradually. And I believe this is the right way.

246

PARTICIPANT VARIABLES IN PATIENT-PHYSICIAN RELATIONSHIPS

by JOSE BUSTAMENTE

The hypotheses of the hypnotists, Freud's concept of transference, Sullivan's about personal interrelationship and Moreno's about tele, constitute the most outstanding contributions to the comprehension of the physician-patient relationship.

The hypnotists are, without doubt, the pioneers on this road, since it is their techniques that set forth clearly, for the first time, the influence that one human being can exercise over another when he enters into relationship. It doesn't really matter that Mesmer tried to explain the phenomenon as the product of animal magnetism, or that Charcot ascribed it to sensatorial fascination, or that it was only Bernheim who offered an adequate interpretation, conceiving it as a special phenomenon of suggestion. If one thing is certain it is that every competent hypnotherapist brought about cures which gave validity to and consolidated the method as adequate therapy.

Freud offered us a new contribution in his effort to cure neurosis, separating himself from hypnosis, which, although a product of the interpersonal relationship between hypnotizer and hypnotized, because of a series of neurophysiological manifestations produced by its technique, leaves hidden the essence and complexity of this relationship.

The concept of transference is a visible step ahead, since it brings us into the heart of the relationship fully uncovered; that is, with both subjects fully awake, in a mutual relationship not dimmed by a hypnotic situation, and with a marked influence on the part of the hypnotizer and a passive attitude — without any apparent participation—on the part of the hypnotized person.

247

Of course, Freud conceived of transference as a concrete experience of two basic preconceived factors in his theory: the libido and iteration. It is, then, a manifestation of the libido expressed in the relationship, and is an obligatory repetition of the one established with the parental figures. His determination to include it within the erotic frame of his theory does not reduce Freud's contribution, especially if we know how to separate both aspects and understand that the phenomenon described under the name of transference includes, according to Freud's conception, the transfer or displacement of erotic sentiments; but we also must capture its dynamism, which is established in accordance with the relationship created between two subjects.

We can either agree or differ with Freud about his concept of the libido and can even reject his criterion about iteration in the psychological phenomenon; but even if we do not accept either of these, we must still understand the sense and value of his contribution, which situates the axis of the therapeutic action in what he calls "the management of the transference," which describes the action of the therapist over the action of the patient. It is this mutual action that is at the center of the treatment and, as we can see, remains situated in the interaction of the two projections created by the patient-physician relationship.

Sullivan goes even further and considers neurosis a result of a specific sum of personal interrelationships. His therapy, then, has to direct itself towards the consequent use of the elements which will function in this personal interrelationship. In this way, psychotherapy becomes an active frame of interaction between physician and patient, in which comunication plays a leading part.

Communication is to be considered in its most extensive expression; that is, verbal as well as non-verbal, not only in its intellectual or cognitive aspect, but also in its emotional or affective background, as well as in its facility or difficulty. Communication, or the defense, as well as the lower emotional basis, or anxiety, is the center of the physician-patient relationship, and its competent management leads to therapeutic success.

In the same way that Freud passes from hypnosis or hypnotic sleep to free associations, so Sullivan passes from free associations to the study of communication and the defense during the interview. He considers that liberty cannot be reached in association, since for that to happen it is necessary to have a very low level of anxiety, a level which would be difficult to find in a neurotic patient.

The viewpoint of Moreno—which establishes a clear difference between the transference (which he considers, as Freud, the projection of the patient's sentiments upon the physician) and the tele (the communication in two currents) — is not reduced to these limits, but implies a clear differentiation between communication as a product of the personality of each member of the situation (physician and patient) in the tele and the intervention in this of the two factors created by the neurosis and made present by it in the transference.

It is because of this that Moreno attributes value to role, pointing out that the patient has to be observed in his role as a patient and in his role as a person (personality), and also as the medium, the reason for his concluding that these four variables are the fundamentals for the understanding of the psychotherapeutic process.

As we can see, hypnotic techniques, Freud's transference, Sullivan's interrelationship and Moreno's tele are the four most important contributions that have been developed, in an ascending manner, in the study of the physician-patient situation.

SOME ASPECTS OF GROUP PSYCHOTHERAPY AND PSYCHODRAMA

by Kohei Matsumura

Our work lies somewhere between counseling and group psychotherapy.

If there are any adequate techniques of developing the "triadic" relationship between client, therapist and therapeutic instrument, much progress would be made in improving group psychotherapy.

1. In therapists, or professional change agents, there is a difference of cognition as to how purposive the relationship should be.

2. There is a second difference in the type of cognition of the therapist. We can divide it into three major types: the "monadic", the "dyadic" and the "triadic". Freud is the first, Marx is the second, Moreno and we are the third.

3. Our "trialectic" theory considers an individual as a "groupal" being, as relatively independent of the determination of outside social influences and of inside heredity.

4. There is a fallacy in assuming a direct relationship between the therapeutic instrument and ensuing behavior or group process. But, they are based on the relational situation, in which the therapist, patient and therapeutic instrument are interacting.

5. Each individual interprets the therapeutic instrument in a slightly different manner. This is the key factor that develops the group process. By operating and changing the instrument we can partly direct the group toward a goal for the future.

6. The instrument has qualities of material. These qualities are the determinants by which common recognition will grow in the group. But these qualities are not interpreted equally by each individual. By these two characteristics the instrument will have the role of change agents in groups.

7. We have had a technique that is effective in improving the

triadic relationship. It may be called "The Tripling" technique.

8. Some other techniques are as follows:

A. (1) Grouping by object-intervening (Technique of Marketing)
   (2) Group-stratifying by object-intervening

(3) Focusing	(4) Localizing
(5) Tracking	(6) Radiating
(7) Ramifying	(8) Search Lighting

B.
(1) Situation-limiting	(2) Situation-retracting
(3) Situation-unifying	(4) Situation-developing
(5) Situation-overlapping	(6) Region-providing
(7) Region-invigorating	(8) Position-stabilizing

C.
(1) Situational monologue	(2) Dyadic role-playing
(3) Triadic role-playing	

D.
(1) Intro-overviewing	(2) Extro-overviewing
(3) Connecting-overviewing	(4) Locomoting between local parts
(5) Reflect-mirroring	(6) Technique of moving-with, standing-with, follow-up, back-up, clean-up
(7) Back up by position-changing	
(8) Clean up by passage-clearing, by object-excluding, by region-magnifying, etc.	

PSYCHOTHERAPY, GROUP PSYCHOTHERAPY
AND ETHICS

by CARL JORGENSEN

I dare say it would be superfluous to dwell for any length of time on the question of the aims of working with psychotherapy and group-psychotherapy. For my purpose in the following, it will be sufficient to say that the aim is to help relieve our patients of certain psychical sufferances which torment them, and to try to help them to greater vitality.

Then comes the question of what afflictions and torments are involved. We have before us a great, diversified world, with its myriads of problems, its millions of situations to be treated individually. I shall neither give examples of these problems nor attempt a classification of them. I only want to point out this macrocosm which is the daily element of the psychotherapist and then pass on to my actual question: What can we do for our patients; what remedies are at our disposal for solving their conflicts, allaying their stresses and improving their vitality?

The first answer to this question is not difficult. Our chief remedy is to make the patient speak, to make him express himself. The many dialogues between patient and physician, which have been used as long as medicine has been practiced, serve this purpose. The protracted monologues, which the psychoanalyst has attempted to cultivate, serve the same purpose. Likewise, in modern group therapy where, stimulated and assisted by the physician, a group of patients throws questions and answers back and forth among themselves, and also in psychodrama, which penetrates behind traditional conversation and tries to re-create situations and conflicts which have been in the patient's life — all these procedures serve to make the patient open up, relieve his thoughts, motions and urges, relieve his teamwork and conflicts with other people. The methods may be different, but they all serve the same purpose.

So far the position is clear. But now the question is, can the physician ever have other tasks? In my opinion other tasks may occur. I shall point out three.

First and foremost it should be a task of the therapist to instruct the patient, now on one thing and then on another, which he does not know and which, after all, it is necessary for him to know if he is to regain his health. Let me mention an example.

I once worked with two small groups of neurotic men, among whom there were some alcoholics. When I asked them what they considered to be chronic alcoholism, not one of the ten was able to give an even fairly sensible answer. As good luck would have it, my knowledge of alcoholism was rather well founded. For one thing I have seen a number of patients who were disabled with alcoholism as the main or substantially contributory cause and secondly I have performed post-mortems on several such patients and seen with my own eyes the damage alcohol had caused to their hearts and nervous systems. Therefore I could say to my groups: It looks as if a daily consumption of three to four drinks can be taken with impunity to health by an otherwise healthy person. At a consumption of six to ten drinks a day the person in question is in the danger zone. With a consumption of ten to twenty drinks a day I consider a person a slight alcoholic, and with a daily consumption of over twenty drinks as a serious alcoholic. But, of course, this is said without any admonition; man must be at liberty to use his organism and experiment with it as he wants. It seems a harmless pleasure to get blind drunk a couple of times a year. It may be found unaesthetic, and many people do stupid things in a state of intoxication, but that is another story. It does not seem to have any lasting injurious influence on the organs.

Many other examples of dangerous ignorance could be mentioned. Men's ignorance of women's emotional life and their outlook on the values of life often are deplorable, and the same can be said of women's insight into men's emotional life and their outlook on the values of life. This shall not be taken to mean that men are very apt to understand each other, or that women are very good at understanding each other. In short, endless varieties of ignorance present themselves to the psychotherapist during

253

his work; he must try to grasp the most dangerous of the phenomena when he meets them, and to remedy them to the best of his
ability.

Now I shall speak of another kind of task. Now and then it
may be right, without actually admonishing him, to give the patient a piece of good practical advice. From one of my groups I
remember a young man of 21 years, a clerk, who was seriously
neurotic and very reticent. His childhood had been rather unfortunate, and he had been knocked out by a number of bad
employments. Under group treatment he quickly cheered up,
and when he was discharged I said to him: "Now you must go
out and find a new position and don't worry! I think you will
do well. I admit that you have been unfortunate with your working places. I also admit that there are many bad working places;
but there are also good ones, you can be sure. It is only a question of finding them. But, therefore, I must give you a piece of
advice. Never stay less than three months in a position. Even if,
on the very first day you can see that here you cannot stay in
the long run, still stay there for three months. There is no job
so bad that one cannot endure it for three months. You should
not think of accommodating yourself to all kinds of high-handed-
ness and every form of muddle. Even in a bad job you can acquire
knowledge of human nature. Stay there for three months and then
look for another chance."

About one year later I happened to meet him in the street,
and he was all right. His first two jobs had been bad, but the third
one was excellent. This bit of good advice had saved his new
existence.

I find that at times the therapist should be permitted to give
advice over a broader front. You will remember that on several
occasions we have discussed the education of children, and I
find it very good that children have much more freedom now
than they had fifty years ago. But still I have repeatedly said
one thing to my groups which one may be inclined to forget: It
must be remembered that before children are 15-16 years old and
emerge from childhood, they must have learnt two things — not
to molest their fellow-men and not to deceive. This is necessary
to enable them to move among other people to equal satisfaction
of both parties. These two rules of conduct, not to molest others
and not to deceive, must be practiced. When such practice can

best begin must be left to the parents, but it will be wise to bear the point in mind.

This, then, is the therapist's second task: now and then to give a piece of good advice; but, of course, still without any admonition.

Then comes the next question: Does it hold good at all times and in all situations that the therapist must never admonish?

If it holds good that we must never on any occasion admonish, then I have offended only once. I remember that patient and that situation as if it were yesterday, although it is now forty years ago. My patient was a married woman of about thirty years (let us call her Mrs. Brown) who suffered from an ordinary diffuse neurosis with unrest, fears and failing sleep at night. The cause of her neurosis was exclusively due to quarrels with her husband, and the reason for these quarrels was always the same. Once or twice a month the husband went out to have an evening drink together with a couple of his old friends. He always came home from these evenings out at a suitable time, he was always sober, the binges did not cost him much money, and no girls were involved. But Mrs. Brown nourished an invincible fear that on these evenings away from home her husband would try to contact a woman to whom he had formerly been engaged. He definitely maintained that all connection between them had been broken off, and the woman had no basis for believing in any connection; still, the fear was in her blood. The consequence was that she once sneaked after him to watch where he went, and with whom he spent his time; the trouble was that the man's comrades discovered her spying. They scorned and teased the man for having a jealous wife, and the result was that he was furious when he came home. His bad temper lasted for days, during which periods he would be taciturn and unresponsive. Mrs. Brown promised to turn over a new leaf; but next time it was the same thing, she again set out to spy on him.

I asked the patient if she found it right to spy on her husband, and she answered, no, she could very well see that it was wrong.

"But why do you do it then?"

"I cannot help it."

And here it was that I failed in my role as a passive therapist. In a gentle way I admonished her:

"Well, but this won't do, Mrs. Brown. You cannot leave it at

255

just saying that you cannot help it. In some way you must try to overcome this."

As you will agree, a gentle admonition.

The decisive thing was not that the man found it wrong of her to spy on him. Her husband's opinion could not bind her. She must be at liberty to have her own opinion of spying. Nor was it decisive that I — in my capacity of her physician — found such spying objectionable. A physician can only guide and give advice. No, the decisive thing was that she herself condemned spying in such cases. Her behavior was a sort of inconsequence. It might be called ethical inconsequence.

I had to condemn this, even if I were the most tolerant man in the world. Tolerance means giving other people freedom to evaluate good and evil according to their own nature and their own disposition. But what happens to it when a person's conduct conflicts with her own evaluations?

Therefore, I termed the phenomenon "ethical inconsequence." And by looking around among my fellow-men I quickly found out that Mrs. Brown's case was not unique. By recollecting his circle of clients, any other therapist will also be able to find twenty examples. It must be borne in mind that ethical inconsequence is not met among neurotic patients only. It is a universal human phenomenon. If, in a quiet hour, we turn our gaze towards ourselves, we all know that it is a daily struggle to bring one's conduct and one's actions into accord with one's evaluations.

What I want to say on this occasion is that if, as psychotherapists, we find ourselves permitted to condemn ethical inconsequence, if, as a matter of principle, we consider ethical inconsequence as rejectable, then the situation forces us to settle with all the philosophical ethics that have been thought and written from the time of Plato and Aristotle to the present day.

For it was typical of all philosophers, from antiquity up to Kant, Bentham and Mill, that they sought some good towards which all mankind ought to strive, a good of universal validity, and some universal evil. Or they sought universal virtues and wanted to point out universal vices. And we know how things developed. In antiquity Aristotle, Zeno and Epicurus had already pointed to widely differing things, and this has continued down through the ages to Nietzsche and the present. The development in ethics has been far from those in physics and medicine, where scientists have gradually arrived at agreement about more and more facts, agreement about a steadily increasing number of maxims. But all that the philosophers proposed as universal proved frail and untenable, and finally the task was put away as insoluble: Philosophical ethics could not offer mankind any sort of a prescriptive, normative ethical system.

SOME ASPECTS ON THE PRACTICE OF GROUP
PSYCHOTHERAPY IN CZECHOSLOVAKIA

by F. KNOBLOCH, J. SKALA, and J. RUBES

We are going to describe here two representative psychotherapeutic systems in Czechoslovakia, one for neurotic and one for
alcoholic patients. Both of these have been developed at the Psychiatric Section of the Charles University Hospital in Prague, in
two departments. Although they differ profoundly in many respects, they still have two basic ideas in common: 1. group psychotherapy is their chief therapeutic instrument; 2. they are interested in finding the most economical ways of solving the problem
of mental disorder in the population as a whole.

It may be mentioned here that the National Health scheme in
our socialist state gives special opportunities for such attempts
on a big scale. And more than that, it cultivates this attitude on
the part of the doctor, who is unable to escape epidemiological
problems by enclosing himself exclusively in a private practice.

Both of the above departments have already achieved some
popularity with the medical and lay public because, besides their
clinical work, research and lecturing, they are very active in
health education, the emphasis upon which is spread by print,
radio and television. The necessary result is, of course, that new
patients who came for treatment have more and more information
and less and less prejudice; their emotional attitudes towards
treatment have been more and more structured. At the same time,
both the departments improve their screening techniques of patients suitable for treatment. This is directed by follow-up studies,
the aims of which are to avoid unnecessary expenditures of time,
by excluding patients who are unmanageable by the therapeutic
system. Now, let us describe briefly the therapeutic system developed for neurotics in the department led by Dr. Knobloch. He

was trained in individual psychotherapy and psychoanalysis and stimulated by direct observation of group therapists at Tavistock in London and at the Social Rehabilitation Center at Sutton. In 1949 he designed a therapeutic system for neurosis suitable for Czechoslovakia, and gradually was able to establish it. Since 1949 he has used therapeutic community treatment with psychodrama and psychotherapy on closed outpatient groups. At present the therapeutic system is best represented by the Prague University Outpatient Department and its two centers, a neurosis center in the country and an improvised day center with its club in Prague.

It was discovered that individual psychotherapy is unable to solve the problems of neurosis in the population. The main strategy of the system is: psychotherapy used in steps and that no methods that are expensive in terms of time expenditure are used before less expensive methods have been tried. In the hierarchy of methods, every method has its maximum of efficiency. For example, to use individual psychotherapy at the beginning of the cure is regarded as a waste of time, not only because it may be substituted by group methods, but because group methods are more efficient in the first stages than individual psychotherapies.

The hierarchy is as follows:

1. *The Open Group and the Day Center.* The district psychiatrist sends more difficult neurotic patients to the University Outpatient Department. After an individual interview the patient is sent to an open group consisting of about 25 patients. He meets there patients who have just returned from the Country Neurosis Center in Lobec, and is generally favorably impressed by their improvement and their optimism. By their example he is quickly induced to take an active part in discussions and psychodrama. In some cases, the attending of this group once a week for a few times, with a final individual interview, is quite sufficient as a short-term psychotherapy.

Another variety is an open group of married couples and family members, in which again the patients coming back from Lobec represent the most active members. It has been proved that it is useful to mix neurotic patients, who quite often are not aware of any marital or family problems, with couples sent by courts of justice and solicitors and who seek counselling for their marital discords but are not aware of any psychopathology.

2. *The Neurosis Center in Lobec.* Seventy kilometres from Pra-

gue an isolated group of thirty neurotic patients and three rehabilitation workers live at a state farm. The psychiatrist comes only once a week, so that only one and a half hours are spent with one patient altogether per month. From this it may be seen that the main therapeutic instruments are the rehabilitation workers, but first of all, the patients themselves. The chief tasks of the psychiatrists are to find out new methods and techniques which can be used by the rehabilitation workers and the patients themselves, and to give emotional support to the rehabilitation workers. Although the psychiatrist has the least direct share in the therapy, and the treatment lasts only five to six weeks, the therapeutic results are the most striking of all the forms used. The patients vary according to the form of neurosis and to the motivation for treatment, and the improvement is of different quality, from a symptomatic one to changes of personality that do not occur by any other treatment used within such a short time. During the last ten years, the percentage of improved patients has increased gradually, and at present it has reached ninety percent. The latest follow-up study finds only five percent of patients unimproved or in worse state now than before the treatment, but only one third of the patients feel well to the degree attained immediately after the treatment.

We find that the efficiency of the Neurosis Center is especially connected with the following circumstances:

1. The therapeutic community is isolated, has high cohesion and, although consisting of thirty patients, has the character of a small group.

2. The outer tasks (some amount of work to be done for the State Farm), and the group tasks (the patient feels responsible for the outcome of treatment of other patients), and stressful conditions of life (physical work, outside work in winter and less comfortable accommodation than the patients are normally accustomed to), contribute to the cohesion of the group and make the situation more similar to real life. By the sum of verbal and non-verbal activities, the community becomes a suitable model of the patients' natural-groups. However, the community is plastic enough so that each patient can structure his typical pattern of relations and show his hypothesis on other people. By means of other patients, who function as fine diagnostic instruments, maladaptive

260

relations are discovered and changed as much as possible.

3. Closed outpatient groups. These consist of seven to eight patients and are groups wherein maladaptive relations among patients, as well as relations towards the therapist, can be analyzed. This differs with the Neurosis Center in Lobec, where it is not advisable to analyze in detail patient-therapist relations due to the fact that the therapist is at the same time both the psychotherapist and the administrator.

4. Individual psychotherapy. There are some cases of neurosis in which we are unable to achieve fully satisfactory results in any other way than by individual psychotherapy. In these cases, however, the treatment in the open group, as well as in the Neurosis Center in Lobec has also great importance, since it is superior to individual psychotherapy in the first stages of treatment and shortens the individual psychotherapy.

PSICOLOGIA ANALITICA E POLITICA

per GIAN TEDESCHI

Uno degli aspètti più salienti della psicologia analitica è il riconoscimento dell'importanza che hanno i dinamismi inconsci collettivi nel determinismo della realtà umana. É nell'incontro con le problematiche insite nel giuoco delle immagini archetipiche che si configura, si realizza il destino non solo del singolo individuo ma anche di una civiltà. La società è infatti la depositaria di quel collettivo psichico che noi ritroviamo nel profondo di ogni psiche individuale, base essenziale del suo divenire. Lo studio approfondito del singolo e apre quindi tra l'altro, la prospettiva di uno studio scientifico delle grandi determinanti un era storica.

La politica, componente essenzialmente concreta, esecutiva di un determinato zeitgeist, deve necessariamente essere ancorata ad una sociologia dinamica, questa ultima a sua volta permeata dalla psicologia del profondo. Quando un orientamento politico non tiene conto di questa realtà, è necessariamente destinata all'insuccesso, perchè non storico, nel senso profondo, filosofico, sociologico di questo concetto.

É necessaria una conoscenza del significato implicito nei simboli dell'animo umano, nelle loro formulazioni mitologiche, e saperli riconoscere nelle immagini viventi del nostro tempo.

Quando un orientamento politico tiene conto di queste premesse, la sua azione trascende gli aspetti puramenti concreti, immediati, economici, per aquistare un significato terapeutico, nel senso ampio, umano, di questa accezione.

POINTS OF VIEW AND HORIZONS
IN GROUP PSYCHOLOGY

by HELEN E. DURKIN

The time has arrived for a reassessment of values in the now
greatly expanded field of group behavior and this book, which
represents so many different points of view, offers us a unique
opportunity to begin such an undertaking. A new whole has
emerged, but most of us who constitute its various parts (subdivisions) have not yet accommodated ourselves to the necessary
restructuring. There are many forms and levels of group therapy
which are being practiced by our members which might profitably
be delineated with a view to setting up the highest possible standards and training requirements for each, in terms of the needs
of the group each meets and the mode which we perceive to
be most suited to it.

SECTION 3: ANALYTIC GROUP PSYCHOTHERAPY

SHIFTING OF THE GUILT FEELING IN THE PROCESS OF PSYCHOTHERAPY

by Vytautas J. Bieliauskas

The aim of this paper is to examine various meanings of guilt feeling and to describe a procedure of shifting the guilt feeling in psychotherapy. An attempt will be made to demonstrate the practical application of this technique to individual and group psychotherapy by providing sample cases where this approach was used.

Feelings of value, inferiority and guilt

According to Lersch, each human individual as a person is a

265

bearer of value and dignity. This metaphysical fact becomes a personal experience through the feeling of self value. The feeling of self value can and must be reinforced by the individual's observations of the attitudes of other people toward him, or their evaluation of him. In order to gain more acceptance and more value in the eyes of the others, the individual can use various ways to impress them. The most normal way to impress others would be through achievements that one can reach or accumulate. The feeling of self value derived on this basis could be called an objective or normal feeling of self value. In this feeling of self value, the individual depends upon the environment but also has a certain right to expect a positive attitude by the environment, because he has achieved something valuable. Of course there is a possibility that one may seek the approval of others without presenting them with objective reasons for it. In this case the feeling of self value would primarily depend upon the good impression one makes upon others and his value will be expressed in terms of his good reputation among others.

When the feeling of self value suffers, the individual experiences a feeling of lack of value that results in a feeling of inferiority. The feeling of inferiority can be experienced either on the basis of a lack or breach in inner value or a lack or breach in good reputation.

If the individual experiences the lack or reduction of inner value he will feel inferior. However, this feeling of inferiority will at first indicate to him that he is limited, not perfect. Such an experience belongs to human reality because we as human beings are limited, and only the one who fails to face reality will deny this fact. The feeling of inferiority could therefore be considered at first as a normal and necessary experience. If the individual realizes that he is not only limited as a human being, but that he made an error or committed an action which reduced his value, the reaction of this person will be that of sorrow. Facing reality, however, such an individual will not despair, and he will not look for excuses, or blame others, for his status. Since the action he completed lowered his inner value, and since this affected his existence, the person in question will regret his deed and will make a decision not to repeat the action. His decision will be an "existential decision", meaning total and unequivocal commitment to change. At this point, with the acceptance of his limitations

266

and with the decision to change, the individual will realize that he still has some value left within himself and that his future goal will be to restore and increase his own value. Therefore, by reaching the existential decision one already restores his feeling of self value and is able to move on into the future.

If the feeling of self value, which is based upon superficial reputation, is reduced, the individual will experience a feeling of inferiority, too. However, he will not accept his limitations as being imposed upon him by his nature. This individual will feel inferior because others may not think well of him. The guilt feeling which will be generated in this case will not be accompanied by facing reality and accepting one's own error, but rather will be associated with "feeling bad" that he was not circumspect in his actions and that others saw him. This type of guilt feeling does not include any kind of existential decision to change. On the conscious level, as usually happens with people suffering from unconscious level a plan will be included on how to repeat the same act. In this case the guilt feeling includes a self-perpetuation, a desire for repetition and a lack of mature approach to reality. In order to compensate for his inferiority, experienced on the unconscious level, the individual may exaggerate his value on the conscious level, as usually happens with people suffering from an inferiority complex. However, the inferiority complex includes a neurotic need for abnormal compensation; therefore, the individual using it will remain entangled in his neuroses and will not be able to restore the feeling of his self value. The guilt feeling in this case will remain as a continuous personality characteristic and will lead such a person nowhere in terms of his personality growth and development. The guilt feeling will increase anxiety and reduce the individual's capacity for experiencing his feeling of self value on an objective basis, and thus will encapsule him in a vicious circle that will lead to the need for additional adjustment mechanisms and additional failures in dealing with reality.

Psychotherapeutic shifting of the guilt feeling

While the individual experiencing guilt and inferiority will be able to maintain his equilibrium, another one will need special psychotherapeutic help to achieve a re-education of his attitudes and his feeling of self value. It will be important for a psychotherapist to identify the type of guilt feeling to which his patient

267

is subject and help him to reorganize his position in relation to his self value. This can be accomplished in helping the patient to develop a feeling of self value based upon his normal accomplishments, which have a realistic basis. It is true that the patient may have many limitations and that it may require much effort to discover his positive assets. However once the areas of the strengths are identified, the therapist should encourage the patient to utilize his positive assets. In doing so, the patient will slowly notice that he really can achieve something and thus will begin little by little to derive the feeling of self value from his achievements rather than from superficial reputation only. Through encouragement at first, then through reinforcement later on, the therapist will help the patient develop a stronger ego. Once the vulnerability and fragility of the patient's ego is reduced, the therapist will be able to help the patient to accept his limitations. Only an individual who is able to experience the objective feeling of self value can face his limitations without being overpowered by undue anxieties and without need for recourse to various neurotic mechanisms. Once the patient is ready to accept his limitations, he will be ready to accept the fact that he can make mistakes. He may slowly develop the capacity of accepting his past mistakes without undue disturbance. The frequent guilt feeling which has prevented the patient from making a decision will slowly be reduced and changed into infrequent but necessary feelings of real sorrow. When this point has been reached, the therapeutic progress will be noticeable. This is the point at which the therapy really begins (cf. Meehl, 1960). Many times the patients at this point will start reporting that they feel freer than before, that they are able to get along better with others and that the mistakes of other people with whom they live or interact do not aggravate them as much as before. It is quite interesting to note that one of the chief characteristics of a neurotic is his lack of freedom. A neurotic lacks freedom in relation to himself and in relation to other people. The guilt feeling and the anxieties resulting from it do not permit him to be generous toward himself and toward other people. Such a person usually has serious difficulties in his interpersonal relationships.

Therefore, the shifting from neurotic guilt feeling to the normal feeling of being guilty helps to free the individual and to open him up to positive emotional interaction with others. In this sense "guilt feelings are reminders that we have been remiss toward those we love and want to love us in return. These signs of trouble help indirectly to maintain positive and affectionate relationships" (Piotrowski, 1960). The shift thus accomplished has important implications not only for the individual involved in the process, but also for society. The normal feeling of guilt, and the sorrow associated with it, enables us to set and maintain rules in our social lives. It also enables the individual to evaluate his behavior from the standpoint of a morality which a neurotic is far from being able to understand.

MULTILATERAL RESISTANCE IN GROUPS OF PATIENTS

by Udo Derbolowsky

Whoever undertakes to alter the direction of moving bodies must study the laws governing the principles of inertia, *i.e.* of resistance, if he is to be able to cope with this when it appears. Freud and his successors did this. They went deeply into the question of the overt and concealed ways in which resistance manifests itself. Freud himself said, in his *Interpretation of Dreams* in 1899: "Anything which hinders the progress of work is resistance." (Vol. II/III, p. 521). In 1910 he wrote: "We are now aiming our efforts directly towards discovering and overcoming 'resistances', and are justified in believing that 'complexes' will be solved without difficulty as soon as the resistances are recognized and eliminated." (*The Future Prospects of Psycho-Analytic Therapy*, Vol. VIII, p. 107).

We must now ask *what* it is in psychoanalysis which influences the patient to change his direction. According to Freud it is all those factors which restore to consciousness whatever had been repressed by the patient.

If through recall of a repressed event the equilibrium of the patient be upset, the emergence into consciousness of such a memory would be opposed by the inertia principle as resistance. Direction-changing impulses, however, may appear in forms in which the patient plays no active part; for example, neurotic symptoms, dreams, or transference. It is understandable, therefore, that the resistance of the patient may on the one hand be directed against his own inner psychic contents where, as Freud says, the result is repression. On the other hand resistance may be directed against the analyst, and so endanger the progress of treatment. This is always the case where the analyst appears as the changing force. Should he do this, he makes himself the object of resistance of his patient.

Freud, therefore, says that the patient should be well prepared for every interpretation; through the interpretation of a changing impulse, the patient should recognize it as his own individual impulse, and not that of his analyst. It is a familiar fact that in daily life there is never much to be gained from telling people the truth. The phenomenon of resistance sees to this. And self-knowledge is known to be painful. By this I mean to say that a cure comparable with psychoanalysis does not as a rule come about spontaneously, either in the individual, or among friends.

Since resistance may be directed against intrapsychic content or against any outside person attempting to bring about a change, the old trend generally continues to exist. How did Freud then make the psychoanalytic process possible? In our opinion he achieved this through a stroke of genius, by diverting resistance on to an artificial plane, where resistance becomes perceptible to the patient and can be made use of in furthering the analysis.

Freud introduced the basic technical rule. In 1916 he wrote: "In setting up this basic technical rule our first aim is that it becomes itself the starting point for attacking resistance" (*Lectures on the Introduction to Psycho-Analysis,* Vol. XI., p. 297).

If we wish to apply the experience gained in the technique of individual analysis to a psychoanalytic group, it, too, is primarily a matter of the drawing up of basic technical rules which can be specifically applied to groups. The aim of such strategy must be to offer to the resistance an object of attack, in order to draw it away from the analyst on the one hand, and from the intrapsychic contents of each member on the other.

If the analyst plays an active part in the group in such a way that he appears to the group members as an 'autocratic' changing force, he provokes the resistance of the entire group upon himself. In sport too a referee gets into trouble if he does not restrict himself to watching over the rules of the game. The majority then feel a threat to their usual ways of life — or of play — and resist because they are unwilling to change. This provides both the pattern for a revolution and the background of the stoning of the prophets.

Perhaps many analysts keep away from group analysis because they are aware of this danger, or they cannot play an interpretative part and the analytic process does not come about. All that is achieved are patient-clubs, which are very useful and helpful, but

271

no analytical developments take place which handle repressions.

The following considerations have pointed the way to a solution of the dilemma: (1) In individual treatment the activity of the patient and the analyst is for the main part restricted to conversation. Any "acting out" is examined as to whether it is not an expression of resistance. In the group very much more "acting out" takes place owing to the nature of the situation. The members sit in a circle instead of lying down. There is a constantly changing interrelationship between them. (2) In the group, transference and projection fan out simultaneously in several directions, different to individual treatment. They are multilateral, as has been pointed out by many authors. (3) In the group acting-out, transference and projection may be more easily employed in the service of resistance. This is expressed in the familiar saying that a person would rather remove the mote from his neighbor's eye than the beam from his own. That, by the way, is certainly a sublime reason for the choice of profession of certain psychotherapists.

In the process of treating one's neighbor's eye, transference plays a part in the first place, whoever may be our patient's neighbor at that time; secondly projection comes into play, so that what the patient fails to see in himself at the time becomes apparent and irritating in his neighbor, and thirdly, "acting out" takes place, that is, the urge to correct his neighbor instead of himself. These considerations raised the question whether it would be possible to utilize the three aspects of resistance just mentioned in groups in order to intensify the analytical process. In fact, we have been successful in making a virtue of necessity and in working out basic technical rules for group analysis, which induce every patient in the group to use these principles.

In this fashion each group member is assigned an interpretative function towards every other member in the group, thus producing changes in a systematic manner with the effect that the resistance of each patient is spread out multilaterally and made productive at the same time.

For since the patient turns away from himself towards his neighbor by reason of the inertia principle and presents him with his interpretation, and this neighbor to the next, and so on, the analytic process is kept going and even intensified by the resistance itself.

Resistance is no longer evoked unilaterally against the analyst, but multilaterally against all members of the group. And the analyst can once more become guardian of the rules.

In my opinion this multilateral resistance and its control is a basic requirement of psychoanalytical group treatment.

ETUDE DIFFERENTIELLE DES PHENOMENES DE TRANSFERT AU TRAVERS DES VARIANTES DYNAMIQUES DANS LES GROUPES DITS STABLES OU INSTABLES

par Jean Kestenberg et Simone Decobert

Introduction

Nous nous proposons d'exposer les résultats d'une étude effectuée sur des groupes thérapeutiques de malades de structure psychotique, suivis dans le Cadre du Centre de traitement de l'Institut de Psychanalyse de Paris.

Le but de notre travail est la comparaison de l'évolution dynamique et des résultats, par la description et l'analyse des manifestations du transfert.

Les groupes étant définis "stables" ou "instables" par leur durée — limitée ou illimitée — dont découle leur composition et l'organisation matérielle de leur fonctionnement, la notion de temps prend une valeur fondamentale dans l'étude différentielle.

La constatation intuitive et clinique d'une meilleure qualité des échanges et de leur évolution dans les groupes stables nous a conduits à une étude plus détaillée et comparative des phénomènes spécifiques de groupe en fonction de leur durée et de la signification inconsciente de cette durée pour le patient.

Le choix des termes "stables" et "instables" correspond aux caractéristiques suivantes du fonctionnement des groupes:

A) La durée du groupe stable est présentée dès le départ comme limitée, le choix de la date de fin de traitement étant laissé aux patients qui la fixent avec les thérapeutes au cours de l'évolution du traitement. C'est un groupe "clos" dans lequel les arrivées et les départs s'opèrent globalement.

B) La durée du groupe instable n'est pas fixée: il accueille les nouveaux arrivants au fur et à mesure des vacances de places.

C'est un group "ouvert" à l'arrivée comme au départ et "permanent." L'instabilité se rapporte au mode de succession des patients renouvelés individuellement après une période d'environ 18 à 24 mois et non à la fréquentation qui reste régulière et généralement très assidue.

Dans les expériences rapportées le groupe stable a duré 9 mois; le groupe instable fonctionne depuis 3 ans.

Deux particularités de la technique seront notées:

1. L'originalité de la méthode thérapeutique employée dans ces groupes qui est celle de la psychanalyse dramatique, comportant une partie verbale et une partie dramatisée.
2. L'orientation vers le groupe d'un certain type préférentiel de patients de structure psychotique qui, en dehors de leur symptomatologie spécifique très riche, présentent un isolement qui a besoin d'être explicité par l'analyse du vécu dans un groupe privilégié. Cet isolement est apprécié au cours de l'orientation thérapeutique par l'étroitesse et la rigidité des rôles que les malades sont susceptibles d'assumer dans leurs groupes naturels.

Les groupes sont hétérogènes quant aux diagnostics psychiatriques et souvent comportent des éléments ayant présenté des états graves.

Par exemple, le groupe instable était composé de trois femmes dont: une hystérique, une névrose obsessionnelle grave, une névrose d'échec avec tics; et de trois hommes dont: un maniaco-dépressif, un hypocondriaque avec troubles somatiques et une personnalité psychopathique avec tentative de suicide.

Le groupe stable était composé de: deux schizophrènes (hommes), une névrose obsessionnelle grave (homme), une personnalité psychopathique avec tentative de suicide (chez une jeune femme).

Un autre groupe stable plus âgé comprenait: deux hommes, avec névrose de caractère; une femme avec névrose obsessionnelle grave, un déliré érotomaniaque chez une femme; une personnalité psychopathique avec épisodes délirants, hallucinations, fugues (femme).

La coexistence de malades graves et de malades moins psychotiques ne semble pas entraîner de difficultés durables dans les groupes: la communauté des phantasmes et des souvenirs réduisent rapidement celles-ci.

La notion de temps nous a paru déterminante dans les variations de structuration et d'évolution des deux types de groupes considérés. Nous venons de voir qu'elle est introduite par celle de durée limitée ou illimitée de la vie du groupe.

A. Dans notre expérience, la limitation du temps a paru présenter une valeur structurante et aider au dépassement de l'angoisse ou des mécanismes de défense pathologiques au sein des groupes stables.

Par contre elle a semblé entrainer une attitude régressive, nuisible à la cohésion au sein du groupe instable dans lequel les patients ont tendance à prolonger leur traitement, afin de conserver et de renforcer leur relation avec les thérapeutes à l'occasion des départs d'autres participants.

Dans le premier cas en effet, la limitation du temps est non seulement un élément sécurisant (parce qu'elle réduit les rivalités de fraterie) mais encore elle introduit deux éléments particulièrement favorables à l'évolution de la dynamique des groupes thérapeutiques qui sont: la réduction des bénéfices secondaires; la valorisation identificatoire.

Il y a en effet réduction des bénéfices secondaires de groupe par le groupe. Le jeu des réactions de prestance avec leurs contre-réactions, la satisfaction ambiguë d'essayer de manoeuvrer les autres members du groupe, ou les thérapeutes et le plaisir qui en découle, pourraient conduire les patients à une véritable "installation" dans le traitement. Bien qu'ils existent dans les deux sortes de groupes, on constate que l'exhibition plus ou mois spectaculaire des troubles et des faits anamnestiques, l'attrait de la fréquentation d'un milieu valorisant par rapport au milieu habituel, l'occasion renouvelée d'une participation voulue comme ésotérique, se trouvent exacerbés de façon répétée dans le groupe instable. C'est ce qui pourrait y expliquer — comme peut-être dans le cas des groupes verbaux — la tendance à l'analyse interminable, ou tout au moins la difficulté à renoncer au traitement en fonction de la persistance d'apport de bénéfices secondaires.

Dans le groupe stable ce risque est détourné par la fixation de la date de fin de traitement. Pour le cas étudié il semble que ce besoin de fixer une date soit apparu, dans les séances, au moment où les patients étaient devenus capables de se réunir en dehors des thérapeutes — par exemple au café — où chez l'un d'eux, c'est à

276

dire au moment où ils n'avaient plus qu'un besoin atténué ou transposé — des bénéfices secondaires du groupe.

On pourrait considérer également en reprenant la remarque de Foulkes qu'il s'agit du moment où l'angoisee change de qualité: de verticale et génétique (pré-oedipienne ou oedipienne) elle devient horizontale et socialisée, portant sur un ensemble d'inter-relations.

Le second élément est la valorisation identificatoire constituée par l'implication d'un contrat d'égal à égal entre les patients et les thérapeutes lors de l'accord commun de la limitation du temps de cure. La passation de ce contrat précipite et cristallise l'évolution des phénomènes de groupe en renforçant l'identification aux théra-peutes. Ainsi il est courant que les malades ne soient pas au même niveau quand l'un d'eux provoque la discussion de fin de traitement — Nous avons pu constater qu'il se produit alors un remaniement interne du groupe qui tend à l'égalisation des niveaux. Le même phénomène survenant plus précocément dans le traitement serait vécu comme une tentative de passage à l'acte, et le "déviant," en avance dans sa structure sur celle du groupe, serait rejeté, pour avoir donné, de l'évolution des patients, en miroir, une image anti-cipée, insupportable. Il y aurait dans ce cas resserrement autour des thérapeutes, alors que dans le cas de fin de traitement il y a, à partir du "contrat," établissement d'une relation plus lâche mais aussi plus adultisée avec les thérapeutes.

La fixation du terme en commun a finalement une valeur anti-régressivante, et l'on peut voir, après la passation du contrat, les malades les plus avancés s'efforcer d'arracher les autres à leurs tentatives de régression, c'est à dire prendre à peu près la position du médecin qui, dans l'analyse individuelle, propose de fixer un terme parce qu'il sent le patient guéri mais au bord de ces mêmes risques de régression. Ce maniement fécond de la "limitation du temps" ne saurait nous étonner car notre expérience quotidienne nous apprend l'intérêt de la limitation du temps dans toute tâche humaine et notre expérience d'analyste ne nous permet pas d'ignorer combien l'utilisation adéquate du temps de la séance par le patient est significative de progrès dans le déroulement de la cure.

B. Un autre aspect de la notion de temps est la possibilité de réduire la durée des séances à 30 minutes ou moins en conservant un maximum d'efficacité. Cette possibilité résulte de l'emploi du jeu et de la valeur hédonique inhérente au jeu. On sait que le plaisir est un des éléments les plus refoulés et les plus culpabilisés chez tous les malades. La technique du jeu lui restitue une présence intense sous la double forme: du plaisir direct à jouer; et de l'autorisation au plaisir par les thérapeutes.

Ce remaniement de la censure ne va d'ailleurs pas sans difficultés ni sans appels au surmoi pour éviter l'apparition de l'angoisee qui dans l'organisation pathologique des patients peut s'intensifier en même temps que l'hédonisme.

C'est ce qui explique la nécessité technique de couper la séance à certains moments favorables, même en deça des 30 minutes. En l'absence d'interruption et d'interprétation — surtout dans les groupes instables — la situation "se refroidit," mais surtout, se déstructure et le groupe régresse.

L'hédonisme du jeu augmente au cours de l'évolution du traitement en particulier dans le groupe stable, plus clos.

La fixation du terme de la cure en même temps qu'une certaine souplesse dans l'utilisation du temps de la séance ont certainement une valeur surmoïque utile: par la limitation et la prise de distance qu'elles introduisent dans l'exercice du plaisir du groupe. En ce sens, certaines tensions dues à la recherche d'interdiction du plaisir qui pourraient sembler des risques de passage à l'acte (peut-être plus fréquents dans le groupe stable) doivent être comprises comme le besoin de restaurer le surmoi et de trouver des limitations obligatoires au plaisir.

MOTOR PHENOMENA AND THEIR IMPORTANCE
FOR GROUP THERAPY

by M. Mitscherlich

The following is an account of the motor phenomena the author studied during an analytic group session. It should be pointed out at the outset that Freud's fundamental concepts and their further development by Anna Freud and Harald Schulz-Henke have been taken as the basis for the analytic procedure.

The group is mixed and consists of 6 to 8 members. Once a week a session is held lasting 90 minutes. In the group are 1 to 2 observers who sit apart from the other members of the group. In each case, the movements of one, or at the most two members, are recorded, and at the same time, what they say. If a patient, whose movement is being observed, moves, he is first asked whether he noticed the movement. This is frequently not the case. At first, the patient relates afterwards the thoughts that have occurred to him concerning the movement.

A 38-year-old professional man dreams: I am in a park with many paths; I don't know which path I should take; I become quite confused and remain so after awakening. While he is relating this, he frequently grasps at his chin and says that at school he was given the nick-name "the breast." His chin had always been somewhat fleshy and bulging, with a split in the middle. From the discussion of the movement it became clear that he identified himself with his mother. She is a schizophrenic, leads a disorderly life and is divorced from his father. Sometimes she walks for hours on end around the town in a confused state of mind and also bothers his family with her visits. He has consciously dismissed this irksome problem from his mind. Unconsciously, he is trying to solve it by identifying himself with his mother. The movement discussed with him reveals his femininity and latent homosexual impulses. He realizes that his inability to

279

face up to the male members of the group in an adequate fashion is connected with this. His attitude towards his father may be illustrated in the light of the movement.

A 42-year-old woman jurist, withdrawn, lacking social contacts, and who tires easily following the amputation of a breast, dreams: I am in a large house. Rats come running towards me; I am afraid and try to ward them off; I succeed. While she is speaking, she stamps her right foot several times. Aggressions that arise cannot be expressed adequately, except in the form of movement. It is obviously a case of an expression of opposition. The patient is only capable of infantile forms of aggression, "stamping impulses." As a child she could not express her rage towards her parents. Now, even in the transference, it cannot be verbalized, but only finds expression in movement. In early childhood, emotional states and movement are concomitant. Maturity also means the ability to experience emotional states without motor expression. The patient had such heavy guilt feelings that she was unable to accept the interpretation given. She did not return to the group therapy.

A 21-year-old male apprentice, suffering from complete loss of hair (alopecia generalis), gave an account of the great difficulties he had with his father. He was completely helpless in face of the latter. While relating this, he pinched his right cheek forcefully several times. The patient identified himself with his former strict mathematics teacher who was in the habit of pinching him in the right cheek when his performance in class was unsatisfactory. (In this connection, Anna Freud speaks of identification with the aggressor.) Careful study and discussion of the movement enabled the patient to recognize the latent aggressions and the way in which he dealt with them.

A further way of making motor phenomena useful for the group is as follows: When a member of the group describes physical discomfort, the individual members are called upon to make a movement they think might lead to the described discomfort.

A 48-year-old chemist, an obsessive-neurotic, now living in straitened circumstances as an unskilled worker, complains of pains in his right elbow. As I have already described, he is asked to assume a corresponding posture. He leans on his right elbow and assumes the posture of the thinker as depicted by the Rodin sculpture. He is a monument. All life has grown rigid. Dangerous impulses cannot find outward expression. His great urge to assert himself (ambition) is of significance, which he was not even able to begin to realize in his life.

A 21-year-old student has a torsion dystonia, a serious illness still held to be purely organic. He lives in constant conflict with his hard and brutal father and finds no support in his depressive mother. He clenches his fist, thrusts it forward as if to strike and pulls it back just as suddenly. This movement is a classic illustration of his ambivalent attitude, his mounting aggression and his heavy guilt feelings. The case of this seriously ill student, who could hardly walk when he came for treatment, is especially indicative of the great therapeutic importance to be assigned to the study of movement. Since there is up to now no analytic technique capable of healing the illness just mentioned, it may be assumed that such forms of motor disturbances cannot be influenced unless a careful study of their movements is carried out.

A 22-year-old apprentice suffers from essential hypertension, just as his father did. He held his right arm stretched out behind him and said he wanted to strike. The patient had a domineering mother who gave him no opportunity to develop his personality. He had always been submissive and was unable to assert himself in the group. The repressed aggressions found expression in the described movement. It is important that this did not take place in the form of motions alone, but as complete readiness for action. This constant readiness for action appears to be a root-cause of essential hypertension.

To sum up, it may be said that careful study of the motor phenomena in groups reveals the repressed impulses, the nature of the opposition and that of the transference. If movement occurring in the group is treated in the manner described, the patient himself has an opportunity to experience directly the conflict arising in the immediate group situation — a process the dynamics of which he can hardly escape.

ANALYTISCHE GRUPPENTHERAPIE IN DER PRIVATPRAXIS

von C. van Emde Boas

Eine ganze Reihe unvorhergesehener Umstände — u.A. eine langwierige abwechselnde Krankheit beider Psychotherapeuten, die beide — zur Hälfte geheilt — einander ersetzten mussten, anstelle gemeinsam, wie es normaliger üblich war, die Gruppen zu leiten; wozu sich ausserdem noch wiederholt unerwartete und nicht angekündigte kürzere Unterbrechungen der Sitzungen gestellten — haben seit Januar 1962 die sieben therapeutischen Gruppen, die in meiner Privatpraxis auf psychoanalytischer Grundlage behandelt werden, in eine Lage gebracht, die meines Erachtens mit einer weitreichenden emotionellen verglichen werden muss. Die Folgen dieses unbeabsichtigten "Experimentes" sind durchaus beachtenswert; obwohl sie therapeutisch wahrscheinlich nicht ganz unerwartet kommen.

Es ergibt sich nämlich, dass jede einzelne von den Gruppen — die alle offene Gruppe sehr verschiedenartigen Alters sind — in völliger Übereinstimmung auf die frustrierende Situation mit der "Reife" reagiert hat, welche die "Gruppe" in der gruppen-analytischen Arbeit erreicht hatte, und dabei ihrem eigenen, spezifischen Gruppencharakter treu blieb.

Innerhalb jeder einzelner Gruppe ergab sich bei den einzelnen Mitgliedern ein analoges Symptom: auch die Einzelreaktionen spiegelten weitgehend die pathologische Charakterstruktur wieder, die den Anlass zu der Behandlung gebildet hatte, mitigiert durch den verschiedenartigen Grad der therapeutischen Fortschritte, welche die Patienten inzwischen gemacht hatten.

In der Praxis bildeten die reëllen Frustrierungen, die wir der Gruppe auferlegten, die wirkliche Vernachlässigung, der wir unsere Patienten aussetzten mussten, eine wirkliche "Herausforderung," auf die im Allgemeinen sehr offen reagiert wurde, und die bei

282

einigen der mehr rigiden Charakterstrukturen zu einem beinahe spontanen Aufdecken analoger Jugendsituationen führte, die nachher erfolgreich durchgearbeitet werden konnten. Das Gleiche kann von der sehr kurzfristigen Einführung einer Stellvertreterin der zur Zeit noch immer kranken Psychotherapeutin gesagt werden, die über ihre eigenen Erfahrungen in dieser Gruppe selsbtändig berichten wird. Das vorzeitige Beenden der Behandlung war in dieser Periode nicht zahlreicher als sonst, abgesehen von vielleicht einer einzigen Gruppe, in der eine auffallende Zahl von Schnellheilungen auftrat, die möglicher Weise als "Flüchte in die Heilung" zu qualifizieren sind.

CLINICAL DATA TO THE PHENOMENOLOGY
OF THE CONCEPTS "REALITY" AND "SOCIETY"

by PAUL SENFT

What is meant by 'private'? A man's exclusive relationship to himself is private (for he can also relate to himself socially and publicly). A man, again, can relate to another man in a way that is exclusive of all aspects that are not personal to these two individuals. Interpersonal relations, too, can be purely private (there is a great deal of confusion about this in modern psychiatry). Thus, a therapeutic relationship is private even though it may aim at the socialization of the person. For what we call "permissiveness" as a therapeutic principle makes sense only if it enacts the unconditional understanding of the exclusive private realm of personal experience in which all law is suspended. And not only that of punitive social injunctions, but also forgiving charity, a moral law of compassion, for both charity and compassion — not just hostility and suppression — are incompatible with the autonomy of the person at which therapy aims in creating the sphere of complete privacy.

Is complete privacy the same as freedom? This is a very difficult question and should not be answered here. Negatively it can be defined as a state of lawlessness, an absence of all regulative law. The realm of fantasy and the realm of autonomous private relatedness must be lawless; in fact, it is what sociologists call *anomie*. "Free Association" suspends logical law; affective self-expression is exempted from all ethical rule or social law. Deep individual psychotherapy which takes place in such a state of anomie recapitulates, therefore, not only psychological ontogenesis, but the social history of phylogenesis and seems to incline, in the Freudian conception at least, towards Hobbes' primordial nihilism rather than Rousseau's primordial goodness of nature. Does then, by contrast, group psychotherapy recapitulate onto phylogenesis from a later level onwards — as some group-analysts implicitly seem to claim when they place the emphasis on the stronger prominence of Ego-processes? I do not think so.

Let us recall what a therapeutic group is. A certain number of solitary individuals agree to make the private realm of their existence public. They, who live in a private state of isolated lawlessness, set out on the search for a law which will serve as a measure for what counts as fact and what as fantasy, where and what is *available* in satisfaction, desire, aggression and love, and what is not. Social validation, in other words, is the key to full individual reality, be it in private or public. Acute fears of this unknown law on the one hand, and the clinging hope for security which this law will grant on the other, are immediate and will last to the end. And the whole process of therapy in between is nothing but a searching-out, a testing-out on each other, of whether such a law exists, if and how and when one has been split off from it, and whether it will be in the future a danger or a benefit. Patients come and patients go; they stay or leave according to when and what answers they will find to these questions during the whole length of the therapy. "Reality-testing" would be an appropriate term, provided that it is not applied in the psychoanalytical sense: as a metaphysical clash between the falsely dichotomized principles of organismic pleasure *versus* fixed environmental reality. "Reality-testing" in the group refers to the authentic field for the becoming of, for the structurization of, reality. In this testing, personal experience continuously oscillates between polarized locations: reality is either to be found in the ultimate private core of the Self, the Ego., *i.e.* in an inner system of subjective intentionality, or in the existence of the group, in an outer system of contacts with others. These alternatives may frequently be diametrically opposed to each other and lead to the postulation of those aims which go under the name of "education" or "re-education" to "adjustment" and "adaptation." In effect, however, "adjustment," whether psychoanalytic or behaviorist, is a hollow concept; not because it threatens to reduce the uniquely rich road of the individual to a mechanical stereotype — as some well meaning existentialists will say — but because it is itself based on a fallacy. One cannot "adjust" a personal Subject to a Reality which is still to be structured by him, if it is ever to confront him as 'objective' environment.

This postulate of 'adjustment' in the dichotomized world of psychiatry puts the patient into a labyrinth where he feels completely lost. In a Patient Club which I am conducting on group therapeutic lines, spontaneous discussions arise from time to time on these themes. One member said: "When I was certifiable, I was alone, utterly lonely. This was very real to me. Whenever I come nowadays into this Club, I cease to be real for I submerge somehow in this—how to say—group mind; in this circulation. I am exposed from all sides and all these activities tear me to pieces." "I feel just the opposite," another member remarked. "In loneliness I feel unreal; here, however, there is reality, even when I do not manage to get into it myself and remain outside of it. The club *is* reality. Alone I lose myself."

Outside/Iside, inner and outer realms and systems, private and public states, may in this way extend, inter-change, overlap and proliferate. For a third patient the Club Group was 'artificial' reality, not a genuine one. She found in the Club real contacts with real people which contrasted with the shadows of her solitary fantasies, but this was precisely why the Club as a whole became quite unreal. Behind the real contacts with real individuals there was the group as their framework, as a total situation, as an emotional horizon which was too fluid and uncertain to have the character of reality. She shifted, therefore, the locus of reality into a 'world outside' altogether; into a reality where the normal and healthy were living and where all transactions were rational, calm, and if not exactly friendly, at least free from upsetting hostility. She well accepted loneliness as her particular condition of personal reality. It was, however, void of all human content: so its emptiness had to be filled in with fantasies. These fantasies were again matched against the real contacts in the Club, and the Club again, measured against 'the world outside,' became unreal. This circle was an existential paradox — the paradox perhaps of being ill: to go on existing neither quite within life nor having definitely crossed its boundaries. To take up residence, as it were, in the constricted area of a no-man's land yet where movement was so open in all directions that real action, for this very reason, has had to be suspended.

TRANSFORMATION OF PARENTAL GROUP GUIDANCE INTO ANALYTIC GROUP THERAPY

by Leon Tec

In recent years, guidance has come to be regarded as the appropriate form of group treatment for parents of emotionally-disturbed children. From the onset of treatment and continuing through its duration, attempts have been made to maintain the group meetings on a guidance level. The very fact, however, that such attempts have had to be made, and that parents of disturbed children when seen in groups have been carefully prevented from moving into any other form of treatment, suggests that there is a tendency for guidance groups to be transformed into other forms of therapy. This transformation, with all its possibilities and implications, remains at the present, virtually unexplored.

In my own clinical experience with such guidance groups, I have had the opportunity to observe changes and modifications. It has not been unusual to see a group start out in guidance, but become, during the treatment, modified into an analytic group therapy. The modification was sometimes spontaneous, but often grew out of the particular needs of the group members combined with the therapist's willingness and ability to go along with them. When these modifications took place they had further significant impacts on the goals and effects of the treatment.

Whether such changes should be viewed favorably and under what conditions, are questions worth exploring. I myself, do not agree with the accepted idea that a guidance group of parents of emotionally-disturbed children should at all times be prevented from becoming an analytic group therapy. I feel strongly that given the proper setting and conditions, the transformation from guidance to analytic therapy may provide benefit for both the parents and the children involved.

Let us concentrate first on group guidance of parents and explore both the changes such groups may undergo and the implications of these changes. A great deal has been said and written about the careful selection of members for guidance groups, a selection based on the appraisal of psychopathology and common interest. These bases for selection, naturally, are not the same as those used for analytic groups which are not child-centered. In the former groups, the adult comes as a parent who recognizes a difficulty in his child and is frequently reluctant to admit his own conflicts. In the latter, adults seek help for themselves because they are already aware of their problems. It is therefore impractical and even unwise to suggest to groups of parents that they participate from the start in analytic group therapy. The initial contact between parents and therapists necessarily involves a certain degree of tension. Guidance, with its specifically delineated goals, helps to structure an emotionally tense situation for the parent. It is only after he has learned to relax in the guidance group that a more meaningful form of treatment may be contemplated. At this stage a partially spontaneous shift from guidance towards analytic therapy may be taking place. But even though the group may be ready for a change, certain factors present in the situation may work to inhibit this transformation or to encourage it.

An inexperienced therapist, rigidly applying what he has learned from books and supervision, will tend to be less flexible and more dogmatic. He will participate more actively in the group discussions and provide guidance just at the point when the group might be ready to move away from it. He may interfere actively in any attempt of the group to move beyond guidance, refusing to permit the exploration of genetic material such as self-evaluation, connection between past and present, discussion of repetition compulsion, identification with the aggressor and analysis of transference phenomena. Essentially here, it is the lack of experience on the part of the therapist which prevents him from granting the group a greater degree of autonomy. His active participation may range from frequent explanations to direct suggestions about practical issues concerning parent-child relationships.

Inexperience is not the only reason for active participation on the part of the therapist. His theoretical orientation may have convinced him that guidance is preferable to any other form of treatment for these groups of parents. And even if he is not rigidly dedicated to this form, he may, on occasion, after evaluating the members of a particular group, decide that its members are only suitable for guidance. However, if he makes this decision before the group starts, he sometimes finds, to his surprise, that it is ready for a shift in treatment after it has worked on a guidance level for a while.

The role and orientation of the therapist, therefore, is important in preventing a group from moving out of guidance. Conversely, his role is equally important in fostering such a change. The shift from guidance to analytic therapy stems from two sources. It may stem from a spontaneous movement of the group which the therapist encourages rather than hinders. But it is also partly due to the therapist's conscious or unconscious desire to see it happen. His remarks are often the catalysts which stimulate the exploration of genetic material. These remarks may serve as hints to the group, suggesting a direction in which it is allowed to go. This process, incidentally, destroys the myth that the group has freedom of selection of topics for discussion.

To a great extent the tone and trend of discussions are dictated consciously or unconsciously by the therapist. The group picks up not only verbal communication, but gestures, facial expressions and moods of the therapist which frequently suggest a tacit approval of some topics and disapproval of others. The group's need of expression and the therapist's selective support of certain topics leads to the formation of the specific character assumed by an individual group. The balance is established in a dynamic fashion, not a static one, moving from analytic therapy to an occasional attempt at guidance and back again.

The impact of the therapist's influence on the character of the group has been greatly underestimated. It is up to him to decide whether to limit a given group to guidance therapy or whether to lead it into analytic therapy. I am in agreement with those who feel he should be allowed to make these decisions, adjusting his treatment to the particular group he is working with, rather than adjusting the group to preconceived ideas of appropriate treatment.

While the role of the therapist is of great significance in promoting or curtailing the character of the group's functioning, at this point it should also be emphasized that the composition of the group itself can also be an equally determining factor. Movement into analytic group therapy presupposes a certain level of sophistication of its members. Where sophistication is absent, such

289

a movement cannot be successful and any attempt to make one artificially will result in failure. It is just as unwise to force some groups away from guidance therapy as it is to prevent others from shifting to analytic therapy; an unsophisticated group may not be capable of moving in the direction of analytic treatment, while a highly sophisticated group may feel uncomfortable when kept on a guidance level. For instance, in the latter group, direct suggestions coming either from the therapist or from other members of the group itself, sometimes lead to resentment and resistance whereas interpretation can result in clarification of issues, acceptance and sometimes in character change.

When the change from guidance into analytic group therapy takes place, it is usually gradual with occasional lapses back into guidance. It is not necessary for all members of the group to make the shift simultaneously. There are usually some members who initiate the transition, while others resist it. With the support of the therapist, the acceptance of the transition spreads and maintains itself with occasional reversals usually stimulated by those who originally were reluctant to abandon guidance. The reversals into guidance, however, become less frequent in time.

In these instances where guidance groups are successfully transformed into analytic group therapy, a number of significant consequences can be seen. One of these consequences, for example, can be improved marital relations. When both parents, in their respective groups, come to understand themselves better and to revise some of the expectations they have of each other, the marriage becomes vastly improved. As a result, the climate in which their child lives, improves accordingly. Similarly, empathy with the child and respect for the child emerging from a review of parents' own childhood experiences can be of considerable help. Take, for example, the outrage one parent felt when his teenage boy was caught with literature considered unsuitable for him. The discussion in the group moved away from guidance, away from what should be done with the boy, and concentrated instead on an analytic exploration of how each of the members experienced handling of prohibited, censored material when they were the same age as the boy. This threw light on the problem and helped the father to understand it in a completely different way. In this case, guidance and analytic therapy were highly interwoven.

Still another consequence resulting from a shift in therapy is a clearly observable movement towards greater group cohesion and greater independence from the therapist. This, in turn, can provide not only much better insight and ability to cope with reality, but also can prepare each individual member of the group for independent action at home and eventual termination of treatment.

Apparent also, is a greater flexibility in handling parental responsibilities. When the therapist is an active leader, the group remains in guidance through identification with his role and the parents are helped to assume responsibilities with their children. Gradually, when the shift into analytic therapy is accomplished, removing the therapist to the background, the parents identifying with the therapist's new position, remove themselves more to the background and become more tolerant and flexible in their own actions towards their children.

Finally, in analytic therapy, the frustration of not being given an answer to a question, initially gives rise to hostility and aggression, but eventually results in greater cohesion and provides more insight. Both of these, in turn, lead to an improved self-esteem.

PSYCHOANALYSIS IN GROUPS:
SEPARATION ANXIETY IN THE ALTERNATE SESSION

by Irving A. Goldberg and Gerald J. McCarty

In the format of psychoanalysis in groups, individual sessions are not routinely provided. The patients meet for sessions regularly with the analyst (the regular session) and meet on a regularly scheduled basis without the analyst (the alternate session). Goals in this form of treatment are reconstructive. The rationale and theory underlying psychoanalysis in groups and the use of the alternate session have been amply described and documented in the literature. Here we will describe how the alternate session facilitates the emergence and analysis of separation anxiety with both oedipal and preoedipal origins. It is our intention to discuss clinical and theoretical constructs which arose from the observations of the authors that some patients develop acute anxiety, panic, phobic reactions, or resistance to attendance at alternate sessions in group psychoanalysis.

Separation anxiety has been described as a disruption of the attachment to the mothering love object. There is evidence that object loss produces separation anxiety and that death and other incidents of object loss may lead to mood disorders which constitute a refusal to accept separation. People tend to ward off and insulate against the anxiety attendant to separation. The literature contains many case descriptions and much theoretical discussion about the relationship between analysts' vacations and separation anxiety, termination of analysis and separation anxiety, and the whole process of psychotherapy being directed toward effecting separation, individuation, growth and maturity.

Clinical experience has led us to realize that the alternate session may create a deprivation and frustration for the patient which is similar to object loss and which occurs regularly within the treatment matrix and can be continually worked-through. This

292

separation from the "therapist-mother" may be either on the overt level of separation (as in separation from mother in going to school and peer relatedness), at the earlier level of separation and individual mastery (as in anxiety at the loss of omnipotent and magical control of the mother), or at the more archaic level of individual identity (as in anxiety attendant to separation from fusion with mother).

An analysis of this anxiety and the defenses against it, as manifested and reenacted in the transference, led to an understanding that it had its roots in oedipal competitive strivings on the part of some patients, struggles for mastery, autonomy and control on the part of other patients, and in an unresolved maternal tie and the underlying symbiotic attachment with still other patients.

We found that separation anxiety is based on heterogeneous determinants. As a phenomenon it is experienced by individuals who fall into various nosological categories. When our patients manifested such anxiety or resistance to the alternate we used this as an opportunity to help them work through the underlying factors involved. Very often this necessitated offering the patient additional individual sessions as support. On other occasions getting the patient to verbalize and associate to his anxieties led to his being able to tolerate the alternate while still working on the problem.

GROUP PSYCHOTHERAPY, GROUP PSYCHOANALYSIS, AND SCIENTIFIC METHOD

by Norman Locke

There is a growing acceptance of the concept that psycho-analysis can be accomplished in groups. A certain reserve can be seen, however, in the manner with which therapists will acknowledge their interest in the field. It is not clear whether this is a timidity, proper scientific caution, or what. Notable is the dearth of written material issued as experiences in or observations on group psychoanalysis. In contrast, there is a considerable body of writing appearing as representative of "psychoanalytically oriented group psychotherapy," or "group analysis," or "analytic group psychotherapy." Since these presentations must be taken literally — whatever they might mean, for they are not defined — they exclude themselves from our discussion.

In all save one of the published work which has been seen, no definition of group psychoanalysis has been presented, let alone essayed; there is no systematic presentation of what group psycho-analysis purports to be; there is no descriptive or explanatory statement of the process of group psychoanalysis. There are merely claims. And this is perhaps the greatest shortcoming in the entire field of group psychotherapy today. If the listener were interested and wanted to learn of the theory or of the technique of group psychoanalysis, he would be told that, like peace, it is wonderful and replete with advantages, but in only one source would he find an attempt at an answer. Just how adequate, if at all, this one answer is remains to be seen.

Just as there are proponents whose argument for group psycho-analysis consists of saying, "We practice it," so there are opponents who argue against it. Their reply to their colleagues is to say, "you can't be practicing it." It is to be regretted that the most significant new movement in group psychotherapy today has degenerated to an empty bandying about of words. There is no *experimentum crucis* — indeed there is no *experimentum* at all.

There is one difference that makes itself felt immediately. Although the proponents of group psychoanalysis merely state "It exists," and say no more, the opponents go beyond this. They reply, "It doesn't," and then proceed to state why it does not exist. This is most disconcerting. And apparently so much so that no one has answered any of the arguments. I would like to present the arguments, as I understand them, and offer a refutation for your consideration.

Most of the opponents base their position not on experience, but on theory. Their theoretical system is over-determined to the individual, cathected if you will, and permits of no alternative. Their most frequent argument against group psychoanalysis centers around the couch: if there is no couch, there is no free association, if there is no free association there is no psychoanalysis. Here, the couch is being made the *sine qua non* of free association, but by itself the couch has no meaning and never can have. Patients can lie on the couch and say nothing, or tell stories of what happened at work, or fall asleep. The couch does nothing to *produce* free association — it is only a device to *facilitate* it.

It is sometimes stated that long periods of time are significant as a criterion of successful psychoanalysis. This is an emphasis upon a concomitant of psychoanalysis rather than the method itself. If the rationale is that only through long periods of time can we come to the ultimate conflicted material, the meaning is more clear. The *material* is the significant fact then, not the passage of time.

Of those who argue against group psychoanalysis, there is a small number who have had experience in conducting groups of their own. These are highly skilled and knowledgeable practitioners in the area of individual psychoanalysis whose comments are not only serious but also significant. The questions they raise are telling.

These critics state that in the group there is no real work with free association. Memory productions are limited by the group setting, they say, and by the other members of the group who will inevitably cut into the association of the patient. They conclude that the association is thus prevented from developing. I agree that the verbal output is less in the group, but I ask the critic to note the increase in non-verbal production. It is the psychodynamic

295

process which underlies the verbal production that is important, not the words as words. The regression and the unfolding of buried material continue in the unconscious of the group patient regardless of setting and regardless of interruption. The *appearance* of the process merely shifts from words to gesture or to facial expression or behavior *vis-a-vis* another group member.

There are those who state that there is no group psychoanalysis because the group lacks "depth." To my knowledge, there has never been a written definition of "depth," and only one verbal one. Some five years ago a conference speaker characterized depth by the appearance of oral material, anal material and infantile strivings, and stated that such phenomena are not found in groups. If we accept this characterization of depth, I point out that the speaker was saying only these phenomena had never appeared in the groups that he had studied. I, myself, have presented transcriptions of group sessions which were replete with such material.

It is said that the transference neurosis cannot be developed in a group setting, or if it is developed it cannot be worked through. The latter qualification weakens an argument that begins most powerfully, and it also shifts the basis from a root criterion of the very presence of psychoanalysis, the transference, to an area that is terminal, the least known of the psychoanalytic dynamics, and one shared by *any* aspect of successful group psychotherapy, the working through. Let us assume that the critic had restricted his remarks to the transference. He then goes on to say that there is no consistent, sequential, day-to-day development of the transference, and concludes that it is impossible to reach the transference neurosis in depth (that word again), and in consistency. You will recognize that this argument is based on an unspoken distinction between the transference and transference neurosis. Here the phrase "transference neurosis" is being reserved exclusively for the relationship between patient and analyst. This *same* aspect in any other context, as I understand it, is either ignored, or termed "transference" and regarded as if it were an altogether different phenomenon. There is more and more agreement that the neurotic person transfers on everyone who constitutes a screen for such a phenomenon — transfers in every setting, and at any time. This leaves us with an argument based on a distinction without a difference.

The foregoing seem to be the most substantive arguments

against group psychoanalysis. As I see them, they are grounded in psychoanalytic theory. There are additional comments which are more of a technical nature. Thus, the antagonists of group psychoanalysis hold that in the group there is a super-ego value, a consciousness of object relations which blocks the achievement of depth (!). It strikes me that if a patient is going to resist by structuring super-ego control, he will do so in an individual relationship as well as in a group, and as we all know, this he does. This is equally true of the patient's use, or rather, misuse, of reality to prevent unwelcome unconscious material from reaching consciousness.

Seemingly related are the statements that in the group there is no systematic analysis of resistance, and that there is no possibility of interpretation. Were these comments valid, they would, of course, be fatal. As I see them, however, they appear to have shifted the critical base from the group to the analyst. The failure to analyze or to interpret is a function of the man, not the method.

I would like to repeat a previous comment: the psychoanalysts who have made these criticisms are reputable, competent people who have given considerable thought to the question raised by group psychoanalysis, and whose opinions are not to be treated lightly. Why the continuing sharp divergence in our thinking? I submit the following suggestion in answer. When psychoanalysis came into a group setting, all of its theory, technique, and climate of thinking came with it. It was not recognized that a new integration had been created, and practitioners looked upon group psychoanalysis as old wine in new bottles. I suggest this is not the case. May I remind you of the example of a quantitative change becoming a qualitative one? From $1°$ to $99°$ C, we know H_2O as water. One degree higher than $99°$ and water becomes steam. One degree lower than $1°$ and water becomes ice. So it is in the group. The addition of a third person to two results in a profound change, an integrative shift, a complete reorganization. To bring the thinking of a one-to-one relationship into a group interrelationship is to limit that thinking. We moved into another universe of discourse when we moved from the individual to the group, and we must reorganize our thinking to the requirements of our new integration. Until the group has been systematically studied and characterized, no one can use a footrule designed for an individual to measure a group dimension.

297

I submit that a therapy is psychoanalytic if its method is one of exploration and uncovering; if its material is that of the unconscious: dream, fantasy, slip of the tongue, free association; and if its description and explanation of behavior are in terms of the generation and subsequent repression of overwhelming or forbidden feeling and fantasy. Here, then, is my three-fold measure of psychoanalysis: method, material and interpretation. If these criteria are not acceptable, I suggest that others be advanced.

SOME THEORETICAL CONCEPTS IN GROUP ANALYTIC PSYCHOTHERAPY

by P. B. DE MARE

The salient feature of group analytic psychotherapy lies in the introduction of a maneuverable social dimension, in the form of the group matrix, into the fabric of the actual technique itself. Any approach to group therapy which fails to do this, not only fails to do justice to the therapeutic potential of the group but may indeed become actively anti-therapeutic.

Group analysis offers us a field in which the interplay between the part and the whole, with the emergent evolution of the new, can be seen in continuous operation. Gestalt theory took the view that the wholeness property is given rather than evolved from the combination of simpler elements. In group analytic psychotherapy we see an extension of this, namely, *first* the existence of relatively autonomously functioning individuals; *secondly,* their interaction with each other; and *finally,* as a result of this, the laying down of a network of communication which establishes the contours of a discrete "whole" group identity which Foulkes has called the group matrix. This matrix comes to play a highly significant role in the therapeutic process. Development then follows along the lines of a chaos-logos-cosmos cycle of events, roughly equivalent to the structure, process and content of the group.

Foulkes adopts an inductive approach and avoids arriving at premature formulations. His approach favors a tentative orientation, admittedly less easy to define but preferable to more facile models that bring distortion in their wake. The fact that the group continues to elude adequate definition stands us in good stead, for it acts as a reminder that concepts of group analysis "must be independent and not borrowed ones." In this respect it is refreshing to note that in an article published by him as early as 1944, he tentatively pointed out the therapeutic factors as being (a) the

299

social and group situation, and (b) a collection of factors which can be conveniently grouped under the inclusive heading of communication, *e.g.* mirror reaction, activation and exchange.

These foreshadowed much of what later became further elaborated, with the notable exception of the concept of the group matrix, which was not actually described in publication, I think I am correct in saying, till 1957, when it was acknowledged as being "at the centre of all our thinking about groups."

In the group analytic situation, then, in which group psychotherapy is observed in its "purest and least contaminated form, where the accent is entirely on the free and spontaneous action and interaction within the group with as little interference, interpretative or other, as possible," there is the triad of, first, the small primary group itself with its "T" set of factors, which is distinguished not so much by "the presence of certain unique factors but a particular combination of several factors . . . and the way in which they are used," secondly, of the process of communication —of "all observable responses," and thirdly, of the group matrix namely "the total communicationable network."

The group analytic situation is best reserved as a comprehensive term covering all three constructs of the triad. To date, most of our attention has been taken up by attempts to understand the first of the triad—the small group itself in its initial phases, its establishment, its framework, selection and procedure. To observe its special features and to cover all these aspects, I should like to introduce two main headings under which it is (I hope) possible to reduce and clarify the complexities of the small primary group itself.

The first heading is the *group locus;* it consists of the basic matters of general group arrangements: size, selection and procedure. It is, in fact, the relatively standardized and unchanging framework. Once established, the group locus exercises considerable influence upon all subsequent events, reducing interference from outside sources (including the conductors) to a minimum; it takes on various phantasy meanings at various stages, depending on changes in the configuration of the matrix at any particular moment; for instance, the family, the stage, the forum, the community. Essentially none of these things, it remains a suspended, transitional, "proxy" entity, quasi-fantasy, quasi-real, and equivalent to the analyst in the psychoanalytic situation. With its a-programmatic occupation, the locus can be compared to a stage without a play, or a law court without a legal code.

The group locus is constantly faced with the dilemma of having to remain sufficiently encapsulated to provide protection from the usual social involvements, which enables the members to feel they can afford to drop their defensiveness; on the other hand, it has to borrow some of the authority of the outside community to give the group sufficient weight to stand up to the censorious and predatory nature of neurosis.

The boundaries of the group locus have been compared to a semi-permeable membrace that protects the group both from the disturbing influences within the surrounding environment and from the endopsychic phantasmagoria of the individual members. Within this locus the members should feel free to adopt, shed, assign and test out various social or, alternatively, phantasy roles, as well as various personifications of impulses, trends or traits in free speculation.

The second heading, also referring to the small group itself, is its *plurality,* covering specifically the more "chaotic" collective nature of the group. In a recent paper, Dr. Salomon Resnik talks of "the constitutional plurality of the group situation," and comments that "any group implies plurality of objects which is what characterizes the group as such."

This is more than a play on words, for it not only *counters* any tendency towards a too facile reductive rendering of the group-as-a-whole, such as regarding "the total material produced by *all* the members of the group as if it had been produced by one member in an individual session," or anchoring the group to over-simplified models such as the family, the breast, or the community, but emphasizes the relative freedom with which the individual-in-the-group and his inner perspective can gain expression.

Because Foulkes has refrained from emphasizing either the pluralistic at the expense of the holistic features, or vice versa, he has been represented as attempting to establish an uneasy compromise between psychoanalysis and Gestalt psychology, which is tantamount to saying that because he is not prepared to discard either of these perspectives, he is making a compromise. Even if this were so it would be preferable to excluding any of the delicate emerging processes. In fact we should be prepared to collate all that has been fathered from allied disciplines, rather than feel a

301

need to impose idiosyncratic versions. For instance, there is much in his approach that bears affinities to the existential outlook — the "being-in-the-world" relates to the individual-in-the-group, and "encounter" with confrontation; there is also the emphasis on action, communication and intimacy; and in the concept of the group matrix, historical and temporal and spatial dimensions play their roles. The social situation of the group brings out real anxiety and real guilt in most cogent ways, and the individual, in finding he can no longer hide, discovers his Dasein. The subject/object cleavage, in keeping with other dichotomies, very obviously loses its consequence in the group situation; for instance, the leader/group cleavage.

Like a sounding board, the plurality within the group enhances salient trends already inherent in the individual personality, e.g., splitting, projection (and projective identification) and introjection, for it offers opportunities for dramatization, personification, polarization, amplification and multiple representation, with temporal, spatial and historical sequences that gradually evolve a group matrix — the total communicational network.

On the other hand, the binding power of the matrix leads to a restructuralization and eventual re-socialization within its network, which is itself in turn continuously modified, the pluralistic foreground figures being highlighted (located) in their particular configuration against the background of the emerging group matrix. The matrix therefore lies in an antithetical relationship to the plurality of the group.

The conductor also bears an interesting relationship to the matrix, for as the matrix waxes, his function wanes and leadership quality as a function of the group is delegated in varying ways, the individed leader throughout being the total group. The conductor attempts to be perceptive to the group's leadership constellation by ranging from the didactic to the heuristic. The group, in learning to operate as-a-whole and with the help of the progressively emerging group matrix, is able to take over its own leadership function without feeling divided and without guilt. This is reminiscent of certain passages from "Totem and Taboo," e.g., "the sense of guilt, which can only be allayed through the solidarity of all the participants . . ." or "together they dared and accomplished what would have remained impossible for them singly." ". . . The memorable criminal act which so many things began;

302

social organization, moral restrictions and religion." ". . . A change has really taken place in the form of society, from father horde to the brother clan."

The primitive, authoritarian, conductor-centered configuration of the initial phases with the leader/group cleavage gradually gives way and is taken over by the emerging group matrix — the social solution to the Oedipal conflict.

Unlike most other leadership situations, the conductor does not attempt to block this transformation, but fosters the growing complexity of the matrix *pari passu* with his own "decrescendo," and this he attempts to achieve, in group analytic psychotherapy, as smoothly and evenly as possible. It can in fact *only* be achieved as a result of the work done in the process of learning to communicate and in the course of, often considerable, time, motivated by "this creative sense of guilt which has not become extinct with us."

Selection here plays a paramount role in enabling both the group and conductor to facilitate the process of learning that the potential leader throughout is the total group who guides the conductor. He in his turn responds and guides the group, and it is up to him to harness this symbiosis for therapeutic purposes, rather than to perpetuate the leader/group cleavage.

Freud described the primary group as "a number of individuals who have substituted one and the same object for their ego ideal and have consequently identified themselves with one another in their ego." For the group-analytic psychotherapist, this is a preliminary phase in the group's history — a group without a matrix. He also commented that the family was a reconstruction of the former primal horde which restores a great part of their former rights to the fathers.

When the group, then, in its initial phases of a family configuration, combines with the help of the binding power of the matrix to take over its social as opposed to family function, the decision is guilt free and represents a reduction in tension and hostility between the members themselves, between themselves and the conductor who is then seen in his socially "real" role, and intrapersonally between the Ego and Super Ego, which in the course of this steady take-over become mutually modified in such a way as to function syntonically.

On the other hand, if this does not occur — when the take-over

303

is by another member in isolation — distortions occur, such as the appearance of the "mad leader" on the scene, which are not necessarily inevitable group phenomena but would seem to denote an uneven-ness in the growth of the matrix and a breakdown in smooth communication, for instance, when the conductor withdraws prematurely, before a sufficient matrix has been established. This breakdown may also occur at any time, however late in the proceedings, when the group is faced by a shared problem of incommunicability: for example, a shared neurotic disturbance, typically when the constellation is changing from a homosexual to a heterosexual pattern when the men and women are encountering prohibitions in exchanging with each other, at which point they may evince the recurrence of a leader-centered but hostile pattern of behavior; they share a phantasy that the conductor objects to this exchange, or else that the other members will object or reject, and this prevents their testing it out.

This steady take-over, then, from the rigidly authoritarian/chaos quality by a progressively evolving matrix that permeates intrapersonal as well as intra-group (transpersonal) dimensions, represents the very essence of the therapy. The dilemma for the group-analytic psychotherapy group is that the conductor does not identify with the maneuvers imposed on him by a group in a rudimentary state of communication.

These comments cover only the first and third aspects of the triad — the second, that dealing with the processes of activation, motivation and communication, closely involves the role of the conductor and is more a subject on its own, about which, perhaps, least is known. Certainly it is the most complex.

POLIKLINISCHE ANALYTISCHE DISKUSSIONSGRUPPEN MIT EINER DURCHSCHNITTSZAHL VON 12 GRUPPENMITGLIEDERN

von R. ZIMMERT

In dem Referat werden die Vor — und Nachteile der 12-er-Gruppe im Vergleich zu Gruppen mit 8 Mitgliedern aufgezeigt. Es handelt sich um ambulante Gruppen, um offene Gruppen, um analytische Diskussionsgruppen, um gruppenzentrierte Gruppen.

Gemeinsam ist den 8-er-Gruppen die Gruppentechnik. Die Gruppen sind gemischt nach Geschlechtern, nach der sozialen stellung, den Berufen, nach Familienstand, nach der Symptomatik und der neurotischen Struktur. Alle Patienten sind durch einen oder zwei andere Psychotherapeuten anamnestisch voruntersucht und mit ihrem Einverständnis, nach Rücksprache mit dem Gruppentherapeuten in eine Gruppe überwiesen worden. Dem Patienten wird schriftlich mitgeteilt, er möge sich zum Beginn seiner Gruppenbehandlung an einem bestimmten Abend zu einer bestimmten Zeit in einem bestimmten Raum einfinden. Dort trifft der neu Hinzukommende auf die bereits vorhandenen Gruppenmitglieder, die ihm in lockerer Form die Spielregeln der Gruppe bekanntgeben. Straff gefasst sind diese:

1) Der Gruppenabend findet 1 mal wöchentlich zur gleichen zeit statt und dauert 2 Stunden.
2) Schweigeverpflichtung nach aussen.
3) In der Diskussion soll möglichst zur Gesamtgruppe gesprochen werden.
4) Der Patient hat völlige Redefreiheit. Er darf auch schweigen. Er bestimmt selbst, worüber er spricht.
5) Kein Mitglied soll längere Zeit unausgesprochenen Groll gegen ein anderes Gruppenmitglied mit sich herumtragen, es sei sinnvoll, seinen Arger zu äussern.

6) Bei zweimaligem unentschuldigten Fehlen hintereinander kann der Patient von der Gruppenbehandlung ausgeschlossen werden.

7) Ferner muss der Patient zu jedem Quartalsbeginn den Nachweis seiner Versicherungszugehörigkeit zur Allgemeinen Ortskrankenkasse erbringen.

Die Gruppentherapie wurde in Berlin im Zusammenhang mit dem Nachlassen der Arbeitslosigkeit intensiver aufgegriffen. Plötzlich standen für die Zeit nach 17 Uhr für viele Patienten keine Behandlungsplätze zur Verfügung. Die Erhöhung von 8 auf 12 Gruppenmitglieder erfolgte teils mit dem Einsetzen der Vollbeschäftigung, teils aus der Tatsache, dass mir für die Gruppenbehandlung eines Tages ein anderer Raum zur Verfügung gestellt wurde. Dieser Raum war grösser als der vorherige, und 8 Personen kamen sich ein bisschen vereinsamt darin vor. Die Gruppen wurden daher auf nominell 14-15 Mitglieder aufgefüllt. Da meistens etwa 2-4 Gruppenmitglieder abwechselnd fehlen, ergibt sich eine ungefähre Anwesenheit von 12 Mitgliedern. Wenn zufällig einmal nur etwa 8 anwesend sind, wird darauf verschieden reagiert, teils positiv, weil die Einzelnen mehr sagen können, häufiger aber wird es bedauert, da man weniger Stellungnahmen zu erwarten hat.

Zur gemeinsamen Technik der Behandlung in 8-er und 12-er-Gruppen kurz Folgendes: Es ist wichtig, die Passivität der Patienten zu überwinden. Deshalb erscheint der Gruppentherapeut etwa 10 Minuten nach dem angesetzten Beginn der Sitzung. Bis dahin hat sich schon ein Gespräch entwickelt. Die Gruppenmitlieder sitzen im Kreis. Der Therapeut hat einen bestimmten nicht weiter gekennzeichneten Platz. Innerhalb dieses Kreises befindet sich kein Tisch oder sonst etwas, so dass die Gesamtgestalt jedes Gruppenmitgliedes wechselseitig voll im Blickfeld ist. Der Therapeut nimmt eine möglichst abwartende Rolle ein. Auch direkte Fragen leitet er an die Gruppe weiter mit der Frage: "Was meint die Gruppe dazu?" Die Gruppe als solche wird noch lebendiger durch die verschiedenartige stammesmässige Herkunft der Patienten, die alle in der Grossstadt Berlin zu Berlinern geworden sind.

Die Vermittlung der Patienten zur Gruppentherapie erfolgt zwar nach den Massstäben der Vermittlung für eine Einzeltherapie, wobei aber für Gruppentherapie prognostisch schwierigere Fälle bevorzugt zugewiessen werden.

Von den bestellten Gruppenpatienten bleiben innerhalb von 6

Wochen etwa 20-30% fort. Meine Kollegin Fuchs-Kamp ist dabei zu untersuchen, aus welchen Gründen diese Behandlungen so früh abgebrochen wurden. Etwa nach 4 Gruppenabenden wird mit jedem neuen Gruppenpatienten ein Einzelgespräch durchgeführt, eine etwaige körperliche Untersuchung durch unsere Facharztzentrale eingeleitet und dem Patienten erklärt, dass er bei Bedarf jederzeit um zwischengefügte Einzelstunden bitten könne. Ferner wird ihm mitgeteilt, dass etwa 75-100 Gruppenabende zur Verfügung stehen. Diese würden sich über 1 1/2-2 Jahre erstrecken. Nach mehr als 150 Gruppenstunden — also 75 Gruppenabenden — ist nach meiner Beobachtung die produktive Spannung zwischen den Gruppenmitgliedern so weit gesunken, dass eine Neueingliederung bzw. Austausch von Gruppenmitgliedern zwischen den Gruppen erfolgen sollte.

Welches sind nun die Vorteile der Gruppentherapie mit 12-er-Gruppen? Nach meinen Beobachtungen ist das Ergebnis der Behandlung in einer gruppenzentrierten Gruppe gleichwertig einer Eizelbehandlung, und das Therapieergebnis in einer 12-er-Gruppe dem Ergebnis in einer 8-er-Gruppe gleichwertig. Daraus ergibt sich, dass an ärztlichem Zeitaufwand im Vergleich zur Einzelbehandlung 1/8 in einer 8-er-Gruppe und 1/12 in einer 12-er-Gruppe beansprucht wird. Der ärztliche Zeitaufwand pro Patient verhält sich also bei der 12-er-Gruppe im Vergleich zur 8-er-Gruppe wie 2 : 3. Die Leistung der Gruppe wird von Seiten unserer Krankenkasse anerkannt. Bei einer Mindestteilnehmerzahl von 7 Gruppenmitgliedern werden für den Gruppentherapeuten für 2 volle Gruppenstunden 5 Arbeitsstunden honoriert.

Bei der Betrachtung der Vor — und Nachteile der 12-er-Gruppe zieht man am besten zunächst den Vergleich mit einer Einzelbehandlung, d.h. also einer 2-er-Gruppe heran. In der Einzelbehandlung weiss der Therapeut sehr viel über die Biographie seines Patienten. In der 8-er-Gruppe weiss er wessentlich weniger, und in der 12-er-Gruppe wäre es eine Illusion zu glauben, sämtliche Details wissen zu können. In der 2-er-Gruppe besteht eine Übertragung und Gegenübertragung zwischen nur 2 Personen. Dies kann therapeutisch ausgenutzt werden. Es fällt dem Patienten aber oft schwer, die verschiedenen Übertragungsmöglichkeiten deutlich auszudrücken, und dem Psychotherapeuten schwer, sie in ihren Nuancen richtig zu erkennen.

Bei einer gruppenzentrierten 8-er-Gruppe gibt es $n(n-)$ also 8 mal 7=56 Übertragungen und Gegenübertragungen, bei der 12-er-Gruppe 12 mal 11=132 Übertragungen bezw. Gegenübertragungen. In der 12-er-Gruppe gibt es also mehr als doppelt so viel Übertragungsmöglichkeiten als in der 8-er-Gruppe. In der 8-er-Gruppe hat der Patient die Möglichkeit, seine Übertragung auf 7, in der 12-er-Gruppe auf 11 Personen aufzuteilen. Dies ermöglicht ein simultanes Ausagieren sehr verschiedener aktueller Konflikte. Die inhomogene Zusammensetzung der Gruppe erleichtert dies. Für den Therapeuten erschwert diese Vielfalt den Überblick, ist es doch unmöglich, 132 Beziehungen auf einmal zu überblicken. Vergleichsweise muss man ad hoc mehr Details aktuell verfügbar haben, je grösser die Gruppe ist In der Therapie verfolgt man das Geschehen wie ein Fussballspiel, man muss aber dabei immer ein Gefühl für die Gesamtatmosphäre haben.

Als Vorteil der 12-er-Gruppe erweist es sich, dass vielfältigere Stellungnahmen und Nuancierungen zu erwarten sind. In jeder Gruppe nehmen 2-4 die Rolle des Schweigens ein. In einer 12-er-Gruppe bleibt eine grössere Zahl von Nichtschweigern, es wird lebhafter diskutiert, vielseitiger interpretiert, und es werden mehr produktive Erwägungen angestellt. Es hat sich für mich gezeigt, dass ich in der 12-er-Gruppe viel leichter die Rolle des Schweigens einnehmen kann als in der 8-er-Gruppe.

Die grössere Zahl von Gruppenmitgliedern führt leichter zu Nebengesprächen, wobei sich aber doch fast immer spontan ein Gesamt-Gruppengespräch entwickelt. Gruppendynamisch wirkt sich also die grössere Mitgliederzahl in der leichteren Bildung von Untergruppen aus, die in der Zusammensetzung während des Abends mehrmals wechseln. Es gelingt meist einer Untergruppe, die Gesamtgruppe für sich zu interessieren. Häufig kommt es auch vor, dass ein Schweiger bei Bestehen von Nebengesprächen den Gegenübersitzenden unterbricht und sagt: "Ich kann Sie nicht verstehen, bitte sprechen Sie zur gesamten Gruppe". Dabei wird der Schweiger meist noch von anderen unterstützt, und so kommt ein Gesamt-Gruppengespräch zustande. Ein permanentes Zerfallen der 12-er-Gruppe in 2 Untergruppen ist in den letzten Jahren nur einmal erfolgt. Infolge einer Unbedachtheit meinerseits hatte ich in einer Gruppe 5 Abiturienten. Es entstand eine typische Klassenkampfsituation, die durch die verschiedenartige Sprech — und Ausdrucksweise der Untergruppen von der Gruppe nicht produktiv bewältigt werden konnte. Ich löste dies Problem, indem ich 3 Abiturienten in meine beiden anderen Gruppen übernahm.

Einen weiteren Vorteil der 12-er-Gruppe sehe ich in dem grösseren Mut, der erforderlich ist, unter 12 statt unter 8 Personen zu sprechen. Ferner bietet die 12-er-Gruppe für den Einzelnen eine erhöhte Chance, Unterstützung zu finden, er findet leichter Hilfs-Egos. Während der Therapeut in der Einzeltherapie vorsichtig nuanciert in seinen Ausserungen sein muss, ergibt sich als willkommene Konsequenz der Hilfs-Egos, dass sich in der Gruppe die Einzelnen ruhig auch unbekümmert und drastisch ausdrüken können. Eine Patientin erzählt z.B.: "Oh, das war schlimm mit meinem ersten kuss. Den ganzen Abend glaubte ich, ein Zacken sei mir aus der Krone gefallen. Als ich morgens aufwachte, fand ich, das Gefühl dabei sei doch sehr schön gewesen. Ich konnte vor Aufregung nicht frühstücken. Da gab mir meine Mutter Rhizinusöl".

Ein weiteres Positivum der 12-er-Gruppe sehe ich in dem intensiveren Wir-Erlebnis und den vielseitigeren Formulierungsmöglichkeiten bei der grösseren Mitgliederzahl. Ein Beispiel: Ein 27-jähriger, gut aussehender Patient hat Kontaktschwierigkeiten gegenüber dem anderen Geschlecht. Er beteiligt sich lebhaft am Gespräch der Gruppe. Es werden von der Gruppe u.a. zahlreiche Möglichkeiten vorgeschlagen, Kontakt mit dem anderen Geschlecht zu suchen, z.B. für ihn als Nichttänzer der Besuch einer Tanzstunde. Alle diese Versuche beantwortet der Patient mit einer abwehrenden matten Handbewegung: "Hat ja doch alles keinen Zweck." Da sagt in gutmütogem Zorn ein anderes Gruppenmitglied: "Hören Sie mal, Herr So-und-so, Sie sind sehr eingebildet, Sie tun, ja so, als ob wir alle miteinander nur erzeugt worden wären zu dem Zweck, dass wir hier zusammenkommen und Ihnen Ratschläge geben, zu denen Sie dann sagen können 'hat ja doch keinen Zweck'." Daraufhin musste der so angesprochene Patient lachen und sagte: "Das war gut". Darauf der Erste: "Das war auch meine Sternstunde". Hierauf der Angesprochene: "Ach wo, ein blindes Huhn findet manchmal auch ein Korn". Die ganze Gruppe lachte.

In der grösseren Gruppe wird eine gewisse "Geometrie der Gruppe" deutlich sichtbar. Die Gruppenmitglieder können ihre Plätze selber wählen. Fest steht lediglich der Platz des Therapeuten. Ich habe die Beobachtung gemacht, dass ein Patient, der sich in aggressiver Auseinandersetzung mit dem Therapeuten befindet, sich den Platz ihm gegenüber aussucht. Dagegen suchen Angstliche, Anlehnungsbedürftige den Platz links und rechts neben dem Therapeuten, gewissermassen im Schutzwinkel, wobei meistens der Patient rechts der Anlehnungsbedürftigste ist. Auch innerhalb des Kreises habe ich festgestellt, dass Opponenten häufig einander gegenübersitzen oder durch das Gegenübersitzen zu Opponenten werden. Es ist wahrscheinlich, dass ein problemgeladenes Gruppenmitglied eher früher zur Gruppenstunde kommt, die Auswahl unter den Sitzplätzen hat und dann gegenüber den später Gekommenen schon das Vorrecht des Einheimischen besitzt. In der Wahl der Sitzplätze durch die Gruppenmitglieder konstelliert sich so schon vor Beginn der Gruppenstunde die innere Situation der Gruppe. Ich habe beobachtet, dass nach gemeinsamen Alkoholgenuss innerhalb der Gruppe die Opponentenbeziehung gestört war. Jeder sprach mit seinem Nachbarn und drang mit seinem Gespräch nicht auf die Gegenseite des Kreises vor.

Dass die Gruppe gruppenzentriert ist und nich in Detailgruppen zerfällt, ergibt sich aus dem Verhalten der Gruppen bei plötzlicher Erkrankung des Psychotherapeuten. Sie führten im Allgemeinen von sich aus die Sitzung alleine durch, eine meiner 3 Gruppen sogar 3 Wochen hintereinander, und alle 3 Gruppen berichteten, dass die Diskussion sehr lebending gewessen sei. Ein Patient sagte mir: "Doktor, so wichtig bist du gar nicht".

Nach meinen Eindrücken zeigt sich die erste Wirkung der Gruppentherapie schon nach 2 Monaten und zwar in der Änderung der Gestik und Mimik. Zuerst kommen die Patienten entweder passiv desinteressiert oder ängstlich gespannt, während nach dieser Zeit die Gesamtmimik und Gestik deutlich lebhafter und gelöster werden. Verhaltensweisen werden im Vergleich zur Einzeltherapie rascher geändert. Als letztes kommt die Beseitigung der Symptomatik, wobei, auffält, dass es vor und bei Erledigung von anstehenden positiven Lebensaufgaben zu einer vorübergehenden Verschlechterung kommen kann. Im allgemeinen wird von allen Patienten betont, wie schön es wäre, einen Ort zu haben, an dem man alles aussprechen könnte und doch keiner Gehässigkeit ausgesetzt sei.

Der Psychotherapeut greift eigentlich nur in 3 Fällen ein:

1) Wenn ein Gruppenmitglied völlig allein gegen die anderen steht, im stützenden und bejahenden Sinn.

2) Wenn es der Gruppe nach längerer Zeit nicht gelingt, sich auf ein Thema zu einigen.

3) Wenn wichtige Gesichtspunkte zu einem Problem nicht

gebracht werden. Aber auch das erfolgt nur, wenn es aktuell notwendig ist, sonst ist Zurückhaltung besser. Meist bringt die Gruppe selbst am nächsten oder übernächsten Gruppenabend die entsprechende Ergänzung.

Die Lebendigkeit dieser 12-er-Gruppen ist möglich einesteils durch die Anonymität des Grosstadtmilieus, zum anderen durch den Witz und die Schlagfertigkeit der Berliner, die von sich selber gern sagen, sie haben "Herz und Schnauze". Ihnen habe ich es zu verdanken, dass mir die Gruppentherapie so viel Freude macht.

SECTION 4: PSYCHODRAMA

GROUP ORIENTED PSYCHODRAMA

by SYLVIA ACKERMAN

The unique feature of group-oriented psychodrama is the involvement of the individual members of the group directly in interaction with the protagonist, without playing the roles of auxiliary egos or doubles. Thus we maintain group psychotherapy throughout the psychodrama by involving the group in the action continuously. First, they created the problem by stimulating the discussion in the warm-up; then they aided the protagonist as auxiliaries and doubles; then they became directly involved in the action by interacting as themselves; and finally, in sharing their experiences, they identify with the problem and form a common bond.

I shall give a single abridged version of group-oriented psychodrama where the members of the group, by playing themselves and directly interacting with the protagonist, are able simultaneously to give and receive therapy throughout the session.

In the first psychodrama, Susan, a beautiful young dance instructress in her twenties, suggested the topic, "How to fight the feeling of withdrawing from people." Susan explained that she lacked self-discipline, could not face new situations, and withdrew.

In discussing the question of withdrawal, a teacher, Viola, raised the question of how to handle a 14 year old girl who has had multiple plastic operations on her left ear without success. She has an orifice without an ear and a hare-lip so disfiguring that the children of the class nicknamed her "monkey." As a result, Linda threatened to quit school because she could not face this mortification. Viola felt that unless something could be done to help Linda, she would be permanently damaged emotionally.

Mrs. A., the director, called Viola on the stage and then chose Susan, who had raised the question of withdrawal, to play the role of fourteen year old Linda. There was a gasp in the audience at the selection of Susan for this role since she is graceful and beautiful. The director then asked Viola to play the role of Linda, since she knew the girl, and Susan was asked to play Viola's role.

Viola (as Linda): I won't go back to school. The children all make fun of me. They call me monkey. I won't go back. They all hate me. I won't go back to school.

Susan (as Viola): It can't be that bad. Why won't you go back?

Viola (as Linda): Nothing you can say will make me go back. I just won't. (Susan does not respond.)

Mrs. A.: Reverse roles, Susan, you be Linda, and Viola, you be yourself.

Viola (intellectualizing): Linda, the children don't hate you; they don't mean any harm when they call you "monkey." You can go to a cosmetician and have something done to your face.

Susan (as Linda): They just don't want me. I feel rejected.

Viola (insisting): No they don't, Linda. You are mistaken. Children are always saying things they don't mean.

Linda: I don't want to get hurt any more. I'm not going back.

Viola: A lot of things can be done. You won't accomplish

314

anything by quitting. You'll only be more alone than before. If you don't pay attention to the children, they'll forget about calling you monkey.

Linda (without listening to what Viola is saying): I can't, I can't, I can't.

Mrs. A. (goes on stage, takes Linda's hand and says): Linda, I overheard the whole conversation that you had with Viola. I notice your hair is covering your ear and no one can notice that anything is wrong. I think you look fine. I am sure there are many people who have a handicap. I would like to introduce you to Walter. He was the protagonist last week. He had a very unhappy childhood because his father and mother were separated. Maybe he can help by discussing his handicap.

Walter (on stage): Linda, I can understand how you feel. My mother and father were separated when I was a baby. I never saw my father until I was a grown man. My mother worked all the time and never had any time for me. I felt nobody loved me. I grew up without any friends. I married a girl whose parents rejected me and she wasn't strong enough to love me in spite of her parents' opposition. I have been handicapped all my life. If some one could have helped me when I was fourteen years old, maybe my marriage would not have ended in divorce.

Mrs. A.: Thank you, Walter, you have been very helpful. Walter goes off stage).

Mrs. A. (to Linda): Do you think Walter also suffered under a handicap?

Linda: It doesn't make any difference, it doesn't help me.

Mrs. A. (to Linda): Let us ask your classmates how they feel about you. Maybe some of them really like you and you don't know it. (Mrs. A. tells the audience that they are Linda's class and they should respond as students spontaneously. Mrs. A. takes Linda's hand and sits down beside her, at the second level of the stage facing the audience, and addresses the audience as members of Linda's class.)

Mrs. A. (to class): Linda feels that she wants to stop coming to school because nobody likes her and you all make fun of her. Is this true? Tell Linda how you feel.

Bob: Linda is always by herself and she seems uninterested in us, so why should we pay any attention to her.

Mrs. A. (to Linda): Is this true, Linda? Do you stay by yourself?

Linda: Yes, because I know they will reject me.

Lowell: I like Linda. I think she has a pretty face. I would like to be friends with her.

Mrs. A. (to Linda): See how nicely he is smiling? Doesn't he look nice when he smiles? Let me see you smile.

Linda (spontaneously smiles and says): I like him because he smiled at me.

Mrs. A. (to Linda): Would you like to be friends with him?

Linda: Yes.

Mrs. A.: Lowell, please come on stage and hold Linda's hand and show her that you want to be her friend. (Lowell comes on stage, takes Linda's hand and she smiles again).

Joan: I would like to invite Linda to join my sorority.

Linda: I don't believe her.

Alice: I would like to invite Linda to my home to study with me.

Linda: She doesn't really mean it.

Jack: I like Linda. In fact I would like to take her out on a date.

Linda: Yes, I would like to go.

Mary: We are not rejecting Linda. She is rejecting us. If she would be more friendly, we would be glad to be friends with her.

Linda: It's not true. They don't want me as a friend.

Edith (A maternal-looking woman in her late forties): I know just how you feel, Linda, because I am just like you. I would ask you to come over to my house over and over again until you would finally accept. I would not take no for an answer.

Linda (smiles): I believe her. (This is the first woman she responded to positively).

Arthur: I think Linda is very pretty. I can't believe that she has no friends.

Linda: I have no friends.

Mimi: The problem is not with the class, the problem is with you.

Walter: I have always felt shy too, but I have learned in order to overcome my shyness to take the initiative in talking to people, and they don't reject me.

Mrs. A. (to Adriane, who had missed the opening scenes): Adriane, you are a new student. What would you like to say to Linda. Would you like to be her friend?

Adriane: I don't know what this is all about. This seems like acting; it doesn't seem real to me.

Linda (standing up): She rejects me. I can't go on.

Mrs. A.: All right. You are no longer Linda. Now you are yourself, Susan. Lowell says he wants to be your friend. I would like to see Lowell and you become friends. Dr. A., you be Susan's double.

Susan: I can't be friends with Lowell because Adriane rejected me.

Mrs. A.: Adriane, would you please come on the stage and tell Susan whether you reject her or not.

Adriane (reluctantly goes on stage): I don't know what this is all about.

Mrs. A. (to Adriane): Do you reject Linda?

Adriane: Of course not. If I must be frank, I am jealous of all women who are younger and prettier than I am. How can I reject her when she has so much more than I have? Why should she care what I say, anyway?

Susan: As soon as she came into the room I knew she didn't like me.

Double: I wish she wasn't here.

Susan (laughs): That's right.

Mrs. A. (to Susan): Is there any woman in the audience whom you feel does not reject you?

Susan: Yes (pointing to Edith, who is the motherly type). She does not reject me because she said she would ask me to come over to her house over and over again. (Mrs. A. asks Edith to come on stage.)

Edith (on stage): I know just how you feel, Susan. (She takes Susan in her arms. Susan nestles on her breast).

Susan: This is what I have always wanted: It feels so good. If only my mother were like this. I wish this could go on forever. (Mrs. A. dims the lights to soft red and blue. Susan continues to nestle on Edith's breast for a few minutes without saying a word. Then Mrs. A. turns the discussion over to the group.)

During the discussion period the group identified and shared experiences with the protagonist. They mentioned that they were puzzled about why the director chose some one as beautiful as Susan to play the role of physically handicapped Linda. They then realized, in the course of the psychodrama, that Susan had played herself in acting out her own emotional handicap. They cited instances where they, too, felt inferior in certain areas, because rejected and withdrew.

317

They wondered how anyone could work out the problem of a person who was not present. In identifying with the feelings of rejection and withdrawing, they realized the universals involved in various kinds of handicaps. As teachers they learned how to handle feelings of rejection on the part of the children they taught, and discussed how they would apply it to individual cases.

The meaning of rejection became clear to them when Adriane and Susan felt mutual rejection. They realized it was self-rejection rather than rejection by some one else. They also realized they had reacted to Susan directly as themselves, rather than indirectly as fictitious students.

Some reacted to Susan as Susan, others to Susan as Linda. In either case they responded as themselves. Through positive and negative interaction, Susan was able to select what she was ready to accept. Even an isolate is able to change rejection to acceptance, once accepted by any person. This success helps her build confidence and courage to develop further communications and relationships instead of withdrawing.

RELIGIOUS PSYCHODRAMA

by Rabbi Alvin Bobroff

Religious psychodrama is that type of group psychotherapy which deals with the personal problems of individuals associated with religious feelings. The director starts the group therapy session by asking for volunteers to suggest a religious topic that they would like to have discussed. Then the different members of the group are encouraged to give their points of view on the topic. When the director observes one of the individuals getting emotionally involved, he focuses the individual on some scene associated with his emotion.

In a characteristic session a woman raised the question, "Why doesn't God answer people's prayers?" In the discussion the woman became very angry and said, "God can be very mean at times." She indicated that God had forsaken her in time of crisis. The director asked her, "Was there ever a specific instance in your life when God disappointed you?" At this point the woman revealed that following childbirth she was very ill and had overheard her doctor saying that she would not pull through. She now felt that God had forsaken her and she became very angry. The director set up a scene between her and the Doctor in which she learned that the doctor had really said that she was not fighting hard enough. She passed the crisis, and as the scene unfolded further she revealed that she became angry again with God when she prayed to him to help her recover rapidly so that she could return to her family, and instead it took a long time. The director asked her if she had ever received help when she needed it, and a new scene was set up with her father when she was a young child. It soon became apparent that her father did for her what she should have done for herself. During role reversal, she as father realized all of this, and learned through the auxiliary who was playing her part how to become self-sufficient, instead of dependent.

319

She then played the scene all over again as the young child who was now self-sufficient and happy in her new found strength, and rejected the overprotectiveness of her father. She learned that she had accepted God as an overprotective father, and expected that God would protect her from all harm and grant every wish she made. In a further scene she prayed to God within her, asking for more strength and courage to be a better wife and mother.

In the group discussion we learned that different members of the group identified with this expectation that God would do for them what they were not ready to do for themselves. Because of their disappointment in God, they neglected not only themselves but also their family. With this new understanding they expressed the desire to become more self-sufficient and allow their children the same privilege.

LE PREMIER PSYCHODRAME PSYCHOTHERAPIQUE
DANS LES "GUEPES" D'ARISTOPHANE
par N. N. Dracoulides

Le premier psychodrame thérapeutique se trouve dans les "Guêpes," comédie d'Aristophane presentée à Athènes en 422 av. J. C. Dans cette comédie Aristophane presente un homme hanté de l'obsession judiciaire (accuser, juger, condamner) et son fils qui tâche le guérir, en inventant à cet effet deux sortes de psychodrame, dont l'un de nature compensatoire et l'autre de nature cathartique et dont l'un constitue l'étape progressive de l'autre.

Aristophane nous donne dans les "Guêpes," en dehors des deux psychodrames qu'il place au centre de sa comédie, d'abord l'histoire qui l'a mené à inventer une psychothérapie psychodramatique de son héros et ensuite le résultant vivant de ces psychodrames. Un point intéressant à noter serait que les deux personnages principaux d'Aristophane qui dialoguent, représenteraient la désagrégation d'un seul en deux: l'un névrosé, (le père) et l'autre normal (le fils) réintegrés après ce psychodrame en un seul personnage par identification du névrosé avec le normal (le père, tel qu'il se montre dans cette pièce après le psychodrame) avec création d'un Surmoi normal-freinateur (intervention du fils après le traitement) à la place du Surmoi névrotique-punitif (le père avant le traitement).

Dans ces psychodrames Aristophaniens on distingue trois activités psychothérapiques, dont l'une correspond à la psychothérapie individuelle d'un personnage imaginaire, l'autre à la psychothérapie d'un groupe imaginaire (le coeur de la pièce) et d'un groupe réel (les spectateurs) et la dernière concerne l'autocatharsis d'Aristophane lui-même.

Le besoin cathartique était ressenti chez Aristophane — enclin à la même obsession que son héros — après la désapprobation que le public et le jury exprimèrent contre sa comédie précédente, les "Nues" dans laquelle (à cause de son attachement aux vieilles idées

321

et de son misonéïsme, tous les deux dûs à sa fixation parentale) il ridiculisa Socrate et diffama la jeunesse de son temps.

L'effet cathartique produit par les "Guêpes" sur Aristophane lui-même fut avéré par le changement d'attitude dans ses trois pieces qui immédiatement suivirent les "Guêpes" (les "Campeuses," la "Paix" et la "Vieillesse") et par son propre comportement réel dans la vie.

PSYCHODRAMA
IN A THERAPEUTIC SOCIAL GROUP SETTING
by ROSE GARLOCK

1. *Definition of Therapeutic Social Club Group:* A therapeutic social club is a group of persons meeting within a warm, guided and permissive atmosphere, wherein each person is encouraged to develop his individual capacities for heterosexual and social relationships — to the best of his ability.

2. *Purpose:* To provide an opportunity for creative self-expression, and for realization and catharsis of mutual emotional problems and conflicts. To aid in the rehabilitation, and the return to the community, of the individual as a socially adequate member of society.

3. *Composition of Group:* The group consists of men and women, ages 16 to 45 years, who are currently in individual or group therapy at the Alfred Adler Center or with private therapists.

4. *Program:* The program consists of varied recreational, educational and creative activities. The addition of psychodrama during the last several years has become one of the major areas for aiding the individual in gaining insights into his emotional problems and in creating within the group greater empathy and cooperation, leading to heightened group cohesiveness.

5. *Case illustrations:* Psychodrama sessions are incorporated within the club program, demonstrating the values of these techniques within the therapeutic social group setting.

6. *Results:* Approximately two-thirds of the group have volunteered as protagonists. Four-fifths of the members have cooperated by accepting roles within the action setting. The total membership has, at one time or another, participated in the group discussions following the sessions. The results have been highly satisfactory in terms of individual development, particularly with regard to social attitudes, group empathy, and greater ability to adjust to social demands.

THE PUBLIC SESSION

by JOHN R. HUNTING

Public Session Defined

The *public session* is defined as a psychodramatic presentation in which the participants literally walk off the street to form the audience. The "public" session differs from a regular group therapy session (often called a "closed" session) in that: (1) most members of the group only come once (although some individuals enjoy returning many times); (2) the size of the group may vary considerably, ranging from 2 to 200; and (3) the entrance fee is much smaller than the usual fee for a regular group therapy session. Since the only regular "public" sessions being held today in the United States are those conducted at the *Moreno Institute* in New York City, those sessions will serve as the main source of information for this paper.

Procedure

Essentially, the public session is conducted the same as the classic psychodrama — *i.e.* starting with a "warm-up," proceeding to the "action," and concluding with a "sharing" or "discussion" period. All of the instruments of any psychodramatic presentation — the stage, the director, the protagonist, the auxiliary egos, and the audience — are present in a public session.

A. *The Warm-up.* The warm-up is usually slower in a public session than in a closed session. The audience, consisting mostly of people who "have come to watch," requires more time and effort to warm-up than the participants of a regular group therapy session, where it is often more difficult to keep them off the stage than get them on it. Consequently, several warm-up techniques have been devised for this type of psychodramatic presentation,

324

and, in view of their importance, some of them are summarized as follows:

1. *Group Discussion Warm-up:* In this technique, the director asks the members of the audience to suggest problems, general or specific, which they would like to explore on the stage. After some discussion, a vote is taken and some aspect of the problem selected is portrayed on the stage — the action usually being initiated by someone voting for the problem that was chosen.

2. *Group Debate Warm-up:* A problem area with high argumentative potential is brought up for group discussion by the director, and as various individuals warm up to it, they are placed on the stage to informally debate the issue. As the debate proceeds, the director adds other members of the audience to take one side or the other. When the director finds a cue, or when he feels the person is sufficiently warmed up, he then asks him if he would like to explore some specific or general problem which may be bothering him at the time. By careful selection of debators, the director may eventually choose almost anyone he wishes with a minimum of anxiety on the part of the protagonist.

3. *Chain Warm-up:* Very appropriate with a large audience, this technique is started by the director who picks someone from the audience whom he would like to meet, and after a short conversation asks this person to pick out someone he would like to meet, and so on. After several people have been brought to the stage this way, the director usually is able to involve one or several of them in a sociodrama or psychodrama. Not only does this method reduce the "stage fright" of the potential protagonist, but it occasionally gives some insight into the sociometric pattern of the group.

4. *Conversation Warm-up:* By starting a general discussion on any topic the group spontaneously brings up, an astute director can usually find some problem or topic which one of the group would be willing to act out. This approach, usually more effective with a small group, is often preceded by a general introduction by each member of the group, and is one of the most popular forms of warming up the audience.

5. *Miscellaneous Warm-ups:* Often, other variations of the psychodramatic process can be used to warm up an individual

or group. Using projective tests, such as frustration tests, a "magic shop" or a group situation (an over-crowded hotel lobby, a bus journey, etc.) can be effective. Also, a socio-drama can be started which will lead into a psychodrama. An empty chair (often referred to as "the four-legged auxil-iary ego") can also be used by having the members of the group imagine someone in that chair, and then having them interact with that person.

B. *Action.* The action portion of the "public" session is similar to that of any psychodramatic presentation, and utilizes the usual psychodramatic techniques of role reversal, the double, the inter-view, the soliloquy, etc. Often the action portion concludes on a positive note by ending with a future projection, a magic shop, or a lecture situation where the protagonist is advising a real or imaginary audience. Since the protagonist is not in therapy and will probably not return again, the director always keeps the action on a level that allows for full closure at the end of the session. Very often, members of the audience serve as auxiliary egos, although trained auxiliary egos are usually available.

C. *Discussion:* As with a regular group therapy session, the members of the audience are asked to share their feelings with the protagonist; both for their benefit and the protagonist's. The director has to be alert to make sure that the comments from the audience are supportive in nature, and he should stop any hostile statements or probes into the protagonist's psyche or behavior. Usually, the director will summarize the dynamics of the session after the audience has shared their feelings. Questions concerning the techniques involved are generally held off until the very last part of the discussion.

Why Public Sessions?

The author feels that the public sessions are justifiable for at least three reasons.

A. *Training:* These sessions serve as excellent opportunities to train future psychodramatists under the guidance of experienced directors. Usually the trainees begin as auxiliary egos, and then gradually work into a directorial capacity. Because of the relative normality of the protagonists and their problems, the directors-in-

326

training do not have to cope with severely disturbed individuals. Thus, if mistakes are made, they are of minor consequence. The public sessions are always excellent opportunities for trainees to practice other forms of the psychodramatic process, such as projective tests, sociodramas and role training sessions. They also allow opportunities to experiment with new ideas or approaches — especially with warm-up and projective techniques.

B. *Demonstration:* By allowing interested individuals the opportunity to observe a psychodramatic presentation, the psychodramatic process becomes known to the general public rather than a select few. And since the psychodramatic process (including sociodramas, role training, etc.) is becoming more and more extensively used throughout the world, and used by members of many different professions (teachers, nurses, social workers, psychotherapists, etc.), these public sessions help familiarize people with some aspects of this process. The public sessions are particularly useful to many colleges and hospitals in the area whose instructors bring their classes to experience a psychodramatic presentation as well as just read about it in text books.

C. *Opportunity for Observation:* By having public sessions, individuals, who may be seeking counseling or therapy but do not know where to go or whom to see, may use the protectiveness of the audience to observe both the process and, in some cases, a therapist at work before having a face-to-face encounter. Such an opportunity is seldom presented in other types of therapeutic approaches.

PANTOMIME IN GROUP PSYCHOTHERAPY

by O. Horetzky

Individual problems represented by pantomime and solved by verbalizing in groups — this is a technique of group psychotherapy I have been practicing for more than ten years. Pantomimes, as I will continue to call this form of psychotherapy in the further text, are carried out in open and heterogeneous groups, and the patients are neurotics, psychotics and psychopaths.

According to the diagnosis, we decide upon the problem to be set to the patient, taking his profession, intellectual level, age, sex and stage of the disease into consideration, as well as the number of pantomimes he has already participated in.

How is the pantomime performed?

We are seated in two semi-circles in a fairly large room. We do not discuss, I do not lecture; we have no requisites, and we are not allowed to use requisites during the performance. There are ten patients in each semi-circle, one semi-circle silently participating in the pantomime. One of the patients from the other semi-circle represents the problem by pantomime, the remaining nine attempt to solve it aloud. To solve the problem means to define the concept, *i.e.* to express aloud whatever the patient is representing. This is repeated in turns so that the activities of silence and speech are rhythmically alternated in each semi-circle until all the members of the group have had their turn. The performer performs the problem he has just received from the therapist, the problem being written onto a slip of paper which has been given to the patient-performer immediately beforehand; the therapist has previously shown it to the other semi-circle of patients, so that ten patients are acquainted with the subject the performer is representing, and

328

nine are not. The group which knows what is the task set to the member of the other group will silently participate in the pantomime, and follow how the performer is representing the problem to the others; thus there are ten patients, each of them imagining themselves in the position of the performer, and wondering how they would represent the set concept in their own way. This results in a particular tension within the group, often manifested by various motions of the hands and lips some individuals cannot control. The therapist sometimes has to silence them. This inner contact is a powerful factor which encourages the performer. At the same time it is a group training itself in self-control.

The pantomime involves a marked interaction between the performer and his group, not by speech but by pantomime, which is much more direct than speech and demands a maximum of effort from the performer. He frequently perspires, loses breath, even bursts into tears. He is required to represent, or try to represent, a certain concept by gestures. This is seldom easy or simple, especially if accurate representation in gender, number, and case is required. Nevertheless, among nine patients belonging to the performer's group there is usually one who ventures an approximately correct guess. The first spark of communication is thus created. The performer broadens his manner of representation, another patient steps in, so to say, and draws nearer to the concept behind the word. Focussing the concept into a gradually clearer form demands a considerable effort, the group and the performer achieve complete contact, a member of the group says the set word, and the problem is solved.

When the word stands for a concrete concept, for example "the safe," it is comparatively easy, at least for those who know the set word. For the performer and for those solving the problem, every problem is difficult unless contact is established in one way or another. The procedure during the pantomime is essentially this: between the concept and the mimed expression, tension is established; this tension demands a solution from the members of the group. Invisible threads are cast, somebody catches hold of them and they stretch.

If the performer still holds them, the other person will help him, and relaxation occurs the moment the word is correctly said.

The group usually changes after several pantomimes, because some patients are discharged and others are admitted. When the patient has accurately represented the concept and his fellow-patients have correctly solved the problem, his active part is finished for that evening (pantomimes are always performed in the evening). After his performance, however, he becomes a member of the group helping the next performer or solver of the next problem. Performance and solving of problems alternates with the silence of those knowing the solution; but this silence is not an interruption of the pantomime, it is inner participation without external manifestations. To what extent this really is participation can be best seen if the tension rises so high that a patient forgets himself and says aloud what he has seen on the slip of paper.

In my pantomimes the sequence is as follows:

(1) Each patient gives his anamnestic data himself. This is done during a so-called psychotherapeutic conversation alone with the patient. These data are complemented with heteroanamnestic data obtained from the family and the environment.

(2) From these data the therapist sets the problem in condensed form, so that it is in connection with the origin of the illness or of the neurotic reaction. For example, a patient's escape into illness is transposed into the problem "I seek company." The therapeutic task is a condensation of this escape in a couple of words.

(3) The patient gets his problem on a slip of paper. He reads it immediately before the beginning of the pantomime. He connects the concept "I seek company" with known ideas, and when he devises a means of representing it by pantomime — no other means being available — his imagination broadens his plan of performance, and after a more or less short initial pause for concentration he applies all his attention to the task of representing the concept "I seek."

Since a verb has to be dealt with — *i.e.* an action — the patient will probably stir, move, bend down, and evoke precisely those functions he has repressed in his escape into himself. If he wants his group to help him, he must contribute his share, this being the principle of every psychotherapy: active collaboration of the patient. This can only be achieved if he is in connection with one or another of the members of his group, who are waiting to see him show something. If the patient is embarrassed and does not show anything, wrings his fingers, crumples his piece of paper, or does anything which is not connected with the problem, an uneasy silence ensues, which is more eloquent than words. This silence

330

induces the performer to do something, even if it is not correct. The disharmonious behavior of the performer or of any other individual in the group harmonizes the other nine patients who are allowed to speak, and they will offer the necessary impulse and encouragement. This is the most tense phase, and it is of diagnostical interest. Therapeutically it represents culmination and crisis.

(4) Catharsis and relaxation: the moment someone out of the group cries "where!" or "he's not here!" or "there!," another one says "lost," "found" and the like, and depending on the performer's representation of the concept "I seek," the tension subsides. What had seemed impossible to the patient suddenly becomes possible. "I cannot" is a common neurotic phrase. There is no "cannot" in a pantomime, because no speech is allowed, and if anything can be expressed in pantomime gestures, this is proof that it is possible after all. Fifteen minutes sometimes elapse from the moment the patient gets his slip of paper until he resumes his place again, but the representation usually takes four or five minutes to be solved. If we assume that a pantomime session lasts for about an hour (with a pause of 10 minutes) and twenty patients attend, this would mean an average of five minutes for each of them.

REFLEXION SUR LA SPONTANEITE ET LES COURANTS AFFECTIFS EN PSYCHODRAME MORENIEN

par P. Lemoine

Buts et moyens du psychodrame

Accaparés par leurs rôles sociaux ou familiaux, les patients viennent à nous parce qu'ils osent rarement être eux-mêmes. Ils craignent de ne pas être acceptés pour ce qu'ils sont et offrent d'eux une image plus conforme à leur idéal qu'à leur nature. Ils adoptent vis-à-vis du groupe social une attitude de culpabilité qui les empêche de s'affirmer pour ce qu'ils sont et de se réaliser en tant que personnes.

La psychothérapie de groupe "fournit les conditions idéales pour le passage du Surmoi infantile qui résulte de l'intériorisation des interdits parentaux, au Surmoi social, expression du désir d'être accepté par le groupe." Mais cela n'est possible que si chaque participant accepte sa propre spontanéité, c'est-à-dire tout dire et de tout faire avec cette réserve qu'il est également libre de se taire quand il le désire.

Une limite á la spontanéité: l'expression de l'agressivité

Dans le groupe psychodramatique discours et action ne sont pas soumis aux impératifs de la bienséance, mais la spontanéité est cependant limitée dans son expression par deux ordres de considérations:

—Celui qui s'exprime de façon agressive risque la rétorsion de la part des autres membres ce qui le force à n'infliger aux autres que des attaques dont l'intensité correspond à celle qu'il pourrait lui même supporter.

—Il ne doit pas traumatiser les autres participants et l'animateur est là pour freiner certaines attaques trop directes.

Nous avons observé des somatisations (crises d'urticaires, crises hépatiques, etc. . . .) après des attaques trop directes de la part d'un des participants.

L'agressivité peut aussi se manifester au niveau du groupe dans son ensemble. L'ensemble du groupe peut se montrer trop critique vis-à-vis d'un participant, exagérer la réprobation. Dans la situation inverse, le groupe peut faire taire ses attaques pour épargner celui qui a parlé. Ce sont là deux problèmes d'expression d'une agressivité franche ou refoulée auxquels le directeur de groupe est appelé à faire face. Il faut qu'il en prenne lui-même conscience (c'est parfois assez subtil pour passer inaperçu et son anxiété peut le conduire à "escamoter" une situation désagréable). Un mot, une orientation du propos des participants, et quand cela est possible une mise à jour des sources de cette agressivité sont les remèdes à appliquer.

Ainsi des limitations sont imposées aux participants d'un groupe de psychodrame, autant dans les paroles que dans les actes. Si on compare le psychodrame Morénien à l'Analyse on voit que l'analyse limite moins le discours, mais empêche l'action. C'est par là-même qu'elle pousse le patient à regresser.

Par contre, le psychodrame analytique permet, d'après Kestenberg, une expression de l'aggressivité plus franche que ne le fait le psychodrame Morénien.

Bien que limitée dans sa réalisation par les limites imposées à l'agressivité, l'action est la dimension originale du psychodrame Morénien. Parler de réalisation symbolique ne signifie rien si comme certainson réduit le geste à la parole, si on entend que la succession des gestes à seulement la valeur d'un discours. Le corps peut, en effet, démentir, et il le fait souvent, les paroles. J'en veux pour exemple le cas de cet homme qui ayant souffert, enfant, de l'autorité de sa mère se refusait à l'imiter. En famille il cherche à convaincre, du moins il le croit, plutôt qu'à exiger.

Un participant lui fait alors remarquer la violence sous-jacente à cette soi-disant intention de persuader. Elle s'est révélée dit-il dans son ton et quand au cours du jeu il a fait le geste d'écraser son bureau.

Cet exemple montre que malgré la discrétion de sa manifestation l'aggresivité aparaît cependant en psychodrame Morénien à celui qui sait la voir. Mais que surtout la participation du corps à l'action n'est pas sans donner aux relations affectives une orientation spécifique. Il semble que dans le jeu dramatique ce qui compte c'est moins ce qui est dit que l'intonation, que l'intention exprimée par le ton et l'attitude corporelle.

Ce sont là les restes inconscients de cette spontanéité dont Moréno nous apprend qu'elle est à son maximum à l'âge de 5 ans. Elle décroit ensuite — quand l'Oedipe la modifie en intériorisant l'agressivité de l'enfant sous forme de Surmoi — ce Surmoi qui était jusqu'alors extérieur et personnifié par les parents.

Le ton, la geste, la mimique mentent moins que la parole et peuvent même avoir une signification totalement opposée.

Enseignée par les parents, puis par la Société, la parole reste conforme à ses origines surmoïques .. le sujet y greffe ses propres réactions affectives mais le fait en fonction des sources parentales auxquelles il a puisé.

Par contre, le geste comme le cri sont la réponse directe du sujet au monde, la réponse de l'animal devenu humain. S'il est symbolique de quelque chose, il l'est par une autre voie que la parole. Et il est facile en psychodrame d'interpréter cette attitude corporelle, ce qui est déconseillé en Analyse.

Donc, tandis que la parole s'incarne dans le sujet, se fait chair, le geste est chair et se fait parole.

Avec l'expression corporelle on touche à un point particulier de la communication en psychodrame.

Le problème du transfert et du télé

Par analogie avec l'analyse on a appelé transfert la relation des participants aux animateurs, transfert latéral des relations affectives des participants entre eux.

Moréno a raison de mettre l'accent sur le fait qu'il ne s'agit pas de la même relation thérapeutique en psychodrame qu'en Analyse et de soutenir qu'on ne peut parler de transfert que lorsque les sujets, au lieu de communiquer réellement entre eux, répètent de façon anachronique et déphasée une attitude ancienne — par exemple en manifestant envers un des participants, ou envers l'animateur une haine ou un amour sans rapport avec celui qui est "renvoyé" par l'autre protagoniste.

Lorsque les sentiments et émotions exprimés comportent une participation réciproque, actuelle, Moréno parle alors de télé. Cette distinction entre transfert et télé étant faite on remarquera que les membres d'un groupe de psychodrame Morénien adoptent une attitude différente envers les animateurs et envers les participants.

1) Bien qu'ils participent au groupe, s'y mêlent, s'offrent au regard et à la parole, s'impliquent davantage que ne le fait un psychothérapeute ou un Analyste, *les animateurs* n'en sont pas moins investis d'une autorité que leur confère leur fonction et leur science et qui tient à la convention qui préside à l'origine du groupe. C'est l'aspect transférentiel de la situation.

Mais, parce qu'ils s'exposent, ils doivent, plus qu'un Analyste, justifier leur fonction, et donc posséder réellement cette autorité, comprendre la direction que prend le groupe, posséder un degré de connaissance et d'expérience qui leur permette de répondre aux attentes du groupe, et cette chaleur humaine qui, à travers les liens humains qui se créent, rende la vérité vivante.

C'est de l'autorité de l'animateur que dépend le respect des règles du groupe donc sa sécurité et sa cohésion: un participant peut tout dire et, en principe, tout faire, mais l'animateur doit protéger chacun des attaques excessives et des passages à l'acte.

Selon le sexe de l'animateur, le thème du groupe aura tendance à se centrer davantage sur les relations avec l'une des figures du sexe opposé à celui (frère ou soeur, conjoint ou épouse) des animateurs. C'est pourquoi il est souhaitable que les animateurs soient de deux sexes différents et qu'ils dirigent à tour de rôle le groupe en tenant compte du thème dominant (l'animateur ne dirigeant pas, jouant alors le rôle d'observateur). Celà s'est avéré un moyen très sûr de manier l'inconscient du groupe.

De même un groupe suit un progrès continu si son thème se poursuit au long des séances, ce ne peut être un pur hasard: un groupe ne va pas n'importe où, il enchaîne plus ou moins consciemment sur le propos de la séance précédente et des thèmes se perpétuent, se développent de séance en séance. Vouloir contrarier un tel courant serait aller au devant d'un échec, c'est, pour reprendre l'image du courant, risquer d'être balayé par le flot. Et ce rôle du directeur du groupe est de se maintenir sur la crête de la vague, de *comprendre la direction que prend le groupe.*

Mais parce que du fait même de la convention qui préside à l'origine du groupe, il est celui qui détient une vérité, l'animateur ne peut en faire usage au même titre qu'un participant. Il doit s'inspirer de la prudence qui doit présider à toute relation psychothérapique, qu'elle soit ou non analytique.

2) Si le groupe prend une direction déterminée cela ne peut résulter que de la recherche de ses membres qui veulent établir entre eux une communication (laquelle résulte de leurs échanges affectifs) et trouver ensemble une vérité.

C'est cette recherche qui aboutit à un thème et ce thème est le commun dénominateur des exigences intimes des participants à tel moment de l'évolution du groupe. Le thème permet d'aboutir pour un certain degré d'échauffement à un psychodrame où le leader parle au nom du groupe.

On sait que chez chacun des membres les échanges affectifs peuvent s'inscrire dans un sociogramme qui montre comment ils se situent l'un par rapport à l'autre: attitudes positives ou négatives. Mais surtout, et c'est là une différence essentielle avec l'analyse, tous les éléments du conflit peuvent être vécus en même temps parce que les projections sont rendues possibles par la multiplication des figures fraternelles ou parentales. En d'autres termes la bonne et la mauvaise mère (la fée et la sorcière), le bon et le mauvais père (le bon génie et l'ogre) le frère et la soeur sont là *en même temps* alors qu'ils ne sont présents que successivement en Analyse. Ils s'offrent dans le même instant aux attaques ou à la tendresse des participants.

C'est une des sources de la spontanéité.

Il peut être intéressant d'étudier la naissance et la mort du groupe.

Un groupe qui a été vivant et bénéfique meurt en se désagrégeant. Pourquoi? Il est devenu vivant quand ont éclaté les préjugés et la suffisance, quand la recherche en commun a eu lieu. Mais il cristallise de nouveaux préjugés, la recherche disparaît et le groupe devient un groupe de bons copains, puis s'éteint. Il n'existe une mort naturelle de tout groupe. Que faire? Avoir un groupe "ouvert" qui se renouvelle par l'apport de nouveau membres. Par leur arrivée, les nouveaux créent un début, un rafraîchissement; puis ils sont intégrés et leur intégration modifie les rapports des membres entre eux.

Mais cet apport d'un sang frais n'est pas sans danger. Il faut être très prudent et on ne peut introduire un nouveau membre à tout moment. Il serait intéressant de voir comment en fonction du thème du groupe et de la personnalité du nouveau membre cette introduction est possible. Notons simplement que certains nouveaux sont très vite acceptés tandis que d'autres le sont moins rapidement ou risquent de ne l'être jamais. Notons aussi qu'un groupe ayant atteint sa maturité est moins perturbé par les départs et les entrées de nouveaux membres: il fait plus facilement son deuil d'un départ et n'est pas géné dans sa marche par la survenue d'un nouveau visage.

On voit que les courants affectifs qui relient les participants d'un groupe sont différents selon qu'il s'agit des courants qui soudent les membres entre eux ou de ceux qui les relient aux animateurs.

Du fait de son statut l'animateur provoque une attitude affective (de dépendance ou de contredépendance) qui se situe davantage sur le versant tu transfert que du télé, tandis qu'entre les membres on observe une certaine facilitation du télé; le transfert étant le fruit de la répétition névrotique.

En Conclusion

Les courants affectifs qui apparaissent en psychodrame sont des courants complexes qui tiennent:

1° à la nature même du psychodrame qui fait intervenir le corps plus que la parole, le geste et le ton plus que le langage. L'expression du corps est une voie différente de celle du langage, a des sources et des modes qui lui sont propres: moins élaborée elle corrige les erreurs et les illusions du langage dans le domaine de la communication. Elle peut faire apparaître un désir qui est nié par le langage.

Parfois même l'intention exprimée par le corps est ignorée de celui qui joue; le sujet exécute parfaitement le rôle de celui qu'il imite mais il ne le sait pas, il a même le sentiment contraire: l'affect est annulé.

2° à la nature et à la simultanéité du "transfert": la présence des animateurs (figures paternelle et maternelle) celles des participants (figures fraternelles) déclenchent des réactions par rapport à des figures présentes, en celà le psychodrame provoque la spontanéité.

Le transfert sur les animateurs est plus dilué; il n'atteint qu'exceptionnellement un niveau aussi élevé que dans l'analyse. Les courants affectifs et les échanges entre les participants en modifient considérablement la nature et l'expression.

L'agressivité est, en particular, plus cachée, moins exprimée qu'en analyse.

Les somatisations sont possibles, quoiqu'assez rares, elles montrent l'importance de la participation du corps en psychodrame.

BREF HISTORIQUE DU PSYCHODRAME EN FRANCE

par Mireille Monod

On peut diviser en trois grandes périodes le développement du psychodrame en France.

Introduit à Paris en 1946 au Centre Psycho-Pédagogique de l'Académie de Paris, le psychodrame fut d'abord utilisé comme une forme de psychothérapie de groupe, auprès d'enfants et d'adolescents souffrant de troubles de comportement et d'inadaptation scolaire. Durant la première période (1946-1954), le psychodrame est une forme nouvelle de psychothérapie relevant de la neuropsychiatrie d'enfants et d'adultes, en traitement ambulatoire ou à l'intérieur de services hospitaliers.

Les premiers psychodramatistes français étant avant tout psychothérapeutes, les problèmes théoriques et méthodologiques que pose une compréhension du psychodrame dans une perspective psychanalytique, ont très rapidement été d'objet d'expériences et de publications en France.

A partir de 1954-1955, le psychodrame devient une branche des jeunes disciplines que sont la psychosociologie et la sociométrie. La pédagogie, comme la psychologie appliquée à la sélection, ont recours au "rôle playing" ou "jeu de rôle". Le psychodrame pédagogique et le psychodrame diagnostique deviennent ainsi aussi importants que le psychodrame thérapeutique des premières années.

Le développement des méthodes et de l'étude des phénomènes dynamiques des groupes, sous l'influence des travaux anglosaxons, caractérise l'évolution des préoccupations de nombreux spécialistes. Depuis 1959-1960, le problèmes des inter-relations humaines devient prépondérant, aussi bien en psycho-pathologie qu'en psycho-sociologie et en psycho-anthropologie.

La richesse et la variété des orientations des sciences humaines telles qu'elles sont pratiquées en France, de nos jours, donnent au terme même de psychodrame un sens fort large et parfois assez éloigné de sa signification originelle de technique psychothérapeutique.

THE INCIDENTAL AND THE PLANNED PSYCHODRAMATIC SHOCK AND ITS THERAPEUTIC VALUE

by Joseph Mann

The origin of psychodrama goes back to the theater. Moreno's discovery of therapy through action and acting out was based on his experiences in the theater of spontaneity (Stegreiftheater), which he founded in Vienna in 1921. Here he did not employ professional actors, but rather encouraged volunteers from the audience to play and re-enact scenes and experiences from their own lives. Soon it became apparent that this type of drama brought about an emotional catharsis in the participants. Aristotle was the first to use the term "catharsis" to describe the reaction of the audience upon witnessing the performance in a Greek theater, a reaction that served to purify the audience's emotions by relieving them of some of their own feelings. Freud viewed catharsis from a somewhat different standpoint: "If the function of the drama, as has been assumed since Aristotle, is to excite pity and fear, and thus bring about a 'catharsis of the emotions', we may describe this same purpose a little more fully if we say that the question is one of opening up sources of pleasure and enjoyment from within the sphere of life, just as wit and the comic do from within the sphere of the intellect, through the action of which many such sources had been made inaccessible. Certainly the release of the subject's own affects must here be given first place, and the enjoyment resulting therefrom corresponds on the one hand to the relief produced by their free discharge, and on the other, very likely, to the concomitant sexual stimulation which, one may suppose, occurs as a by-product of every emotional excitation and supplies the subject with that feeling of a heightening of his psychic level which he so greatly prizes."

Moreno's concept of catharsis is focused on the healing effect

—not only in the spectator, but primarily in the producer (actor-patient) who creates the drama, re-experiences a particular event, ventilates and liberates himself from it.

Dialogue is only one of the tools of psychodrama. Many of the psychodramatic methods, as stated by Moreno himself, were rediscovered and adjusted for psychodramatic purposes. For instance, the mirror technique from Shakespeare's *Hamlet,* the double ego method from Dostoyevski's *The Double,* the dream technique from Calderon's *La Vida es Sueño,* and role reversal (Dialogues of Socrates). Let me add here also the "psychodramatic shock" (as I like to call it) from Boccaccio's *Falcon,* which gave Paul Heyse the basis for his formulation of the climax in his theory of the structure of the short story, which he called "the shooting of the falcon."

Moreno's original formulation of psychodramatic shock was given in *Psychodramatic Shock Therapy:* "The patient is asked to throw himself back into the hallucinatory experience when it is still most vivid in his mind. He is not asked to describe it, he must act. He puts his body into the position as it was then and acts as he acted then. He may select any member of the staff to recreate the hallucinatory situations. The patient usually shows a violent resistance against being thrown back into the painful experience from which he has just escaped. His natural bent is to forget—not to talk about it. He is full of fears that his new freedom may be shattered. The mere suggestion, and still more the actual process, frightens him. The psychodramatist is encouraging the patient to act, to throw himself into the psychotic state, to lose himself entirely in it, however awful, ugly and unreal it may seem to him at that moment."

Psychodrama shock does not necessarily have to be used only for re-experiencing a hallucinatory delusion. It can also be used as a cathartic element in a dramatic confrontation. It can be incidental without the therapist's intention, completely unexpected, or planned, as when the shock is applied purposefully as a part of treatment.

The therapist has to be skilled enough to guide a situation in which a spontaneous or incidental psychodramatic shock has occurred or is about to occur. After all, psychodrama is not a play intended to be enjoyed by spectators, but should be used for the maximum benefit of everyone involved, and the protagonist-patient has to be treated as a patient, according to the principal thought in medicine: "salus aegroti suprema lex esto." The applied, or planned, psychodramatic shock allows the therapist a better management of that which is important to the patient and can contribute to his improvement, and such a shock is quite often the turning point in treatment.

PSYCHODRAMA ON A HOSPITAL WARD

A STRATEGIC SETTING FOR TRAINING

by ADALINE STARR

It is the purpose of this paper to indicate the manner in which psychodrama and sociometry can be utilized on a psychiatric hospital ward to promote spontaneity and cooperation of the patients and staff, and so provide an opportunity for the ward population to acquire a fuller knowledge of group methods.

All members of the staff are not necessarily interested in conducting psychodrama; but all may increase their skills in dealing with groups through the experience of being an auxiliary ego, audience member or protagonist. Those who show an interest in becoming directors of psychodrama can be selected by the staff and given additional training, perhaps using their talent and interest on other wards.

The place to begin, experience indicates, is on an open intensive treatment ward — with the staff and patients in attendance. This small community is a group; larger than the family, but facing some of the problems of everyday living, eating, sleeping, playing and working together. They know one another, at least marginally, and continue to be together for a period of time — in some cases, for years.

Psychodrama, with its emphasis on the enactment of relationships, is one of the few therapy forms which can accommodate a large group and still be of therapeutic value. It may be a protagonist-centered therapy in which a patient presents himself to the ward by playing out (with a trained auxiliary ego) the circumstances of his life. The performance quickly transforms the stranger into a man with recognizable problems of relationship — of benefit to himself as well as to others who must live with him. Or, it can be group-centered therapy: the interpersonal relationships within the group are sociometrically tested and drama-

342

tized. These sessions are viewed and evaluated by their day-to-day companions and often result in a learning experience for both the patients and staff. There is a chance to act out special ward problems and discuss them. The advantages of using the ward group seems obvious, but will be itemized and illustrated.

Walk with me on a ward of a large psychiatric hospital. The chairs are arranged in a semi-circle, allowing an area for the psychodramatic action to take place. Some patients are seated there waiting for the session to begin; others are along the wall, sitting with their backs to the group, or they may be lying on the floor. As you look about the room, you see patients who are depressed, confused, overactive, hallucinatory, delusional, pacers, and each category of behavior that exemplifies the hospitalized patient is there. On a closed ward, the number of people in attendance may reach sixty or seventy — with more patients sitting away from the circle than are in it. On an open ward — and this varies from ward to ward — the number attending is smaller, depending on the weather, the attitude of the staff toward attendance, feelings of the patients toward the group and therapy session, the composition of the group, as well as the timing of the session. If psychodrama is programmed after a long ward meeting, the active patients leave, and only the quiet ones remain. After a time some wander back to take part or leave again. The size of the group rarely is under 20 patients, but under favorable conditions, out of a ward population of 70, there are usually 35 patients who attend the session. The staff (ward psychiatrist, social worker, psychologist, psychology trainee, aide, training aide, or student nurse) — all those who meet and interact in this setting — are invited to participate as audience, auxiliary ego, discussion leaders or resource people. The acting area requires nothing more than a table and two chairs. The total ward is the group. Seeing and hearing one another is most important.

The psychodramatist is introduced to the group. She explains that the meetings will be held once a week for an hour and a half and that psychodrama is a form of group therapy. "This is a learning method — learning by doing, by feeling and then through discussing with the group how do they see us, and how do we see them." The director says to the group, "This time can be of value if you bring into the group problems that concern all of you — ward problems, problems of relationship as they occur

343

here on the ward, problems of relationship that occur outside the ward, on your days away from the ward, or family problems. Let's get to know each other. You can, when you feel ready, invite any member of your family to join us and take part in the psychodrama."

A Sample Session on a Male Open Ward

The warming-up period may begin with the director looking over the group and commenting on its composition and exploring some of the feelings of the patients toward each other or toward the staff. Are there any new people to the group? How does it feel to be here? How long have the student nurses been on the ward? Suddenly, the director notices that Warren, a patient, is trying to kiss a nurse. The student nurse wrestles with him. We have a situation. As they sit in the group, the director calls to Warren: "You're treating the nurse as if she were a girl friend." They stop. He retorts angrily: "It's none of your business." "Oh, yes it is," contends the nurse. "He tries this with all the student nurses." The director asks Warren to come up.

Warren: "No, I won't. But I have a juicy problem for the group (smiling broadly). There's a lot of masturbation and fornication on the ward, and I want to learn how to sublimate our sex drive. I don't approve of masturbation, fornication, adultery, but I'd like to know what we should do. I won't mention names, but they know it's disturbing to the rest of us."
Patient: "What does fornication mean?"
Warren: "It's illicit love-making of unmarried people. Adultery is illicit love-making of married people, and I disapprove of both, as well as masturbation."
Staff: "Are you married?"
Nurse: "Yes, he is, to a nice girl. I know her."
Staff: "Are you reassuring the nurses that you only play games with them and have no illicit intention?"
Warren: "Tell them, Miss Student Nurse, what you said to me."
Director: "Will both of you come up, please?"
But at this moment a patient, Mr. V. (42 years old), stalks into the acting area and, in very vulgar language, begins to describe in detail the "juicy" problem of the ward. He names names — recognizes it as a problem — but feels it shouldn't be mentioned unless

344

the "high authorities" sanction it. A few patients try to interrupt him, but one patient reminds the group that since Mr. V. usually only talks to trees and grass, perhaps they should hear him out. The "high authorities" decided that this problem was one of relationship to oneself and to others and so could be dealt with here. Mr. V. thrusts his forefinger at the group, flexes his right arm muscle and shouts at the group: "I am a 14-year-old boy — too young for sex — but strong and old enough to work." Then he calls out to the doctor: "Look at the floor. Do you like how I cleaned it? I'm a good worker."

Staff: "You're changing the subject from sex to work. Have you given up the idea of ever becoming a sexual man — a ladies' man — and settled to be a worker?"

Group: "But he doesn't even work. He doesn't do his ward assignment."

Mr. V.: "Isn't the floor clean? Do you like it?"

Staff: "What happened to you at 14 that made you decide that you couldn't achieve manliness? Work or love was too much for you?"

At this point Mr. V. leaves the ward and goes to find, perhaps in the whispering trees and murmuring grass, the kind of answers he sought. "He may try us again," the director says, "and from this encounter we are better prepared to deal with his social isolation." This explanation calms the group, and a brief discussion follows in which one old-timer on the ward recalls one event in Mr. V.'s life. On his last visit home he had worked as a plumber's assistant to his brother and tried to make love to his brother's wife, with the result that he has not been invited to return. A deep silence falls over the group. His feelings now are better understood by the group.

Staff: "It may be uncomfortable for you, Mrs. Starr, to come here expecting to do psychodrama and find us going off on a tangent."

Patient: "I played an FBI man last week. I'll come up."

Director: "This *is* psychodrama. The spontaneous act we just experienced brought responses from many of you. For a moment you became the trees that Mr. V. usually talks to — but unlike the trees, you responded to him out of your own involvement. Mr. V. emerged from his fantasy world and played, briefly, a social role — a proper man — reprimanding the patients and staff for 'dirty

345

talk' in front of ladies. The counter-spontaneity of the group confused him, so he returned to an environment without counter-spontaneity — the trees."

The director recognizes that the presence of the student nurses has stimulated the patients to speculating on themselves as sexual males, and he returns to the incident of the kissing patient and the wrestling nurse.

It may be of interest to follow this session, in part, as one example of a procedure which seems to provide an atmosphere open enough to allow the patient to observe his behavior and its effect on others, without paying the high price of lowered group esteem; as well as becoming aware that the group is trying to understand him. The director picks a cue from an earlier remark and asks, "Who else in the group has Warren tried to kiss?" All the student nurses raise their hands, and they are instructed to choose a patient and break up in pairs to enact before the group an incident of this behavior. Warren is to sit, watch, and comment as to the accuracy of the occurrence. He is delighted and laughs as each pair of actors shows how he tried and failed — how he chased a nurse around and around and failed — how he teased and never succeeded in getting a kiss. "That's right, that's right, that's the way it was." The director asks Warren to play himself with a nurse, and he does, only this time the nurse, in response to his "I want a kiss," says, "Sure, if that's what you want." And he bolts. A discussion follows with the group membership breaking up in small groups of eight or ten, each with a staff member as discussion leader. The various group reports are that 1) it was clear to them he didn't want to get a kiss, 2) he was running after rejection, 3) Warren needs love, maybe his mother didn't love him enough (a frequent catch-all). The director asks Warren to show how his mother treated him, with the ward doctor acting as Warren. "But my grandmother raised me," says this handsome colored man. "She used to go on like this — You are the finest one of the lot, the only one I can rely on. You are smart, make good high grades in school, work after school and bring me your money. You're a good boy. You'll be something — some day. I just know it."

Doctor (As Warren): "But I'm tired of being good. You keep on expecting so much from me. The only place I seem to have in this family is if I'm knocking my brains out being good. Lay off."

346

Warren: "I never talked like that to my grandma."

Director (As Warren): "But did you ever feel like it."

Doctor (As Warren): "You bet. But it never lasted, as long as I lived with grandma."

Warren (As Grandma): "Now son, don't go and ruin everything and your chances in life by marrying. You've got to finish school or you'll end up on a construction job. . . . And don't you forget it . . . you'll just be nothing. (He lapses into being Warren.) She was right. I couldn't make it after I married. It was hard to study, so I quit. I'll never make it now."

Doctor (As Warren): "But I can make girls squeal. It may not be much — but I can do that successfully — and easily. I like that . . . it's almost as easy as impressing grandma."

After this session the kissing stopped, and Warren began the search for useful ways out of his predicament. The pattern of behavior enacted by this patient with the student nurses helped them to change their role in dealing with him and clarified for Warren the purposiveness of his feelings: to succeed in a sham battle.

Another feature that contributed to the movement of the session was having the nurses act out the episodes with the rest of the patient group, so giving them the opportunity to experiment with a new role. This general approach is effectively used when there is fighting, stealing, smoking in bed, or someone refusing to keep his place in the chow-line. The patients are warmed up to the problem and ask the staff to take some action. "We are helpless — you have power — do something." The emphasis here is on what can *we* do, or what can *you* make him do — to make our life here more harmonious. The psychodramatist helps the group to make the problem explicit through role-playing and empathetic through role-reversal. The situations are enacted with close attention to the action used in dealing with it. (At the time of stealing — a patient wakes up and sees another patient running through his pants pockets and turns over and goes back to sleep.) The group is polled for more and more experiences with the offender. Sometimes the offender jumps into the role to correct the image he objects to; other times he needs to be assured that harmony, not punishment, is the goal. Occasionally, he'll leave the scene. When all the episodes have been enacted, the director suggests that the rest of the session should be spent either in several small group

347

discussions or one open large group: "In what way can we help Mr. D. to keep his place in the chow-line?"

The suggestions may be acted out, if not with the offender, then by other patients. For this problem the following ideas came from the group: 1) give him a poke in the kisser, 2) carry him bodily out of the line, 3) assign a patient to stand by him, 4) take away his pass for the week-end, 5) tell the dietician to send him to the end of the line.

The director turned to Mr. D. and asked, "How about that? Which of these actions would you think to be the most helpful to keep you in line?" He didn't agree with any of them. "Mr. D.," said the director, "will you show me how you stood in line before you came to the hospital — to punch a time clock, to get your check, to get into the cafeteria?"

Mr. D. "I'll stay in line." And he did, from then on.

The ward was impressed with this action learning method. It was a valuable experience for the group to see a patient give up making unrealistic demands on the group, "serve me first, or else," after the careful analysis and role-playing of the psychodrama. The patient saw the effect of this interaction and was able to select another role to deal with his place in the line and on the ward. Reprimand can be supportive.

LE PSYCHODRAME DE GROUPE:
TRAITEMENT ELECTIF DE L'ENURESIE CHEZ L'ENFANT

par Michel Soule

Notre double expérience de pédiatre et de psychiatre d'enfants s'est souvent trouvée désorientée devant le problème du traitement des enfants énurétiques. En effet les traitements banaux habituels parfois efficaces se heurtent souvent à des problèmes psychologiques. En revanche, il est difficile de conseiller une psychothérapie longue pour un symptôme finalement mineur.

La pratique du psychodrame de groupe nous a toujours donné des résultats très favorables lorsqu'on a éliminé les cas qui présentaient un véritable problème névrotique dans lequel l'énurésie n'était qu'un élement mineur. Le psychodrame s'est particuliérement révélé efficace chez les pré-adolescents et les adolescents où l'énurésie apparaît comme le reliquat d'une attitude ancienne qui persiste par suite d'une passivité générale. Il ne s'agit pas de traiter un symptôme mais toute la personnalité à propos d'un symptôme. Le psychodrame permet à l'individu de prendre conscience des bénéfices secondaires, de sa passivité, de sa complaisance inconsciente, de ses anciennes attitudes névrotiques, des liens de type régressif noués avec son entourage, etc. . . .

Il est possible de prendre plusieurs énurétiques en traitement en même temps, avec un ou plusieurs médecins, et le fait qu'ils soient tous "logés à la même enseigne" supprime la blessure narcissique qui leur serait, sans cela, imposée.

Pour les enfants plus jeunes il est possible de jouer certaines scènes portant sur les mêmes problèmes ou sur les instances psychologiques en cause. Ceci permet de renforcer leur Moi face à des bénéfices secondaires intenses.

La consultation elle-même bénéficie beaucoup de l'expérience psychodramatique. Elle permet de prendre rapidement en mains l'énurétique et très souvent de le guérir à bref délai.

Cette attitude psychodramatique peut, si elle constitue le fondement même de l'abord de l'énurétique, s'avérer beaucoup plus efficace que tout autre traitement.

FORMATION DU PERSONNEL PSYCHIATRIQUE PAR LE PSYCHODRAME ET LA DYNAMIQUE DES GROUPES

par Jacqueline Rouquette et Anne Ancelin-Schutzenberger

EXPERIENCE INSTITUTIONNELLE ET IMAGE IDEALE DE SOI

Nous voudrions rendre brièvement compte de l'expérience de la formation du personnel, entreprise depuis plus de cinq ans à l'Hôpital psychiatrique de La Verrière, dans la région parisienne.

Cet hôpital (actuellement appelé Institut Marcel Rivière) a été conçu et organisé dès 1957 par le Professeur Paul Sivadon en vue de la thérapie des malades mentaux adultes, hommes et femmes, appartenant à l'Education Nationale. C'est sous l'égide et grâce aux fonds de la Mutuelle Générale de l'Education Nationale qui groupe les professeurs et instituteur de la France entière, que cette expérience a pu se développer. L'expérience pilote de l'Hôpital psychiatrique de Ville-Evrard, faite depuis 1946 par le Docteur P. Sivadon et son équipe, également dans la région parisienne, a permis de roder l'aspect thérapie institutionnelle, et hôpital ouvert.

L'esprit novateur qui a présidé à l'édification du Château de la Verrière, s'est étendu non seulement aux normes architecturales révolutionaires permettant d'hospitaliser dans un service entièrement ouvert, des malades mentaux de toutes catégories, mais aussi à la formation du personnel para-médical qui devait se consacrer aux soins et à la réadaptation de ces malades psychotiques ou gravement névrotiques.

Dès avant l'ouverture des premiers pavillons, une *Ecole de spécialisation psychiatrique* fut instaurée. Cette Ecole devait recevoir pendant un an des élèves possédant déjà le diplôme de base de leur fonction, à savoir: diplôme d'Etat d'infirmière, d'Assistante Sociale, de kinésithérapeute, de secrétaire médicale, de diététicienne, etc. Nous voulions donner, par un enseignement commun, à un personnel disparate par sa formation, ses origines sociales et géographiques, une formation homogène et un langage commun, intelligible à tous les membres de l'équipe de l'hôpital. Les cours théoriques comprennent la psychiatrie, la psychologie dynamique, la neuro-psychiatrie infantile, la psychologie sociale, la sociologie, associés à des stages dans divers hôpitaux classiques et modernes, tant de la région parisienne qu'en province et dans les pays voisins de la France (Belgique et Suisse), pour ouvrir les yeux de nos infirmières sur tout ce qui peut être fait dans le domaine de la psychiatrie.

De plus, en vue de faciliter les communications indispensables à un travail d'équipe, les *cours* et les *stages* ont *été* complétés dès l'ouverture par une sensibilisation à la Dynamiques des Groupes et une initiation au Psychodrame pour l'ensemble du personnel paramédical, afin de leur permettre en même temps une certaine expérience personnelle de psychothérapie de groupe, dès l'entrée à l'hôpital et à l'Ecole de spécialisation.

Ainsi chaque promotion reçoit chaque année, au cours de l'année universitaire de formation théorique et pratique, un entraînement au groupe consistant en un vingtaine de séances de deux heures, à raison d'une fois par semaine de: *Groupe de base* (T-group), avec jeu dramatique, sociodrame ou psychodrame, c'est-à-dire en fait *psychothérapie de groupe sous forme de psychodrame triadique.*

Les premières promotions, d'une douzaine d'élèves, purent être formées en un seul groupe de base, ce qui eut pour effet de favoriser les relations au sein de ces promotions, qui "essuyèrent les plâtres" de la construction de l'hôpital et de son démarrage.

Par la suite, les promotions atteignant 30 à 40 élèves, il a fallu faire fonctionner en même temps plusieurs groupes parallèles de 10 à 12 participants. Nous verrons par la suite les effets de cette manière de procéder.

Actuellement, *l'année universitaire commence par un séminaire de trois jours,* à temps complet, comportant des *conférences* d'initiation à la psychothérapie de groupe et au psychodrame, traitant des problèmes de communication et de transmission de l'information et de l'approche non directive centrée sur le groupe et de la dynamique des groupes, et un test sociométrique, dont les résultats servent à l'établissement des "groupes de formation." Au cours de ces trois jours, les élèves participent en petits groupes à 6 séances non directives de 2 heures, avec généralement du jeu dramatique, ce qui leur donne une expérience personnelle de ce que pourrait être "le groupe." Le séminaire se termine par une table ronde et une séance d'auto-évaluation, d'abord dans chaque groupe et ensuite, tous les groupes et tous les moniteurs réunis.

Ce n'est qu'ensuite que vont commencer les *séances hebdomadaires* dont la durée, compte tenu des vacances, va s'étendre sur sept à huit mois, c'est-à-dire sur l'année universitaire.

Comme les préjugés sont nombreux en ce qui concerne la psychothérapie, et que les élèves sont à priori effrayés de groupe où l'on "doit parler et se dire tout," surtout entre camarades de classe et collègues habitant ensemble, nous avons mis l'accent sur l'aspect pédagogique et ressenti du groupe, et utilisé pour le personnel les termes de "sensibilisation à la Dynamique des Groupes," plutôt que psychothérapie de groupe. Il est établi dès l'abord que chaque groupe est tenu au secret professionel en ce qui concerne ce qui est dit de plus personnel au sein de ce groupe. Cette discretion lie les élèves comme les moniteurs vis-à-vis, tant de la direction de l'Ecole et de l'hôpital que vis-à-vis des collègues, de la famille et des amis. Nous insistons aussi sur le fait que personne n'est obligé de parler de quoi que ce soit (et surtout pas de son passé), l'accent est mis sur ce qui se passe *ici et maintenant* dans le groupe; les élèves voient bien que le climat est réellement permissif et qu'il s'agit plus souvent de parler des causes et des difficultés de l'interaction, des inhibitions, des craintes devant la situation nouvelle face à une école inconnue, des malades mentaux, etc., que de leur passé personnel (ce n'est qu'exceptionnellement que le passé dans le présent apparaît).

Après ces trois jours obligatoires pour tous les élèves et tout le personnel, les élèves s'inscrivent en connaissance de cause s'ils le désirent aux séances hebdomadaires. A quelques exceptions près, ils y viennent tous et découvrent d'eux-mêmes l'aspect therapeutique du groupe. Nous avons finalement préféré cette formule de choix libre du groupe et du moniteur, accompagné d'un engagement et d'une participation régulière personnelle, à la formule contraignante. Cette obligation de formation s'accompagnerait bien sûr d'excuses pour manquer le groupe lorsqu'il y a des résistances ou des difficultés réelles. C'est une formule flexible dans une école où "le groupe de formation à la dynamique des groupes et au psychodrame" fait partie de l'enseignement au même titre que la psychiatrie ou la gymnastique.

Au cours de l'année de formation, et avec l'accord des intéressés, une ou deux visites se font de groupe à groupe, quelques transferts de groupe peuvent avoir lieu, et quelques séances commune réunissent deux puis trois groupes de formation, soit sans thème, soit pour des conférences discussions ou tables rondes avec les moniteurs, observateurs et conférenciers du Groupe de Sociométrie.

Après quelques mois de contacts avec l'hôpital psychiatrique et l'Ecole de spécialisation, après appréciation des stages et examen des connaissances théoriques, les élèves de l'Ecole sont "admis à signer" le contrat qui va les lier à l'hôpital pour trois ans. A cette occasion, certains partent, soit qu'ils échouent, soit qu'ils ne se sentent finalement pas la vocation ou la résistance nerveuse suffisante pour travailler avec des psychotiques, dans un relatif éloignement de leur milieu social. Il est évident qu'aucune note n'est donnée par les responsables des "groupes de formation," qui ne participent pas avec les autre professeurs à cette opération et respectent le secret du groupe.

Au cours des années précédentes nous avons essayé, tantôt d'apporter aux stagiaires l'aide du group pour parler de toutes leurs difficultés d'adaptation, tantôt de réserver la formation hebdomadaire aux élèves qui restent après avoir signé le contrat. Depuis deux ans, tous les élèves participent à un séminaire de trois jours dans la quinzaine qui suit leur arrivée à l'hôpital, et les groupes hebdomadaires n'ont commencé qu'après les examens probatoires et la signature du contrat.

Personnel hospitalier qui suit cette formation

Il s'agit essentiellement d'un personnel féminin para-médical. Les médecins, exerçant à l'hôpital à temps complet, à temps partiel, ou stagiaires, participent à divers groupes de psychothérapie de groupe à l'intérieur de l'hôpital, ou à des groupes extérieurs, hétérogènes. Nous n'aborderons pas ici la formation à la psychothérapie de groupe et au psychodrame du personnel médical et des infirmières en titre, mais seulement celle du *personnel para-médical entrant* à l'hôpital.

Les participants: l'Ecole de spécialisation psychiatrique reçoit en général des jeunes filles de 20 à 30 ans (90%), célibataires (95%), venant de province le plus souvent et de ce fait appelées à résider dans l'internat adjoint à l'Ecole. La plupart d'entre elles sont des infirmières diplômées; 10% environ sont kinésithérapeutes, secrétaires médicales, assistantes sociales, diététiciennes ou techniciennes (laboratoire, radiologie, EEG, etc.).

Nous voulons, par une formation homogène et complète, créer une unité à l'intérieur de l'hôpital, jeter un pont entre les médecins et le personnel para-médical, et éviter dans les groupes une sorte de snobisme des infirmières par rapport aux autres membres du personnel, et une scission dûe à la formation préalable du personnel de l'hôpital.

En fait, dès avant le début des séances de formation et de psychothérapie de groupe, des *différences* se font jour *suivant divers critères de réalité*: les rares élèves mariées par rapport à la grande masse des célibataires que les envient, le faible pourcentage des jeunes filles d'origine parisienne ou de grandes villes, par rapport à celles venant de la campagne ou de petites villes, ayant donc moins l'habitude de grands ensembles et d'une vie intellectuelle aussi cosmopolite que celle du Château de la Verrière (où l'on reçoit beaucoup de malades cultivés, membres de l'enseignement, et de visiteurs de marque de tous pays); enfin les différences entre celles qui ont l'expérience de l'internat, celles qui viennent directement de leur famille ou y habitent encore, celles qui ont déjà travaillé à l'hôpital. A ces différences dans le recrutement, que l'on peut qualifier de sociologiques, s'ajoutent la rare possession d'une voiture ou d'un vélomoteur (l'hôpital se trouve à deux km de la petite gare et d'un village, et à une demi — heure de train de Paris), d'une famille dans le voisinage, de la connaissance de Paris.

Mais surtout il s'établit une division très nette, d'emblée, dûe à l'apparence entre les jeunes filles de style "mère," celles de style "soeur," dont la neutralité vestimentaire contraste avec le style plus élaboré de celles qui se tiennent à l'avant-garde de la mode en toutes circonstances.

PRINCIPAUX THEMES EVOQUES

I. — *Solitude et Isolement*

C'est le thème de l'*isolement* qui revient le plus fréquemment, depuis six années que nous faisons de la formation avec la même population. Cet isolement touche à la fois chaque participant, ou groupe, en séances de formation, et aussi l'ensemble du personnel de l'établissement, du fait, tant de sa destination psychiatrique, que de sa situation géographique.

1. — *Isolement et solitude de l'individu.* Chaque élève arrive dans un milieu où elle ne connaît personne, et qui de plus est situé loin de son milieu naturel, familial et amical. Elle peut se sentir seule. De plus, elle va avoir à apprendre des choses étranges, voire mystérieuses ou menaçantes: c'est "le monde inquiétant de la folie." On y parle un langage différent de celui de son milieu habituel: un grand nombre de termes techniques passent, avec un sens dérivé, dans le langage du personnel, et paraît à la fois compliqué et ésotérique. Il arrive ainsi qu'on se fasse traiter par les plus anciennes de "schizoïde" ou de "frustrée" sans qu'on sache très bien de quoi il s'agit exactement. Les anciennes semblent former une petite chapelle et il paraît difficile d'accéder à l'initiation. Cette inquiétude n'est pas particulière à la psychiatrie: on la retrouve dans les autres collectivités soignantes (sana, éducateurs d'enfants inadaptés, etc.). Une telle inquiétude est liée à l'isolement vis-à-vis de la famille, généralement éloignée et surtout vis-à-vis de la société normale des bien portants. Quelle que soit sa motivation et son désir de trouver parfait et amical son milieu professionnel, l'infirmière ne peut que soulever le problème des horaires de travail, qui rendent difficiles les communications avec le milieu social familier et les membres des autres professions. Son horaire est tantôt continu, tantôt coupé. Elle est libre à des heures variables et travaille souvent à l'heure des repas ou des loisirs des autres.

Aux difficultés de la vie hospitalière en général, s'ajoute l'isolement géographique de la plupart des hôpitaux psychiatriques. Il est rare qu'avant quelques années, l'infirmière possède une motorisation qui lui permette de ne pas dépendre des intempéries, des trajets jusqu'à la gare et des horaires irréguliers des trains. Il arrive qu'une sortie de théâtre tardive impose de coucher en ville faute de trains après minuit et demie.

Souhaitant se créer des relations amicales qui lui permettront de sortir de son "isolement en groupe," l'élève sera désireuse de tout faire pour les conserver pendant ses années d'études et de travail dans le même milieu, c'est-à-dire qu'elle se sent tenue à une certaine prudence dans l'expression des sentiments et des opinions. Il est important de pouvoir conserver les relations amicales des premiers jours et de ne pas se brouiller avec des collègues dont les opinions politiques, religieuse, les attitudes sentimentales ou sexuelles, les goûts, la culture, le milieu, le degré d'évolution, de maturation ou d'indépendance peuvent être différents.

La sortie de l'isolement par la camaraderie professionnelle entre jeunes filles est rarement la solution aux problèmes de la solitude.

Pour les mêmes raisons d'isolement géographique et social, il est difficile de rompre l'isolement sexuel. L'hôpital, en dehors des malades des deux sexes, ne comporte qu'un très petit nombre d'hommes, et generalement mariés dailleurs.

Aussi le célibat est-il redouté, à moins qu'il ne soit inconsciemment souhaité; la revendication virile, le renoncement à la féminité comme à la maternité physique au nom d'une maternité professionnelle est fréquent, comme la facticité de certaines protestations ostentatoires de féminité.

Cet isolement du groupe vis-à-vis de la société s'accompagne d'autre part de l'impossibilité de s'isoler réellement lorsqu'on le souhaite. La vie collective en internat entraîne en effet une quasi impossibilité d'autonomie, bien que chacune possède une chambre-studio personnelle, dans laquelle elle peut recevoir, et qu'un salon soit mis à la disposition des élèves.

S'isoler trop souvent, souhaiter l'isolement, est conçu par les autres élèves, soit comme une offense qui leur est faite, un rejet de leur camaraderie, soit comme une manifestation pathologique.

De plus, les confidences peuvent être répétées. Elles disent: "tout se sait, les murs ont des oreilles," et c'est en fait souvent vrai. Par ailleurs, souvent s'isoler à deux ou quatre, c'est former de "petites bandes" souvent mal vues par les autres, et parfois donner lieu à des racontars, voire à des calomnies suscitées par tout ce qui est "autre."

L'établissement de sous-groupes amicaux et les efforts que beaucoup font pour "créer une bonne ambiance" est une solution aux problèmes de l'isolement mais non à celui de la solitude. Les cas d'amitié réelle et durable sont rares. Toutefois nous avons pu observer que certains sous-groupes créés dès l'entrée parmi les élèves, se sont maintenus pendant plusieurs années chez les infirmières.

2. — *Isolement du groupe des entrantes dans l'institution.* Les entrantes ont naturellement tendance à se solidariser. Le groupe des élèves se sent d'une certaine façon un groupe celui des nouvelles. Mais il arrive que les élèves se sentent abandonnées, isolées

356

du reste de l'hôpital, voire brimées par les anciennes, qui mangent ensemble, ne les invitent pas lorsqu'elles se réunissent entre elles, ont priorité pour les jours de congé, les horaires et les remplacements.

It n'est pas exclu qu'un certain sadisme latent s'exprime par ce "bizutage" informel, qui consiste à laisser les nouvelles arrivées "se débrouiller seules" en observant la façon dont elles vont s'y prendre. Cette tendance est si forte qu'elle l'emporte sur le désir d'accueil, que certaines promotions ont manifestée. Même lorsqu'une promotion a décidé en fin d'année d'accueillir les nouvelles en octobre, mille raisons ou oublis font retarder l'accueil jusqu'en mars ou avril, lorsqu'en fait, l'intégration des nouvelles est faite et la période d'angoisse passée.

Les anciennes apparaisssent comme des initiées; elles utilisent volontiers un langage hermétique, laissent le groupe des nouvelles à l'écart de leurs conversations et de leurs réunions. Le langage même de l'hôpital ne favorise pas les communications intergroupes, comme nous l'avons vu plus haut.

3. — *Isolement du groupe institutionnel dans la société.* Comme nous l'avons vu à propos de l'isolement de l'individu, deux faits contribuent à favoriser l'isolement du groupe institutionnel vis-à-vis de la "société normale."

D'une part la situation géographique: l'hôpital se trouve à 35 km de Paris, à la campagne, et à 2 km de la gare, qui n'est même pas dans une bourgade. Aussi la possession d'une voiture personnelle est-elle considérée comme le moyen le plus efficace de renouer le lien avec une vie social normale, les trains étant rares, et seulement de jour, et le trajet fatigant, pour qui le fait après une journée de travail (en fait, nous avons toujours apprécié la rapidité avec laquelle se fait le lien par train avec l'hôpital, pour y travailler, et sa proximité de Paris. Mais il est plus facile de s'y rendre en trente minutes pour travailler que de s'en échapper deux heures pour se distraire).

En outre, le fait de travailler dans un milieu psychiatrique est considéré comme "suspect" par les autres membres de la société dite normale. La famille et les amis des élèves ont souvent tenté de les dissuader de s'engager dans la profession, comme cela se voit aussi fréquemment pour la profession d'infirmière en général.

Il est remarquable de constater une fois de plus que le *vieux*

357

tabou aliénant les malades méntaux vis-à-vis de la société dite
normale atteint ceux qui prennent soin d'eux.

A ce propos il faudrait remarquer que dans des séminaires d'autres professions s'occupant d'autrui, des médicins psychiatres, psychoanalystes, prêtres et pasteurs, juges, se sont plaints d'un certain isolement social causé par leur métier, l'image que l'on s'en fait, et même leur attitude. C'est l'isolement des hobereaux de province, aggravé de l'ambivalence que provoque le shaman, le "medecine-man" au pouvoir mystérieux de voir au-delà des choses liées aux remous de l'âme. Le "grand renfermement" depuis 1656, à l'hôpital général des malades, des pauvres, des vagabonds, des voleurs, des adultères, des joueurs, dans des locaux libérés par la disminution de la lèpre et de la peste, crée et entretient la confusion entre la maladie mentale et les outrages à la société, confusion dont nous souffrons encore inconsciemment, car elle est ancrée dans l'esprit public malgré la révolution de Pinel.

Au fur et à mesure que les séances de groupe de formation se déroulent, l'accent est mis par les participants sur le fait que cet apprentissage de la maladie mentale, ainsi que l'enseignement théorique de psychologie et de psychiatrie, provoquent des changements dans leur personnalité et leur manière de s'exprimer tels qu'il leur devient difficile de continuer à parler un langage commun avec ceux qu'ils fréquentaient auparavant. Même lorsqu'il s'agit de ce qui pourrait paraître une "conversation anglaise" d'ordre général, l'appréciation portée sur un film, sur un livre, est différente. Les interprétations des attitudes d'autrui, les commentaires sur le comportement humain, sont, qu'on le veuille ou non, imprégnés des notions apprises, ou libérés de certaines conventions ou de certains tabous. De ce fait, les élèves, encore plus que les infirmières, sentent une certaine coupure vis-à-vis de leur milieu habituel. L'isolement de fait s'accroît donc d'un isolement psychologique et il est parfois difficile de "faire le rétablissement" pour se remettre au niveau de communication verbale habituel aux groupes extérieurs à la psychiatrie.

II — *Dépendance et Indépendance*

En plus du grand thème de l'isolement, on voit apparaître celui de la dépendance-indépendance. Rappelons qu'il s'agit en majorité de jeunes filles de 20 à 25 ans. Beaucoup sortent directement de l'école d'infirmières sans être passées par un travail ou un service hospitalier où elles auraient pu mener une vie professionnelle et une vie personnelle d'adults. Tout se passe comme si elles cherchaient un refuge dans une autre vie protégée, mi-scolaire, mi-familiale, où sont pris en charge à la fois tous leurs besoins matériels (tels que le logement, la nourriture, le chauffage), comme les besoins culturels et sociaux (tels que l'organisation de l'enseignement et de quelques distractions). De plus, durant leur scolarité elles reçoivent également un traitement. Par ce traitement elles se rattachent à l'aspect adulte de l'existence, mais par les autres conditions de leur vie, elles son vis-à-vis de l'hôpital-école comme l'enfant vis-à-vis de sa nourrice, dans une situation de "maternage" ou de désir de l'être, et considèrent leur salaire presque comme l'argent de poche d'une situation "au pair".

La séparation d'avec les parents, qui, en général, n'étaient pas d'accord pour les voir embrasser une profession psychiatrique, est vécue comme une premier acte d'indépendance, comme une libération. Mais elles n'ont pas conscience du fait que ce rejet de dépendance vis-à-vis des parents n'est que factice, puisqu'il s'accompagne de la recherche d'une autre dépendance vis-à-vis d'une institution jouant un rôle parental. Ainsi peut s'éxpliquer l'ambivalence vis-à-vis de l'Ecole: attachement aux études, au cadre qu'elles trouvent exceptionnellement beau et confortable (parfois trop), mais agressivité vis-à-vis de l'environnement. A partir d'un certain moment elles vivent l'ambivalence face à l'Ecole-Mère. Elles voudraient à la fois être totalement prises en charge et trouvent à redire au moindre détail, comme des enfants gâtés; (elles voudraient plus de disques, de livres, de tourne-disques communs, de télévision), et totalement indépendantes, pour jouir de leur première liberté.

Une autre source de malaises est dûe à l'organisation démocratique de l'institution: "la démocratie" est vécue comme l'anarchie, comme le "laisser faire" ou encore comme l'abandon par les parents; "on ne s'occupe pas de nous", "on ne nous dit pas ce qu'il faut faire", "on nous laisse trop libres". Ce sentiment général d'insécurité est vécu comme un syndrome d'abandon et en même temps projeté sur les malades, sur les médecins, sur les anciennes infirmières, sur le poids de l'engagement qu'elles contractent en s'engageant dans une profession qu'elle présentent comme "délivrante".

III — *Problème de la vocation d'infirmière*

Ces difficultés dans l'accession à l'état adulte sont corollaires de la *crainte de la féminité*. Cette crainte d'être femme recouvre le problème de leur vocation. Les infirmières (puisqu'il s'agit de cette profession pour une forte proportion d'entre elles) ont cherché refuge dans un milieu essentiellement féminin dans lequel les malades hommes sont traités comme des enfants, ce qui permet de les "materner". La fonction d'infirmière est vécue pour beaucoup comme un substitut de maternité et une maternité sans hommes. La "bonne infirmière" est identifiée à la mère nourrice ou à la religieuse d'un certain nombre d'hôpitaux où elles ont fait des stages avant de venir. Pour ces stagiaires, il en découle une certaine hostilité contre l'apparence élégante de leurs camarades, hostilité qui traduit ce refus de la féminité.

La fonction d'infirmière permet donc d'être mère sans avoir été épouse, mais cette peur de l'homme, ce refus du mariage, s'accompagnent d'une crainte panique de ne pas se marier et de là pour beaucoup, la "chasse au mari" ou l'installation dans l'état de vieille fille, dévouée aux autres, soeur de charité aux mains secourables.

IV — *Problème de la vocation psychiatrique*

La maladie mentale constitue un pôle d'attraction et en même temps de crainte pour l'infirmière. Cette vocation peut être apparue pour des raisons familiales (parents ou amis malades menteaux), mais aussi par besoin de faire plus que le soins matériels habituels, le désir messianique de "se donner" à une grande cause, le besoin "d'aider en profondeur", de connaître les gens et d'établir avec eux des relations authentiques. Cependant pour beaucoup d'entre elles l'entrée dans la carrière psychiatrique se marque par une déception devant la pauvreté en gestes techniques dont on connaît bien le caractère rassurant.

Mais surtout la crainte est grande devant le mystère du malade mental, qu'il s'agisse de la limite indécise entre le normal et le pathologique, de la crainte que le milieu "déteigne". Pour le publique, le malade est aliéné et celui qui le soigne de même.

Enfin le danger le plus grand est lié au fait que connaître un malade et apprendre à déterminer ses motivations inconscientes, c'est risquer de retrouver en son propre inconscient un type analogue de problèmes et de conflits, et cela pose le problème si lourd de l'identification au malade. C'est risquer d'être ou de devenir comme lui et dans une certaine mesure "complice". Car la maladie continue à être vécue au tréfonds de beaucoup comme entachée de culpabilité, phénomène magique et "punition" d'une faute mystérieuse et peut-être si lointaine, agressivité contre le père, la mère, autrui, refoulement de pulsion inavouées, etc. Le contretransfert de ceux qui s'occupent de malades mentaux est peu etudié.

Cette crainte s'aggrave du fait de l'isotérisme du langage dont nous avons déjà parlé. En fait, a la psychiatrie, tout l'ensemble de l'institution est dramatisé.

Dans ce monde inconnu tout est danger, et chaque entrant se perçoit comme un corps étranger dans quelque chose d'existant, d'organisé, de redoutable. Quelle influence ce monde peut-il exercer sur nous, comment allons-nous devenir lorsque nous serons bien intégrés? On examine avec anxiété les anciennes pour bien vérifier si la maladie mentale risque de "déteindre" sur ceux qui la soignent, et quel est le climat de ce cosmos?

Par ailleurs dans un temps ultérieur se pose le problème de la validité du travail accompli: en cas de rechute, dans quelle mesure sommes-nous responsables? Sommes-nous désarmés devant ces maladies et la peine que nous prenons est-elle utile? Que deviennent les normes auxquelles nous étions habitués, où le blanc était blanc, et le noir était noir quand, dans ce monde mouvant, à chaque instant tout est remis en question?

Cette insécurité si lourde, facteur d'angoisse, est parfois si mal tolérée, qu'elle aboutit à des départs, préférés à une remise en question complète de tout le monde adolescent vécu antérieure- et nous verrons que la dynamique des groupes revêt à ce propos ment. C'est là que nous abordons les difficultés de maturation une importance considérable comme facteur de sécurisation, de sédation de l'angoisse et d'insertion plus rapide dans ces nouvelles structures.

V — *Maturation et passage à l'age adulte*

Après une remise en question nécessaire aux stades si importants de la sortie de l'adolescence et de l'insertion en milieu professionnel adulte, rapprochés ici, les élèves débouchent sur une prise de conscience plus nette que dans des professions de recrutement voisin telles qu'infirmière d'hôpital général, institutrices, éducatrices. Leurs difficultés sont comparables comme nous avons eu l'occasion de le voir ailleurs, mais sans prise de conscience des problèmes qui sont généralement plus refoulés que sublimés. Par cette méthode ils deviennent conscients et peuvent être assumés.

VI — *Craintes devant la situation de groupe*

Il faut faire remarquer que la situation d'un groupe de formation et d'entraînement à la Dynamique des Groupes est assez particulière. Il s'agit d'élèves d'une même classe, de membres d'une même équipe, qui sont mis en situation de groupe et sont appelés à se revoir quotidiennement, aux cours, au réfectoire, dans le salon, le corridor des chambres du foyer. Il s'agit là certainement d'une difficulté supplémentaire par rapport à des groupes hétérogènes de formation ou de psychothérapie de groupe. Quand on se connaît, quand on habite au même endroit, qu'on travaille ensemble, on craint les conséquences *réelles* de ce qu'on peut dire dans le groupe. On peut évoquer le problème du secret professionnel de groupe, il reste le fait de se dévoiler vis-à-vis de collègues, qui un jour pourront en abuser. Vis-à-vis de l'autorité, ce qu'on dira ne sera-t-il pas rapporté? Est-on jugé et noté sur ce qui est dit au sein du groupe? Il est évident que (et c'est formellement dit) le secret du groupe lie aussi moniteurs et observateurs et que rien de ce qui est dit en groupe ne sera rapporté à la Direction de l'établissement, et que le vécu du groupe a un caractère strictement confidentiel. Outre cette crainte des consequences, un sentiment de protection vis-à-vis de la camaraderie provoque un certain degré d'inhibition ou certaines absences car il faut préserver la possibilité de travailler sans heurt ultérieurement. Il est donc difficile d'oser être soi-même, de communiquer d'une façon authentique. Ce thème est abordé en groupe chaque année. Mais petit à petit le groupe s'apprivoise et chaque groupe trouve un équilibre entre le désir et la crainte de communiquer.

Un autre thème est qu'il est presque possible de prévoir ce que l'autre va dire parce qu'on se connaît trop, et les réactions des compagnes sont presque devinées avant même que d'être exprimées, car on se connaît non seulement en groupe mais hors groupe, du moins dans certains rôles.

VII — *Résultants de cette mèthode*

Le bénéfice apporté par cette technique est bien connu: il s'agit d'accroître la compréhension réciproque, d'accepter autrui différent de soi, de ne pas le juger, de s'accepter soi-même non parfait; vis-à-vis de la situation, de comprendre ce qui se passe dans une relation humaine, d'apprendre à analyser ses propres réactions parfois perçues comme suprenantes, de décharger en groupe l'agressivité qu'on ne peut exprimer vis-à-vis des malades, ni vis-à-vis des médecins ou de l'hôpital.

Autrui vécu comme dangereux parce qu'inconnu est ramené à ses justes proportions, donc peut être plus faciliment abordé. On peut à la faveur de ces groupes prendre conscience de son agressivité vis-à-vis des autres et apprendre à supporter le silence et tolérer un autrui différent de soi et de ce qu'on voudrait qu'il (ou elle) fût.

Sur le plan de l'intégration dans le groupe institutionnel, la traduction se fait dans le langage: on ne parle plus de "leur monde", mais de "notre monde".

VIII — *Influence du "Séminaire de Formation" sur l'évolution de la personnalité*

Nous pouvons prendre l'exemple de trois de nos élèves. Elles sont arrivées à l'Ecole très infantiles, avec une immaturation affective considérable. Leur comportement était hésitant, inhibé, et elles présentaient tous les signes dont nous avons parlé plus haut, à savoir: difficulté vis-à-vis de l'indépendance, du contrôle de soi-même, de la sexualité.

L'une d'elle, O... s'est mariée au bout de deux ans et mène une vie heureuse de mère de famille, harmonieusement équilibrée avec son travail professionel. Elle constitue dans l'institution une des meilleures images d'identification qui soient et a regroupé autour d'elle une équipe homogène d'infirmières qui l'admirent et aiment travailler auprès d'elle.

Une autre, J..., est arrivée en déclarant qu'elle ne pourrait jamais se marier (vu un handicap physique) et qu'elle souhaitait être dispensée du groupe de formation et surtout du psychodrame "qui ne servait à rien qu'à égratigner de vieilles plaies avec ces questions de femmes et de relations". Elle s'est fiancée au bout d'un an. Elle a quitté l'établissement pour suivre son mari à l'étranger.

Enfin, Y..., n'a pas trouvé jusqu'à maintenant d'équilibre affectif aussi satisfaisant que les précédentes, mais a investi toute ses potentialités dans des études de médecine et réussit fort bien.

Plusieurs autres se sont mariées ou fiancées, ont eu des enfants, et ont continué une vie professionnelle heureuse dans l'établissement ou ailleurs.

On pourra objecter que ces diverses vocations peuvent représenter une fuite de l'état de soignante, qui les avait amenées dans notre Institution. Nous pensons cependant que la recherche de l'épanouissement de la personnalité de nos élèves leur permet de se réaliser plus pleinement dans une direction ou une autre suivant les situations et les possibilités. On voit nettement l'épanouissement sur le plan physique, vestimentaire, sportif, culturel, le "savoir-faire social."

IX — Evolution du groupe lui-même

Nous l'avons déjà abordé plus haut: Le "groupe de formation" des infirmières ne diffère pas sensiblement des autres groupes habituellement étudiés.

L'évolution notée hors champ par une personne extérieure au groupe et concernant en particulier l'intégration de groupes successifs dans l'institution, nous parait plus intéressante. Le groupe le plus ancien chronologiquement était homogène, avec un vif sens des responsabilités, une fierté, et un sentiment d'intégration au fonctionnement de l'institution.

Lorsque le deuxième groupe arriva l'année suivante, groupe plus fort numériquement, il surgit au sein du groupe 1, un sentiment d'insécurité, d'anxiété, de crainte de ne pouvoir faire face et d'être jugé. Le sentiment de sécurité lié à la conscience de la responsabilité fait place à la crainte de devenir inapte à l'enseignement, la crainte d'être dévoré. Le groupe ancien fait alors bloc devant le nouveau, perçu comme envahisseur et perturbateur. En contre-partie, le nouveau groupe se structure par opposition à ce qu'était le premier.

La troisième année, le 3ème groupe est attendu impatiemment par le 2ème, résolu à l'accueillir de façon solennelle et par opposition à l'absence d'accueil qu'il a reçu lui-même du groupe 1 (cérémonie du baptême, rites d'initiation). Le groupe 1 (les plus anciennes), isolé, s'infiltre peu à peu dans cette nouvelle structure, plutôt individuellement qu'en tant que groupe.

Le 4ème et le 5ème groupes s'intègrent dans l'institution progressivement, et il semble qu'une tradition s'établisse.

Le 6ème groupe, numériquement très abondant (plus d'une quarantaine) a présenté des difficultés internes particulières par la formation de sous-groupes. Il semble que l'intégration à l'ensemble de l'institution se soit faite par l'intermédiaire de ces sous-groupes et au moyen, en particulier, des groupes fonctionnels existant par ailleurs dans l'Etablissement (réunions de pavillons, réunions de travail), bien que ce soit le seul groupe qui ait tenu à écrire aux moniteurs des groupes de formation que le groupe leur avait servi à s'ancrer dans l'institution et permis de survivre aux difficultés.

Actuellement, si on essaye d'évaluer les résultats globaux de la méthode, on voit essentiellement en général, qu'au bout de l'année d'études on n'arrive plus à distinguer de quel groupe chaque infirmière est originaire. L'intégration se fait donc de façon active, facilitée par la structuration pavillonnaire. Cependant il existe une reconstitution de sous-groupes par activité professionnelle, absolument normale (activité commune des kinésithérapeutes par exemple), mais qui dans une certaine mesure aurait pu gêner le fonctionnement de l'ensemble. La structuration en groupes d'origine, chronologique, persiste malgré tout, au cours de l'évolution et facilite fonctionnellement la circulation de l'information.

LES EFFETS D'AUDIENCE DU PSYCHODRAME

par Daniel Widlocher, Bernard Jean et Yvan Tellier

Normalement la pratique du psychodrame exclut la présence d'un auditoire assistant aux séances sans prendre part à l'action. Nous rapportons toutefois ici les effets d'une expérience contraire qui se déroule depuis trois ans à la Clinique de Neuro-Psychiatrie Infantile de la Salpêtrière (Paris), où un groupe de médecins et de psychologues assiste à des séances de psychodrame thérapeutique pour enfants sans y prendre une part active. Il s'agit pour eux d'acquérir une information concrète sur le psychodrame. Pour cela nous constituons des groupes d'enfants dont la cure psychodramatique se déroule avec l'aide de deux psychothérapeutes (un homme et une femme) en présence d'un groupe d'une dizaine de personnes qui s'engagent à suivre régulièrement les séances.

Les enfants sont choisis de telle manière que leur état mental ne constitue pas un obstacle à une telle forme de psychodrame (gravité moyenne des cas, absence d'une trop grande inhibition). Psychothérapeutes, enfants, et auditoire se retrouvent ainsi chaque semaine. Après chaque séance les membres de l'auditoire échangent leurs impressions avec les psychothérapeutes. La disposition matérielle est telle que l'auditoire se répartit en hémicycle autour du groupe enfants-thérapeutes, à quelques mètres de lui.

On explique d'ailleurs aux enfants, dès le début du traitement la nature de cet auditoire et le fait qu'ils peuvent lors du choix des rôles, inviter l'un ou l'autre à participer au jeu. De même à l'auditoire on précise que les enfants peuvent à tout instant les solliciter.

En réalité le recours à cet auditoire dans la distribution des rôles est très rare. Ceci s'explique à notre avis par la focalisation croissante du transfet du groupe sur le couple de psychothérapeutes. Aussi, chaque fois qu'il fut fait appel à l'un des autres participants ce choix prit toujours une signification précise quant à la dynamique du transfert.

Une telle expérience peut-être étudiée de différente point de vue. (1) Effets sur les groupes d'enfants. (2) Effets de l'assistance au psychodrame sur les membres de l'auditoire. (3) Effets sur le jeu des psychodramatistes, sur leurs interventions, et sur leurs relations réciproques.

La première question n'a pas été étudié avec méthode et nous nous contenterons ici de quelques conclusions d'ensembles. La présence d'un auditoire n'a été un obstacle important pour la marche du psychodrame que dans un seul des groupes d'enfants choisis. Il s'agissait d'un groupe de fillettes de douze à quatorze ans, très inhibées. Cette inhibition s'accentuant, en rapport avec une angoisse croissante, nous dûmes renoncer après quatre séances à continuer le psychodrame devant l'auditoire.

Dans tous les autres groupes (huit en trois ans) les séances purent se poursuivre normalement tout le long de l'année scolaire. Il s'agissait, il est vrai de groupes sélectionnés en vue de cette expérience, groupes de garçons entre dix et dix-huit ans, présentant des structures névrotiques modérément graves.

Dans l'ensemble les résultats thérapeutiques furent bons, analogues à ceux observés dans les groupes pris en privé.

Une comparaison très superficielle nous a permis de noter que si au départ l'auditoire constituait un facteur de gène il prenait par la suite un rôle differencié dans le champ. Très schématiquement on peut ainsi préciser ces effets:

—Fixation d'éléments transférentiels latéraux, négatifs ou positifs (par exemple appel à la compréhension de l'auditoire en opposition à l'attitude du couple des thérapeutes ressenti comme hostile et frustrant).

—Effets d'amplification de certaines émotions collectives (par exemple perception par les enfants de l'anxiété ou de la satisfaction de l'auditoire à l'égard de ce qui se déroule dans le groupe).

—Accentuation du caractère de représentation dramatique, au détriment d'une dimension purement ludique du psychodrame.

(la présence de l'auditoire semble en certaines occasions avoir fréné certaines échappées régressives du groupe dans des attitudes de jeu, et en d'autres accentué la dimension du sérieux de l'improvisation dramatique).

Cet effet peut être considéré comme nuisible ou comme bénéfique.

La troisième question, celle de l'incidence de l'auditoire sur l'attitude des psychodramatistes n'a pas non plus été l'objet d'une investigation méthodique. Elle mériterait cependant une étude approfondie. Nous nous bornerons à mentionner deux effets: (1) Incidence très grande de la présence de l'auditoire dans le jeu et les interventions des psychodramatistes. Ceux-ci ressentent très fortement les deux registres (enfants-auditoire) ou opèrent leurs attitudes. (2) Accentuation du rôle prevalent de l'un des deux psychodramatistes, en l'occurence le thérapeute masculin, dans la mesure ou il apparait à l'auditoire en position d'enseignant.

L'objet de ce travail porte sur la deuxième question, celle concernant les effets de l'expérience sur l'auditoire. On peut à cet égard poser plusieurs problèmes: Dans quelle mesure l'expérience entraîne une participation émotionnelle; Quelles relations affectives s'établissent avec les psychodramatistes, avec les enfants; L'auditoire acquiert — il une connaissance precise de la technique psychodramatique.

PROTOCOLE DE RECHERCHE

(1) Le Questionnaire: C'est en vue de réunir des informations à ce sujet que cette recherche a été conçue. Dans ce but nous avons construit un questionnaire comprenant 36 questions (confer annexe). Les questions se rapportent directement ou par un biais aux types de réactions énoncées plus haut. Plusieurs questions se recoupent, mais il a semblé utile d'élaborer des questions assez semblables quelquefois pour favoriser le plus possible l'expression des multiples expériences de chacun des individus. Le questionnaire est demeuré anonyme; par contre, chacun a répondu (sur une feuille détachée) à d'autres questions concernent l'âge, le sexe, la professions et ses connaissances théoriques et pratiques du psychodrame.

Un problème méthodologique particulier s'est posé pour l'analyse des résultats. Devions-nous recourir à l'emploi de statisques? Nous avons choise de traiter les résultats d'une façon différente en raison du petit nombre de sujets et parceque ce qui fait l'objet de cette étude n'est pas tant le nombre de personnes qui ont éprouvé tel sentiment ou tel autre, mais bien plutôt la nature de ces sentiments. Le fait qu'ils soient éprouvés par un seul membre de l'assistance a ici la même importance que s'ils sont éprouvés par tous les autres. Pour ces raisons, nous renonçons à l'emploi de statistiques, quitte à introduire à l'occasion certains chiffres qui seront utiles.

(2) Le Groupe Etudié: L'étude a porté sur un auditoire qui a assisté à des séances hedomadaires de Psychodrame de Novembre 1962 à Mai-Juin 1963. Le groupe se compose de cinq hommes et de cinq femmes. L'âge médian est de 31 ans. Tous posèdent une formation psychiatrique ou psychologique. La plupart ont assisté régulièrement aux séances de psychodrame depuis au moins six mois. Aucun n'a participé a des séances de psychodrame au préalable. Au début aucun n'avait de connaissance théoriques sur le sujet. Depuis, cependant, à l'exception d'un des participants, tous ont enrichi leurs connaissances théoriques en lisant des livres ou des articles relatifs au psychodrame.

ANALYSE DES RESULTANTS

Même si tous les aspects du questionnaire son étroitement liés, nous avons cru préférable, pour faciliter l'exposé des résultats, de grouper les questions par rubrique. Ceci nous a permis de diviser le travail en deux parties: la première traite des réactions affectives aux séances de psychodrame, la seconde de l'aspect didactique.

Participation Affective de L'Audience: Une première série de questions (Q. 1, 2, 8, 11, 12, 16, 17, 23, 26, 28, 36) visait à mettre en évidence chez le spectateur:

—l'existence d'une participation affective
—la nature des situations dramatiques à forte charge émotionnelle
—la réaction du spectateur devant ces situations
—le degré d'Insight atteint par le spectateur.

Une deuxième catégorie de questions visait à comprendre la façon dont le sujet percevait son rôle de spectateur. (Q. 7, 34, 18,

19, 20). Une troisième tentait finalement de préciser le type de relation spectateur-thérapeute. (Q. 4, 9, 14, 15, 21, 22, 24).

A. *Les Réactions affectives*

De façon générale, la tension chez le spectateur est à son maximum au cours du choix du thème et de son élaboration; il y a une détente progressive au cours du jeu. Le spectateur surtout au cours des premières séances, supporte difficilement le silence des enfants. Ces périodes de latence sont habituellement interprétées par le spectateur comme étant un refus de la parte des enfants, une opposition au thérapeute.

Le spectateur n° 9 se révèle beaucoup à ce sujet. Il dit à la question deux (2) : "au début, il existe une vive curiosité s'accompagnant d'un léger sentiment d'anxiété (crainte des silences prolongés). Cette anxièté disparaît assez rapidement alors que croît l'attention développée en vue d'essayer de saisir ce qui se passe exactement au cours de la séance . . ." Il semble qu'à ce moment, le spectateur parvienne à maitriser sa participation émotive du début en recourant à sa compréhension intellectuelle. En effet, le même spectateur continue en mentionnant que ce qu'il essaie de saisir dans le jeu, c'est "la valeur du thème, l'importance de la distribution des rôles, le processus d'identification etc. ..."

B. *Influence des Thèmes*

Le spectateur n° 8 a été pour sa part très sensible aux thèmes d'exploration. Se mettant à la place des enfants, il perçoit chez eux une demande à l'adresse des thérapeutes. Cette demande ne recevant pas de réponse provoque une frustration qui est vivement ressentie par lui. Ce sentiment existe tout au long du questionnaire, mais semble avoir évolué. En effet, à la fin du semestre, il dit que la compréhension qu'il a acquise l'a beaucoup aidé à controler ces sentiments.

Sous des thèmes différents, le spectateur n° 4 est sensible aux situations de frustrations et ressent des émotions semblables à celles du spectateur précédent.

En égard aux différentes personnalités présentes chez les spectateurs, on aurait été en lieu d'attendre une gamme beaucoup plus variée d'émotions ressenties. Or, il n'en fut pas ainsi. Sous des thèmes divers, ce sont les mêmes situations dramatiques qui éveillent des résonances chez les spectateur. Ils semblent être sensibles à deux positions fondamentales: la frustration et l'opposition.

De façon générale, le spectateur à tôt fait d'identifier les sentiments des participants du psychodrame et ses propres sentiments. La conscience qu'il a du caractère projeticf de cette identification varie. Elle va de la reconnaissance vague, de déjà vécu (cf. Spectateur 5: Q. 8) à la reconnaissance de ses propres désirs infantiles suscités par la situation dramatique.

Il semble bien qu'à l'instar du groupe des enfants, le groupe des spectateurs subisse une régression marquée en participant aux séances de psychodrame, mais ils ne voient pas en cela aussi qu'ils s'identifient aux enfants. A une question précise à ce sujet la plupart répondent négativement. Cependant, quelques-uns (3) se sont rendus compte qu'ils se mettaient à la place des enfants à certaines occasions. Ceux-ci, voient alors que grâce à cette identification, ils ont été plus à — même d'analyser leurs propres réactions. De façon générale, on a l'impression que cette participation n'est pas suffisante pour influencer les attitudes professionnelles, personnelles ou familiales. Cependant, certains (2) ont retiré une plus grande compréhension ou une plus grande sensibilisation aux problèmes affectifs des enfants.

Un spectateur en particulier croit avoir mieux compris sa propre situation familiale. Un autre mentionne des changements dans certaines de ses attitudes personnelles, sans toutefois préciser la nature de ces changements. (Fait intéréssant: ces deux témoignages viennent des deux seuls participants qui sont en cours d'analyse.)

Tous (excepté un) ont d'ailleurs ressenti à la suite de certaines séances le besoin d'une psychanalyse personnelle ou d'utiliser cette expérience dans leur analyse (Q. 28). Il semble donc bien que le simple fait d'assister à des séances de psychodrame chez l'enfant aut modifier certaines attitudes personnelles.

Un autre fait intéressant â noter ici, est qu'à la dernière question (Q. 36) la plupart disent qu'ils n'ont pas éprouvé de sentiments très profonds. Ceci est en contradiction avec ce qui précède. L'analyse des autres questions a montré des sentiments d'angoisse, d'hostilité et d'agressivité. Cette négation finale peut s'interpréter comme un refus ou une gêne à admettre qu'on puisse réagir en tant que spectateur à des situations impliquant principalement des enfants.

C. *Rôle de Spectateur*

On serait porté à croire que la position des spectateurs est de tout repos. Il n'en est pas ainsi. La tension dramatique, nous l'avons vu plus haut, trouve une résonnance affective chez le spectateur; il croit gêner le jeu des enfants et celui des thérapeutes. Autre moment anxiogène, celui où il est susceptible d'être choisi pour jouer le rôle de thérapeute auxiliaire (cf. Q. 7-18).

Spectateur, il est susceptible de provoquer l'hostilité des participants (cf. Q. 18 — Spectateurs 9-5-4). Se mettant à la place des enfants, il se perçoit comme "un intrus," "un voyageur," "quelqu'un qui n'ose se mouiller les pieds" (cf. Q. 7 — Spectateur: 8-5-4). Par contre, sous le regard des thérapeutes, il se veut "nécessaire," "indispensable"; il prétend à un rôle sécurisant pour les thérapeutes (cf. Q. 34 — Spectateur: 9-8-5-4).

Le spectateur a une demande précise: son désir d'être "nécessaire," "indispensable." Dans la séance de psychodrame cette demande n'est pas gratifiée; d'où hostilité. Ce qui explique parfaitement bien la grande sensibilité aux situations dramatiques de frustration; ce qui rend compte également de son anxiété parfois marquée lors des séances d'opposition, devant le silence des enfants.

ÜBER DAS POLITISCHE MIKROSOZIODRAMA

von Hans H. Floeter

Es ist sehr schwer, wenn nicht oft unmöglich, mit Anhängern geschlossener totalitärer Systeme in ein Gespräch zu kommen, das nicht propagandistisch oder terroristisch ist. Die Anhänger der geschlossenen Gesellschaften identifizieren sich mit ihren Systemen und sind daher von aussen — und oft auch von innen — her nahezu unansprechbar. Die Lage erleichtert sich, wenn man unter vier Augen spricht. *Diese* Situation bewusster zu machen, dienen diese Zeilen, die auf Erfahrungen aufbauen.

Zwei Personen, unter sich, gewillt etwas und sich auszusprechen, das ist eine günstige Lage. Es gibt keine Zuhörer, vor denen der Anhänger eine geschlossenen Systems sich nach gewohnten und gewünschten Mustern verhalten müsste. Der äussere Zwang, sich mit der geschlossenen Gesellschaft zu identifizieren fehlt also. Den inneren Zwang kann man abbauen, wenn man — nachdem das Gespräch eine Zeitlang gelaufen ist und dabei möglichst viele gemeinsame Dinge berührt worden sind, die dem Alltag angehören mögen — vorschlägt: "Nun werde ich einmal alles aufsuchen und aussagen was mir'am Westen'missfällt." Die gefundenen Punkte kann man auch notieren. Dann wird der Gesprächspartner gebeten, seinerseits ähnlich zu verfahren. In dieser Situation identifiziert sich keiner mit seinem Gesellschaftskörper, sondern scheidet sich kritisch von ihm ab. Die Unter redner finden sich ausserhalb ihrer 'Häuser' — sind aus dem Häuschen — in einer offenen geistigen Landschaft, die ihnen neue und freie Blicke gewährt und sie auch zu neuen Einstellungen und Verhaltensweisen auffordert, herausfordert. In nicht wenigen Punkten der Aussagen bestätigen sich zumeist die Gesprächspartner. Das gilt inhaltlich wie auch in der moralischen Ebene des Menschlichen und Vertrauenswürdigen. Etwas nicht nur vom Verstehen, sondern vom Kritischen bleibt und lässt Selbstverständlichkeiten fragwürdig werden und lässt Voraussetzungen bewusst werden. Es vollzieht sich in solcher Situation ein

Prozess des Reifens, da durch die Sachkritik das Selbst befreit wird vom Wunschsystem (in der totalitären "Selbstkritik" wird exakt umgekehrt verfahren und das gewonnene Realitätsverhalten rückgängig gemacht durch opportunistische oder fanatische Anpassung).

Zu solchen politischen Mikrosoziodramen kommt es nach meinen Erfahrungen verhältnismässig leicht dann, wenn Anhänger totalitärer Systeme z.B. in Vorlesungen über Erkenntnistheorie oder Geschichtstheorie merken, dass 'westlische' Anschauungen von den ihren sich nicht weit entfernt befinden — dadurch *und* durch den 'kleinen' Unterschied beunruhigt und an Aussprache darüber interessiert sind (womit die Einstellung des ideologischen Besserwissens bereits weitgehend abgebaut sein kann).

Unbetroffen geht keiner der beiden Unterredenden aus solchem sachlich harten politischen Mikrosoziodrama heraus.

THE DEVELOPMENT AND PROGRAM OF THE ST. LOUIS STATE HOSPITAL TRAINING INSTITUTE FOR PSYCHODRAMA AND GROUP PSYCHOTHERAPY

by Leon Fine

A. *TYPES OF GROUP THERAPY*

In the period March, 1959, through February, 1963, 54 groups were conducted by the Psychology Department. These 54 groups included patient therapy groups and staff training and communication groups. The descriptive titles of the groups submitted by their leaders will give a sampling of the approaches that were used: "Intensive Group Psychodrama," "Vocational Rehabilitation-Job Seeking," "Psychodance Group," "Psychodrama Workshop for Senior Staff and Section Heads," 'Psychodrama Workshop for Chaplains," "Non-Directive Counseling Group," "Open Discussion Group," "Discussion-Supportive Group," "Rational Therapy Group," "Analytic Group Therapy Using Psychodrama," "Problem Discussion Group," "Supportive Group With Relatives," "Adolescent Group Using Psychodrama Techniques," "Didactic Group," "Rehabilitation Group Focusing on the Return to the Community," "Rehabilitation Group-Non-Directive Counseling," "Experimental Psychodrama Workshop," "Intensive Psychotherapy Group."

You can see by the titles reported by the therapists describing their groups that there are a very wide range of rationale and techniques employed. These groups only report work done within the Psychology Department. Psychiatry, Social Service, Pastoral Counseling and Nursing are also involved in group approaches with patients and staff.

(1) *Intensive Group Psychotherapy*: These are small long-term groups for intensive psychotherapy. These groups utilize psy-

chodrama and action techniques in their operations. It is typical to have about 8 patients and 2 therapists in each group. Groups meet once or twice each week and are usually open-ended. Each session runs from 1½ to 2 hours. Patients may be in these groups as much as 3 years. Currently two such groups are conducted for the Outpatient Clinic; one is conducted for hospitalized schizophrenic patients, and, one for hospitalized alcoholics who have also been diagnosed as psychotic.

(2) *Milieu Projects*: These groups are usually conducted for specific wards. The prime purpose is to influence and change staff attitudes as well as to provide therapy for patients. Typically, the groups will have from 10 to 30 patients and will include all Nursing Personnel, and, where possible, all professional staff associated with the ward. Usually, there is a team of two staff members who have been trained in Group Psychotherapy and Psychodrama who take prime responsibility for the group. Currently such groups are being held for the Youth Center, on the Admissions Unit, and on three regressed wards. Milieu Project Groups usually meet for one hour sessions with the patients and staff together and for another hour with the staff alone. As our specialists in Group Psychotherapy and Psychodrama are limited, attempts are made to train the ward staff to carry milieu groups after one year of operation. Psychodrama and action techniques are used in the Milieu Projects.

(3) *Vocational Rehabilitation Groups*: These groups are short-term groups which focus on assisting the patient in practicing life roles integral to securing employment. Groups typically meet for an hour and a half and utilize role playing techniques in assisting patients to practice and analyze their approaches in securing jobs and getting along with people on the outside.

(4) *Discussion Groups*: Small discussion groups are run on different sections by psychologists, psychiatrists, social workers, pastoral counselors and nurses. The nature of discussion and the depth and intensity of each group depends upon the training of the therapists involved and the nature of the patients involved.

(5) *Ward Government Groups*: These are large groups which include the entire staff of the ward and are held for the purpose of improving communications and to conduct administrative functions. These groups are usually initiated and conducted by psychiatrists.

376

(6) *Remotivation Projects*: These groups follow the design set up by Smith, Kline and French and are conducted by Nursing Personnel, particularly aides and attendants. The prime purpose of these groups is to stimulate the regressed patient to renew contact with his environment.

You can see then that the types of therapy are varied and are designed to suit particular patient groups and also depend upon the type of training that the leaders of the groups have experienced.

B. *PERSONNEL*

The Psychodrama and Group Psychotherapy section of the Psychology Department has been set up as a source of stimulation, training, and guidance for other professional units of the hospital. This unit is composed of psychologists whose prime frames of reference have been influenced by Moreno's psychodramatic approach, by psychoanalytic theory, and by learning theory. Their mode is eclectic. The Co-Directors of our accredited Training Institute for Psychodrama and Group Psychotherapy are Chief Psychologist A. G. Ossorio, Ph. D., and Director of the Psychodrama and Group Psychotherapy Section, Leon Fine. Three other psychologists and a pastoral counselor are assigned to the Psychodrama and Group Psychotherapy unit. This unit provides supervision for all groups conducted by the Psychology Department, the Vocational Rehabilitation Department, and the Admissions Unit, and is available for consultation by other departments upon their request.

Groups are independenly conducted by psychiatry, social work and nursing service. Supervision is usually provided by staff psychiatrists in these cases.

Intensive Group Psychotherapy is usually provided by psychologists, less often by psychiatrists and social workers. Supportive Group Therapy is provided by all professional disciplines and by the nursing staff.

C. *TRAINING AND SUPERVISION*

Group Therapists are first expected to be trained in their primary disciplines. Those who join the Psychodrama and Group

Psychotherapy unit and who are fully engaged in Psychodrama and Group Psychotherapy activities are provided with extensive training in Psychodrama, Group Psychotherapy, and Group Dynamics. This training is provided primarily through an apprenticeship period in which the therapists participate with more experienced therapists in the ongoing groups. Training and supervision is also provided by individual supervision, through experimental and training workshops, and by sending the staff for such training experiences as are provided by the Moreno Institute, the National Training Laboratories and the American Group Psychotherapy Association Workshops. We also employ a consultant in Group Psychotherapy (analytically oriented) and sponsor consultants of renown in the Group Psychotherapy area when they visit St. Louis. Basic minimum experience for someone who is planning to work extensively in Group Psychotherapy is a one-year internship with the section. The applicant becomes fully involved and participates in ongoing groups with patients and staff and later conducts his own groups under supervision. Continuing supervisory experience is provided internally by the section; by each therapy group in after-session meetings; and in weekly consultation with a consultant. Medical supervision is provided by the psychiatrists responsible for individual patients and by an advisory committee to the Training Institute.

Training and supervision of professionals not to be fully engaged in Group Psychotherapy or Psychodrama is much less vigorous. The training usually follows the same pattern of apprenticeship in ongoing groups for the beginning therapist. However, the Psychodrama and Group Psychotherapy unit functions as part of the Psychology Department and is therefore available only upon the request of other units. Other group therapy approaches are established and internally supervised by Psychiatry, Social Work and Nursing Departments.

D. *INVOLVEMENT OF FAMILIES*

There have been several projects which attempt to involve family members, but this is not yet a major emphasis in the treatment program. Some groups have been set up specifically for the parents or spouses of hospitalized patients. Some patient groups are held on visiting day and we encourage relatives to attend the large milieu project meetings. There have also been abbreviated attempts working intensively with the family units as a prime group.

E. SIZE OF GROUPS

Groups vary in size depending upon the purpose of the treatment. Intensive Groups usually have 6 to 10 patients; Milieu Projects average over 20 in a group; supportive groups and remotivation groups usually have about 10 patients.

F. TRAINING INSTITUTE

The St. Louis State Hospital is recognized as an accredited Training Institute for Psychodrama and Group Psychotherapy by the American Society of Group Psychotherapy and Psychodrama and by the Academy for Psychodrama and Group Psychotherapy. Dr. Ossorio and Mr. Fine, Co-Directors of the Training Institute, hold Director's Certificates from the Moreno Institute. Less than 50 such certificates have been awarded. The St. Louis State Hospital Training Institute has programmed three phases of development: (1) Internal Development — training for the hospital staff; (2) Training for the staff of the Division of Mental Diseases of the State of Missouri; (3) Training for other public institutions. The Institute is now engaged in the second phase of its operation in providing training and guidance for the other state hospitals and training schools of the Missouri Division of Mental Diseases.

G. STATE-WIDE SERVICES FOR DIVISION OF MENTAL DISEASES

The staff of the St. Louis State Hospital Training Institute for Psychodrama and Group Psychotherapy has been engaged in advancing group psychotherapy in the other state hospitals under the Missouri Division of Mental Diseases. Three years ago, two-day workshops on Psychodrama and Group Psychotherapy were held at Fulton, Farmington, Nevada and St. Joseph State Hospitals. More recently an intensive one-week Workshop was held at the St. Louis State Hospital for twelve delegates representing the four State Hospitals and the St. Louis State Hospital and Training

379

School. Consultative relations have been established with Fulton State Hospital and Farmington State Hospital. Consultative relationships involve visits by our staff to the other hospitals; visits by staff of the other hospitals to our hospital to observe our ongoing program; and letter and telephone communication. Visitors from many other public institutions are permitted to observe ongoing programs, but as yet no formal workshop programs have been established for any groups outside of the Division of Mental Diseases.

TREATING THE ALCOHOLIC WITH PSYCHODRAMA

by HANNAH B. WEINER

Psychodrama is of inestimable value in treating the alcoholic, for it offers by comparison to other methods the keenest way to create a harmony and balance of one's mind and actions. In one part of my mind I can see where the psychodrama is similar to alcohol, with the exception that in alcohol the individual uses pathological means of dispelling painful memories — the inadequate behavior of escaping or defending himself. In psychodrama he gains a more healthy satisfaction from his initial experience, which is heartened not by the conviviality of the drinking crowd but by the sincere interest of the other participants in the psychodrama. Pathological acting-out is replaced by therapeutic and controlled acting-out. Destructive, irrational transference in real life is replaced by interaction, feedback and open discussion.

The groups were composed of people not really indiscriminately chosen, but also not particularly chosen. They had one thing in common — a problem with alcohol — either they were alcoholic or were married to alcoholics. In the beginning, the groups were segregated. Of the three groups, one was composed totally of alcoholics, another of a mixed group of alcoholics and non-alcoholics, and the third of non-alcoholics related to alcoholics. We began to realize that a mixed group was satisfactory as long as everyone agreed to be the "victim." In this way we soon discovered that the same problems could be handled in a number of ways, and each member of the group could profit by seeing himself mirrored or by reversing roles with another member so as to see what it might be like to be in the other person's shoes.

Once the patient entered the psychodrama group he became involved in a therapy that was not synthetic and which often involved direct confrontation, bodily contact and fantasy, and was

381

always on a conscious and consciousness-expanding level. In the groups we had men, women, young adults and children, all of whom were present because they had trouble with alcohol. Whatever else they were was not clarified except in the action and interaction of the group. The group became a therapeutic community similar to Moreno's public sessions, in that anyone could or could not show up; but those who did became responsible for whatever happened. Often the director became a co-director with a member of the group, who would feel that he knew better what was happening.

In my psychodrama work with the alcoholic, one fact was confirmed over and over again: the sober alcoholic faces the same difficulties we all face, with the difference added that he must also come to his own terms with the "stigma." My work has been with the diagnosed alcoholic. It has not mattered whether or not the member of the group accepted this label. What has mattered is that he wanted to learn how to live more satisfactorily and realistically.

The psychodrama sessions I have directed have been successful because of the feelings of love and support that were generated through acceptance and non-acceptance in appropriate situations. The auxiliary egos were not professional people but were members of the group who learned, as auxiliary egos and as group members and protagonists, just how to have feelings again and what to do with them. Everyone in the group maintained the same status, therapist and all. There was no authority; rather, there was participation. One of the highlights of the psychodrama was that it diminished the differences between therapist and patient, thereby creating an atmosphere of true feelings and real reactions; for one does not have to be perfect in order to survive. If love is a special way of feeling, then this was the force in the group, because everyone learned how to feel, how to take disappointments, and how to be.

There isn't any one form of the psychodrama — there are many forms; thus, I feel it safe to say that over our four year period we used just about every form and every technique. The most effective techniques were the auxiliary chair, self-presentation, the double, role reversal, mirroring, and the Magic Shop. We used the rehearsal form of psychodrama in role-training an individual to be able to refuse the first drink that is offered to him after sobriety. On a deeper level, we assisted in ridding the individual of "ghosts" by causing the "deceased" to re-appear, permitting actions and words that were never said to be actualized, and providing at the same time an integration of the abandoned "other" into the life force. At other times we prepared individuals for successful divorces, as well as for successful marriages. We dealt precisely with the problem of alcoholism by giving life to Antabuse, to Alcoholics Anonymous, to alcohol, to suicide, and to the future, and by permitting an extension of living with each one or all of these. We developed means of psycho-sexual maturity; we explored the areas of death, life, the intoxicated group member and immediate social problems.

We had no set schedule or procedure in these sessions. Very often we extended the therapy hour to two hours in these sessions, or for as long as was needed to complete the experience. Sometimes we went out into the actual community and assisted in the getting of jobs, and shared in social experiences. There was a great deal of permissiveness on the part of the therapists to become members of the group and to have their roles understood. These were but some of the points of our procedure.

Quite frequently we had sessions revolving around what it is like to be a little child who has lost the love and affection of one or both of his (her) parents through death, divorce or just plain disinterest. In most instances, the "child" became socially isolated, feeling the "pain" resulting from a deprivation of the guidance and support needed to make an adjustment to the complex world around him. One evening we had a "little boy" (age 45) run away from his "rejecting mother," who was nursing a young baby. He "ran away" because he was unloved — he ran and sat on a low table (he later described it as a low) and cried for his "Daddy." When "Daddy" appeared, the "little boy" asked him why he had died and left him. The "Daddy" embraced him. The "child" clung to the "Daddy" and they kissed and hugged and cried together. Suddenly, the majority in the room ran to "Daddy" and all felt he was their "Daddy." He hugged them all. Later he explained that he felt they were all his children, and he was perplexed that he might not reach them all, but was happy that he tried.

At another session, a writer in the group confronted a member of the group who had been his former psychiatrist. The following week he came in very angry because this psychiatrist had chided him on being an alcoholic and actor instead of a person. We made a wall, and the Doctor and the writer smashed a cup against it.

Another member of the group, in trying to communicate with his wife, kept asking her to tell him the truth about himself. In a psychodrama session he was told, "Let us hear you talk to her this way." He did, saying repeatedly, "Tell me the truth, just the truth, that's all I want to hear." It became obvious to him as well as to the group that despite his verbal willingness to listen to his wife, he held his hands extended with a pushing motion towards her whenever he said, "Tell me the truth," and in practice continually blocked her off, giving her no chance to break through to him.

In another scene, it was obvious to the group, because both the husband and wife were in therapy, that the only justifiable action at the moment was for the couple to separate. But the wife could not do this. Stepping in, as she did when the moment seemed to call for something to be done, the director took the role of the woman's two-year-old daughter — but in this case a two-year-old who was trying to share some of the feelings of her parents, even though she couldn't talk about them because she did not have the words. The mother turned immediately to the "little girl." There followed one of the most touching sessions, with mother and "child" actually clinging together and crying over the necessity of parting from the father. The mother hated to face the parting because she was afraid of the distortion she was giving the child about the father. The session helped enable her to face the necessity of making the parting, and as a result the couple had a chance to develop by themselves, away from each other.

Another member of the psychodrama group, Oscar, was a young man of thirty-one. In his one year in the group he had gone from being overweight, lethargic, and never working, to taking part in therapy sessions, making friends right and left, working at a job, and thinking well of himself.

I'd like to mention one more session in which a case of *Folie à Deux* became apparent. It involved a married couple — a very domineering husband and a passive wife who shared years of alcoholism together. First, she was requested to leave the room during his session, and then he was asked to do the same during hers. He became very angry after the session was over, refusing to come back to future sessions. In his next drinking bout she didn't join him, but remained sober, and was able to handle the situation adequately. She felt that this was due to the psychodrama, which gave her role-training as well as insight into the home situation.

Often the action episode of the psychodrama supplied therapy or experience, or both. Often there was a profound inner "transformation" accompanied by a new ability on the part of the patient to respond to a situation as required. This change may occur so quickly that the patient is unaware of the change until he recognizes, and others recognize, that he is acting differently. This may well be considered a change in his spiritual makeup — a development of his spontaneous creativity. This may be accrued to the patient through his ability, either as a protagonist or an auxiliary ego, to lose his self and to become a free-flowing individual, reacting to his environment through action rather than through intellectualization and with new responses preceeding frozen responses. Psychodrama enables the alcoholic to have that authentic encounter, and moves the action forward. This is accomplished not through analysis, but by creating conditions in a climate which make it possible for the alcoholic to discover, through his own willingness, his own potentialities. This action portion provides conditions for the development of spontaneity, in order to: (1) create insights; (2) change behavior; (3) improve performances; and (4) to actually become involved and live through a real experience. Psychodrama sensitizes individuals to their own behavior. By developing this kind of awareness within the alcoholic, we develop his considerations and values in a sphere of action, and lessen his need for absolute control by developing his spontaneity. This establishes inherent skills, so that the patient can recognize and give support to the groups — his reference groups — which in turn will give him a greater equality of status, influence and liberation.

There were some remarkable changes in many of the people in the groups. They felt more accepted and more secure, with greater self-esteem; they had less hostility and anxiety and more trust and faith in others; they developed a greater willingness to see other people as separate and distinct from themselves rather than as objects to be manipulated or manipulative. They recognized that others have problems different from their own; they were able to objectify themselves and develop means of socialization and a greater sense of self, with an increasing appreciation of the dignity of themselves and relevant others; and, they developed a more real social sense, with abilities to enter into social situations away from the group. The treatment was a matter of adequate interpersonal testing and training, with an emphasis on the process of gaining compliance with one's self as well as with others, through understanding the "exploitation of values," through clarification of expectation, and though an increasing awareness of the presentation of self. This was done in the milieu of developing freedom.

The success of these groups is partially due to the creativity of the individual members. Many became co-therapists, thus adopting a new status role and practicing behavior patterns in a miniature society. Psychodrama encourages an almost immediate emotional involvement through action and experience, which frequently has been difficult to attain in the type of patient who has often been refused as a patient because of his willingness to accept defeat through withdrawal, reticence, hostility, isolation, relentless self reliance, or ignorance, and who has a deep need for social re-connection. The psychodrama offers a suitable approach for research in interpreting alcoholism as a problem in adjustment and learning as well as a disease problem.

In some of these sessions, the individual became aware that alcohol may have assisted an adaptation of the self to the environment, but that it did not offer stability. In the psychodrama, the individual learned means of stable adaptation; the psychodrama method was accepted because psychodrama did not have a definite meaning to the participants — it did not seem to be a therapy but rather a means of developing existential behavior, as well as an opportunity to deny the problem and yet receive help. The conversion to therapy became automatic and was consistent with the values of others. Another significant factor in the use of the psychodrama as a therapeusis is that the therapeutic aspects are more consistent in terms of our "American belief" of individual responsibility as a value. Many patients refer to their group as the class where each has the responsibility of developing the potential of himself and others, where he trades-in ignorance for education, and where he can develop his sense and his imagination in dialogue. In the psychodrama, the individual participates in a system of checks and balances wherein freedom, liberty and recovery are believed by the individual — and it is actually true — to be developed by himself and not by the therapist. He receives therapy by helping others, either in his own role or in the role of a significant "other," whereby he may ventilate rage, love, hostility, anger, compassion, or depression in a socially accepted atmosphere, and thereby help someone else. This is similar to the twelve steps of A. A. In the psychodrama, responsibility is put on the shoulders of the group members. The members of the group feel greater responsibility for each others' actions and their own actions. Change provides a framework wherein feelings of helplessness can be counteracted.

I believe that psychodrama reaches out to the individual far beyond other therapeutic methodologies and proves to be more successful in probing deeper to the source of conflict and frustrations; it discloses valuable data and at the same time provides the individual with modes of acting through the power of practice, reliving, and retraining, whereby he may gain greater personal freedom. Psychodrama gives the participants heightened encounters, wherein mutual feelings of trust and support are generated and group members develop courage to show their covert attitudes, guilts and ways of living. We were not only treating drinking patterns but general behavior as well.

In summary, one might say that psychodrama: (1) gives a greater depth of feeling to the group therapy experience; (2) enables the patient to discover his spontaneous self; (3) activates the individuals' unconscious to bring forth conflicts, fantasies, memories, past life eperiences and emotional phenomena; (4) develops the need for motivation; (5) provides an atmosphere where the patient can try, succeed, and fail — can learn by experience, rational thought, and action; (6) removes subconscious inhibitions and develops problem-solving ability; (7) teaches patients to work out and solve their own problems; (8) helps set realistic goals; (9) develops insights and reassurance; (10) intensifies the patient's affectivity and reduces excessive intellectualization; (11) trains for family, work and community roles; (12) provides rock bottom; (13) decreases the transference reaction; (14) develops personal freedom; (15) helps educate patients to the addiction or disease of alcoholism; (16) provides the opportunity to develop family roles and changes; (17) lets off steam and rage; (18) develops and explores the self concepts; (19) restores or eliminates old roles as needed; (20) intensifies reality; (21) develops and encourages community spirit, group identification, and citizenship; (22) betters patient-personnel understanding; (33) educates; (24) re-educates; (25) modifies isolated behavior by reducing social deprivation and anxiety-creating conditions; (26) develops emerging social situations; (27) changes self concept in terms of picking up others' cues and expectations as well as own; (28) narrows grandiose feelings and in their place develops responses to reduce conflicts; (29) provides an educational method with a high quality of feedback; (30) repairs the loss of love and affection of parents, guardians, or spouses through death, separation or disinterest; (31) reduces the effect of social deprivation; (32) trains how to live; and (34) develops the courage to be.

In conclusion, I feel that psychodrama, above all, challenges the alcoholic into action and stops him from becoming a spectator to his auto-telic moving picture of life. By exploring the alcoholic's social roles and skills we explore his life; we extend our psychodrama into life itself — *in situ* — by attending important functions of individual members of the group, helping those who need jobs to get them, and going to dinner with others.

A member of one of the psychodramatic groups stated one evening: "After I stopped drinking, what I needed to do was start feeling again. Psychodrama has done this for me. It has ended the intellectualization and has propelled me into action." If I were to conjecture on this statement, I would affirm that psychodrama creates within the individual a greater freedom than he has known before. In his presentation of himself in scenes constructed of his everyday life, fantasies, and past recollections, he can in psychodrama reach where the ordinary methodologies cannot venture; for psychodrama is as close to living as we as creative therapists can achieve. Not only is it a therapy, it is an experience where insights can be gained and skills developed on the spot in an almost immediate reassessment of living and life action.

SECTION 5: MENTAL HOSPITALS

THE EXPANSION OF GROUP PSYCHOTHERAPY IN MENTAL HOSPITALS

by CURT BOENHEIM

Group psychotherapy plays a major part in mental hospitals today. While in 1950 about 50% of mental hospitals used group psychotherapy in the U.S.A., at present all of them make use of it to a varying degree. Group psychotherapy serves a double purpose. It reaches a large number of hospital patients who are accessible to psychotherapy. Secondly, it provides valuable training facilities for the resident training progress.

Group psychotherapy in mental hospitals follows the general principles of dynamic psychotherapy as it is used by the majority

389

of present day psychiatrists. Technical applications, however, have to be modified to meet existing conditions. Some of these are the fact that the patient lives in a hospital, whether in open or closed wards; as well as the anxiety, the weakness of defenses, and many more elements connected with this mode of life, away from reality, partly deprived of freedom of action and decision.

Selection of suitable cases is as important as it is for groups outside of the hospital, although the criteria naturally are different. If all cases of character disorders or mild psychotic processes were excluded, the range of group psychotherapy would be rather limited. We select patients who show a certain amount of insight and cooperation, who have some contact with reality, who can express themselves verbally and who are not in acute psychotic episodes. There are many cases in our hospital population who fall into this category and can therefore be treated in groups. It has also been pointed out that "Doctors Groups" are a valuable method of preparing residents for conducting groups. Our task of training our residents for group work consists of two phases. First, we have to provide basic knowledge pertinent to psychotherapy in general, and then to group work in particular.

We have three years at our disposal. The main items in our training program are fundamental lectures in psychopathology, individual and group psychotherapy, neurology, and so forth. During the second year these lectures are supplemented by group discussions, supervision, and journal club meetings. At the center of these training activities is a weekly workshop in which practical and theoretical questions can be discussed. This group workshop is open to all the disciplines which are engaged in our extensive program; residents, psychologists, social workers, and nurses. Any therapeutic and didactic system has to have the cooperation of the whole hospital if it wants to succeed. We are fortunate in having this cooperation to a full measure. Our former Superintendent, Doctor Lowell O. Dillon, now Commissioner of the Ohio Division of Mental Hygiene, clearly foreseeing the impact of group psychotherapy on a mental hospital, has done his utmost to put our ideas into practice. Doctor Benjamin Kovitz, our Clinical Director, has actively cooperated in giving group therapy its place and scope.

In the latter part of the second year and during the third year, residents take part in groups which are conducted by more experienced leaders, first as observers, later as co-therapists. We make ample use of co-therapists, since we see far more advantages than disadvantages in having two therapists in a group. So much, then, for the part which deals with theoretical knowledge and practical experience.

We feel that to provide knowledge is not enough to prepare our residents for group work. Our residents have little chance to undergo a personal analysis, which by common consent is the most effective way to get the necessary empathy into dynamic phenomena. We expect that many of our residents will have the chance to have a personal analysis after their residency, which is regarded by many authors as the best time in any case. To sit in front of a group of patients is no easy matter for a young psychiatrist. There is no hiding behind the couch; the resident sits in a "gallery of mirrors", as Grotjahn once said. To enable our residents to deal with their natural great anxiety, especially in the beginning, we introduced our Doctor Groups. In such groups they experience how it feels to sit in a group like their patients, and here they can learn to come to grips with their own anxieties.

Counter-transference has rightly received increasing attention in modern psychiatry. The time has passed when the therapist was regarded as a sort of catalyst, or a screen on which the patients' problems can be projected as on a movie screen. Instead, most of us see the therapeutic situation as a partnership between two human beings. We have learned to pay as much attention to counter-transference as to transference. Problems of counter-transference are indeed the main phenomena with which we have to deal in training our residents.

Although we concede that therapists have their problems as human beings in their own right, we do not mean that they can claim the same freedom to express their anxieties that the patient has. To be partners does not mean to play the same role in the partnerships. Parents, for example, do not play the same role in a family as their children. If misunderstood equality is practiced in families, we see very disturbing effects on children. We see similar happenings in individual and group psychotherapy. To learn to cope with anxiety, to be able to take aggression without retaliation, to sympathize without over-identification, these are some of the reasons why we incorporated these groups into our

391

program. They are not compulsory, but there are very few residents who do not make use of them. Our five years of experience have shown us that the groups can work efficiently and that those difficulties can be controlled which arise from the fact that the residents work and often live in a small community. They do not want material to leak out which may do harm to their prestige in hospital or at home. On the same plane is another point of interest: the group leader, himself a member of the senior staff, has to be aware that his loyalty to the group has to come first, even before his loyalty toward the hospital and its administration. Time has taught us that difficulties of that sort can be overcome.

Some of our residents have applied group orientation to their wards. Aware of the fact that they do not often have enough time to see patients, especially new admissions, they very soon decided to divide their respective wards into four to six groups. Every day they met with one group, so that each group is seen at least once per week. Groups composed of relatives of patients nearing discharge have also proved to be useful. It depends to a large extent on the attitude of the patient's relatives whether an improved patient can live at home or whether he has to return to the hospital. It is therefore valuable to discuss the problems of the home in which a patient has to live.

Additional areas in which groups have been introduced are the Trial Visit Clinic and the Admission Service. It is time-saving to see patients during their trial visit period in groups, and to help their adaptation to life outside of the hospital.

In the Admission Service, groups help to acquaint a newly admitted patient with the hospital routine. Since it takes time for a patient to be staffed and for a comprehensive therapy plan to be put into effect, the interval waiting period can be used productively, and treatment on general lines can start at once. Orientation is one of the main advantages in this type of group.

Recently we have added a new dimension to our group activities. In certain wards of severely disturbed patients the observation was made that the cooperation between the different classes of personnel was not smooth and effective. This does not mean that there was any obstruction or silent resistance. But there was insecurity and vagueness, some indecision and wavering to be noticed. In this way the necessary wholeness of the therapeutic approach was impaired. A particularly difficult case brought these

392

facts to the surface and it was decided to try to help the entire complement of a ward to achieve a better working atmosphere.

A group was formed consisting of all ward personnel, from ward doctor to junior members of the attendant and nursing staff. This group meets once a week under the leadership of two therapists, and it seems to alleviate some of the anxieties and indecisions which had a hampering influence on the common task of controlling a disturbed ward according to the principles of modern psychiatry. We intend to introduce this sort of group on a larger scale.

We are very much aware that group psychotherapy can only have a restricted influence by itself. It is part of the general plan which includes many other aspects, such as individual psychotherapy, medication, electric shock therapy and other forms of treatment. In recent months, the Activities Therapy Department, which is very close to our own work, has been developed to a much larger extent. This form of treatment I regard as a sister institution to group psychotherapy. We see a patient once a week in a group, in some cases twice a week. What happens to the patient during all the remaining hours of the day? Here Activities Therapy comes in. We now have an efficient department which can offer various forms of activities to many patients. I regard group and activity therapy as a most important working unit, utilizing common principles to help our patients to get well as quickly as possible.

GROUP PSYCHOTHERAPY WITH CHRONIC SCHIZOPHRENICS

by Inoue Syogo

The aim of our first study was to compare therapeutic efficiency during psychotherapy before and after six consecutive months. The aim of our second study related to change significantly before group psychotherapy.

In the first therapeutic situation, the subjects of the study were restricted to male, long-stay, chronic patients between the ages of 25 to 60. In the second, the subjects were contained, female and male patients between the ages of 20 to 45. Each sample was confined to patients with an uninterrupted stay in a mental hospital of at least two years, and who were able to cooperate in psychological testing.

FAMILY CENTERED GROUP THERAPY WITH CHRONIC SCHIZOPHRENIC PATIENTS

by RUDOLF LASSNER

The project concerns itself with seven male schizophrenic patients who have been hospitalized for periods from 3 to 16 years. Six of these have maintained personal contacts with their immediate families, some through weekly home visits. The seventh, Alex, is an exception to this, as will be discussed later on. Other relatives and friends, as can be expected, have over the years withdrawn from these men. The only persons with whom they have been in contact have been hospital employees, fellow patients, and, occasionally, their close kin. They are thus hospital-habituated patients who cannot visualize themselves any longer as parts of the outside community. Their ages presently range from 22 to 48 years. They are all single.

When I first encountered them they were spending most of the day on the ward. They would do one of the following things: work for an hour or two on insignificant housekeeping jobs, such as polishing floors; watch television shows indiscriminately; sit, smoke and stare at the opposite wall, or, even worse, lie on their beds dozing away. Except for one or two of them, they did not converse with anyone. Occasionally some of them would be engaged in a two-person card game. Their participation in hospital recreation, with one exception, was nil. They all enjoyed unsupervised ground privileges, but alas, only two took limited advantage of this; one in order to stroll about in splendid isolation, with plenty of opportunity for an uninhibited fantasy existence; the other, an athletically minded young man, to participate in ball practice. Three took advantage of their liberal weekend privileges, while three others visited their families only for a day at a time. The seventh, an alien from Yugoslavia, has no relatives or friends in town, or elsewhere in the United States. He spent all of his time on the ward. Under the traditional program, home visits were granted as reward for "good" behavior in the hospital, which actually is unhealthy behavior, namely, idleness, seclusiveness and withdrawal. The patients' activities, or lack of any, their interpersonal interactions, if any, and their mood while visiting their homes, were not taken into consideration. Home visits were granted as long as the relatives did not express concern over troublesome behavior. A routine signing-out and signing-in procedure, handled by ward personnel, was all the contact the hospital maintained with the families.

Our group therapy with the patients started in May, 1962. Meetings were held first twice weekly but reduced to one per week as our friends became engaged in useful occupations. At the time of this writing 52 sessions had been held.

Meetings with the relatives were started in August, 1962, and held once a week. After seven sessions with these people we decided, with the consent of everybody concerned, to invite the patients as well. Thus, since October, 1962, we have had conjoint meetings with relatives and patients. All in all, there had been 34 sessions as of the time of this writing.

For the patients themselves, these joint meetings were a rather unique experience. For the first time in many years, some of them have had the opportunity to be introduced to "normal" people and sit among them as equals, *"pares inter pares,"* outside their narrow family circle. On two occasions, evening parties, which were also attended by some of the ward personnel, replaced the late afternoon sessions.

At the time of this writing, our patients' living standards have been raised in the following ways:

1. Their physical appearance has become more attractive, with more attention being given to grooming, clothing, shaving, etc.

2. They are taking ataraxic drugs in smaller dosages than formerly.

3. With one exception, they are engaged in useful occupations at least five days a week, either attending school, or leaving the ward to fulfill an industrial therapy assignment.

4. They not only recognize each other's existence and names, but occasionally compare notes with each other, commenting on each other's assets or shortcomings, and even make

useful suggestions, implementing these by helpful actions. They also react to humor in an appropriate way.

There have been several set-backs throughout the year, whereby some of our patients temporarily regressed, displaying aggressive behavior, having hallucinatory experiences, paranoid thoughts, or just withdrew. Some of these set-backs were occasioned by my absence from the hospital due to vacation and prolonged illness. Others could have been avoided. They had been caused by unfortunate decisions made by other staff members without my knowledge.

In using a fresh approach to patients' families, hospitals, like ours, that have been in the habit of practically ignoring them, must proceed slowly, though steadfastly. I think there are two phases to it: In the first phase, the relatives become acquainted or re-acquainted with the hospital, develop confidence in their kin's therapists and learn to express their feelings before each other, including the sick relatives. So far, our project has been in this first phase. I visualize another phase in which a therapist is welcomed by the families in their homes, preferably during the patients' home visits. There he conducts family group therapy; he becomes intimately acquainted with their interactions and thus assists the returning patient in assuming his role as an independent adult. This procedure would continue, if indicated, after the patient's release from the hospital. Should it be found to be more feasible that he live on his own or even get married, thus finally breaking off a symbiotic living pattern with a parent, the therapist would be in a position to give continued support to everybody concerned during the period of re-adjustment. This again might entail re-grouping: old family on one hand, patient and new spouse on the other hand.

Thus, our project is only a modest beginning. To make it really work, at least another year would have to elapse. Also, a closely knit psycho-socio-medical team would have to cooperate diligently and with shared optimism for the patients' ultimate rehabilitation. We have not been as fortunate as to have such a situation. However, we are hopeful that it will come soon. On the whole we feel confident that a family-centered approach to hospital-habituated schizophrenic patients, using group therapy in various combinations, will bring beneficial results.

397

CATALYZING ELEMENTS IN THE GROUP PSYCHOTHERAPY OF SCHIZOPHRENICS

by PIERRE BOUR

The best common denominator in a therapy group of female schizophrenic patients was the introduction of the four elements: water, fire, air, and especially, earth. The latter was a point of reference concretely present in the form of clay or of ordinary earth, which the patients could manipulate during the session. Actually, in some sessions, earth played the part of the ground-conductor in a wireless set — for example, in regard to the mobilization of electric energy.

In comparing the group therapy technique applied to this type of patient to the techniques of psychodrama for more conscious neurotic patients, one is impressed at one and the same time by the more direct and pared-down expression of the "affects" in depth and by the existence on the psychological level of a "common medium" which can be used as a basis for reconstruction processes.

Besides, the best results were obtained in the group when certain concrete objects were chosen to underlie the chosen theme.

398

THE DEVELOPMENT OF A SENSITIVITY TRAINING PROGRAM FOR HOSPITAL PERSONNEL

by Ralph S. Long

Initiating any type of program in an on-going situation meets with resistance — both overt and covert, subtle and obvious — from those who view it as foolish (meaning in some way threatening to their sense of security) or useless and unnecessary (meaning, more work for them). This resistance may be manifest anywhere in the hierarchy from those who "must" participate in the experience to those who have the prerogative of approving or disapproving the activity. It is evident, then, that successful implementation of any program is predicated on how well the idea is "sold."

A particular characteristic of the military hospital is emphasized in the dual roles *expected* of its personnel, *i.e.* military and medical — expected because these roles are accepted and emphasized differentially. These dual roles often require attendance at many administrative meetings, special training lectures, etc., thus reducing time on the job and crowding an already tight schedule. All of these factors have to be considered in developing a meaningful Sensitivity Training Program.

Since most of the groups "had" to attend, it was decided to make the initial meeting as stimulating as possible in order to maximize the positive valence. A film entitled "Eye of the Beholder" was shown, depicting 24 hours in the life of a talented artist during which he interacts with five people, each of whom "sees" and describes him differently. It is a provocative film and, when stopped at appropriate places, usually provokes a lively discussion concerning interpersonal perception and the role of projection in such perception. We are all concerned with the accuracy of our perception—that it should report the world to us as we shall later find it. Most of us realize, though sometimes

399

dimly, that by acting on our assumptions we make our world, in part, as we go along—particularly that part of it which has to do with our ability to experience and act, *and* interpret the way others experience and act. This is often referred to as "subjective reality." Thomas puts it quite succinctly: "If men define situations as real, they are real in their consequences."

In the next phase of training, the Case Method is introduced. Essentially, it involves the presentation to the group of concrete human situations—situations with some temporal and developmental span in which multiple determinants of behavior are at work. These may be film clips, tape recorded or printed vignettes, or merely photographs and pictures. Trainees are asked to analyze these situations in terms of why events *happen* as they do—why the people involved *act* as they do. When such situations are analyzed in a group setting, the trainee begins to appreciate the variety and complexity of factors that function in an actual situation. Although the stimulus presented has been the same for all, he may be surprised to find a difference between *his* viewpoint —which assumes some implicit or explicit schema of human motivation or social determination—and the viewpoint of others in the group. Thus, he may discover gaps and inconsistencies in his perceptive ability, blindspots to certain kinds of factors and forces, overweightings of some kinds of variables as compared with others, and projections of subjective interpretations which he may find difficult to distinguish from the "objective" evidence presented. With continued practice in such activities, he will hopefully acquire some of the attitudes required for dependable and accurate perception—a withholding of judgment, an active awareness and perhaps acceptance of variety in people and situations, and maybe even humility before the complexities of organizational, group and individual behavior.

Since the goal of Sensitivity Training is change (the term *modification* is probably more acceptable because it engenders less resistance) in the *behavior* of the person being trained— merely adding to his knowledge or creating a shift in his attitudes are not enough and do not usually bring about a change in the way the individual *actually* behaves—he must develop behavioral skills to carry out this new knowledge. Therefore, the traditional approach of teaching facts and ideas, *or* exhortations to change attitudes, are not usually in and of themselves the most effective methods.

400

While discussions of this type are extremely fruitful, the introduction of role-playing and psychodrama adds a vital new dimension — action! A problematic situation is presented to, or invented
by, the trainees. The theme is developed in skeleton form only,
with those involved in the drama supplying the lifeblood and
developing the situation toward some sort of resolution. The other
trainees are now observing "live" behavior and critiqueing the
individuals' *actual* reaction to the problem situations. In addition,
the "actors" *describe* their feelings and thoughts as they experienced the role. This method brings the trainees' own behaviors
and actions into the open for analysis and guided practice. But
the situation is still not completely "real" — the players are acting,
but they are role-playing characters who are, at least in part,
"other people" in an activity which, in a measure, is projected
beyond or outside the actual training situation. Of course, many
of their own personal projections into the roles played are revealed
in the action *and* discussed in the analysis of the action, but the
situation is still "make-believe." We know that experimentation
is essential if new patterns of thinking and acting are to become
part of the individual. To gain security in behaving differently, we
also need to *practice* new approaches — practice in an atmosphere
that does not condemn mistakes, for these are the "grist for our
mill." Essentially we are *re*learning how to learn because so much
of our formal education has led us to believe that we learn from
listening to authorities rather than from a sequence of exposure
— feedback and *experimentation* — feedback and *practice* —
feedback.

401

COMMUNICATION SUR UNE PREMIERE EXPERIENCE DE PSYCHOTHERAPIE EN GROUPE BIFOCAL

par E. DE PERRET

En Europe, *R. Schindler* et *O. Arnold* ont annoncé, en 1952, un nouveau style de "traitement en groupe bifocal": celui-ci rassemble d'un côté un groupe de six à sept schizophrènes, représentant la famille du patient, et de l'autre côté un groupe comprenant un parent de chacun d'entre eux, représentant le patient. La formation de tels groupes, utilisant essentiellement la discussion, et parfois la situation psychodramatique, a pour objet de promouvoir une transformation du style d'existence des familles participantes, par le développement psychologique des parents, qui leur permette ultérieurement de reconnaître et de prévenir les déviations de leur attitude et d'accepter l'émancipation du patient, projetée dans le groupe de celui-ci. La méthode recourt à l'interprétation psychodynamique des situations qui se créent au sein du groupe.

Notre observation

Notre maître Christian Muller nous a conduit à entreprendre un tel traitement de groupe bifocal, en janvier 1962. Il s'agit de deux groupes ouverts, composés de six à huit participants chacun, y compris deux thérapeutes. Les circonstances ont voulu que seules des mères et des soeurs participent au groupe des parents, sans que nous ayons exclu les pères et les frères. Notre intention n'était pas former un groupe de mères.

Le deux groupes ont manifesté le désir d'être environ au nombre de huit. Nous pensons aussi que ce chiffre est optimum.

Nos critères de choix ne sont pas restés fixes depuis la création du groupe, en relation avec des circonstances extérieures. Le groupe des malades se rencontre deux fois par semaine, pendant 3/4 d'heure; le groupe des mères, une fois par semaine, pendant une heure.

Le groupe des patients a été remanié plusieurs fois. Il compte actuellement six patients, moitié hommes, moitié femmes, dont quatre de la première heure. Trois d'entre eux ont été traités auparavant, sans succès, l'une par une psychothérapie d'orientation analytique, les deux autres par des psychothérapies dites "de soutien". Tous, âgés de 20 à 30 ans, ont plusieurs séjours hospitaliers à leur actif et ont été traités par des cures biologiques majeures. L'appartenance au groupe n'exclut aucune autre forme de traitement. Un patient a une structure pré-psychotique; les cinq autres sont des schizophrènes avérés. Six autres patients ont passé dans le groupe sans y rester, différents de la majorité par plusieurs côtés.

Ce groupe s'est structuré rapidement. Une patiente a d'emblée conquis le rôle de leader et s'y est maintenue activement. Elle est reconnue par les autres patients. Elle règle l'allure et l'état d'humeur du groupe, par son attitude, et définit ses positions face au thème traité. C'est elle qui a, peu à peu, déterminé les avantages d'un tel traitement et les raisons d'adhérer au groupe. La position qu'a prise le leader est certainement en relation avec le fait qu'elle était suivie individuellement par l'un de nous, en dehors du groupe. Cette particularité lui a d'ailleurs permis d'y participer. Nous avons encouragé son attitude, garante de la cohésion du groupe, par l'intérêt que nous lui portions. Nous avons essayé de remédier à cette inégalité apparente en voyant en tête-à-tête chaque patient, une fois tous les quinze jours. Nous avons ultérieurement abandonné ce système, qui ne répondait pas à une nécessité, nous contentant de voir les patients en cas de besoin. Deux patients tentent de s'opposer au leader; les autres jouent des rôles plus neutres.

Au début du traitement, nous avons dû faire conduire les patients au lieu du rendez-vous, car ils étaient tous en divisions fermées. Actuellement ils viennent seuls, étant pour la plupart, en divisions ouvertes. Mais nous leur rappelons toujours l'heure du rendez-vous. Cette contrainte apparente n'a pas retenu ceux qui voulaient nous quitter.

Nous nous sommes montrés d'emblée très stimulants, le but étant d'abord de permettre à chacun de parler, voire de réapprendre à parler. Cette importante fonction du groupe a fait l'objet des premiers mois de traitement. Ce n'est qu'une fois ce résultat atteint que les liens de chacun au groupe se sont renforcés.

Evolution

Le groupe des patients a évolué de façon homogène, en consolidant sa structure, centrée sur le leader. En effet, celle-ci a quitté l'hôpital, effectuant une réadaptation difficile dans un cadre proche de son métier, encore non terminé. Cette circonstance a permis au groupe d'apparaître comme un ensemble qui se dresse et se défend contre le monde extérieur, ses contraintes et ses frustrations. Un double mouvement s'est alors manifesté: celui répondant aux difficultés avouées par le leader, apportées comme preuves du rejet socio-familial dont est victime le malade en voie de réadaptation, et de façon générale toutes les fois qu'il s'affirme, et qui a été utilisé comme défense opposée à tout changement; et celui où le leader, sûr de sa position dans le groupe, conscient de l'effort qu'il a fourni pour sa réadaptation, a pris la défense de la réalité contre le groupe, qui tendait à attribuer sa réussite à l'existence d'un passe droit.

Ce double mouvement a permis au groupe d'approcher de la prise de conscience des mécanismes de projections qui soustendent l'hostilité du monde extérieur, vécue par chacun d'eux. Parallèlement, l'angoisse devant l'emprise du monde extérieur a été mobilisée, voire même explicitée par la discussion, au cours de séances où tous ces mouvements étaient vécus comme autant d'agressions subies.

Il est frappant de souligner que les femmes du groupe, en moyenne plus âgées, s'affirment davantage que les hommes, sont plus actives et plus entreprenantes qu'eux. De sorte qu'une certaine opposition entre sexes s'est développée parallèlement à cette différence, et s'est exprimée par la répartition des participants autour de la table de séance, de part et d'autre des thérapeutes: les hommes d'un côté, les femmes de l'autre, alors qu'au début du groupe, les sexes étaient mélangés.

Le groupe a connu une importante modification: l'un d'entre nous, femme, l'a quitté, remplacée par un homme. Cette transformation a été acceptée passivement, sans commentaire, sinon sans réaction déplacée.

404

Un autre point nous paraît devoir être souligné, c'est la différence qui règne presque toujours entre l'attitude du patient au groupe et celle en division, objectivée par les rapports du personnel soignant. Le groupe apparaît effectivement comme une situation privilégiée, conditionnée par la communauté des buts des participants, par la stabilité du groupe, enfin par le rapprochement des médecins. La malade s'y insère dans un nouveau style de relation, qui dépasse celui qu'il a connu enfant, et qu'il retrouve plus ou moins passivement dans le reste de l'hôpital, et en général dans l'existence. Ce nouveau style de relation repose sur des bases solides, stables et sécurisantes, qui appartiennent au groupe en propre, en tant que champ d'expérience clairement défini par rapport à l'extérieur. Le problème du traitement nous semble revenir alors à mettre en évidence le changement pofond qui permet au patient de vivre ce nouveau style de relation, et à réduire la distance existant entre celui-ci et le style habituel, de façon à ce qu'il devienne utilisable en dehors de cette situation privilégiée.

Enfin, nous avons été amenés à utiliser deux artifices, qui méritent d'être signalés, parce qu'ils nous ont permis d'expliciter certains mécanismes transféraux, en réduisant de façon indirecte des déplacements habituels.

Le premier consiste en l'enregistrement sur bande magnétique des séances, avec l'accord préalable des patients. L'introduction de cet appareil a permis de mobiliser une angoisse jusqu'alors latente, concernant les buts du groupe et plus particulièrement des thérapeutes, qui voyaient aussi les parents. L'appareil en effet a été immédiatement identifié au monde tout puissant des parents, et plus généralement au monde de "l'autre", toujours menaçant. De plus, la présence de l'enregistreur a permis de mettre en évidence le manque de contact profond entre parents et enfants, la bande apparaissant comme le moyen d'y suppléer. Enfin, il a permis de faire apparaître un des buts des patients en venant au groupe: "que celui-ci serve à transformer le monde extérieur".

L'autre artifice a consisté à introduire, au cours de certaines séquences, le jeu psychodramatique de situations, où des répétitions d'attitudes apparaissaient comme des moyens de défense jusqu'alors inattaquables sur le plan verbal. Là encore, la structure rassurante du groupe a paru bouleversée par les changements de personnages, mobilisant des affects directement utilisables et secondairement analysables. Cependant, le rapprochement causé par l'échange des rôles entre patients et psychothérapeutes s'est montré encore trop anxiogène.

Notre position varie donc dans le groupe des patients entre deux extrêmes: le bienveillant et le malveillant. Nous sommes l'ami quand nous comprenons et acceptons, l'ennemi quand nous ne transformons pas le monde réel selon les phantasmes du patient.

Le groupe des parents a connu moins de vicissitudes. Il compte actuellement quatre mères et une soeur, substitut de mère. Une mère et deux soeurs ont quitté le groupe; il nous a paru qu'elles n'étaient presque pas culpabilisées par la situation.

Ce groupe s'est structuré moins nettement que l'autre. Quelques participantes ont successivement pris la place du leader, sans s'y maintenir; c'est ainsi que la mère du leader du groupe des patients a pris ce rôle, favorisée peut-être par l'intérêt que nous portions à sa fille. Finalement, le groupe s'est réuni autour des deux thérapeutes.

Les participantes ont montré une résistance moins massive que les malades, mais plus intense et plus durable. Elles ont envisagé avec difficulté l'importance que peut prendre la réaction familiale sur l'état du malade, excitant à ce sujet toutes les causes possibles et déculpabilisantes de maladies mentales, du facteur rhésus au déséquilibre glandulaire.

Enfin, elles ont montré un grand attachement au maintien du malade dans son statu quo ante, se montrant pessimistes, anxieuses de l'avenir, suspectant les qualités de leurs enfants, les surprotégeant et les brimant la plupart du temps.

A NEW APPROACH TO THE USE OF FREE ARTISTIC CREATION IN GROUP PSYCHOTHERAPY: GROUP IMAGE THERAPY

by GEORGE VASSILIOU

Method

The purpose of this project was to study a new approach to the use of free artistic creation — paintings, drawings, doodlings — in group psychotherapy and to explore its therapeutic possibilities.

For a period of twelve months a total of ten hospitalized patients, with ages ranging from 17 to 45 (mean 29) and an intellectual functioning from average to very superior, were studied in groups of four to five patients at a time. Both psychoneurotics and psychotics in relative remission were included for a wider range of observation. Previous interest or experience in drawing or painting was not a necessary requirement for their participation.

The painting was done during leisure time in order to keep the creation as spontaneous as possible and in order to exclude the alarming and censoring presence of the group and the therapist, thus securing the freest possible emergence of dynamics. Materials used were crayons, chalk, water colors or oils, paper or canvas.

During the group sessions (ninety minutes each, twice a week) one patient at a time was asked to present his creation, or creations if a number of paintings were done simultaneously or in a sequence. He would first comment on it, mentioning the title if any, talking about its meaning, the biographical or other content involved, symbolisms, allegories, etc., the feelings he tried to discharge, under what circumstances and emotional states he did it, his own associations, etc.

Then a spontaneous discussion, based upon the artist's comments, would develop among the members of the group. They were encouraged by the therapist to include their own associations, projections, feelings, etc., triggered by the painting. They were then encouraged to shift from the painting to the painter himself and to other members of the group, and to discuss what feelings were discharged, what their needs, wishes, conflicts were, what defenses were operating, etc. It was thought that focusing the whole discussion on one patient's creation at a time would not only trigger the emergence of more dynamics from the painter, but would also serve as the common crossing point of dynamics needed for a successful group transaction. We left the rotation to the group's initiative for the same reason that we left the interpretations primarily to them, thinking that this would prevent premature overexposure of a member.

The therapist followed the rules generally accepted in psychoanalytically oriented psychotherapy. A clinical psychologist, who functioned as an observer, kept detailed notes on proceedings, observing especially the second level communication and transference-countertransference phenomena.

Observations

The development of the processes involved in the patient's paintings appeared to be similar to those involved in dream work. Condensations, displacements, turning into opposite, the function of censorship, etc., would often become obvious during the discussions.

Jerry, a 17 year old patient who was dealing with a very destructive, castrating, unpredictable mother and a passive, inadequate, alcoholic father, painted an ugly woman's face. The title was "very insulting", as he put it. "The Tobacco Chewing Woman" (Painting No. 1). He explained that he started drawing "a crucified Jesus whom people think to be powerful, beautiful, sweet, and a man praying in front of the cross. Then I drew the face of a beautiful woman in the place of the cross. I don't know how it happened but the outline of a woman's face was there. I started painting that . . . the eyes . . . oh the eyes looked mean! . . . and then I saw this man, this crawling figure in front of her. That made me furious! I started splashing colors and I finished it in a few minutes."

The image of an "everloving" Jesus had been recurring in his paintings and phantasies. It represented, according to him, his wish to have "a parental figure so powerful and so benevolent, sweet, quiet to love me and do things for me instead of torturing me." The theme of crucifixion, in addition to other dynamics involved, presented for him, unconsciously, a parental figure in which his perception of his mother as a phallic one, his longing for paternal masculine support to face her threat, and his negative oedipal wishes, were merged. This figure was coming to fulfill this wish by giving everything for Jerry's — the praying figure's — sake. As this theme came closer to his conscious, it slowly took the less threatening form of the "beautiful woman" — the ideal Mother-Figure. However, by the completion of the drawing, his conscious perceived something different, a Woman; and in front of her the configuration of a "crawling, bowing man" who, according to his and the group's associations, was Jerry's father and Jerry himself. The "Man's" humiliation in front of a "Woman" triggered all his anger stemming from his family situation. He made the "Man-Father" what he was in real life — a shadow, "a decorating shadow in my mother's life" as he said when a member of the group pointed out that this shadow (which according to Jerry was a "Man") looked to him like a decoration in the woman's dress. Then he distorted the woman's face, got revenge by calling her "The Tobacco Chewing Woman" ("a very insulting title" as he said), and "triumphing" (again his expression), he covered all the upper left part of the painting with his signature — a thing that he only once did in his paintings. He would usually sign them at the right lower corner with very small letters.

Often one particular theme would be used repeatedly by a patient. It was observed that the group using the patient's associations recognized the repetitious theme as representing a crystallization of prevalent dynamics. Thus, in Jerry's paintings the sea was one main theme. The group recognized in it "Jerry's own changing moods", his conflicts with his mother and women in general, his ambivalence towards them, his aggressive wishes and his fear connected with these wishes, his insecurity, etc.

The desert, or deserted landscapes, was a main theme in Sam's paintings. The group recognized in it his loneliness, his withdrawal and isolation, his subjective interpretation of the world as a "desert full of unknown danger", etc.

The struggle between evil and good on a universal scale was

often presented in Earl's symbolic paintings. This was interpreted by the group as a projection of his own conflicts on a universal setting. They saw in it his conflicts with his mother, who deserted him after birth, his anger stemming from his basic unfulfilled infantile wishes, and his denial mechanisms.

Increased ease of communication was noticed from the beginning. Members who were withdrawn and silent most of the time on the ward and very evasive during interviews would start talking spontaneously during the sessions. Two patients, who became quite active in the group, were reported to remain inactive in a different group under conventional group psychotherapy. Patients who withheld personal material in individual psychotherapy found themselves discussing it with the group "quite naturally."

It was observed that, usually, *resistance* was taking the form of artistic or technical discussions during which the painting was treated as a mere art product, the form of intellectualizations and rationalizations, of misleading stories, etc.

Manifestations of resistance were observed even immediately after the onset of free creative processes. A splash of colors, a blot, a configuration would become then part of an abstract or even geometrical design. In such a case the painter would insist during the group session that "this is simply a study and nothing else" or "this is a pure design — an abstract."

However, the group proved able to break all similar forms of resistance quite successfully. One of their most "striking experiences" — as they put it — was that even from completely abstract or unintelligible paintings they would have significant and productive discussions. Raymond, in commenting upon his experiences in this therapy, writes: "There is more than dramatic astonishment in seeing how much of oneself and one's nature and conflicts and problems can be extracted from a painting or drawing, no matter how simple it appears to be."

On one occasion the therapist presented a painting to Earl, before he was introduced to the group. No one knew who had painted it or anything about the painter himself. The comments that followed, although projections of the group members, reflected Earl's problems. One member even felt that Earl grew up "motherless."

The differences in interpreting the painting and the differences of individual projections in relation to it caused difficulties at the

410

beginning. But very soon the group turned it to an advantage: they realized the psychological origin of these differences and were able to attribute them to the individual dynamics. They started using them in subsequent meetings as clues in order to further understand the presenting patient and his paintings. Frequently they confronted each other with their previous statements and paintings to make the interpretation they were offering acceptable.

Our initial fear that after a few sessions the uncovering would increase the members' resistance and that the spontaneity of the art work would be suppressed was not substantiated. In fact, the spontaneity increased in almost all cases.

411

SECTION 6: MILIEU THERAPY

PSYCHOTHERAPIE DE GROUPE ET DYNAMIQUE DES GROUPES EN MILIEU PSYCHIATRIQUE INSTITUTIONNEL

par F. Gantheret, P. Sivadon, R. Amiel, J. Capitaine

Le problème de la psychothérapie en milieu institutionnel est un problème irritant parce qu'apparamment difficilement soluble, et ceci pour plusieurs raisons:

— tout d'abord on ne voit guère comment l'on pourrait se passer d'une pyschothérapie, sous quelque forme qu'elle se présente: ceci tend à devenir une idée-force, partout où l'on se rend compte qu'il n'est pas de thérapeutique, aussi résolument somatique, qu'elle se présente, qui ne prenne son sens réel, et sa réelle valeur, que comme support de *signification*, — et qu'il n'est pas d'action d'un individu sur un autre individu qui ne dût être envisagée pour ce qu'elle est, c'est à dire comme *rencontre* et *dialogue* —

— mais pour une autre part, les contingences matérielles rendent difficile, voire impossible, cette psychothérapie, du moins tant qu'on ne l'envisage que dans la nécessité d'une rencontre inter-individuelle régulière et de long cours. Dans les meilleurs des cas, il n'est pas d'institution psychiatrique qui puisse offrir cette possibilité —

— aussi bien, le pourrait-elle, qu'on se heurterait à un problème lui aussi difficilement soluble: la formation des soignants à la pratique psychothérapique. Pour ne prendre que l'exemple de la Psychanalyse, comme la plus répandue et la plus strictement définie des méthodes psychothérapiques, il apparait impensable actuellement que même une majorité des soignants y soit formée —

— enfin, et comme le rappelait gentis, il existe un troisième et important écueil: à savoir l'incompatibilitè au moins apparente entre les rôles d'autorité, à tout le moins d'intervention, des soignants dans le pavillon, (et particulièrement du médecin) et les rôles de neutralité qu'exige la pratique psychothérapique.

I. Les conditions de réalisation d'une "communauté psychothérapique"

A) Le problème dans sa généralité

— Le problème se posant au départ de définir "la psychothé-rapie", nous accepterons comme nôtre la formulation de Bonnafé, formulation "adjective" qui definit comme *l'action* psychothèra-pique "la connaissance et le maniement des champs de significa-tion variant autour des relations soignant-soigné", action fondée sur un *savoir*, qui "tend à approfondir la connaissance et la maîtrise des significations pathogènes et des significations cura-tives".

414

—par rapport à cette définition, la psychothérapie de groupe apparait comme une *technique,* utilisant ce savoir et employant cette action psychothérapique dans la situation particulière d'un *groupe de malades,* réunis selon certains principes d'unité de composition, de lieu et de temps, en présence d'un ou plusieurs *psychothérapeutes.*

—dans le milieu psychiatrique institutionel, la psychothérapie de groupe ne prend sa signification que dans la mesure où on la considère dans sa réalité, c'est à dire comme technique psychothérapique en conjugaison étroite dans le temps, l'espace et les significations avec d'autres techniques curatives, au sein d'une institution donnée, de structure et fonctionnement bien précis et qui ne se définit elle-même que comme élement d'un contexte plus vaste, d'ordre sociologique.

—à partir de ces mises en places, et si l'on envisage la *dynamique psychothérapique* comme mobilisation dans un sens jugé duratif de cette relation soignant-soigné, il apparaît que cette mobilisation ne saurait avoir lieu sans la mobilisation corrélative du contexte institutionnel. Une progression dialectique de cette mobilisation ne peut-être conçue qu'en référence à une double polarité antithétique: un pôle de rigidité de cristallisation, qui rend compte de la nécessité d'une structuration ou d'une organisation, et un pôle de fluidité, de mouvement, de contestation, qui rend compte d'une souplesse nécessaire de cette organisation. Il est clair que le groupe de psychothérapie, porteur et pénétré dans son sens même du contexte qui le définit, ne saurait être opérant si ce contexte institutionnel n'est pas le siège d'un mouvement identique. Ceci implique donc de porter l'instrument d'analyse et d'action au niveau même des soignants, et de l'institution.

B) *Le problème dans sa spécificité*

—est-ce à dire que nous devions promouvoir la même technique au niveau des soignants, c'est à dire une psychothérapie de groupe sans malades, une "dynamique des groupes" qui tenterait d'élucider et de traiter les relations intersubjectives entre les soignants? Nous pensons qu'il y a là une erreur et une méconnaissance de la réalité structurelle de l'institution.

Comme le souligne une analyse déjà citée, il existe une différence fondamentale entre soignés et soignants, dans le sens même de leur présence à *ce lieu de rencontre* qu'est l'institution, et plus particulièrement le groupe de psychothérapie: les malades sont présents en ce lieu en une *période* de leur vie, dans la totalité actuelle de leur existence. Les soignants y sont présents en un *secteur* de leur vie, le secteur de leur activité professionnelle.

Le mouvement commun qui les rassemble s'instaure dans la spécifité des sens de leur présence. Il apparaît donce que ce mouvement doit animer le groupe des soignants *dans leur praxis,* dans leur technique, porter à ce niveau, et à ce niveau seulement. Mais, cette limitation n'en inclue pas moins l'éventail très large qui définit cette praxis, de la simple insertionpsychologique personnelle en cette praxis, jusque et y compris les conditions *sociales* de cette activité professionnelle (les problèmes syndicaux par exemple).

C) *Le "groupe de recherche en psychothérapie de groupe" comme tentative d'application de ces principes*

— en partant de ces données à la fois relativement simples et fondamentales, nous avons constitué un "groupe de recherche en psychothérapie de groupe", réunissant des soignants (médecins, psychologues, infirmières) qui sont effectivement engagés dans une activité de psychothérapie de groupe, et qui se donnait:

— pour buts: l'éclaircissement de "ce qui se passe" dans les groupes de psychothérapie: l'auto-formation et perfectionnement des soignants.

— pour mode de travail: la position dans le groupe de recherche des problèmes actuels de l'évolution des groupes de psychothérapie, et leur éclaircissement, à l'aide de l'examen, — chaque fois qu'il apparaissait utile — de la dynamique même du groupe de recherche engagé dans cette tâche.

— disons dès l'abord que le groupe de recherche n'a pu s'adjoindre un observateur de son propre fonctionnement. Cette carence a conduit à une auto-analyse de sa dynamique, avec les inconvénients et limites que celà comporte.

416

—le groupe de recherches en psychothérapie de groupe a travaillé sur tous les groupes de psychothérapie de groupe qu'animaient les participants, et s'est tout particulièrement contré sur un "groupe expérimental," dont il a suivi par séance par séance le déroulement, à partir de leur enregistrement sur magnétophone. Ce "groupe expérimental" était composé de névroses obsessionnelles ou phobo-obsessionnelles: il s'agissait d'un groupe stable et fermé, dont la durée avait dès le départ été finé à 20 séances (2 mois).

Conclusions

Tous les changements ne vont pas dans le sens des tendances centrales dégagées. Dans un cas par exemple, l'affaiblissement des défenses obsessionnelles a laissé s'extérioriser des tendances psychotiques auparavant maîtrisées (sans pour autant que ceci handicape ce malade dans la reprise de ses activités profesionnelles). Mais ce n'est que par un troisième entretien, quelques mois après la fin du groupe qu'il serait possible de déterminer dans quelle mesure les changements constatés se sont stabilisés. On peut entre temps faire les constatations suivantes:

1. La psychothérapie est d'abord conçue par le malade selon le modèle de la médecine somatique traditionnelle à structure dyadique verticale.
2. Plus on s'engage dans le devenir du groupe, la conception de la psychothérapie se modifie en faveur d'une conception interrelationnelle horizontale, et plus il y a un changement thérapeutique manifeste.
3. Ces résultats semblent être en faveur de la psychothérapie du groupe comme addition positive à l'effort d'ensemble du rétablissement des malades dans l'institution.

Nous sommes enclins, à partir de cette expérience privilégiée, à voir en une telle entreprise d'analyse, définie précisément comme nous l'avons fait, une condition essentielle de la psychothérapie de groupe en institution psychiatrique. Nous serions même tentés de dire: de toute psychothérapie réelle en institution. La somme d'énergie et de travail qui semble devoir y être investie reste dans le domaine du possible: un tel groupe de recherche, premier pas explorateur, l'a été. Elle est en tout cas infiniment moindre que

417

toute l'énergie dépensée dans les inhibitions et les conflits liés à la psychothérapie, en tant qu'elle est ressentie comme nécessaire, et ne peut être réalisée. Soulignons enfin que la position de ce groupe de recherche dans l'institution en tant qu'explorateur d'un nouveau mode de fonctionnement, ne pouvait être, à certains niveaux, que conflictuelle avec le reste de l'institution. Ce problème s'est intégré a la dynamique du groupe comme analysable lui aussi, mais n'a évidemment pas toujours favorisé sa progression. Il en sera évidemment tout autrement quand, cette forme de travail étant plus généralement pratiquée, ce sera au sein d'un mouvement de même nature qu'évoluera un groupe de recherche de cet ordre. Soulignons pour terminer que l'entreprise d'analyse d'un *groupe de travail*, c'est à dire poursuivant un but défini à l'avance, bien que contraire aux normes du "groupe de diagnostic" classique, ne nous a pas paru poser de problèmes insolubles dans ce cas précis.

REMARQUES A PROPOS D'UNE INTERVENTION PAR GROUPE D'ANALYSE DANS UN MILIEU "NATUREL" (HOPITAL PSYCHIATRIQUE)

par Raymond Fichelet et Robert Meigniez

La mise en forme d'expériences de groupe antérieures, et plus spécialement les discussions d'une équipe d'analystes, au cours d'une intervention dans une institution psychiatrique effectuée auprès du personnel soignant et au moyen du "Groupe-centré-sur-le-groupe" (T-Group centré sur l'analyse hic et nunc), ont amené cette équipe à relever un certain nombre de points théoriques et techniques qui lui paraissent stratégiques, spécialement pour l'intervention dans un milieu "naturel".

a) Le mode de résistance opposé à la centration sur le hic et nunc dans les séances de groupe semble spécifique à la nature du groupe naturel où se situe l'intervention. C'est ainsi que le personnel soignant, en milieu psychiatrique, a adopté des résistances semi-analytiques consistant à "lâcher du terrain" sur le plan de la reconnaissance des symboles et de leur signification, afin d'éviter une prise en charge analytique des problèmes structurels. Ceci paraît exprimer une loi générale du développement de tout groupe d'analyse, celle de la *conduite d'économie* (le groupe ne livre que ce qui lui paraît le minimum nécessaire au stade considéré).

b) La dichotomie "stade de progression — stade de résistance" (de même que la dichotomie "mécanismes de progression — mécanismes d'entretien") est critiquable: tout processus tend à être progression et résistance, selon l'angle sous lequel on l'envisage.

c) L'analyse "bicéphale" (deux analystes), centrant les membres du groupe sur la relation perçue entre les analystes, ainsi qu'entre toutes les personnes de l'équipe analytique présentes aux séances (y compris les observateurs) paraît avantageuse à

419

ιa maturation du groupe. La présence de figures féminines dans l'équipe analytique va aussi dans ce sens.

d) Le problème des analystes: travailler en vue d'une prise de conscience explicite de sa situation par le groupe, ou viser à une maturation affective qui n'implique pas toujours cette prise de conscience, est une option qui exige d'être étudiée sur le plan théorique. De même pour le problème connexe de la manière dont les analystes utilisent le vécu "rituel" spontané du groupe (repas de communion, etc.), soit en l'analysant comme passage à l'acte, soit en s'y impliquant au niveau de l'assomption d'un rôle spécifique.

e) Le problème de la restitution ou non au groupe des partιcipants de ce qui est dit dans les discussions intérieures au groupe des analystes, ou même éventuellement le problème de l'observation de ces séances de discussion par les participants (et alors comment éviter "l'analyse sauvage"?).

A PROPOS D'UNE EXPERIENCE DE PSYCHOTHERAPIE
DE GROUPE EN MILIEU CARCERAL

par Yves Roumajon

Une expérience est actuellement en cours dans certains établissements pénitentiaires français, afin d'y introduire des méthodes de psychothérapie de groupe qui n'ont jamais été utilisés en France pour le traitement des délinquants.

Après d'assez nombreuses discussions, il a été décidé de n'utiliser dans cette expérience qu'un seul type de psychothérapie: "L'Entretien de Groupe" (Group Counseling).

Cette forme unique de psychothérapie de groupe a été choisie comme la plus propice à surmonter les grandes difficultés devant lesquelles les promoteurs se sont trouvés, aussi bien sur le plan du recrutement du personnel techniquement spécialisé que sur celui des problèmes propres à l'introduction dans le système pénitentiaire français de ces méthodes nouvelles.

Sans doute, l'Administration Pénitentiaire Centrale s'est-elle montrée tout-à-fait compréhensive en autorisant l'introduction de telles méthodes dans quatre établissements, mais c'est pour prévenir les réticences du personnel d'encadrement et de gardiennage que la méthode a été choisie en raison de sa simplicité apparente et, surtout, de la facilité avec laquelle on pouvait l'expliquer à ce personnel.

L'expérience a commencé depuis dix mois dans cinq types d'établissements choisis pour la diversité de leur population:

1° une maison centrale de femmes condamnées à de longues peines,

2° une maison centrale d'hommes de type classique,

3° une maison centrale d'hommes de type "rénové" pour peines de longue durée,

4° une maison centrale d'hommes de type "rénové" pour peines de durée moyenne,

5° un foyer de libérés

Des premiers résultats qui nous sont parvenus, et malgré la relative brièveté de cette expérience, il est déjà possible de préciser combien il est nécessaire de faire précéder l'introduction de telles méthodes, dans un milieu comme les prisons, d'une information longuement détaillée qui puisse, à l'occasion, revêtir elle-même la forme d'un entretien de groupe avec le personnel d'encadrement et de gardiennage.

Chez les détenus, le recrutement des patients se fait sous la forme exclusive du volontariat, mais le recrutement des libérés s'avère beaucoup plus difficile.

Les habitudes françaises n'ayant jamais, jusqu'à présent, été très favorables à l'établissement et l'extension des méthodes psychothérapiques collectives, cette expérience paraît ainsi pouvoir être un test particulièrement intéressant bien que, pour le moment, il ne soit pas encore possible d'en tirer des résultats statistiques ayant une valeur réelle en fonction même de la brièveté de la recherche.

En résumé, l'expérience, actuellement en cours dans les maisons d'incarcération françaises, porte sur l'efficacité de "L'Entretien de Groupe" en tant que méthode préférentielle en milieu carcéral.

SECTION 7: THERAPEUTIC COMMUNITY

DIE KONSOLIDIERUNG EINER POLIKLINISCHEN OFFENEN GEMISCHTEN GRUPPE

von D. Fuchs-Kamp

Im Jahre 1956 — nach 5 jähriger Erfahrung mit mehreren parallel laufenden Frauengruppen — hatte ich mit meiner ersten gemischten Gruppe begonnen. Ich lernte in dieser eine erheblich lebhaftere Gruppendynamik kennen, als ich sie vorher bei den eingeschlechtlichen Gruppen erlebt hatte. Wie zu erwarten war, wirkte sich diese für das therapeutische Geschehen in der Gruppe recht positiv aus. Daraufhin stellte ich im Januar 1959 unter Einbeziehung einiger Restmitglieder aus einer ehemaligen Frauengruppe meine zweite gemischte Gruppe zusammen. Die Mischung hinsichtlich Neurosenstrukturen, Symptomatik und Altersgruppierung entsprach durchaus unseren Vorstellungen von einer günstigen Inhomogenität einer Gruppe, ebenso lag eine soziologische Inhomogenität vor, soweit sie unter den Versicherten unserer Allgemeinen Ortskrankenkasse vertreten ist. Das Alter der Gruppenmitglieder bewegte sich zwischen Ende 20jährig bis reichlich Mitte 40jährig, das Durchschnittsalter lag bei Mitte 30jährig.

Entgegen meinen Erwartungen blieb in dieser Gruppe die Diskussion schleppend und neigte zur Verflachung. Ich brachte dies damit in Verbindung, dass in dieser Gruppe im Jahr 1959, dem ersten Jahr ihres Bestehens, ein ungewöhnlich starker Patientenwechsel erfolgte. Die Gruppe selber kritisierte diesen Patientenwechsel, als wir gemeinsam Überlegungen über die Ursachen für die Diskussionsverflachung anstellten. Bei Durchsicht der das Jahr hindurch geführten Anwesenheitsliste dieser Gruppe stellte sich heraus, dass von den anfänglichen listenmässig 9 Gruppenmitgliedern aus dem 1. Vierteljahr 1959 zu Anfag des Jahres 1960 nur noch 3 der Gruppe angehörten. Normalerweise ist mit einer Gruppenzugehörigkeit von 1½ bis 2 Jahren mit rund 75 bis 100 Gruppenabenden zu je 2 Stunden zu rechnen. Bei den hier in der Zwischenzeit ausgeschiedenen 6 Patienten handelte es sich in 2 Fällen um das regulär eingetretene Behandlungsende, 4 Patienten gehörten nur kurzfristig der Gruppe an. Im weiteren Verlauf des Jahres 1959 waren ausser diesen 6 Patienten auch noch 3 neu hinzugekommene Patienten nach kurzer Zeit wieder aus der Gruppe fortgeblieben. Insgesamt waren also im Laufe eines knappen 9 Patienten, rund die Hälfte, nach verkürzter Zugehörigkeit zu dieser Gruppe wieder ausgeschieden.

Die Frage, aus welchen Motiven 7 Patienten, die nur vorübergehend an der Gruppenbehandlung teilgenommen hatten, wieder weggeblieben sind, möchte ich hier nicht näher aufrollen. Ich möchte dazu nur aufgreifen, dass sich bei nachträglicher nochmaliger Durchsicht der Krankengeschichten dieser Patienten für die Prognose besonders ungünstige Merkmale fanden, die für den Voruntersucher bei der Anamneseerhebung nicht in allen Fällen so gewichtig in Erscheinung getreten waren. Ich plane, dieser Sonderfrage an Hand einer grösseren Zahl früher Abbrüche von Gruppenbehandlungen noch weiter nachzugehen.

Die Stellungnahme der Gruppe zu dem lebhaften Patientendurchgang ging dahin, dass die übrigen Teilnehmer eine Scheu empfunden hatten, in einem immer wieder veränderten Kreis ihre Probleme aufzurollen.

Auf Grund meiner früheren Gruppenerfahrungen war ich bis dahin der Meinung gewesen, dass eine unter Umständen nur kurzfristige Teilnahme neuer Patienten an einer Gruppe sich für diese nicht störend auswirke. Nachdem ich in der hier zur Diskussion stehenden Gruppe aber eine andersartige Erfahrung gemacht habe, musste ich mir den Grund hierfür überlegen. Die geschilderte Patientenfluktuation hat sich von März bis Oktober 1959, also innerhalb von nur 8 Monaten, in die auch noch die Urlaubspause der Therapeutin fiel, abgespielt. Sie lag prozentual erheblich höher, als ich das jesonst in einer Gruppe erlebt hatte und habe.

Der häufige Wechsel in dieser Gruppe hatte sich nach meiner Beobachtung besonders deshalb als Störfaktor erwiesen, weil diese noch nicht zu einer Konsolidierung gelangt war. Dass wiederum so besonders viele Patienten nicht in das Gruppengeschehen hatten einwachsen können, lag bei den meisten — vie schon erwähnt — in deren starren Neurosenstruktur mit ungünstiger Prognose begründet. Dies wäre aber vielleicht dennoch nicht in jedem Fall geschehen, wenn ein spürbarer stabiler Gruppenkern vorhanden gewesen wäre, den ich inzwischen für eine gruppenzentrierte offene Gruppe für einen ganz wesentlichen Faktor erachte.

Der Gruppenkern bietet der sich erweiternden Gruppe in der Festigkeit seines Beziehungsgefüges eine Möglichkeit der Hinwendung und Ausrichtung. Er entspricht etwa einer kleinen Familie, die wechselseitig an Wohl und Wehe interessiert und auch aufeinander angewiesen ist. Ihr können dann neue Familienmitglieder zuwachsen, sich ihr einfügen und schliesslich sich auch wieder daraus verselbständigen.

Wenn aber die innere Konstellation einer solchen Klein-Familie flirrend ist, wird für neu Hinzukommende eine Orientierung sehr erschwert unter Umständen unmöglich. Gleichzeitig wird eine solche unfeste Familie ihrerseits bei Konfrontierung mit neuen personellen Beziehungen in ihren Bezügen aufeinander verunsichert. Sie droht auseinanderzufallen, statt sich zu festigen und zu entwickeln.

In der erwähnten Gruppe bildete sich ein solcher Gruppenkern gegen Ende des Jahres 1959. Zu diesem Zeitpunkt gehörten der

Gruppe insgesamt 8 Mitglieder an. Die 4 Mitglieder dieses Gruppenkerns möchte ich Ihnen kurz vorstellen. Ich nenne sie A, B, C und D. Die Altersangaben beziehen sich auf den Zeitpunkt der Konstellierung des Gruppenkerns Ende 1959. Nun also die Personen in der Reihenfolge ihres Eintritts in die Gruppe:

1) Herr A., 33jährig, verheiratet, gehört der Gruppe seit März 1959 an. Er leidet an einer Ejaculatio ante portas, Magen- und Darmstörungen, Erregungszuständen. Es handelt sich bei ihm um eine Mischstruktur mit Überwiegen zwangsneurotisch-hysterischer Züge.

2) Frau B., 39jährig, verheiratet, gehört der Gruppe seit Oktober 1959 an. Sie leidet an schweren Appetitstörungen, Stimmungsschwankungen, Herzbeklemmungen und Schwindelgefühl, Druckgefühl im Hals. Bei ihr handelt es sich um eine depressiv-hysterische Struktur, wobei auf den hysterischen Strukturanteilen das Hauptgewicht liegt.

3) Frau C., als 28jährige die Jüngste in der Gruppe, verheiratet, kam am gleichen Tag wie Frau B. im Oktober 1959 in die Gruppe. Sie leidet an Atembeklemmungen, Schlafstörung, Frigidität, starker Reizbarkeit. Bei ihr treten die hysterischen Strukturanteile am ausgeprägtesten hervor.

4) Herr D., 37jährig, verheiratet, gehört der Gruppe seit November 1959 an. Er leidet an einer Claustrophobie als Hauptsymptom, ausserdem an depressiven Verstimmungen, Sauberkeitszwängen, Schweisshänden, gelegentlichen Jähzornsausbrüchen. Bei ihm handelt es sich um eine depressivzwangsneurotische Struktur mit nur angedeuteten hysterischen Zügen.

Dem Gruppenkern nahe steht ein 47jähriger Patient, der der Gruppe seit deren Beginn im Januar 1959 angehört. Er wird von den Frauen des Gruppenkerns "Papa X." genannt. Es kommt mir bei ihm nicht auf die Symptomatik an, sondern auf die Tatsache, dass er als Schichtarbeiter jeden 3. Gruppenabend versäumen muss. Hierdurch ist der emotionale Anschluss an das Gruppengeschehen erschwert.

Mit diesem letzten Gesichtspunkt der durch Schichtarbeit bedingten unregelmässigen Teilnahme an der Gruppe ist noch ein Thema angeschnitten, das uns hin und wieder bei Gruppenpatienten eine Schwierigkeit bereitet. An der zur Diskussion stehenden Gruppe nahm im Frühsommer des Jahres 1959 für einige Wochen noch ein weiterer Patient mit Schichtarbeit teil, durch die für diesen jeder 2. Gruppenabend ausfiel. Er konnte zwar jeweils sachlich kurz über die Thematik des versäumten Gruppenabends informiert werden, aber es fehlte wechselseitig der emotionale Anschluss. Er ist dann nach wenigen Wochen aus der Behandlung weggeblieben, obwohl ich die Behandlungspausen durch eingeschobene Einzelstunden überbrückte und geglaubt hatte, mit ihm in gutem therapeutischem Kontakt zu stehen.

Heute würde ich sagen, dass es nur ausnahmsweise gelingt, dass ein Patient mit einer Teilnahme im 14tägigen Rhythmus in der Gruppe mitarbeiten kann. Als Voraussetzung dafür hat sich mir ergeben, dass er über einen längeren Behandlungsabschnitt mit regelmässiger Teilnahme in der Gruppe eingewachsen und mit ihren Hauptproblemen vertraut sein muss. Bei Gruppenpatienten deren Behandlungsende bevorsteht, handhabe ich es gelegentlich so, dass sie im Auslaufen der Behandlung nur noch etwa zu jedem 2. Gruppenabend kommen, um noch etwas Zeit zu gewinnen. Diese sind dann meistens auf Grund ihrer langen Gruppenzugehörigkeit in der Lage, sich jeweils voll in dar Gruppengespräch einzuschalten.

Nach dieser kurzen Nebenüberlegung zurück zum Gruppenkern. Während ich für die Gesamtgruppe die Inhomogenität als einen wesentlichen positiven Faktor angeführt habe, gilt dies für den Gruppenkern in nicht so strenger Form. Die Patienten, die spontan zu einem Gruppenkern zusammenwachsen, stehen zunächst unter dem Eindruck von Gemeinsamkeiten. Sie finden wechselseitig Parallelen in ihrem Leben und Erleben, ohne dass es aber dabei zu völliger Übereinstimmung käme, die die Gefahr der blinden Flecke in sich tragen würde. Besonders wichtig ist ausserdem, dass sie nicht passiv erwartungsvoll — oder skeptisch abwartend — in die Gruppe gehen, sondern von vornherein darauf eingestellt sind, sich aktiv um Änderung in sich und Gesundung zu bemühen.

Das aufkommende Gefühl der Verbundenheit und der Verstehbarkeit, zugleich aber auch ein Stück emotionaler Aufgeschlossenheit sind für die spontane Bildung des Gruppenkerns eine wesentliche Grundlage. Diese ist bei solchen Patienten zu erwarten, deren Struktur eine hysterische Auflockerung enthält. Bei allen vier

Patienten des genannten Gruppenkerns fanden sich hysterische Züge in mehr oder weniger ausgeprägter Form, während zwangsneurotische Züge bis auf einen Patienten mehr in den Hintergrund traten oder in einem Fall ganz fehlten. Als ebenfalls noch wesentlich hat sich mir ergeben, dass keine erstarrten ideologischen Haltungen vorliegen dürfen.

Welche Faktoren haben nun die Entwicklung des speziellen Gruppenkerns, von dem ich sprach, begünstigt?

Frau B. und Frau C. waren, wie erwähnt, am gleichen Tage neu zur Gruppe gekommen. Schon durch diese Tatsache fühlten sie sich gewissermassen als Schwestern. Ausserdem fanden sich in ihrer äusseren aktuellen Lebenssituation weitere Parallelen: Beide hatten je 2 Kinder. Die beiden Ehemänner, der eine in Lehrerausbildung, der andere Polizeiwachtmeister, kamen nie mit ihrem zufällig gleich hoch angesetzten Taschengeld aus, während die Frauen kaum etwas für sich persönlich beanspruchen konnten. Beide hatten in ihren Familien im Übrigen die Zügel fest in die Hand genommen, weil die Männer eigener Verantwortung aus neurotischen Gründen auswichen. Dennoch waren weder die Frauen noch deren Ehemänner mit dieser Rollenverteilung zufrieden.

Da beide Frauen unter starkem Leidensdruck standen durch ihr sehr gespanntes Verhältnis zu ihren Ehemännern, brach vor allem bei Frau B. schon am ersten Abend ein Sprudel von erregtbewegten Mitteilungen, zum Teil von Weinen begleitet, heraus. Ich habe auch sonst mehrfach beobachten können, dass Patienten, die frühzeitig mit emotionaler Bewegtheit in der Gruppe über ihre Probleme sprechen, rasch und fest in die Gruppe einwachsen und wesentlich zur Gruppendynamik beitragen.

Herr A. und Herr D. wurden zu Gegenspielern von Frau B. und Frau C. und umgekehrt. Zwischen ihnen entspann sich ein bewegtes fruchtbares Hin und Her, das ich hier nur vereinfacht andeuten kann.

Frau B. wurde von Herrn A. in ihrer vielfachen Kritik an ihrem passiv weichen Ehemann bestätigt und bestärkt. Ausserdem bemerkte sie mit Neid, dass Herr A. seiner Frau verantwortliche Fürsorge zukommen lässt. Dann aber bemerkte sie, dass er dabei doch auch von seiner Frau für seinen Handwerksbetrieb einen erheblichen Arbeitseinsatz erwartete und auch von ihr erhielt.

Herr A. seinerseits zollte notgedrungen der Tuchtigkeit von

Frau B. Anerkennung. Gleichzeitig übte er aber auch Kritik an solcher Tüchtigkeit, weil sie emotionale Bedürfnisse zu kurz kommen lassen kann.

Aus diesen kurzen Hinweisen ist schon zu ersehen, wie aus der Beziehungnahme dieser beiden Gegenspieler bereits intensive Übertragungserlebnisse auch in die weitere Grupe gebracht wurden. Frau B. wurde von Herrn A. in ihrer vielfachen Kritik an ihrem völlig un-ideologische Unbekümmertheit und die oft drastische Ausdrucksweise ihrer Mitteilungen vorwiegend Sympathien auf sich. Vor allem Herr D. fühlte sich von ihrer Kontaktbereitschaft sehr angesprochen, während Frau C. ihrerseits die Verlässlichkeit in ihm schätzte. Dann aber kam von ihrer Seite Kritik an seiner Pedanterie und Neigung zu Knauserigkeit auf, während Herr D. an der geringen Toleranzbereitschaft von Frau C. dem Mann gegenüber Anstoss nahm.

Damit kamen entscheidende neurotische Reaktionsformen der Partner des Gruppenkerns ins Gespräch und es war der Boden für deren klärende Bearbeitung und allmähliche Korrektur bereitet. Mit den positiv-negativen Bezügen aufeinander entstand zwischen diesen vier Partnern ein wirksames Spannungsfeld, und es kam nun — Ende 1959 — innerhalb weniger Wochen eine lebhafte Gruppendynamik in Gang, von der die übrigen Gruppenmitglieder mit erfasst wurden.

Anfang 1960 bestand ein festes Gesamtgruppengefüge. Zu diesem Zeitpunkt gehörten der Gruppe 8 Mitglieder an, die sich in intensivem therapeutischem Gespräch miteinander befanden. Die Vertrauensbasis untereinander erwies sich als stabil. Kritisch eingreifende Stellungnahmen untereinander wurden vertragen und wirksam aufgenommen.

Bei Überlegungen mit der Gruppe, nachdem eines der Gruppenmitglieder aus beruflichen Gründen hatte ausscheiden müssen, ob wir nun wohl die Aufnahme neuer Gruppenmitglieder bewältigen könnten, meinte Herr A.: "Wenn die sich gut einfügen." Nun, einfügen kann man sich nur in eine vorhandene Gemeinschaft, deren Existenz damit also bestätigt wurde. Die Auffüllung der Gruppe auf seither laufend 10-11 Mitglieder ging dementsprechend ohne neue Erschütterungen vor sich, wobei die Zusammensetzung des Gruppenkerns auch wechselte, z.T. seine Mitglieder sich auch austauschten.

Aus den in dieser Gruppe gemachten Beobachtungen ergab

sich für mich die Wichtigkeit eines Gruppenkerns in einer gruppenzentrierten offenen Gruppe. Ich musste mir also die Frage stellen, auf welche Weise ich bei der Zusammenstellung einer neuen Gruppe und auch beim Auffüllen einer bestehenden Gruppe die Bildung eines Gruppenkerns begünstigen kann.

Die Gesichtspunkte, die sich mir hierfür herausgestellt haben, sind folgende:

1) Bei Neubestellungen empfiehlt es sich, immer auf eine bunte Mischung hinsichtlich Neurosenstruktur, Symptomatik und soziologischer Auffächerung bedacht zu sein, um für die erwünschte engere Gruppierung eine grössere Auswahlmöglichkeit zu bieten. Die Erfahrung hat gezeigt, dass auch eine grössere Gruppen-Mitgliederzahl von mindestens 10 Patienten sich im gleichen Sinne produktiv auswirkt. Von besonderer Wichtigkeit ist es dabei, dass einige Patienten deutlichere hysterische Strukturelemente aufweisen.

2) Patienten, deren Krankheitsbild die Prognose besonders ungünstig erscheinen lässt oder die eine starke Misstrauenshaltung aufweisen, sollten nur ausnahmsweise and dann nur in eine bereits gut konsolidierte Gruppe aufgenommen werden.

3) Ebenso ist daran zu denken, Patienten mit Wechselschicht nur in Ausnahmefällen in eine Gruppe zu übernehmen.

4) Es ist sinnvoll, einige Patienten mehr zu bestellen, als es der erstrebten Teilnehmerzahl der Gruppe entspricht, da im Allgemeinen innerhalb der ersten 4-6 Wochen etwa 2-3 Patienten wieder abspringen. Auf diese Weise wird vermieden, dass zu frühzeitige Neueingliederungen notwendig werden und Unruhe bringen.

Mein heutiges Referat hat sich mit einem speziellen Problem hinsichtlich der Konsolidierung einer offenen Gruppe beschäftigt, und ich hoffe, damit einen Beitrag für unsere Diskussion zu geben.

COMMENT UNE INSTITUTION MEDICO-PEDAGOGIQUE DEVIENT UNE COMMUNAUTE THERAPEUTIQUE

par R. Portugaels

Les institutions humanitaires satisfont tant de besoins individuels ou sociaux secondaires que leur efficacité n'est pas une condition nécessaire de leur existence.

Le problème de leur efficacité n'est que rarement soulevé parce que leurs objectifs sont rarement ou conscients ou formulés correctement.

Comme dans la plupart des instituts médico-pédagogiques de mon pays, l'institution à laquelle j'ai été appelé à collaborer, accueillait dans une optique de garderie bien plus que de traitement, des enfants (de 5 à 14 ans) retardés mentaux ou arriérés pédagogiques, avec des troubles caractériels assez graves, et privés de milieu familial normal.

La vie d'un groupe de 35 ou 40 enfants, dirigé par une éducatrice, sans formation appropriée, aidée par une personne s'occupant des aspects matériels de la vie commune, était réputée suffisante pour ré-éduquer les enfants pendant leur séjour à l'institution.

Ce que les enfants devenaient dans la suite n'était pas perçu comme ayant un rapport avec la période passée à l'institut.

Les échecs marquants étaient interprétés à partir d'un diagnostic sur la constitution ou l'hérédité, impliquant l'incurabilité.

Certaines institutions ont adopté, en suivant des modes de notre époque, divers types de traitements individuels en différenciant davantage les diagnostics de base et ont créé des sections plus spécialisées, des services de ré-éducation psycho-motrice, de logothérapie, voire de psychothérapie. Sans nier l'expérience bienfaisante de ces processus de traitement, on n'en a pas obtenu ce que l'on en escomptait.

431

Pour ma part, j'ai pensé qu'avant d'équiper une institution de différents services spécialisés, il importait d'abord de créer une communauté de vie ayant par elle-même une influence thérapeutique.

C'est pourquoi mes efforts ont été centrés pendant cinq ans sur la vie de l'institution comme totalité dynamique orientée vers des buts qu'il importait de clarifier progressivement.

Cette totalité dynamique institutionnelle doit être vécue et observée dans ses tendances dominantes pour qu'elle devienne consciente d'elle-même at qu'elle puisse reformuler, à son propre compte, des objectifs réalistes à court, moyen, et long terme.

Comment se rendre compte de la dynamique institutionnelle réelle, sans disposer de moyens de laboratoire, dans la vie spontanée de l'institution?

1°) Le travail le plus important consiste à observer et aider le chef et la cellule directionnelle de l'institut. Ceci est une condition sine qua non pour percevoir correctement et pour avoir une influence thérapeutique. Il est important que le chef de l'institut devienne progressivement capable d'exercer une autorité de type coopératif.

2°) Le travail de groupes d'éducatrices et d'enseignants est reflété (avec déformation) dans les diverses réunions instituées dans la maison. En ce qui concerne les éducatrices (personnes chargées des enfants en dehors des heures d'école) trois types de réunions hebdomadaires ont été institués.

a) réunions informelles centrées sur le groupe, qui ont pour objectif la sensibilisation et la saisie de processus de la vie de groupe (group centered meeting),

b) réunions centrées sur des problèmes de travail éducatif (problem centered meeting) où on demande une attitude de "problem solving",

c) réunions de synthèse dont l'objectif formel est le diagnostic et l'élaboration des orientations éducatives et curatives à donner à l'enfant.

Les membres du personnel enseignant ont aussi une réunion hebdomadaire centrée sur les problèmes d'enseignement.

432

Ces diverses réunions sont analysées:

a) en fonction de leur objectif propre,
b) en fonction de la découverte de la dynamique institutionnelle.

3°) Il est important de noter spontanément toutes sortes d'éléments assez difficiles à définir comme des réflecions d'enfants, des membres du personnel domestique, de personnes extérieures à l'institution qui expriment très souvent sans le savoir des éléments hautement significatifs de la vie institutionnelle.

Par example un jour que j'arrivais dans l'établissement, un groupe d'enfants me pose la question de savior qui est le chef dans la maison "Est-ce vous ou telle autre personne?" m'a permis de me rendre compte de ce que les rôles de la direction et du conseiller, n'étaient pas clarifiés dans l'institution.

Voici comment on peut décrire à grands traits l'évolution de l'institution.

Dans une première phase les éducatrices ont surtout présenté et étudié des cas individuels d'enfants en vue de rechercher de meilleures manières de résoudre, sinon des problèmes d'éducation, au moins des problèmes de vie commune.

Mon objectif dans cette phase était d'aider:

a) à mieux observer la réalité,
b) à se rendre compte de leurs sentiments exprimés ou éprouvés et de leur incidence sur les évènements,
c) à analyser des situations jusque dans leurs détails matériels,
d) à découvrir les besoins réels des enfants et d'essayer d'y répondre de manière réaliste avec les moyens dont on dispose.

Au cours de cette première phase la plupart des membres du groupe des éducatrices ont mieux perçu et tenu compte de leur implication dans la réalité éducative; peu-à-peu ils ont découvert les difficultés liées à la structure de l'établissement et caractérisées par:

a) une structure hiérarchique de type autoérotique,
b) une organisation de la vie en masse d'enfants (35-40) dans une installation inadéquate.

Cette phase a duré un an.

433

Dans la seconde phase, les groupes d'éducatrices sont devenues capable de formuler des objectifs éducationnels qui tiennent compte de la situation des enfants perçue plus clairement et de la nécessité d'adapter les moyens dont on dispose aux objectifs poursuivis.

Il faut dire que la cellule directionnelle de l'institut avait évolué plus vite et avait des propositions à faire; mais ces propositions n'ont été faites qu'au moment où les groupes d'éducatrices avaient une conscience claire de la nécessité d'une nouvelle organisation.

Les décisions communes suivantes ont été prises:

a) les enfants d'âge vivraient en groupe de dix,
b) les enfants auraient un appartement séparé,
c) le mode de vie des groupes se rapprocherait de celui d'une famille et serait autonome,
d) l'éducatrice disposerait d'une large autonomie pour organiser la vie de son groupe et s'efforcerait d'établir un contact aussi coopératif que possible avec les enfants.

Ces décisions sont devenues effectives après une année de travail. Dans la suite, pendant trois mois, les éducatrices ont éprouvé beaucoup de difficultés dans l'exercice de l'autorité lors du passage d'une relation d'autorité plus autocratique à une relation plus démocratique.

La troisieme phase s'est développée à partir de la constatation que dix enfants formaient un groupe avec une dynamique plus visible que dans les grands groupes de 40 enfants; c'est à ce moment qu'on a donné aux éducateurs une formation à la dynamique des groupes.

Au cours de ces trois phases, on a fait des constatations encourageantes: je ne signalerai pas les nombreuses décisions prises au plan de l'organisation qui ont remobilisé la vie institutionnelle, notamment la construction de 11 maisons familiales pour dix enfants chacune dont le programme architectural a été étudié.

En ce qui concerne le "fonctionnement" des éducatrices relevons simplement sur le plan de la communication verbale: les éducatrices s'expériment (sans connaître les théories) en termes d'existence de vécu et de structure au lieu d'essence, de pensée, d'élément.

Les communications passent du plan impersonnel au plan personnel (en 1ère personne) les éducatrices ne s'expriment plus en terme d'une pédagogie normative (il faut, on doit) mais en terme de constatation, d'objectifs à atteindre, de mode opératoire.

Au début, on rapportait surtout les cas d'enfants difficiles pour l'éducatrice (par exemple les enfants agressifs). De plus en plus on rapporte des cas difficiles pour eux-mêmes (les enfants non difficiles mais qui n'évoluent pas).

Un fait important à signaler est que l'institution s'efforce de résoudre les problèmes et non de les éliminer. Ainsi des enfants étaient souvent éliminés en cours d'année quand ils étaient "difficiles". Actuellement les enfants quittent l'établissement à la fin de leur séjour normal.

La quatrième phase que l'institut aborde en ce moment serait la phase du travail fonctionnel.

Les éducateurs commencent à saisir qu'ils ont plusieurs rôles à unifier dans leur personne, que ces rôles impliquent des appartenances à des groupes différents. Notamment dans le travail ils commencent à percevoir correctement qu'il y a des objectifs communs au niveau de l'institution, que ces objectifs sont contrôlables, que l'institut est inséré dans un contexte socio-économico-culturel. C'est en ce moment que des *décisions institutionnelles* peuvent être prises pour équiper l'établissement en services spécialisés appropriés aux différents besoins selon les possibilités budgédaires de la maison.

Grâce aux informations collectées et correctement analysées, il est possible de formuler ce que Merton appelle des "self fulfilling prophecies" constructives.

Le résultat important de tout ce qui précède est la création d'un milieu où l'enfant peut exister pour son propre compte avant d'apprendre ce que la société lui demande. Il importe dès lors que tous les members du personnel aient les uns pour les autres une existence propre et personnelle qui peut s'exprimer dans leur rôle d'éducative.

Cette communication n'a pas de prétention scientifique; elle raconte comment à l'aide des connaissances et des techniques psycho-sociologiques contemporaines, on peut remobiliser des institutions qui étaient vouées à la stagnation, là où l'on n'a pas toujours la possibilité d'en créer de nouvelles.

D'autres publications exposeront en détail les méthodes et techniques utilisées.

ORGANIZATIONAL BEHAVIOR, PREVENTIVE PSYCHIATRY AND GROUP PSYCHOTHERAPY

by Eugene S. Uyeki

Introduction

It is an interesting phenomenon that the U.S. military forces have recently taken the leadership in utilizing a more organizational, interpersonal, and behavioral slant to their psychiatric operations than many civilian facilities. There are a number of factors which account for this. First, the military is one of the class of total institutions which has almost complete control over its members. It is possible, therefore, to attribute behavioral manifestations to salient factors in the social-psychological environment. Second, there is persistent and technical concern with the effectiveness of its members as fighting men. All of the health facilities are mobilized to support this dominant goal. The conjunction of these two factors makes possible "experimentation," in which environmental factors are readily manipulated with observable results in behavior. Third, the fact that the military organization is intimately involved with physical danger increases the range of behavioral reactions to stress in a variety of contexts. Fourth, the changing nature of warfare requires that the military keep abreast of the latest technology, with fortunate consequences in the health field. Finally, it might be noted that the leadership in psychiatry in the military services is committed, as a result of experiences in World War II and Korea, to a very broad approach.

Put in another way, it is apparent that all individuals have their breaking points. We can also characterize units as having different breaking points. This is an area too vague to define precisely. As an approximation, we might visualize a situation in which enough individuals become disaffected from the main purpose of the unit so that it is unable to function as a unit. There is no numerical way to pin-point this, since any unit is not an aggregation of individuals, but is a social organization in which individuals are related in terms of subordination to a hierarchy with differential subjective investment and responsibility in the unit. This simple axiom is emphasized by pointing out that it makes little difference if a private is the soldier who becomes disaffected. However, if it is one of the platoon sergeants, the impact on the rest of the soldiers is of great consequence.

Stress as Index of Morale — Its Measurement

In the "normal" course of daily living, individuals have accidents, get sick, get into trouble with constituted authorities, and so on. This is to be expected, for there are certain strains which recur regularly. But the degree of stress will differ from day to day. Stress can be handled in a number of ways which may be broadly categorized into three general types of reactions: (1) cooperation, (2) withdrawal, and (3) aggression.

If we can measure the frequencies of withdrawal and aggression, we can infer something about the morale of the unit.

The Kinds of Data to be Utilized

No attempt is made to classify reactive behaviors in terms of withdrawal or aggression, since we have pointed out that both forms of reactions are indications of poor morale. At a later stage, such a classification may prove to be very useful. We chose the following data from those available as the basis on which to measure morale:

1. Reductions in grade.
   a. By court-martial.
   b. By Article 15.
   c. By own request.
2. Dropped as deserters.
3. AWOL's.
4. Other unauthorized absences.
5. Company punishments.
6. Courts-martials.

    a. General.
    b. Special.
    c. Summary.
7. Requests for transfers.
8. Direct admissions to hospital.
9. Outpatient visits at dispensaries.
    a. Accidents.
    b. All others.

Conclusions

There are two conclusions which I would like to draw. The first is that the method described for studying morale is quite analogous to the use of ecology in the study of other social problems. By itself, however, it can lead to solipsism. It spots the locus within which there appears to be a morale problem. The confirmation that there is one and the ascertainment of the causal factors must be undertaken by other means. Used properly, this gross approach to the study of morale is applicable to other kinds of organizational situations. It is necessary, however, to supplement this approach with other methods — i.e., participant observations, systematic questionnaire surveys, panel techniques, perusal of other kinds of administrative records, to name a few.

CO-CREATIVE GROUP PSYCHOTHERAPY

by Max Ackerman

In co-creative group psychotherapy the individuals of the group inspire each other by identifying themselves with the assets of their personalities rather than with their defects. Its main objective is the integration of the group members so that they can feel, think and act in unison. The integration enables each individual to overcome his limited self-interest, which blocks his development. Self-interest, when examined carefully, proves to be pathologically defensive rather than self-satisfying. By participating in the sharing of the group, the individual loses the need for self-interest and gains the strength of secure relationships. This relationship is kept active by the continual flow of emotional support in which each member exerts himself for the benefit of the others, producing maximal identification and emotional security. He can express his most desirable traits and innermost feelings without fear of misunderstanding or ridicule. He can deal with his problems with the confidence that he shall ultimately solve them. In the process he experiences emotional satisfaction so that he is able to feel and act better. He becomes receptive to re-education for a new style of life, consistent with his potentials and with the group's approbation.

Each individual stimulates the others to create new patterns of behavior that they can test on each other. This enables them to form a stable, rather than a transitory, relationship. By concentrating on his success, the negative factors are overcome, without the need to dwell on them. It becomes unnecessary to enter into endless discussions of all his failures. His previous anxiety is dissipated by the love and regard that the group feeds him. He no longer focuses on himself but on the needs of the group, and he rises above his own inferiorities. He satisfies his healthy needs, which he finds more rewarding than his defensive ones. Since most problems are based on poor interpersonal relationships, the ability to establish successful relationships through a cooperative attitude enables the individual to solve his problems. This contrasts

439

with group therapy, which starts with the problems confronting the individual. Unfortunately he becomes so involved emotionally that he can scarcely deal with his problems. His efforts to overcome them are held in abeyance because of past rejections and penalties which have branded him a failure by society and himself. This makes him feel isolated and detached from the others because he believes his problems to be unique, as he thinks only of himself. It may take a long time before he learns that others have similar problems.

In co-creative group psychotherapy he finds a common goal that he can share with the group from the beginning. This common goal is each individual's responsibility for each other, which acts as a therapeutic agent in promoting emotional health. The frustrations of fruitless struggle no longer haunt him as he proceeds at his own pace. He learns which of his actions promote or restrict his relationship with the group. In his previous relationships the individual was faced by a constant flux of vacillation in being accepted and rejected, with rejection occurring more frequently. In the integrated group, where acceptance of the individual is consistent, self-confidence replaces self-doubt and the individual becomes increasingly more secure. He is respected for what he is and what he can become. He is important to the others and to himself. He respects himself because he is a man now. He can go out into the world and use his abilities instead of his crippling defenses, which were defeating him before. Through the mechanisms developed in the group, the individual is able to function on a higher level on the job, in the home and in the community, because he can control the pressure through his satisfaction, acceptance and belonging in the group. When he is attacked on the outside, he does not experience self-rejection. Instead he realizes that the individuals who are attacking him must be as frustrated as he was. He remains confident because he does not become involved emotionally. He is able to accept them kindly, which has a calming influence and stimulates them positively. If he meets with hostility and obstruction, he can always find another way. If he experiences any weakening of this determination, he can renew his confidence with the support of the group, which acts as a constant source of revitalization. If he needs a better approach to his objective or goal, he can always depend on the group to discuss the matter, stimulate him and each other, and come up with new answers.

SECTION 8: FAMILY THERAPY
AND MARRIAGE

FAMILY THERAPY: AN APPROACH TO THE
TREATMENT OF MENTAL AND EMOTIONAL DISORDER

by Virginia M. Satir

This is a paper about *family conjoint therapy*. This term refers to a method of psychological treatment of persons with emotional, mental, and social disorders, whereby these persons are treated in the family units of which they are currently a part. Each treatment unit consists of all the family members and deals with their action, reaction, and interaction with one another, as this is manifest in how family members look and sound to one another, and what each says and does in relationship to himself and the others.

441

The family member who has the label of any disorder (symptom) is treated as one who signals whether symbolically, or in some other way indirectly, the presence of some kind of pain which cannot be directly acknowledged. In general, this pain directs attention to distortion in growth, a threat to survival, and/or an inability to get close to others.

More specifically, the symptom-bearer is interpreted as signaling pain in himself and the presence of pain in the figures who have survival significance for him. We find that if one person in the family has a symptom, everyone has a reaction to it and forms a part of the context within which the symptom is perpetuated. Symbolically, this same survival significance may exist in a dysfunctional marital pair, where one partner apparently invests the other with a survival significance similar to that which he invested in his actual nurturing adults. This is when one of the marital pair is the symptom-bearer or identified patient.

The following are the basic premises that underly the family therapeutic approach, together with the implications for diagnosis and treatment:

1. *Every human is the product of a three-person learning system:* the male and female (the parents) who provided nurture, financial support and direction (guidance, discipline), and the child for whom this was provided. The child's basic blueprint for what he is expected to be is derived from this learning system. Therefore, to understand any one person as he is today, one must understand that person's perceptions of who taught him, what and how he was taught, what he learned, and how he is using today what he learned then. In dysfunctional families, the "curriculum" seems unspecific, unclear, contradictory, and incomplete, as well as the persons who taught it.

2. *Every human develops his self image and his self esteem* through a process of being exposed to the world outside himself, reacting to that exposure, and integrating that reaction with his internal operations at that point in time. Therefore, to understand any one person means getting the person's picture of what he was exposed to, how he reacted to it, and how he fitted this reaction into his own internal operations at that point in time. Thus, behavior is an interactional as well as intra-psychic phenomenon and depends for its perpetuation on current interactional

442

support. The primary figures present in the infant's outside world are the male and female adults who are usually labelled "his father and his mother." Since the human infant is helpless at birth and, without the care of adults, would die, there develops an essential nature of the relationship between self and other, of which survival is the base. We ask, what are the kinds of data which any developing infant must integrate? What does the child see and hear about himself and each parent in the presence of each parent separately and in the presence of both parents? What is the child told directly about himself and the other parent, with each parent separately and together? What is the child permitted to do in the presence of each parent separately and together? What does the child see and hear about himself, about a sibling, said or done to a sibling in the presence of a sibling with each parent separately and together?

3. *No human being is so continually aware of his internal self and his external manifestations that he is at all times able to present himself consistently.* Therefore, each parent needs to know that gaps will exist between what he intends and how he manifests himself, between what he meant and what the other received, and between what he expects and what the other manifests. Otherwise, the child may get the credit or blame for the gap and get corresponding messages. He will not always be able to tell the difference. The child, not being born with a blueprint, but only with one set of ingredients for developing it, must depend on his clues for what each of his parents looks like, sounds like, says and does to him, about him, to and about each other, the siblings, and the objective world in which all live, away from each others' presence and in each others' presence to get a blueprint for how he shall be. The survival figures, both male and female, then become the most powerful shaping forces of the child's self image and self esteem.

4. *In the presence of another, one cannot not react.* His reaction cannot be clearly known or completely understood by an other simply by observation. If one sees or hears (observation), one automatically makes conclusions about what he sees or hears. That does not mean that the interpretation he makes of what he has seen or heard is obvious to the other. If the observer cannot or does not check out his observations, he will be in the

position of treating his conclusions as "the facts" and treat that which he observed in relation to "his facts", with the result that the other may get reactions that do not fit his intention and a "comedy of errors" begins, with tragic results.

5. *Every human is geared toward survival, growth, and closeness to others.* Therefore, if he perceives his survival as being threatened, his growth as being distorted, or he is not achieving closeness to others, he will act to make a change. This effort at change is reflected in behavior. The behavior of any person then can be seen as efforts at surviving, at growing, and at getting close to others. The effect of some of these efforts can turn out to be pretty destructive of the self, of others, or of the context in which the behavior takes place. The extreme picture of this is suicide of the self, murder of the other, and destruction of things outside of self and others. All behavior then is seen primarily in the service of the self, regardless of the outcomes to the other or the context. I think behavior which we label a symptom breaks out in a human being when he can no longer find any way to make any kind of fittingness of things that really don't fit.

6. *Every human is dependent in some way, at some time, in some place, in some circumstances upon another.* Therefore, each human has to have reliable, effective, predictable techniques for engaging others when the life needs of the self so direct. Not having reliable, effective, or predictable techniques leads to frustration and isolation. It simultaneously calls for a reaction on the part of any others present, and leads to an interaction which may only further frustration and isolation.

7. *Every human being has to develop a means of giving and receiving meaning to and from others.* The kind of means, the specific symbols used, and the means of checking out the accuracy of the meaning intended and received obviously will depend upon the "rules" one has developed for reporting and commenting on and about himself and on and about others. The way in which communication is carried on will contain the clues about the techniques utilized for manifesting each self and for handling the presence of differences, and will contain clues to the nature of the self-esteem and self-image of those communicating.

We therefore start our therapeutic efforts by seeing the whole

444

family together to observe how family members at this point in time communicate (act, react, and interact) in terms of what is seen, heard, said and done. We call this complex maze *family homeostasis.*

We see the family homeostasis at a given point of time as the result of the evolvement over time of the efforts of the marital pair to survive, grow, and get close to one another. Into this will come a child, who in turn will react, act and interact. Each adult, as a self, as a member of the marital pair, and as a parent reacts, acts, and interacts with the child. The whole is not the sum of its parts. Each experience in reacting, acting, and interacting serves to solidify and crystallize the basic perception which, because of changes brought by growth, time and the environment, may assume quite a different appearance.

Things are not what they seem. The function of the symptom basically seems to be to announce that things are not what they seem, to get acknowledgement of this "delusion," and to find ways to treat things as they are, rather than as what they seem to be.

The therapeutic task, then, is to make explicit *what is? how did it come to be? how is it interpreted? what use is made presently of the conclusions? what are the outcomes? how do the outcomes vary from the hopes for survival, growth and closeness to others? what is seen as the handicap to achieving the hopes?*

THE THERAPEUTIC IMPACT OF CO-THERAPIST INTERACTION IN A COUPLES GROUP

by ASYA L. KADIS and MAX MARKOWITZ

During the past nine months, the authors have been jointly treating a group of four married couples. Within this period marked changes have occurred in two couples and significant changes in the other two.

This paper will be focused on the co-therapists' own interaction, as the dynamic source of therapeutic movement and change in the couples.

The two therapists, ALK and MM, have long known each other as colleagues and collaborators. They have for many years been leaders of therapy groups.

Early in the group's development, it became apparent that the female therapist was being invested with the projection of the ego ideal of each patient — the magical, all-powerful mother prototype. This was the key factor in their disturbed capacities for adequate relationships with their mates and with others, constituting the central core of their character structure. Their need to live up to this ideal image resulted in a compulsive drive to acquire absolute acceptance and approval from her, in the absence of which the patients experienced guilt and shattered self-esteem.

A recurring central aspect in each couple's interrelationship was the man's expectation of his wife's continuing happiness and contentment. Whenever she seemed depressed or dissatisfied, he felt rejected by her and unconsciously blamed himself. This pattern of vulnerability and defensive projection of blame made him less able to perceive and fulfill his wife's realistic dependency needs. She, in turn, was intensely disappointed in her husband and reacted toward him with subtle or overt contempt. The vicious cycle of mutual resentment and devaluation was thus perpetuated.

ALK felt that it would be salutary to introduce a male therapist

446

into her group to counter: (1) lack of male identification in the husbands; (2) lack of an adequate father model in the wives; and (3) tardy psychosexual maturation with fixation in the symbiotic pregenital period (i.e., an early and undifferentiated child-mother relationship). It was anticipated that both therapists would be free in their interaction to assert separateness in their feelings, attitudes, and values. Acceptance of this freedom in each other would, hopefully, provide a model for couple interaction permitting separateness and self-expression. However, the female therapist recognized the importance of overt expressions of the male therapist's "fatherly" or self-assertive position in the group, to promote growth and to reduce the dyadic, symbiotic relatedness between her and her "children." Her recognition of this factor was effective in frustrating the members' alliance fantasies with the female therapist. The demonstration of this healthy or realistic alliance sanctioned the spouses' separateness and freed them from their neurotic interlocking reactions.

Beginning phase

The predominant phenomenon observed in the beginning phase of the group was the pattern of the wives' reactive contempt to their husbands' need to please them, and the men's remarkable capacity for guilt at failing in this endeavor. It is noteworthy that in all four couples, husband and wife have compulsively perceived differences between themselves as rejection. The therapist "couple", recognizing their own differences, were aware of the necessity to live with them constructively rather than competitively and sought to so demonstrate this in the group.

In the beginning, the male therapist was set up by the various patients to satisfy their concept of the ideal father and husband. The men demanded that he live up to their impossible self-standards, and the women communicated their contemptuous conviction of his inadequacy. Perceiving the female therapist as the all-powerful mother figure, the spouses felt that their security lay in making an alliance with her. The necessity for co-therapist interaction to break into these unhealthy residual pregenital symbiotic patterns was quite clear.

In the first session, Husband #2 and Wife #3 reacted aggressively to the presence of the new male therapist, each in his own

447

way. The man issued an open challenge: "Let's see if you can measure up to being the big man in this group." The woman was overtly and boldly seductive, making a play to be the father's favorite, as was the case in her nuclear family. Husband #2 expressed group feeling to ALK by saying: "Why did you need to bring MM into the group?" implying, "Mother, how could you marry a guy like that?"

The couples complained that one-and-one-half hours would not be a long enough session and stressed the fact that they were accustomed to two hours, which cost them less. MM merely said his own needs dictated the shorter time. The course open to MM was clear: consistent behavior in line with his own feelings and best judgment independent of expectations.

The female therapist expressed her view of MM's significant place in the group by giving him the most comfortable and impressive chair in the room. MM accepted this as a symbol of responsibility rather than undermining or competing with ALK's significance. Neither therapist wished to reproduce in himself the typical cultural pattern of submission-domination, rivalry, and power struggle.

Working through

MM's and ALK's attitudes and interaction are subject to questioning and testing. The couples' need to preserve an alliance with ALK, as the omnipotent source of security, tended to cast MM in the role of an intruder who threatens this alliance.

The third session marked the first real assault on MM's significance by a group member. ALK had looked in on the assembled group just before the session and warned MM that his chair was occupied by Husband #3. MM decided to resist this maneuver promptly and to expose it to analysis. As he walked in, the group awaited his response, watching for signs of his humiliation on having to sit elsewhere. Instead, MM informed Husband #3 that he would like to have his chair. Husband #3 refused to get up, saying that his painful back called for a more comfortable chair. Not impressed with this excuse, MM insisted on repossessing his chair. The group members allied themselves with Husband #3. "Look at that selfish S.O.B. demanding his chair. Asya wouldn't do that." Nevertheless, MM persisted until his chair was vacated.

Husband #3, furious because he felt humiliated by MM, said, "What if I had fought with you?" MM replied, "I would have had no choice but to defend myself." Husband #3 tried to arouse MM's guilt by bringing up his heart condition, adding indignantly, "MM could have killed me by making me so angry and humiliated about the chair." ALK, seeking to analyze Husband #3's motivations, alluded to the oedipal implications. She gave the chair to "Papa", where formerly her only concern had been for her children. Husband #3, as her "son", thought he had a prior right to it and was, therefore, taking it away from "Papa." There was no recognition of "Papa's" right to claim the chair for himself. During the ensuing interaction, Husband #2 identified with both ALK and MM, pointing out to Husband #3 that his stated need of the chair because of backache and heart trouble was a rationalization; another comfortable chair was close at hand. Husband #3 thought this over and then said earnestly, "I can't see it that way." Although MM verbally insisted on having his chair, ALK felt that his nonverbal behavior during the incident was friendly, communicative, and benevolent, which Husband #1 and #3 could not appreciate. In fact, none of the members grasped the meaningfulness of MM's action, whose purpose was not to humiliate the usurper but to maintain his own position — an attitude he would like the other group members to assume in their own lives.

The importance of the chair incident became increasingly clear as time went on. It came to symbolize the right to have a place in life and to assert that right; it was repeatedly referred to as similar changes began to take place in various group members. At the time, all the husbands except #2 misinterpreted the significance of the incident. Husbands #1 and #3 reacted as to an assault which downgraded their own masculinity. Husband #4, identifying with the overriding powerful father figure, justified MM's action solely on that basis.

From the outset it was evident to MM that in the group transference, the male therapist's importance to the members was in terms of the use the female therapist (mother) had for him: he was reacted to largely as a necessary irritant with little if anything to contribute and little that was worthy of emulation. " 'Papa' is here only for the children's needs, not as a need of 'Mama's'; unimportant to her personality, he is needed by her only for the children's sake." This formulation fits into the patients' alliance fantasies with the mother figure. MM was alert for opportunities to bring reality testing to bear on these fantasies.

On one occasion ALK had the idea of introducing another couple into the group. Taking for granted MM's interest and consent, she failed to consult with him before putting it up to the group near the close of a group session. Truly concerned with their reactions, she tended to identify with them in their wish to reject any newcomers. As was to be expected, the members' reaction to the proposal was negative. It was clear to the male therapist that "Mother's" sympathy for her "brood" would unwittingly favor their alliance fantasies. Feeling indignant at the whole procedure, he rose just before the meeting was over and said, "Well, I've learned something here tonight. I'm going home to ask my children if I may be permitted to have another child." ALK's horrified gesture plainly said, "How could you do this to the group?"

In the post session (without the therapists) members expressed resentment toward MM for failing to treat them as adults. When faced with the male therapist's reactions to their transference wishes, they tended to fall back on reality testing and become more aware of their adult status, handling discomfort related to their own transference behavior by projecting blame onto the offending parental-authority figure.

During the next session, numerous significant working through reactions were evident in the members. Husband #1 was angry and expressed the group's feelings of "being treated like children." Husband #3 declared that MM's way of making a point was unkind (ignoring the fact that MM might consider this criticism unkind) and went on to say that MM should have reacted directly to ALK instead of "taking it out" on group members — a very significant interpretation from the viewpoint of maturity. "Max doesn't care whether the group members like him or not; he wants them to know he's around and that Asya has to deal with him." When one or all members launched such an attack, MM remained silent looking as if he found their accusations rather amusing. Whereas some members interpreted this attitude as one of contempt, it actually reflected MM's inner pleasure about their common facility of self-expression and self-assertion and his role in stimulating and eliciting it.

450

In the previous session, MM had made clear that he, as a "father", could not be disregarded, and also that he would not permit the "mother" to ally herself with the "children." Husband #3, identifying in a healthy way with MM, was able to accept MM's "rights" as the father of the family, and the mother's and children's place in relation to it. On the other hand, Husband #4, now allied himself with ALK; he felt that MM was angry and was implying criticism of him for this reason, thus reflecting his own deep problem with his wife. At this point, he was in the process of exposing his core problem and had not been able to identify with the male therapist's self-assertive actions. Husband #2 had already asserted himself by leaving the group for an extended business trip.

Wife #3 missed this particular session on grounds of illness, but both therapists thought her absence was more likely due to anxiety over what had transpired between them at the previous meeting. Wife #1 agreed with her husband's view of MM's action as "demeaning", thus supporting him in his neurotic need to please the woman and acting out the cutting off of his own self-assertion. Wife #2 mentioned her plan to join her husband on his trip, leaving the children in her mother-in-law's care. MM's referring obliquely to his previous action, said "Did you ask your children if you could leave?" Her grin said she got the point, and also was pleased to be able to gratify her need to recognize that her place was with her husband, even if the children might be temporarily unhappy. Wife #4 characteristically took no part in the group response, withdrawing and smiling anxiously.

At the next meeting, Wife #3 said she was sorry to have been absent; although she was interested in seeing how "Mama" and "Papa" would "fight it out", she was also frightened at the thought. She had felt bad for ALK when MM "slapped her down." MM pointed out her competition with the father for the mother and her need to show up the father as a S.O.B. Wife #3's position confirmed MM's perception of her early attempt to seduce him not as a sexual assertion but as a means of gaining power over him so she could eliminate him from competition for the mother. She had clearly set up the parents to compete with each other, as if saying, "I'll side with you, Mama. If Papa gets hurt, he'll act like a bastard and compete with me, his daughter. This will

451

prove that he's not only ineffective but unreliable." If Wife #3's maneuver to split the parents were to succeed, *i.e.* if "Papa" should "slap down" the "daughter" and "Mama" take her side, she would have bested him in the competition for alliance with the mother. Fully cognizant of this ploy, ALK said, "It seems that you can't accept the fact that parents have different views. They *should* have; they're different people." Indicating her ability to accept as a necessity differences between herself and the male therapist, and to work constructively with them, ALK told the group that she definitely did not feel "slapped down" by MM. "You see us fighting out our differences, but don't notice that we live with them too."

Husband #3 said to MM, "Weren't you angry with Asya?" and MM replied, "I was indignant but not angry." Husband #3 then brought up his feeling of resentment over his wife's need to ally herself with women, in effect leaving him "out in the cold." However, he put his arm around her shoulder in a reassuring gesture. ALK asked, "Do you feel guilty about bringing this up? Is that why you're putting your arm around your wife?" Withdrawing from the embrace, he said, "No, I don't feel guilty and I'm not angry." He could at this moment fully share MM's perception of the wife's competitive behavior toward both of them, and his indignant reaction without hostility or helpless anger. Husband #3's ability to identify with MM in this way indicated a breakthrough in his neurotic pattern which the group recognized and verbalized.

Husband #1 and #4 were convinced that MM *had* been angry with ALK, refusing to accept the idea that he could be indignant without being angry. Here is the core of the conflict in the couples' interaction: in the transference they maintain their identification with the oedipal mother who is wronged by the father; they must not emulate him or they will lose the oedipal competition. Each man perceives his wife's unhappiness as his own failure; he is, "like Papa, no good." As Husband #4 expressed this feeling, "If I were good, my wife would be the happiest woman on earth." But several sessions later he said, "Things between my wife and me are easier now. When I come home finding her depressed or complaining, I don't blame myself. I just say, 'Let's have dinner.' I know she'll get over it." A man who is not hampered by his own guilty responses is better able to fulfill his wife's realistic dependency needs.

Summary of Progress

The couples group has met once a week from September to July, each therapist having missed only one of about 40 sessions. None were canceled.

Couple #1: In this marriage, the most difficult problem in the group, both partners are still maintaining a negative transference relationship to the male therapist and are reluctant to acknowledge to themselves or to the group that he cares about them and for them. On one occasion when the wife openly rejected MM, he indicated his wish for better communication with her by saying, "Let's bury the hatchet" and then jokingly acknowledged his counter-transference by adding, "but not in my head." Recently MM sided with Husband #3 who was having a dispute with Wife #1. When she charged that MM was allying himself with Husband #3 against her, MM openly stated that he loved her and that his opinion in the dispute had nothing to do with his feeling for her. In this way he showed his awareness of her transference to her own father, who she insisted was more interested in her boy friends than in herself. MM now feels that his relationship with her is improving but there is a long way to go.

Couple #2: The personal and marital relationships of this couple are markedly improved. Their sexual relations are now frequent and mutually satisfying. Each is freer in relation to the other to assert his needs; feels he has the right to do so; and is less concerned about injuring the other. Insofar as each can accept the other's assertions and separateness, he is becoming increasingly capable of fulfilling the partner's realistic dependency needs. The breakthrough point for the husband came when he was faced with the fact that he could expect no magic from ALK's maternal warmth and MM's strength and power. When he asked, "Where do I go from here?", ALK said firmly but gently, "How about your own resources?" After a pause he said, "I didn't think that maybe my own strength counts. This really gives me hope; it's something I haven't thought about before." Shortly after this incident he was able to overcome his hypochondriacal fears about air travel. He left on an extended business trip without being unduly concerned about his wife and children remaining at home.

Wife #2 had been afraid to ask him for anything: money, clothes, household items, or sex. In the previous couples group,

453

her relationship with ALK was completely nonverbal and her behavior was fearful and guarded. She became more verbal and communicative in the new group, as it became clear in the transference that she perceived MM as the strong father who would protect her against the destructive mother. In this transference she was never able to relate freely with the mother. As she began to sense the friendly and cooperative communication between ALK and MM in the group, through their interaction, her fear of offending the protective father by acknowledging her need to turn to the mother diminished. She said to ALK: "I'd like to have more to do with you! I'm not really afraid of you any more."

Couple #3: The marital relationship in this instance is significantly better. Improvement in the self-image of each partner appears to be the salient development thus far. Husband #3 has become more self-assured and able to assert himself on the basis of his own needs, expectations, and limitations, and he shows less guilt about his inability to be constantly pleasing to his mate. He is able to make definite decisions relating to his career and, during the past few months, has been less preoccupied with his physical condition. As a result, his wife, who had abandoned any idea of being helpful to him, shows a remarkable change. She has found a highly rewarding and gratifying position to augment the family income while he is working through his own occupational ambitions. She is more contented with herself and with her husband. Husband #3 has grown as a person, man, husband, and father. The main factor contributing to his maturation seems to be his ability and readiness to accept, through identification, what MM symbolized for him. "I never thought I had the right to a special place in life," referring to the chair incident. "Now I know I have the right to go after a creative vocation that I never dared to pursue. I always felt that I had to bring home a good paycheck every week, first as a good son and then as a good husband."

Wife #3 had denied her own need for creative work in view of her neurotic need to maintain her femininity by being supported by her husband, yet at the same time she had little regard for him as a man. Her poor feminine identification resulted from a conflictual situation between her parents in which she basically sought alliance with the mother at the expense of the "contemptible" father. She acted out this pattern in her own marriage, seducing and then dominating her husband. Through observing the co-therapists' interaction, she has been helped toward more realistic self-perceptions. Her increasing respect for MM is beginning to be reflected in her attitude toward her husband. Her relationship with ALK has become less symbiotic, in that she perceives and has emotionally accepted ALK's real place with her "mate." Despite a considerable breakthrough into the fantasied alliance with the mother figure, both therapists feel that more working through will be required.

Couple #4: There has been a noticeable abatement in Wife #4's depressions. Although more animated in group interaction, she still tends to remain silent. In individual sessions with MM, she is less dependent, supplicating, and helpless; MM has recently challenged her openly. She clings to her security with him, avoiding any direct involvement with ALK. Lack of any active attempt to assert her own femininity with the mother indicates that her oedipal resistances are yet to be reached and worked through.

Husband #4 came into the group, without any preparation, to help his wife. Although he reserved the right to leave after one month, he missed only one session throughout the nine months — when the babysitter failed to appear. Early in the group's development, his continuous complaints about not understanding what was going on led to the group's charge that MM was ill-advised if not stupid to introduce such a *nebbish* into a sophisticated group. Husband #4's pattern was to deny his oedipal strivings by adopting a position of fixed passivity toward the unquestioned father figure. He transferred his own expectations of achieving results for his wife to MM, as the strong, all-powerful and all-knowing father image. He has been able to meet a direct challenge and to criticize the idealized father more overtly, finding MM more human and less threatening as a result. Like Husband #2, he has achieved a better sense of his own separateness and power. He, too, can hit a "home run." His increasing ability to separate himself from his wife's moody behavior and critical attitudes has been noted earlier. He has slowly accepted the idea that he is in the group not only because of his wife; he knows he too is being helped but does not yet understand *how.* Considering how slight were his insight and personal motivation for therapy, his growth in a relatively short time is all the more remarkable. He has earned the group's wholehearted acceptance as an equal member.

COUNSELING THE MARRIED COUPLE

by Aron Krich

My recent studies have addressed themselves to the theory and practice of marriage counseling, with emphasis on the recent trend toward joint interviews with the spousal pair. The shift from client-centeredness to couple interaction is examined as an extension rather than a departure from traditional marriage counseling patterns of work. The early recognition that a paired relationship, symbolized and institutionalized by marriage, required a shared therapeutic experience is identified as a special contribution of marriage counseling in the United States.

L'EXPERIENCE D'UN GROUPE DE PARENTS D'ENFANTS PSYCHOTIQUES

par M. SOULE et S. DECOBERT

Les auteurs rapportent le bilan pratique et théorique d'un groupe de parents d'enfants psychotiques qui a duré deux années. Les enfants souffraient de troubles graves et bénéficiaient parallèlement ou antérieurement d'une psychothérapie. Le bilan pratique fut la réussite inespérée de tous les traitements entrepris et une prophylaxie manifeste des troubles qui commençaient à apparaître dans les fratries. L'amélioration des parents fut celle habituelle aux participants des groupes thérapeutiques de cet ordre. Cette expérience permet de dire que la meilleure formule de soutien des parents d'enfants psychotiques paraît être ce type de groupe. Celui-ci leur permet rapidement de prendre conscience de la blessure narcissique que leur inflige leur enfant et des formations réactionnelles de leur comportement. Il leur permet aussi de supporter mieux l'approche des anxiétés suscitées en eux par les fantasmes psychotiques de leur enfant. Rapidement s'atténue l'effet de réverbération parent-enfant qui gêne souvent longtemps les psychothérapies. Le groupe évite aussi l'intrusion anxieuse des parents dans les psychothérapies. En dehors de cela, le groupe a été conduit de façon classique par interprétation du transfert de groupe et du fantasme commun. Fait particulier, le groupe était conduit par un thérapeute homme et un thérapeute femme non mariés entre eux, qui structura tout de suite le groupe dans un schéma oedipien, ce qui contribua à canaliser et à apaiser l'angoisse non formulée. Le groupe fut dissous mais certains de ses membres ont entrepris une psychothérapie individuelle conduite sur un mode particulier qui fera l'objet d'une autre communication.

GROUP TREATMENT FOR THE ONE
PARENT FAMILY

by Miriam Proctor

Family disintegration is accelerated rather than prevented by certain prejudices our society entertains against the one parent family, whether such a family results from death, divorce, deser-'ion or illegitimate birth.

Since our society has consistently ignored the problem created by a steadily increasing number of one parent families, a group of single parents decided to remedy this situation in 1957 by establishing an organization, Parents Without Partners Inc. Its purpose is "to bring our children to healthy maturity with the full sense of being loved and accepted as persons, and with the same prospects for normal adulthood as children who mature with their two parents together."

PWP employs principles of group therapy, group dynamics and modern educational methods as a type of self-help "milieu" or "social" therapy. Self-understanding for the adult means prevention of ills for their children. Lectures and discussions led by professionals, organized social activities, collaboration on Committees, Workshops and Conferences have been instrumental in making PWP an invaluable organization for the successful large-scale treatment of this urgent social problem.

SECTION 9: GROUP PROCESSES

HUMAN INTERACTION AND MUTUAL
MENTAL CONTAGION

by Joost A. M. Meerloo

Introduction

It has been known for quite some time that an individual case of panic can induce collective panic in a group of people, or that hysterical behavior of the one can be conducted to a crowd. We find, however, that not much systematic attention has been given to the concepts of mental contagion, psychic infection and behavioral contamination.

459

Man as an Individual Crowd

The fact that man is not a well-boundaried individual with a constant self, but turns out to be the centerpoint of a field of influences and the nucleus of various participations, will come as a shock to many. Man is not the sum total of what he consciously experiences; there is a larger pyramid of unconscious and biological drives leading him to his actions. He is not only that well-rounded, unique human being that his visual illusion shows him, he is not that purely original, creative thinker the poet sings of, but from his epoch and the *Zeitgeist*, from history and tradition he accumulates and absorbs as much as he is able to mould and transmogrify, as an individual creator, into some personal *Gestalt*. The collectivity of listeners has as much an equal share in composing the music as the composer himself while creating and re-creating the harmonies in his listening mind. A Mozart born in the twentieth century would have evolved as a different composer. This, of course, does not alter the fact that there are real geniuses, *i.e.* transformers of their actual world, that there are also talented moulders, and that there exist mere plagiarists as well. Politicians, so dependent on election and public approval, are even more products of the *Zeitgeist* and are continually moulded and conditioned by the mass-emotions of their epoch.

Direct Mental Induction and the Common Regression to Archaic Communication

Various synonyms are used to designate the phenomenon of mental contagion. We all are "moved" by other people's emotions. Sometimes this transfer is spoken of as moral contagion, sometimes as infectious defamation or contagious blaming. Infectious and stimulating propaganda is often called inflammatory propaganda; a politician may speak of people being susceptible to other political currents because of their persuasive impact. One can speak of infestation with panic or of behavioral contamination or of the suggestive sloganization of a group. The psychiatrist may speak of mass psychoses or of *psychoses à deux* or *psychoses à trois*, considering them as a special aspect of human intercommunication. In non-pathological cases he speaks of family interaction.

To gain a better knowledge of these subtle interactions one should be aware of the intricate and complicated web of commu-

460

nications surrounding man. Man lives in a field of continuous intercommunication. Stimuli from inside and outside, of which he is more or less aware, reach him. Exploration of the psychotherapeutic process has brought to light the existence of unconscious pre-verbal communication as well as an unobtrusive, subliminal communication both of which make use of infinitesimal clues. There is rhythm and sound, and gesture; and at the very summit of mutual contact there is the verbal semantic exchange. In this paper I do not want to elaborate on the intrinsic network of stimuli directly influencing man, but I want to draw special attention to the direct mental induction caused by various forms of archaic communication.

Archaic communication is the social intercourse established by the innate signal code which man and animal have in common. Everyone understands and reacts to distress calls of animals. There exist emotional expressions that are immediately understood. Crying, laughing, rhythmic tapping, yawning, fright-reactions, fainting, itching, dancing movements, convulsions, erotic gestures arouse immediate empathy and response. Nothing is more contagious, for example than yawning, or the rhythmic emotional shout of a crowd of people, like, for instance, the "Sieg Heil, Sieg Heil" call in Hitler days.

Mental contagion is related to man's deep symbiotic needs and his utter dependency. It is as if the gap between humans has to be bridged by various new means of communication. The biological basis is the direct empathy which exists in the individual mother-child relation. The greater the distance grows between mother and child, the more urgently other means of communication have to be found. In every group relation where the old symbiotic relation is re-enacted — e.g. in all participation societies — the facts of mental contagion are obvious. Even the outsider is affected, may it be in a negative way; the group directs his opposition nonetheless. We can observe that mental infection increases when established social institutions collapse and the group regresses to more primitive means of intercommunication. When the individual's ego-boundaries and mental defenses are weak, he is more easily suggestible, and invariably also feels himself to be a more passive victim of outside stimuli. In schizophrenic doxasm the patient feels as if his brain lies open to every bad intention of other people, which he secondarily interprets as being victimized by mysterious rays.

Man's regression under the burden of group action and mental contagion should not only be interpreted as something negative. True, there exists a negative regression leading to chaos and decay, but there is also a positive side of regression leading to revitalization and towards new adaptations. We must keep this ambivalence in mind. The group, by its greater chance to contamination, tends to incite the individual to regress to primitive actions, but by its continuity and its protective influence the group can also prevent the individual from regressing too much.

The ambivalent relation between group and individual is also clearly demonstrated by man's motivation for mutual participation and symbiotic bliss. The group comes together not only for mutual collaboration and co-operation, but also for exclusion of others, to ban and persecute the black sheep and the scapegoats. This unwitting urge to vent common hidden aggression is — by the way — one of the fundamentals of group prejudice. Such inner tension may lead to groups imposing on themselves the maximum of rules and laws and the burden of legalism as a defense against this ambivalence. We see this for instance in totalitarian régimes. A democracy founded on freedom, however, wants to impose a minimum of law, thereby demanding from the individual more humanism, dignity and self control than the law requires. The essential difference between dictatorial legalism and the freedom of commitment is the way men have confidence in their mutual intentions toward each other. This gain is a psychological component stimulated by personal example and emotional transfer of mutual trust.

Mental Contagion and Man's Vertical Conditioning

The fact that man realizes he is a product of historical tradition comes especially to the fore at times when he feels threatened in his social and private existence. Everywhere in the world where a conqueror and tyrannical occupier tries to change the social and economical relations in a country, we experience a revival of historical interest. It is almost a form of escape towards old glory and the heroic myths of the past. They are the mental roots that give life to the group under pressure. This *identification with the past* can be inspiring indeed and give rebirth to the most vital

462

energies a group or nation possesses but can also lead to the most primitive regression towards obscure myths and primitive magic, as we experienced them in Nazi mythology with its glorification of the blond beast and ancient Germanic Nemesis.

Man's vertical historical understanding takes place unwittingly already through the means of communication he uses. The very word he speaks is rooted in a history of meanings which unconsciously reverberate in the actual word symbols he now uses. Linguists ably describe how our thinking is determined by the treasure of verbal tools at our disposal. Our thinking is tied to our language, and because of our language we are unwittingly tied to the historical modes of thinking that language represents (Whorf). The language given to us in turn directs our modes of perception (Sapir).

Another example of vertical conditioning of behavior is given by what we might call pseudo-heredity, the subtle interaction from generation to generation which can be so easily explained as true heredity. Without denying the facts of biologically bound heredity, Ehrenwald gave a crystal clear description of how generations of obsessive-compulsive people (the Obscomp family) prepared a conditioning milieu for the next generation so that the same kind of pathological psychic defenses had to be built up in the next generation.

Another intrapersonal historical development is very extensively investigated in psychopathology and psychoanalytic therapy. There exist specific sensitive phases in the development of the individual in which traumatic occurrences may have a tremendous conditioning impact. Through the traditional clinical sequence of libidinal evolution in oral, anal and genital phases we become acquainted with developmental conditionings which can be recognized in later character traits. However, many more sensitive developmental phases exist, such as the teething period, the walking crisis, the Weltschmerz period in adolescence and others that can make the growing individual temporarily more vulnerable to conflictious impact and to moulding from outside. The educator has to become more aware of this fluctuation of formative impact.

Horizontal Social Conditioning

When reading about ecological and psychological factors that condition and direct human behavior, we usually think in terms of conscious persuasion or, more forcefully, of mental coercion. Yet, there exist many unobtrusive influences in society that direct our lives just with often as great an impact. For example, technicalization and institutionalization have taken away — more than any other cultural phenomenon — man's belief in being an autarchic individual. He is caught in a network of inadvertent suggestions difficult for him to oppose with his own opinion and his own ethical evaluation. A society usually gives its members a cluster of articulations and justifications of why they are expected to adjust to its code, its prejudices and its ceremonials. This tends to make the fact of our psychological submission usually unaware and obscure.

Man witnesses the world through his prejudiced and moulded emotions. The slave can be made to believe that he lives in a paradise while those who have the luxury of freedom and independence can be talked into daily feelings of deprivation and dissatisfaction. Indeed, in our technical age the emptiness of leisure time has for many become a new burden calling for new adaptations.

How man is influenced by his horizontal social conditioning can easily be seen through the relatively small world of psychologists and psychiatrists. The theoretical schisms we notice are usually determined rather by the school the student happens to visit and by his teacher's opinions than by initial verification of facts and thoughts. The student's initiation into a specific psychological group is usually determined by similar social and ecological factors — suggestion, coercion, prejudice — rather than through elaborate study of all the pros and cons of his adopted system and the parallel ones.

THE INFLUENCE OF UNINTENDED PHENOMENA
(PLACEBO EFFECTS) ON THE RESULTS OF
GROUP PSYCHOTHERAPY

by STANLEY LESSE

The vast literature dealing with psychotherapy, including group psychotherapy, has considered the changes in a given patient that take place during the course of treatment to be secondary to the intended efforts of the therapist. This is particularly true of positive reactions, while negative reactions often are inferred as occurring secondary to unintended effects. As a result of these naive concepts there are very few instances in which the changes that occur as a result of psychotherapy can be documented as to whether they were the result of 1) intended or 2) unintended phenomena. In great measure this attitude accounts for the great conflict in claims of psychotherapeutic efficacy, claims that are usually unsubstantiated. It leads also to the development of cults and *isms* chartered upon metaphysical beliefs rather than sound documentation.

All therapies, whether they are organic or non-organic in nature, must be evaluated as to whether the changes that occur are due to the specific action of the given treatment. If psychotherapy is to become a mature science, these factors must be taken into consideration in the planning of any research project.

As I have pointed out in a series of papers an *unintended effect* is synonymous with a *placebo reaction,* if the placebo effect is considered from a broad perspective as pertaining to procedures as well as drugs. This broadened concept of the placebo is in keeping with the accurate definition of the term. The limiting of the term to drugs is purely one of tradition.

My definition of a placebo effect is an extension of a description by Shapiro. "The placebo effect is the psychologic, physiologic or psychophysiologic effect of any medication or procedure given

465

with therapeutic intent which is independent of or minimally related to the effects of the medication or to the specific effects of the procedure and which operates through a psychologic mechanism. The relative or complete remission or exacerbation of any symptom, sign or syndrome as the result of the administration of any drug or technique cannot be ascribed to the specific effect of the drug or technique on the symptom, sign or syndrome unless it can be demonstrated that the improvement or worsening is not due to a non-specific placebo effect". Detailed classifications of unintended or placebo effects, their relationship to each other and to specific therapeutic effects, have been outlined in detail in previous publications.

These classifications emphasize that unintended or placebo reactions may enhance or negate specific positive therapeutic reactions, or may cancel out a positive placebo or unintended effect. Positive and negative reactions may be seen in different patients in the same studies, or in the same patient on different occasions, all in response to the same unintended effect. All therapies that have a specific effect, in all probability, have an unintended or placebo reaction that will add or detract from the impact of the specific effect.

The unintended factors may pertain primarily to the milieu, the therapist, the patient or a combination of all. Various factors will be more prominent than others depending upon the type of psychotherapeutic procedure used.

A. Influence of the therapeutic environment

The term *therapeutic environment* pertains equally to the broad cultural milieu and the more immediate office of the therapist. Different therapeutic techniques have been popular in different cultures at different times. The positive benefits of dances like the tarantella, the specific healing powers of various spas, the ministrations of holy men, are all examples of techniques that are based upon cultural expectancies at certain times. Today, in the western world, particularly in America, the psychotherapist's task is made easier by the conviction, held in some groups, that psychotherapeutic techniques are the treatments of choice in the care of emotional illnesses. The allure of group psychotherapy as well as individual psychotherapy has been enhanced by dramatizations of successful results in books, plays, on television, and in the cinema. Patients who have obtained positive results are in themselves the best "salesmen" in the propagation of a popular cultural expectancy. Therefore, in many instances, the therapist is aided even before the patient enters his office.

If the individual who refers the patient for therapy is a very prominent and respected person, for example, a prominent physician, the psychotherapist temporarily "borrows" the prestige of this source of referral. Temporarily the psychotherapist is merely a surrogate of this party until a direct positive transference develops.

The therapist's office setting is of importance. If the office is in a large medical institution that has a prominent reputation, the institution's reputation enhances the prestige of the therapist. It has been pointed out that the type and amount of illumination may be very relevant to psychological activities and movement in group psychotherapy. Similarly, various types of noise affect the group therapy patient. The group climate may be related to the time at which the group meets and even by the relation of the meeting time to meal time. Finally, the appearance of the therapy room, including such factors as the presence or absence of a mirror, the color of the walls, all affect some patients.

B. Unintended influences referring to the psychotherapist

The intensity of the therapist's optimism and enthusiasm as to the results to be derived from his particular psychotherapeutic tool influences directly the results that will be obtained. This may be considered a positive unintended or placebo reaction. The psychotherapist's expectations appear to have a greater effect upon the patient's personality change than does the patient's own expectations. The very duration of therapy is also positively affected by the therapist's early prognostications as to the length of treatment. A factor such as this may contribute significantly to the efficacy of brief psychotherapy.

The therapist's positive expectations depend also upon whether the specific psychotherapeutic tool is the only tool in his psychiatric armamentarium. The therapist who utilizes only one technique for all patients is completely dependent upon this technique for results, for pride and pleasure, for his positive self-image and for his very economic security.

An apathetic or hostile therapist will promote negative placebo reactions. Emotional attitudes on the part of the group therapist definitely affect the progress of group psychotherapy. The attitude of group analysts may be indicated by the composition of the group that is not based on any clinical experimental criteria. The fact that a group may be composed exclusively of men or women or of patients with one type of complaint may reflect the therapist's emotional matrix. A limitation in the techniques used in group psychotherapy may reflect the attitudes of behavior of the group therapist. In these instances the patients are fitted to the technique rather than the technique being adjusted to the patients.

Locke, in a recent paper, lists a number of attitudes towards group psychoanalysis that would greatly affect therapy. Some of them are 1) need for one to one relationship; 2) need to be the parent image; 3) need to dominate; 4) fear of involvement; 5) fear of spontaneity; 6) fear of loss of importance; 7) fear of lack of order; 8) need for vicarious participation; 9) need to perform; 10) fear of reacting.

The need to dominate on the part of the therapist, and the expectancy to be dominated on the part of the patient appears to be the rule, at least in America. This does not mean that the therapist is aware of his desire to dominate, and since this pattern would run contrary to popular concepts of the patient-therapist relationship, the therapist tends to suppress this desire very strongly.

I pointed out in a previous paper that a positive unintended or placebo effect may result from the enthusiastic expectancy in an inexperienced therapist in the treatment of a patient with a very difficult psychiatric problem, because the therapist was "unaware that he should fail with a particular patient." Older, more experienced psychotherapists may have a negative expectancy toward a particular type of patient based upon a knowledge of the literature and a series of failures with a particularly difficult problem.

Much of the intricate phenomenon of communication between therapist and patient, whether it be on a verbal or non-verbal level, is unintended. The quality of voice, facial expression, manner of walking, etc., may express the therapist's attitude much more forceably than hours of detailed intellectualized interpretation.

The problem of reinforcement or conditioning has been little appreciated in psychotherapy. Reinforcement is an important factor whether the therapy is directive or non-directive.

A true conditioned reflex of the "second signal" system type may be established depending upon the intensity and frequency of the reinforcement of the therapist's expectations. Frank has pointed out that this may be accomplished, when the therapist repeatedly gives approval of a patient's statements or actions.

Other factors such as the professional or public prominence of an individual therapist play a definite role in the initial effect of therapy. An older therapist is considered by some to be "wiser", while a young therapist might be deemed by others to be "more up to date."

C. The unintended influences pertaining to the patient

Unsophisticated, uneducated and superstitious patients, anyone who is suggestible, are prone to develop positive placebo or unintended reactions. Positive unintended reactions in psychotherapy depend in great measure upon the patient's desires that psychotherapy will relieve his symptoms and problems. In some patients this expectancy may be narrowed down to a particular type of psychotherapy.

Patients who had marked relief of discomforts tend to have high levels of expectancies from psychotherapy. The first patient-therapist contact appears to be an important determinant of symptom reduction. If the patient believes that he will be the main source of help in therapy, meaning that he expects to take a large amount of the responsibility, this type of expectancy has a high correlation with subsequent improvement.

The patient's previous experience with authoritative persons such as parents, teachers and physicians, etc. will determine in part his expectancies in relation to psychotherapy. The duration of illness also determines in part whether or not a positive placebo effect will develop. Those who have long unremitting illnesses do not commonly develop positive placebo effects. Sociopaths and schizophrenic patients develop at best very fickle and transient positive placebo reactions. Conversion hysterics do not commonly develop positive unintended reactions.

The patient's conception of psychotherapy determines in part the role he will assume and the role he expects the therapist will assume. If there is harmony between these two assumptions a positive placebo reaction may be expected; a negative reaction will occur if these expectations are at odds.

469

There are many other unintended influences that pertain to the patient that have not been worked out as completely as those enumerated. For example, the problem of the patient's motivation for psychotherapy is of great importance.

In previous papers the author pointed out in detail that the transference phenomenon is usually an unintended or placebo reaction in that it is usually unplanned. It should be considered as a placebo effect in psychotherapy in that the "formation of the transference relationship depends upon all those unintended factors enumerated that determine a placebo reaction." For example, it depends in great measure upon the patient's expectancy that the therapist will assume a certain role or behavior. The entire concept of role expectancy is intimately involved with the concept of transference. The mutuality of expectations by the therapist and patient greatly affect the transference phenomenon. Lack of congruence in role expectations leads to a negative transference reaction. The factors determining the so-called "transference cure" are all unintended. They should not be belittled for their benefits may be very lasting on many occasions.

Counter-transference could perhaps best be considered under unintended influences pertaining to the therapist. However, it is so closely interrelated with the concept of transference that it may properly fit at this point. Counter-transference is always an unintended or placebo effect. A positive counter-transference may result, if the therapist's role expectancies of the patient are strongly fulfilled. A negative counter-transference reaction may result, if the therapist has a hostile role expectancy of the patient that is fulfilled by the patient.

The concept of transference should not be related entirely to the concept of regression. If the therapist's counter-transference is quite negative or overly positive, the patient very realistically may react in an adverse fashion (negative transference). All of these phenomena are unintended.

D. Miscellaneous unintended factors affecting psychotherapy

The "Law of Initial Value" has a profound effect on all therapies and on all research. This law, as proposed by Wilder, states that "the change in any function of an organism due to a stimulus depends to a large degree on the pre-stimulus level of that function.

This applies not only to the intensity (i.e., extent and duration) of response, but also to its direction. The higher the pre-stimulus level (the initial value) the less the tendency to rise in response to function-raising stimuli. With more extreme high and low levels there is a progressive tendency to no response or to a paradoxic reaction (i.e., a rise instead of fall and vice versa)." In connection with this the author pointed out, using various types of psychiatric treatment, that patients manifesting a high degree of anxiety prior to the onset of therapy were more likely to show marked improvement to any therapy. Conversely, patients manifesting very little overt anxiety prior to the onset of therapy did not show good responses. Patients with very little overt anxiety also rarely developed positive placebo reactions.

In another study the author demonstrated that the direction of change in a patient's pre-treatment clinical status is of great moment in determining the effect of therapy. In other words, if a patient is improving at the time any therapy is instituted, better results may be expected than if the patient's status was becoming worse at the time of onset of treatment. This is of prime importance. Too often a therapist will take credit for improvement when, in reality, the patient was improving at the time treatment was initiated.

This particular factor is related to the concept of the "Law of Initial Value", except that the "Law of Initial Value" originally dealt with the concept of a single evaluation whereas my studies dealt with multiple pre-treatment evaluations made over a period of two or more weeks (a continuing base line).

The concept of biologic rhythms is poorly understood in medicine and particularly in psychiatry. In this regard only a few papers have appeared dealing with spontaneous remissions and exacerbations. The consensus is that most so-called spontaneous remissions are really not spontaneous. The term spontaneous when used merely indicates that the causes of the change were not appreciated. Many of the factors producing the so-called spontaneous remissions or exacerbations have been described in detail in the body of this paper under the description of unintended or placebo reactions.

However, as I indicated previously, this does not take into account the possibility that rhythmic cycles might not affect the course of a patient's psychiatric problem. Rhythmic or cyclic fluctuations refer to those variations in size, number or quality that occur with reasonable regularity, that is, with a beat. Some studies dealing with medical and non-medical phenomena have pointed out rhythmic fluctuations that were considered to be significant (due to a non-chance cause). Are there *circadian* (24 hour) rhythms in psychic functioning such as there are with body temperature, or *near-rhythms* (every few hours) such as there might be with blood microfilaries or blood sugar levels, or possibly are there psychologic rhythms that change every few days? Phenomena such as sun spots appear to have rhythms that are of several years' duration.

DIE GRUPPE ALS THERAPEUTISCHES MILIEU

von R. Battegay

Die Gruppe ist in allen geschichtlichen Epochen und in allen Lebensphasen das Existenzmilieu des Menschen. Der Gruppenverband ist für das menschliche Individuum der Hintergrund, auf dem es sich abzeichnet, Gestalt annimmt. Nur in den Reaktionen der ihn in der Gruppe umgebenden Mitmenschen kann er sich erkennen und nur dort verwirklichen, wo er mit einer Umwelt, die an seinem Verhalten, an seinen Entäusserungen und Reaktionen Interesse hat, verbunden ist. Ohne teilnehmende Gruppe hat der Mensch keinen Widerhall, keinen Wirkkreis und keinen historischen Bestand. Im Gedenken der Gruppe bzw. der Gruppen, in die das Individuum mit einbezogen ist, überwindet es seine Zeitlichkeit. Erst in und an der Gruppe wird der Mensch zu dem, der er ist. Wäre er allein auf sich abgestellt, ohne ein ihn umgebendes, gruppenstrukturiertes Beziehungssystem, würden seine Leistungen und seine Existenz ins Nichts verpuffen. Ein Mensch kann daher erst dann ganzheitlich ermessen werden, wenn er in seiner sozialen Verstricktheit, in den Interaktionen mit seiner mitmenschlichen, gruppenzentrierten Umwelt erfasst wird. Auch in seinem Kranksein ist der Mensch nicht nur als Individuum, sondern auch als geselliges Wesen, als "Zoon politikon" *(Aristoteles)* zu verstehen.

Wohl ist, wie *Freud* betont, die soziale Umwelt im Seelenleben des Einzelnen mitenthalten. Doch kann das Kommunikationssystem, in das hinein ein Mensch verwoben ist, niemals aus dem, was an Ab-, Vor- oder Zerrbild in seiner Psyche enthalten ist, ermittelt werden. Es ist deshalb wesentlich, dem psychisch Kranken in einem sozialen Rahmen, wie ihn eine therapeutische Gruppe darstellt, zu begegnen. Wir gingen deshalb in der Basler psychiatrischen Universitätsklinik vor Jahren dazu über, mit ganzen Spitalabteilungen wie auch mit kleineren, diagnostisch einheitlicheren Kranken-gruppen kollektiv-psychotherapeutisch zu arbeiten. Daneben haben wir auch das Lernpflegepersonal und, seit einem Jahr, die Klini-kärzte, sofern sie Interesse daran hatten, gruppenpsychotherapeu-tisch erfasst *(Battegay)*. In der Therapiegruppe zeigt es sich, bzw. deutet es sich an, wie sich ein Individuum in der Gesellschaft bewegt. In jeder gegenwärtigen Auseinandersetzung eines Indi-viduums mit einer Gruppe schwingt seine infantil-familiäre Situa-tion mit. Es bietet sich so dem Therapeuten Gelegenheit, zu prüfen, ob die sozialen Aktivitäten eines Gruppenmitgliedes der momen-tanen Situation adäquat oder ob sie das Produkt kindlicher Grup-pen-Erlebnisse ist. Das Mitglied seinerseits wird im Spiegel der Behandlungsgruppe erkennen, was an seinen Verhaltensweisen der neuen Lagen angepasst und was im Gegensatz dazu ein Gebaren ist, das seinem ursprünglichen Gruppenerleben in der Kindheit entspringt. In der therapeutischen Gruppe werden jedoch auch Reaktionen und Verhaltensweisen der Einzelnen und der Gesamt-heit manifest, die weder in frühen, noch in späten eigenen Erfah-rungen der Beteiligten ihren Ursprung haben sondern, wie *Jung* formuliert, "Niederschläge des Ahnenlebens" sind. Wir werden also in Gruppen Manifestationen der Einzelnen und des Gesamts erkennen, die eigentlich nichts anderes als reaktivierte urtümliche Menschheits- bzw. Urgruppenreminiszenzen sind. Da die Gruppe seit den Uranfängen der Menschheit deren Organisationsform darstellt, spiegelt sich in ihr, die alle Generationen überdauert, ein transzendentes Geschehen. Demgemäss offenbart sich die Trans-zendenz auch in der therapeutischen Gruppe.

Wenn wir ein therapeutisches Kollektiv vor uns haben, werden wir uns also bewusst, dass sich zwar in jedem Gruppengeschehen die individuelle Lebensgeschichte der Beteiligten spiegelt, jedoch auch das Erleben und das Erfahrungsgut der gesamten Menschheit von Anbeginn und damit ein transzendentes Geschehen mit ent-halten ist.

Die in den therapeutischen Gruppen beobachteten Gesetzmässig-keiten sind demnach das Produkt multipler, in den mitwirkenden Einzelnen und in kollektiv-menschlichen Erfahrungen begründeten Determinanten. Wir wollen nun versuchen, einige der ein therapeu-tisches Kollektiv kennzeichnenden Charakteristika herauszugreifen und sie womöglich auf die erwähnten Entstehungsbedingungen hin zu untersuchen.

474

1. *Partizipation-Isolierung*

Die an einer therapeutischen Gruppe Beteiligten nähern sich im Verlaufe der Zeit in einem für ein bestimmtes Kollektiv wie auch für die es zusammensetzenden Individuen charackteristischen Ausmass. Damit dürfen die Mitwirkenden eine mitmenschliche Partizipation und Nähe erfahren, die sie vielleicht bisher in ihrem Leben noch nie erfahren hatten. So sehen wir in der Gruppenpsychotherapie gelegentlich, dass Schizophrene, die bisher infolge ihres Krankseins in bedrohlicher Weltferne lebten, nun im Kollektiv erstmals eine zwischenmenschliche Nähe wahrnehmen, die sie ermutigt, wieder in die reale Welt zu steigen. Die partizipierenden Mitmenschen sind in der therapeutischen Gruppe die neue Erfahrung, die die Menschen, wenn sie durch ihre Erkrankung in ein Mengen-Dasein gedrängt waren, gewinnen können. Wie wir in den therapeutischen Gruppen beobachtet haben, können sich die Einzelnen in einem Kollektiv allerdings so nahe kommen, dass sie vom Individualitätsverlust bedroht werden. Wir haben bereits verschiedene Male beobachtet, dass die Konvergenz *(Hofstätter)* in einer therapeutischen Gruppe tatsächlich bis zum drohenden Verlust der psychischen Eigenständigkeit der Einzelnen gehen kann. Die Beteiligten können in diesen Fällen nicht mehr nach freiem Ermessen entscheiden, sondern sie führen das aus, was "die Gruppe" von ihnen fordert. Ihre Handlungen und Verhaltensweisen erfolgen nicht mehr aus intellektueller Erwägung heraus, sondern sie sind das Resultat trieb- und affektbedingter Anpassung. Diese Entwicklung ist eine potentielle Gefahr für jede Gruppe; sie wird besonders dann immanent, wenn es einem Monopolisten *(Slavson)* gelingt, sich in eine Führerrolle aufzuschwingen und von dort aus das Kollektiv zu dominieren. Mit diesem Vorgang ist eine Entdifferenzierung der Gruppe zu einer Masse verbunden, die nach *Freud* nichts anderes ist, als ein "Wiederaufleben der Urhorde." Die Urgruppe ist demnach potentiell in jedem therapeutischen Kollektiv mitenthalten.

Doch kann der Einzelne im Behandlungskollektiv durch die übrigen Zugehörigen etwa recht hart angepackt werden. Der Patient muss in diesen Fällen oft Belastungen ertragen lernen, die er in der Zweiersituation der Psychoanalyse nie hätte aushalten müssen. Die Gruppenkameraden gehen nicht mit der Subtilität vor, welche bei einem erfahrenen Psychotherapeuten Selbstverständlichkeit ist. Ein

Patient kann sich so gelegentlich inmitten einer Gruppe durch deren vermeintliches oder wirkliches Unverständnis gänzlich isoliert fühlen. Selbstverständlich ist es dann Sache des Therapeuten, dem Betreffenden beizustehen und ihn aus seiner Isolierung herauszuführen.

2. Regression-Reifung

Die therapeutische Gruppe vermittelt den Zugehörigen durch die gefühlsmässige Teilnahme der Uebrigen die Möglichkeit, eine bergende Umsorgung zu erfahren. Wir haben besonders bei den in unserer Klinik hospitalisierten milieugeschädigten und verwahrlosten Jugendlichen gesehen, wie eine durch einen Arzt und eine Fürsorgerin geleitete therapeutisch Gruppe als eine familiäre Gemeinschaft erlebt wird. Diese Patienten übertragen auf die Gruppe jene Gefühle, die sie ursprünglich für ihre, um die Eltern oder entsprechende Ersatzpersonen zentrierte Familie hatten oder aber nicht hegen konnten. Diesen jungen Menschen kann so etwa jener affektive Rückhalt geboten werden, der es ihnen ermöglicht, über die Verkürzungen ihrer Kindheit hinwegzukommen. Es entsteht dabei naturgemäss auch die Tendenz der Gruppenmitglieder, in ihrem Verhalten auf infantile Stufen zu regredieren. Die therapeutische Gruppe führt bei den Beteiligten durch eine Reaktivierung der kindlich-familiären Situation zu einer Mobilisierung kindlicher Erwartungen an die Gruppe und deren therapeutische Leiter. An diesen liegt es dann, ob es den Betroffenen gelingt, in der Regression ihre frühere affektive Frustrierung bzw. Uebersättigung zu überwinden oder aber für immer an das früh Erlittene fixiert zu bleiben.

Schon allein die Einsicht in Regressionstendenzen kann beim Gruppenmitglied zu einer Reifung seiner Persönlichkeit führen. Aber auch wo keine regressiven Strebungen vordergründig sind, bringt der Gruppenprozess, in dem sich die Beteiligten gegenseitig abschleifen, eine Bereicherung der sozialen Erfahrung mit sich. Diese Erweiterung der Gesellschaftskenntnis bewirkt bei den Beteiligten eine Reifung, die sie besser instand setzt, sich mit ihren realen Möglichkeiten abzufinden.

3. Dynamik und Statik in der Gruppe

Im Vergleich zur Zweierbeziehung der klassischen Psychotherapie sind die gegenseitigen Einwirkungen im Rahmen einer therapeutischen Gruppe bedeutend komplexer (*Foulkes, Friedemann, Langen, Moreno, Slavson, Stokvis,* u.a.). Die mannigfaltigen Interaktionen zwischen den Gruppenmitgliedern einerseits und zwischen diesen und der Gesamtheit andererseits bedingen einen ständigen Wandel in der Erscheinungsweise des Kollektivs, im Verhalten der Einzelnen und in deren Übertragungsgefühlen. So fiel den Mitgliedern der Selbsterfahrungsgruppen mit Ärzten unserer Klinik immer wieder auf, wie sehr sich die Problematik der Gemeinschaft und des Einzelnen und deren Verhaltensweisen von Sitzung zu Sitzung wandelt. Es war kaum voraussehbar, was beim nächsten Zusammensein an mehr oder weniger unbewusster Konflikthaftigkeit hervorkommen wird; es bot sich stets wieder ein neuer Aspekt des Einzelnen und des Gesamts. Im permanenten Wandlungsprozess der therapeutischen Gruppe kommen immer wieder andere Seiten der Einzelnen zur Geltung, und mit dem Wandel der einzelnen Beteiligten verändert auch das Kollektiv ständig seine Gestalt. Die Dynamik der therapeutischen Gruppen lässt uns verstehen, dass sich die Gruppen der Gegenwart aus denjenigen der Vergangenheit heraus entwickelt haben. Diese Erkenntnis führt uns wiederum zu der bereits erwähnten Feststellung, dass in den Behandlungsgruppen auch die urtümlichen Kollektiverfahrungen der Menschheit mitschwingen.

In den Therapiegruppen finden sich jedoch nicht nur Kräfte, die deren ständige Wandlung herbeiführen. Es werden vielmehr auch Tendenzen aktiv, die eine Gruppe in der einmal gewonnenen Situation festhalten wollen. Wir denken an die in jedem therapeutischen Behandlungskreis sich zeigenden Tendenzen von Einzelnen und der Gesamtheit zur "Institutionalisierung" oder "Stereotypisierung" einmal vorgenommener Handlungen oder aufgetretener Verhaltensweisen. Wir konnten beispielsweise in allen therapeutischen Gruppen die mehr oder weniger ausgeprägte Neigung der Mitglieder erkennen, einen einmal eingenommenen Sitzplatz auch an den nächsten Zusammenkünften einzunehmen. Diese Beharrungsenergien, die polar die dynamischen Kräfte in der Gruppe ergänzen, vermitteln dem therapeutischen Kollektiv die für das Entstehen eines Geborgenheitsgefühls notwendige Konstanz. Befänden sich die statischen Kräfte in einer Behandlungsgruppe im Uebergewicht, würde sich bei den Beteiligten wenig an innerer Wandlung ereignen. Beinhaltete die Gruppe nur dynamische Tendenzen, würden die Mitwirkenden zwar gewandelt, doch fehlte

477

damit die notwendige Musse zu einer entsprechend therapeutisch wirksamen Einsicht.

4. *Gegenwärtigkeit-Transzendenz*

Bei der Vielfalt der möglichen Beziehungen zwischen den Beteiligten und zwischen Einzelnen auf der einen Seite und der Gesamtheit auf der anderen Seite ergibt sich eine die Mitwirkenden mehr oder weniger faszinierende Aktivität und Gegenwärtigkeit des Gruppengeschehens. Der in einer therapeutischen Gruppe sich abspielende Prozess trägt Aufforderungscharakter. Im Erleben des Gruppenprozesses wird jedem offenbar, dass jede Stellung dauernd aufs neue erkämpft werden muss. Die Gruppe hat es in sich, die Einzelnen in die kollektive Aktivität hineinzuziehen. Demgegenüber bestehen in einem solchen Rahmen auch Möglichkeiten, sich temporär in eine Ruheposition zurückzuziehen. Der Gruppenprozess wird für die Mitwirkenden zu eine gegenwärtigen Realität, die es verhütet, dass sie sich in der alleinigen Introspektion verlieren. Patienten, die dazu neigen, sich von der Umwelt abzukapseln, beginnen in einem solchen realitätsintensiven Kreise etwa, sich am sozialen Geschehen affektiv und intellektuell zu beteiligen. Autistische Schizophrene oder Involutionsdepressive, die nach *Kielholz* in der überwiegenden Mehrzahl verschlossene, introvertierte, wenig anpassungsfähige Persönlichkeiten sind, bringen es gelegentlich in der therapeutischen Gruppe erstmalig fertig, ihre Schonhaltung aufzugeben, sich zu entäussern und sich an die Realität anzupassen. Doch ist die Gruppe nicht nur ein Kreis, in dem mehr oder weniger sichtbare Interaktionen vor sich gehen. In einem solchen Kollektiv, das, wie erwähnt, die ursprünglichen Gruppenerfahrungen der Menschheit mitenthält, erwächst bei den Betreffenden auch der Sinn für das Transzendentale. Der Umstand, dass die menschliche Gruppe in der Regel über die Beteiligungszeit des Einzelnen hinaus Bestand hat und dessen Wirken in die Zukunft weiterträgt, wirkt sich auch auf die therapeutischen Gruppen aus. Den in den Behandlungsgruppen Mitwirkenden, die das Transzendenzerleben der sie erfassenden sozialen Gruppen in sich tragen, wird nun auch im therapeutischen Kreise das Transzendentale evident. Gegenwärtigkeit und Transzendenz sind demnach in der Therapiegruppe in polarer Ergänzung und Gegensätzlichkeit enthalten.

478

5. Unterordnung-Freiheit

Bei der Integration in eine therapeutische Gemeinschaft muss es das Individuum erlernen, sich an deren Gegebenheiten anzupassen. Der Einzelne kann seine Anliegen nur dann durchsetzen, wenn sie nicht mit denjenigen der anderen oder mit den Erfordernissen der Gesamtheit in Konflikt geraten. Und ist dies der Fall, so wird er, falls er weiter an der Gruppenaktivität teilnehmen will, seine Wünsche und Strebungen den Verhältnissen der Gruppe anzupassen suchen. Wir bemerkten etwa bei den bereits angeführten milieugeschädigten und verwahrlosten Jugendlichen mit ihrem vorherrschenden Lustprinzip *(Aichhorn)*, dass sich bei der Gruppenpsychotherapie etwa die Einsicht in die Notwendigkeit einer Anerkennung des Realitätsprinzips mit seinen Anforderungen anbahnt. Die Patienten haben es mit Hilfe dieser Behandlungsmethode leichter, sich mit der Wirklichkeit abzufinden und sich, trotz persönlicher Schwierigkeiten, in die Gesellschaft einzufügen.

Die therapeutische Gruppe zeigt damit den Beteiligten die durch die soziale Situation des Menschen gegebene Freiheitsbeschränkung auf. Auf der anderen Seite wird in einer Behandlungsgruppe meist auch offenbar, dass die Beteiligten in und mit ihr eine Freiheit erlangen können, die sie allein kaum erzielt hätten. Bei unseren gruppenpsychotherapeutischen Erfahrungen haben wir es zum Beispiel häufig erlebt, dass auch scheue, wenig durchsetzungsfähige Individuen mit Hilfe des Kollektivs irgendein Begehren dem Therapeuten oder der Klinik gegenüber durchzusetzen versuchen. In der Behandlungsgruppe ist der Hebelarm des Einzelnen verlängert. Er kann so Anliegen und Wünsche verwirklichen, die er sonst kaum realisiert haben würde. Unter diesem Aspekt vermittelt die Behandlungsgruppe eine Freiheit, wie sie ein Patient allein kaum erlangen könnte. Auf der einen Seite muss sich der an einem solchen Behandlungskollektiv Beteiligte der Gruppenrealität unterordnen. Auf der anderen Seite wird es ihm deutlich werden, dass er innerhalb einer Gruppe, das heisst eigentlich mit dem und durch das Kollektiv samt seiner beschränkenden Ordnung mehr Freiheiten erlangen kann, als wenn ihm scheinbar unbegrenzte Möglichkeiten offen stünden.

6. Selbstbehauptung-Selbsthingabe

In jeglicher therapeutischen Gruppe ist dem Patienten die Aufgabe gestellt, sich in einem gesellschaftlichen Rahmen zu behaupten. Er wird in der Auseinandersetzung mit den anderen und der Hilfe des Therapeuten im allgemeinen an Durchsetzungskraft gewinnen, vorausgesetzt dass nicht eine Ich-Schwäche jede Selbstbehauptung in Frage stellt.

Indem die Einzelnen in den Behandlungsgruppen erleben, dass andere vielleicht noch dringender als sie mitmenschliche Unterstützung und Hilfe benötigen, werden in ihnen oft auch altruistische Tendenzen aktiviert. Patienten, die sonst nur mit ihren eigenen Leiden und Lebensschwierigkeiten beschäftigt sind, wenden sich in den gruppenpsychotherapeutischen Sitzungen etwa anderen Kranken zu, um ihnen beizustehen. Die Behandlungsgruppe weist dementsprechend die Mitwirkenden auf die Proportionen von Selbstbehauptung und Selbsthingabe hin, die für ihr Bestehen in der Gessellschaft adaequat sind.

SOZIOLOGISCHE FAKTOREN BEI DER ENTSTEHUNG UND BEHANDLUNG VON NEUROSEN

von D. LANGEN

Bei der Entwicklung und Therapie psychoreaktiver Zustände oder Neurosen im weiteren Sinne wird unter dem Einfluss der Psychoanalyse die frühe Kindheit des Menschen häufig so stark ins Blickfeld gerückt, dass daneben andere oft wichtigere Faktoren nicht scharf genug gesehen werden. Dazu gehören neben den Anlagekomponenten auch alle die soziologischen Faktoren, die den Menschen seit seines Lebens umgeben. Diese sollen hier beleuchtet werden.

Bei Beurteilung der Lebensgeschichte eines Menschen verhält es sich wie sonst in der Geschichte auch, dass diese durch ein Sammeln von "Fakten" zusammengetragen wird. Dabei erfolgt in jedem Falle eine Auswahl, die vorwiegend durch die Position des Untersuchers bestimmt wird. So sind auch die "Fakten" einer Lebensgeschichte nie "rein, sondern erfahren im Geist des Berichterstatters immer eine Brechung." Dies hat der englische Historiker Carr am Beispiel des deutschen Politikers Stresemann eindrucksvoll dargestellt. Dieser "selbst brachte den Prozess der Auswahl ins Rollen," den dann seine Biographen jedesmal erneut fortsetzten. Dieser "Prozess der Auswahl" lässt sich noch viel ausgesprochener bei dem Bericht eines Patienten und der biographischen Analyse durch den Arzt nachweisen. So entsteht eine doppelte Subjektivität, die beachtet werden muss, wenn man sich verstehend in die Lebensgeschichte eines Patienten hineinzudenken versucht. Hierbei muss diese, die Wirklichkeit unter Umständen besonders stark trübende doppelte Subjektivität bei einer Krankengeschichte berücksichtigt werden, da beide Partner — Patient und Arzt — im Gegensatz zu den geschichtlichen Untersuchungen viel stärker und vor allem zunehmend emotionell aufeinanderbezogen sind.

So lassen sich seit Beginn der Psychoanalyse bis in die Gegenwart Phänomene beobachten, die man in Analogie zu Gubisch als "glaubensgelenkte Anpassung" bezeichnen kann. Erinnert soll nur werden an einige besonders prägnante Erscheinungen, wie die Aenlichkeit der Bilder, die Patienten malten, welche von C. G. Jung behandelt worden waren, bzw. das Auftauchen von bestimmten freien Assoziationen bei Patienten entsprechend der Gedankenwelt des Arztes. Ein anderes Beispiel ist schliesslich die Tatsache, dass die meisten Patienten, bei denen eine Traumanalyse durchgeführt wird, mehr und mehr auf den Arzt zuträumen.

Nimmt man alle solche Beobachtungen zusammen, so wird wohl verständlich, warum bei vielen Arzten ein Bedürfnis besteht, sich von dieser doppelten Subjektivität zu befreien, bzw. diese zu verringern.

Eine Möglichkeit dazu bietet die stärkere Beachtung der soziologischen Faktoren in Entstehung und Therapie der Neurosen. Diese enthalten zwar ebenfalls subjektive Aspekte, daneben aber gleichzeitig eine Fülle von leichten, objektiv greifbaren "Fakten." Ihre Beurteilung beruht ferner nicht allein auf der Darstellung des Patienten, sondern gleichzeitig auf der Schilderung all der andern Menschen, die an diesem sozialen Organismus teilhaben.

Für die Beurteilung der Entwicklung der Neurosen bestehen auf diese Weise mehrere Möglichkeiten zur Faktensammlung, so dass die von Patienten ausgehende Subjektivität erheblich verringert werden kann. Zur Erfassung des Kindheitsmilieus speziell kann die Befragung der Mitglieder der Primärfamilie wesentlich sein und hier wieder speziell die der Eltern. Dabei scheint oft eine detaillierte Objektivierung der vom Patienten erlebten pathogenen Situationen nicht so wesentlich wie die mehr sphärische Erfassung der Menschen, die für die Gestaltung dieses ersten Lebensmilieus mitverantwortlich waren. Das Gleiche gilt für die späteren sozialen Organismen, an deren Aufbau der Patient mitbeteiligt ist. So erweist es sich immer als fruchtbar, im Falle eines Ehekonflikts die einzelnen Mitglieder der Familie kennen zu lernen. Dies erfolgt weniger, um zu prüfen, ob der Bericht des Patienten Tatsachen entspricht, sondern um zu sehen, wie sich die "Fakten" im Geist dieses anderen "Berichterstatters" brechen. Wird dann dieser Vorgang möglichst oft durch Hinzunahme weiterer Berichterstatter ergänzt, so vervielfältigen sich die Aspekte nicht nur, sondern sie erweitern sich noch in einer anderen Dimension, da ja der Patient gegenüber den einzelnen Menschen in diesem sozialen Körper verschiedene Funktionen hat.

Am Beispiel einer Patientin mit einem Ehekonflikt kann dies am besten illustriert werden. Sie selbst erlebt und schildert sich in diesem Konflikt als eine an ihrem Partner in irgendeiner Form Leidende. Der Partner dagegen stellt die Schwierigkeiten dar, die im Zusammenleben mit der Patientin auftreten, die in der Regel ganz andersartig sind, als sie von dieser selbst erlebt wurden. Die einzelnen Kinder dagegen sind wieder in der Lage, diese und jede Seite der Patientin zur Darstellung zu bringen, was sonst nur spät oder unvollkommen, vielleicht gar nicht sichtbar geworden wäre. Leben, wie dies ja gerade bei derartigen konflikthaften Situationen nicht selten ist, noch Personen aus der Kindheitsfamilie in derartigen Gemeinschaften, so werden noch mehrere subjektive Aspekte von einem und demselben Menschen sichtbar.

Erst durch alle diese Facetten und Brechungen, durch die subjektiven Berichte dieser unterschiedlichen Beobachter, kann das Bild des Patienten einigermassen vollständig entworfen werden. Gleichzeitig erlebt der Untersucher den Kranken in seinem "sozialen Netzwerk" und wie er in ihm seine verschiedenen sozialen Funktionen verrichtet.

Noch entscheidender ist die Beachtung soziologischer Aspekte für die Psychotherapie selbst, bei der ja immer wieder die Frage nach dem Wirkungsmechanismus auftaucht, ohne dass hierüber bisher eine klare Antwort gefunden werden konnte. Die Zunahme an Erkenntnis eines Patienten über psychologische Zusammenhänge macht ihn wohl manchmal zwar klüger, ob dies daneben auch immer hilfreich wirkt, muss doch häufig stark bezweifelt werden. Die emotionelle Nachreifung ist sicherlich ein häufiger Erfolg, aber mehr Folge als Wirkung der gefühlsmässigen Erschütterungen in der Therapie. Neben diesen dürfte dann ferner die Fülle neuer soziologischer Erfahrungen eine Rolle spielen, die nun weiter beleuchtet werden soll.

Durch die Psychotherapie wird der Patient von Anfang an in ein soziales Kräftefeld gebracht, das in seinem Aufbau besser bekannt ist und nun seine therapeutische Wirksamkeit besser entfalten kann. Hier ist es zunächst die Persönlichkeit des Arztes selbst und die zu ihm entstandene Zweier-Beziehung oder Kleinst-Gruppe, der der Patient als erstes ausgesetzt ist und die er mitgestalten muss und in deren katalysierande Kräfte er sich begibt. Da in dieser Gleichung mit mehreren Unbekannten der Arzt seine "persönliche Gleichung" relativ gut kennt, zumindest sich in diesem Prozess der Wechselwirkung (Interaction auf amerikanisch) beobachtet und im Interesse der Entwicklung eines Anderen um eine dosierende Gestaltung sich bemüht, kann diese für den Patienten neue erste Kommunikation als optimal bezeichnet werden. Sie soll sich als Keimzelle für weitere soziale Erfahrungen auswirken.

Neben dieser ersten Zweier-Gruppe kommt der Patient, speziell bei Aufnahme in die Klinik, in eine weitere Gruppe, die Krankenstation. Hier sind es die Mitpatienten und die anderen Mitglieder des Arbeitsstaates, die zusammen eine zwar nicht so gut bekannte, dafür aber auch überschau-und steuerbare soziale Einheit darstellen. Alle Faktoren, die von uns als "indirekte Gruppentherapie" zusammengestellt wurden, kommen nun zum Tragen. Der mit ihnen sich auseinandersetzende Patient kann in dieser Adaptation an die für ihn neue Gruppe beobachtet und evt. geführt werden. Erfahrungsgemäss wiederholen dabei die meisten Kranken, besonders anfangs, die gleichen Einstellungen zur Gemeinschaft, wie sie sie vorher im Leben gelebt haben, bis nun speziell unter der steuernden Funktion des Arztes andere in der Gruppe auf dieses Verhalten zu reagieren beginnen und so eine neue Wechselbeziehung eintritt. Die Möglichkeiten zu korrigierenden Hilfestellungen sind vielfältig. Sie unterscheiden sich oft recht erheblich, so z.B. in Abhängigkeit vom Geschlecht der Gruppe, wie speziell von A. Ploeger herausgearbeitet wurde. Diese sozialen therapeutischen Faktoren sind besonders wegen des praktisch dauernd vorhandenen Einflusses so gross, dass eine "Therapie in permanenz" entsteht. Gruppendiskussion und Psychodrama unterstützen diese "klinische Soziotherapie," die besonders wirksam wird, wenn das ganze Personal in irgendeiner Form an ihr teilnimmt. (Die hierüber gesammelten Erfahrungen hat R. Alnaes kürzlich unter Verwertung auch des Schrifttums ausserhalb Deutschlands veröffentlicht.)

Anerkennt man die Bedeutung der therapeutischen Wirkung des "beseelten Organismus" (Wiezmann) einer derartigen Krankenstation, so wird auch die Notwendigkeit zur Verbesserung der diagnostischen Möglichkeiten gerade dieses sozialen Körpers einleuchten. Hierzu leistet eine regelmässig durchgeführte Soziometrie gute Dienste, wie M. Ozek und auch wir bereits vor view Jahren darlegten. In wieweit durch eine soziometrische Verlaufskontrolle auch die therapeutische Wirkung vom Einzelfall beurteilt werden kann, wird durch A. Bonzi und D. Kieser aufgezeigt werden. Die hierbei festgetellte hohe Korrelation zwischen Übereinstimmung der soziometrischen Befunde, der Gemeinschaftsfähigkeit und Veränderung der Krankheitssymptome zeigt, wie entscheidend wichtig es ist, alle in der Behandlung erfassbaren soziologischen Faktoren auch wirklich auszunutzen. Darüber hinaus beweisen gerade diese Befunde, dass der "soziale Masstab" nicht irgendeiner unter anderen, sondern ein in der Tat zentrales Bezugssystem darstellt, das für die Beurteilung von abnormen Entwicklungen und therapeutischen Resultate sehr gut verwandt werden kann. Der hierbei speziell von B. Stokvis bevorzugte soziale Aspekt hat auch so gesehen eine absolute Gültigkeit.

Nach der klinischen Psychotherapie wird ein Teil der Patienten so stabilisiert sein, dass sie im alten Lebensraum gut wieder angepasst werden können, ohne nennenswerte fremde Hilfe zu brauchen. Bei einem Teil aber wird man nach wie vor eine "Psychotherapie in sozial tragbarer Form" für angebracht ansehen. Dann sollte gerade hierfür eine Kombination von Einzelführung mit Gruppentherapie gewählt werden, damit an einem weitgehend bekannten sozialen Körper eine soziologisch ausgerichtete Übungstherapie betrieben werden kann. Hierfür bieten sich Einrichtungen nach dem Modell des "Social Clubs" ("Gemeinschaftskreis") (J. Bierer) an, bei denen die auch räumliche Ablösung von der Klinik eine wichtige Voraussetzung zu sein scheint. Das gruppentherapeutische Fixiertbleiben an die Klinik erweist sich dagegen regelmässig als ungünstig, da die klinische Gruppe realitätsfremder ist und anderen Aufgaben dient, so dass die entlassenen Patienten in ihr nur alte Erinnerungen pflegen können und bald nur noch als Gäste angesehen werden. Für eine weitgehend lebendige, d.h. die verschiedenen sozialen Wechselwirkungen adäquate Kommunikation aber bietet die klinische Gruppe dem aus der Klinik entlassenen nur wenig Möglichkeit. In einer Gruppensituation aber, wie sie einem therapeutischen Social Club entspricht, die ausserhalb der Klinik existiert, deren Mitglieder zum grossen Teil auch im beruflichen Leben stehen, und einen Leidenszustand oder soziale Isolierung durchgemacht haben, kann der Arzt nun erneut beobachten, wie ein Patient z.B. nach der klinischen Behandlung in einem derartigen, meist seit vielen Jahren bestehehnden sozialen Körper hineinwächst. Für den noch betreuungsbedürftigen Kranken

485

aber liegen die jetzt an ihn gestellten sozialen Aufgaben ganz anders als bei Beginn der klinischen Psychotherapie. Das einmal wöchentliche Zusammentreffen der Gruppe stellt zunächst geringere soziale Anforderungen an ihn. So muss er von vornerein mehr eigene soziale Aktivität entwickeln, wobei der Arzt eine gewisse aktive Unterstützung geben muss. Diese erste Phase der "sozialen Implantation" in einem neuen "sozialen Netzwerk" ist für viele Patienten nicht leicht, so dass sie gerade hier Hilfe brauchen. Diese ist besonders wichtig, da das Versagen gerade in dieser ersten Phase vom Patienten schon öfters erlebt wurde, z.B. wenn er nach dem Eintritt in einen neuen Verein diesen bald wieder verliess, weil er keinen Anschluss finden konnte. Ahnliches ereignet sich erfahrungsgemäss auch häufig im beruflichen Bereich: Die Kommunikation mit den Kollegen mislingt und damit die Akzeptierung durch die neue Gruppe. Die Auswirkung spielt sich dagegen oft in der anderen Schicht des Stellenverlustes und häufigen Stellenwechsels ab.

Ist diese erste Phase der "sozialen Implantation" in die neue ebenfalls gut bekannte Gruppe, z.B. des Social-Club, oder einer anderen analogen psychiatrischen Nachbehandlungsgruppe erfolgt, so trägt diese nun den Patienten, bis dann später persönliche Freundschaften entstehen, die sich nun erfahrungsgemäss häufig durch eine grosse gegenseitige Hilfsbereitschaft und Stabilität auszeichnen. Der "Gemeinschaftskreis" als grössere Familie nimmt an ihm in irgendeiner Form teil, bzw. gehört mit zu dieser persönlichen Beziehung, ohne deshalb an Bedeutung zu verlieren.

Wieder hat der Arzt die Möglichkeit, den Patienten auf diesem Wege zu beobachten, falls erforderlich, durch ein Einzelgespräch in einer schwierigen Situation zu helfen, und hat als Primus interpares eine Fülle von Steuerungsmöglichkeiten. Immer wieder bietet sich ihm die Gelegenheit, sich von der Grundbedeutung der soziologischen Faktoren im Leben seiner ihm anvertrauten Mitmenschen zu überzeugen.

GROUP PSYCHOTHERAPY, GROUP SENSITIVITY TRAINING, AND THE NECESSARY GROUP CONDITIONS FOR THERAPEUTIC PERSONALITY CHANGE

by JOHN ALTROCCHI and MARTIN LAKIN

Group sensitivity training has a very different history and set of traditions than group psychotherapy. Variously named group dynamics training, human relations training, leadership development training, and now group sensitivity training, these techniques were developed after World War II by a group of research-oriented but also action-oriented social psychologists who were followers of Kurt Lewin. This training first emphasized the experiential understanding of the dynamics of groups, with secondary emphasis on training in sensitivity to one's interpersonal impact. Recently, however, many group sensitivity trainers have tended to de-emphasize the study of group process in favor of emphasizing enhanced personal insight. For instance, in a book by Bradford and Gibb that will appear this year, Shepard (1963) says: "Implicit recognition that individual development was the lasting consequence in training led to increased focus on individual dynamics. Group level interventions were replaced by more personally oriented interventions. The National Training Laboratories began to focus on the problem of 'giving and receiving feedback' and in recent years, personal feedback has seemed to be the most important feature of the T-Group." (Shepard, 1963, page 16.) Even clearer evidence of this trend is the initiation this year by the National Training Laboratories of a new Continuing Laboratory for individuals who have had one previous Laboratory experience. The announcement of this new Laboratory states, it ". . . will concentrate more thoroughly on self understanding so that the individual may better understand some of the limiting and hindering characteristics of his behavior, may realize more completely his own

487

creative possibilities, and may achieve more authentic communication."

This growing emphasis on individual development in group sensitivity training makes it particularly appropriate to compare group sensitivity training and group psychotherapy. Recognizing at the outset that there are many group psychotherapies and some variations in group sensitivity training, we will try to abstract and to focus on general trends, and will compare the two traditions with a view toward examining some assumptions about the necessary group conditions for promoting effective personal and interpersonal functioning.

Most group psychotherapies and group sensitivity training are similar in the following ways: (1) A small group of people meets repeatedly, for somewhere between one and two hours per session, with a leader, with little prescribed structure. (2) The purposes include personal growth and better interpersonal relationships. (3) Members are encouraged to generate their own unique group culture which focuses on experiencing, awareness, and understanding of each person's feelings, thoughts, and behaviors. (4) There is ample opportunity for forceful and genuine interpersonal encounters. (5) There is a variable group atmosphere produced by members' feelings, topics of concern, individual activities and perceptions, and the interaction of all of these. (6) Finally, there is extensive use of feedback data from the members and the leader regarding individual and group behavior. It is not usually called feedback in group therapy, but we think it is quite appropriate to call it that. The above listed seem to be the most salient similarities between group sensitivity training and group psychotherapy.

On the other hand, group sensitivity training differs from most group psychotherapies in the following ways: (1) *Goals and Expectations.* In group sensitivity training, the members come as culturally and self-defined normal people to a skilled group leader, usually in a laboratory setting, for a learning and growth experience. In contrast, group psychotherapy members come as culturally and self-defined sick people to a doctor for treatment of an illness or disorder. (2) *Frequency and Number of Meetings.* Usually sensitivity group training meetings are concentrated once or twice daily in a two- or three-week period while group psychotherapy meetings tend to occur once or twice weekly over a much

488

longer period of time. (3) *The Atmosphere* in group sensitivity training is more clearly work-oriented and more clearly cognition-oriented. For instance, meetings are usually held around a table, members have notebooks and often take notes, outside readings are suggested, and often the training groups occur in conjunction with lectures on group dynamics, personality theory, small group theory, and other related topics. In contrast, most group psychotherapists eschew a work atmosphere and especially a cognitive orientation because of concern that the patients will use the cognitions defensively rather than therapeutically. (4) *The Leader's Role.* In group sensitivity training, there is a tendency for the leader to decrease status differences. For instance, it is common for sensitivity group leaders to encourage the use of first names for everyone including themselves rather than formal titles. While this is occasionally done in group psychotherapy, this is not usually the case. The leader in group sensitivity training also tends to reduce transference rather than focus on and increase it. This has been made clear in a paper by Leonard Horwitz (1963). "The group therapist encourages the development of transference, particularly to himself, by confining his behavior largely to that of observer and interpreter of group and individual conflicts and resistances. The trainer, on the other hand, not only interprets but often moves in the direction of a 'member' role by 'modeling' behavior and contributing his own reactions to group events as a way of helping the group to understand and learn about itself. These member-like behaviors contribute to an attenuation of transference reactions and to diminished preoccupation with the central figure and increased interaction and interdependence among the members. In terms of the goal of maximum learning about blind-spots and distortions in one's own personal interactions in a brief time-limited group, the 'member-like' role of the trainer seems preferable to the transference role of the therapist." (Horwitz, 1963, pages 15-16.) This raises the question, familiar in discussions of theories of individual psychotherapy, of the importance of dealing explicitly with transference in psychotherapy. Clearly the group sensitivity training leader focuses more on the actual, in contrast to the transference, relationships which are focused on by many group psychotherapists. (5) *Member's Roles* in group sensitivity training more explicitly include helping each other and it is assumed that everyone can take rather direct feed-

489

back. In group psychotherapy there is a tendency to make direct and confrontational feedback somewhat less frequent and less intense and to focus upon motivational predispositions, often assumed to be unconscious. This is presumably because patients in therapy groups are seen as less able to take such confrontation or because motivational states are assumed to be beyond rational control. (6) *The Focus* in group sensitivity training is entirely, rather than partly, on the here-and-now, and there is less emphasis of the etiology of feelings and behaviors in the past — for instance in the original family — and there is less emphasis on current but extra-group relationships, such as with one's wife, husband, children, parents, roommate, and so forth.

In reviewing these similarities and differences, we are led to three tentative conclusions. (1) There is an obvious need for comparative research to answer questions about similarity between these two sets of group techniques in terms of process and results. Some of Dr. Lakin's work has made a beginning in exploring similarities of process (Lakin and Carson, 1963; Carson and Lakin, 1963; Lakin, 1963). Furthermore, in Dr. Lakin's new and expanded work in group sensitivity training at Duke, he will soon be using group sensitivity training with psychiatric patients. He will be researching these groups extensively and this work should help to clarify whether some of the differences between group psychotherapy practices and group sensitivity training are indeed necessary because of differences in ego-strength and adaptability between "normals" and "patients" or whether these differences are only due to the very different historical traditions of these two techniques. This leads into the second conclusion: (2) Some of the differences noted above seem to reflect the emphasis on psychopathology in group psychotherapy and the emphasis on normality and cognitive learning in group sensitivity training. One is led to wonder whether the psychopathological emphasis, which includes the emphasis on past etiology, which group psychotherapy shares with other clinical traditions, is necessary for psychotherapeutic personality change. Many of the differences between group psychotherapy and group sensitivity training may result from differences in stated goal and unstated expectation which in turn result from the very different historical developments of these two sets of group techniques. Group psychotherapy clearly developed out of clinical traditions and group sensitivity training developed out of social psychological laboratories. One wonders whether the emphases which group psychotherapy carries, on the basis of its historical tradition, are any more necessary for psychotherapeutic personality change than are the emphases on normality, learning, and mutual help which pervade group sensitivity training. For instance, there have occasionally been implications from research that patients gain more psychotherapeutically when they are seen more positively by their therapists. Also there is evidence that enduring changes in behavior can result from group interaction which focuses on contemporary motivation rather than predisposing motivational states (Lewin, 1947). (3) Finally, if one is interested in promoting effective personal and interpersonal functioning, both group psychotherapy and group sensitivity training have had their shortcomings. Group sensitivity theorists have tended to overlook personality dynamics. Many group psychotherapists have tended to overlook group dynamics. Group psychotherapy and group sensitivity training, however, do share some common aims, techniques, and processes. These might be summarized by saying that they are similar in emphasizing feedback from current interpersonal encounters in an unstructured group situation so that each person can experience and better understand his own reactions, his effect on others, and their effects on him. It may be that the common factors discussed provide the necessary group conditions for promoting development toward effective personal and interpersonal functioning.

GROUP DYNAMICS OF SLEEP DEPRIVED PATIENTS
AND CONTROLS

by Daniel Cappon and Mario D. Bartoletti

INTRODUCTION

There are very few references to group dynamics of subjects *(Ss)* who have been experimentally sleep deprived, despite the voluminous literature on prolonged wakefulness. This is partly due to the fact that such experiments are usually carried out with one *S* at a time. There are no references, to the author's knowledge, to a comparison of the group behavior of psychiatric patients and their matched controls, exposed, on separate occasions, to the same stress of prolonged wakefulness.

The primary and original purpose of our experiments was the perceptual experience and behavior of depersonalized and derealized patients and their controls, during normal laboratory conditions and in four different experimental conditions known to induce orientational percept distortion. These experiments were designed to test the hypothesis that distortions in orientational perception are the main basis for psychiatric illness. However, our observations of the group dynamics of patients and controls under one of these perceptually distorting conditions, namely prolonged wakefulness, yielded very interesting results and seemed to be unique. Hence they are reported in this paper.

The specific questions for which this study seeks answers were:

1. Did these patients differ from their controls initially in terms of group dynamics? And did they differ in their group behavior over the period of prolonged wakefulness?
2. Was their endurance of prolonged wakefulness predictable?
3. Was there a difference between patients and controls, both

492

initially and over sleep, in terms of a number of personality variables: namely, suggestibility, sex drive and affectivity? The usual restrictions were observed in carrying out the separate experiments with patients and controls and in collecting the data. Appropriate statistical analyses were carried out to answer each question (*e.g.* t-test analyses of variance and non-parametric tests for differences and correlation coefficients for statements on prediction).

METHOD

I. *Population*

The patients (pts) (N-14) were selected for their spontaneous complaints of depersonalization (DP) and derealization (Dr), on the same assumption that their perception would be most readily distorted. Prolonged wakefulness was to amplify the differences in DP and Dr and in orientational perception. Pts were obtained from various settings: private practice, outpatients, psychiatric and mental hospitals. They represented various diagnostic groupings, ranging from major neuroses to borderline psychosis. The controls (C's), N-14, were matched with the patients on the basis of sex, age and education. There were 6 females and 8 males in each group. The age range was 18-41. The education spread was 8-16 years of schooling. All were volunteers and strangers to each other. They were paid $1.00 per hour of time spent in the experiment. Each group was exposed to 50 hours of sleep deprivation on separate occasions.

II. *Data Collection*

A. *Group Dynamics* — the quantifiable data were derived from three sources:

(1) Data on the *S's* actual spontaneous activity (independently noted by the *Ss* and by observers, Doctors, nurses and orderlies as well as our research team).

(2) Data on sociability (sociometrics) — this included such variables as the *S's* position in the group, popularity, participation or degree of involvement, warmth and spontaneity and preferred activity. There are baseline data

493

(questionnaires) for the self-rating of *Ss* in all these areas in terms of their habitual group behavior with strangers and with friends, prior to the experiment. The identical data was obtained from the *Ss* (self rating and rating each other) and from independent observers on the *Ss,* for each period or level of wakefulness, throughout the experiment.

(3) Data from sociogram — this duplicates the above insofar as it delineates the position of each *S* with respect to the group, over the period of wakefulness.

Also, at three regular intervals, the groups were assembled for group discussions on three different topics previously prepared by the Experimenter but unknown to the *Ss*.

B. *The prediction of endurance* — Previous work in this laboratory indicated that certain paper and pencil tests should be used as predictors of endurance under the stress of prolonged wakefulness, namely the Cornell Medical Index, Maudsley Medical Questionnaire, introversion-extroversion scale, and a specially devised dissociability index (D.I.) Throughout the 50 hours, regular observation of the *Ss'* performance was recorded, utilizing various questionnaires as well as independent observations by the research staff. Quitting times and manners of quitting were carefully recorded, and follow-up data were also obtained.

C. *The personality variables* — Emotionality and sex drive data were obtained throughout the experiment with questionnaires, and suggestibility data were obtained with autokinetic and Witkin's body-sway measurements.

III. *Clinical Description*

Clinical description of group behavior follows the organization previously described by one of us. It consists of four stages: initial encounter, consolidating phase, middle phase and dissolution, or ending.

IV. *Method of Analyzing the Quantifiable Data*

Wherever possible, we attempted to predict the group dynamics, that is, the activity and sociability of *Ss* from available data, using correlations. We also attempted to predict endurance to the stress and emotional reaction to the stress. Then we looked at differences between pts and C's in terms of scores derived from self and observer ratings and also in terms of discrepancy in scores between self and observer ratings, initially, and at each level of prolonged wakefulness, using appropriate statistics. All differences stated in this paper were not due to age, sex and education, since pts and C's were matched for these variables.

RESULTS

A. *Quantitative*

I. *Sociodynamics* — The activity of pts and C's, as indexed by our ranking their preference for sports, games, discussions, self initiated solitary or individual activities, or for doing nothing, was not predictable from their baseline self ratings, which had given an indication of their social preferences, nor from their introversion-extroversion scale score. However, analysis of variance showed that C's differed significantly from pts (p % .001) in their preference for sports activity. Wakefulness had no reliable effect.

DISCUSSION

I. *Group Dynamics*

There was a reliable difference between pts and C's in kinetic activities and sports. This may have been due to the greater interest normal persons have in sports, but it was also due to the C's discovering that such activity stimulates alertness. The C's were sufficiently interested in each other and had a strong enough group cohesion to want to keep up the morale and to succeed in the task of staying awake 50 hrs. For anyone who has been through the last war and had the experience of prolonged vigils this is nothing new. Probably there is a constitutional difference between pts and C's in that normal persons have a higher level of libido or sustained psychic energy.

Females tended to be less active in sports than males, especially female pts, until the level of fatigue wiped off the difference (in

495

phase IV). However, there was another pertinent factor. The pt population was chosen for their suffering from Dp and Dr, and there is some evidence that Dp and Dr are commoner in homosexual pts than in other males. This may be a defense reaction. Moreover, there were a number of overt and latent homosexuals among the male pts. And they preferred talking to kinetic activity, as they usually do.

II. *Endurance*

It was predictable from the fact of pt status that they would not endure this stress as well as the C's. This once again, should be of considerable importance in selecting personnel who have to work without sleep for an extended period.

GROUP PSYCHOTHERAPY AS A METHOD
FOR THE STUDY OF AFFECTS

by David R. Hawkins, John T. Monroe, Jr., Mary G. Clarke and Charles R. Vernon

Clinical experience with group therapy impressed us with the fact, already well known, that the group psychotherapeutic situation is a paradigm of much of social living. Moreover, we were impressed with the degree, amount, and variety of significant affective experience undergone by participants.

It gradually dawned on us that group psychotherapy might provide the answer to a troublesome methodological problem which had plagued us in another area of interest — namely, the psychophysiological study of affects. The major problem here is that it is very difficult for an observer to be present and in a position to make reliable observations at the time a human being is experiencing significant affective changes.

It seemed to us that the intensive group psychotherapeutic situation might permit the type of studies appropriate to proper investigation of affective behavior for which we had been searching. While the situation does not lend itself to experimental manipulation one can anticipate that at a given point in time and space the likelihood is great that significant affective changes will occur in the subjects under study. Moreover, through the use of the one-way mirror-screen, multiple observers can obtain useful data.

To study affects properly one has to take into account the immediate social situation, the individual psychology of the subject, including the observable behavior, his subjective state and physiology (including biochemistry).

We have had the experience of about a year's work with a pilot group, during which time we attempted to test our hypothesis that the group psychotherapeutic situation would be a useful one in which to study affective behavior. Moreover, we were attempting to see if these techniques would be useful for studying the process of group therapy.

The group under study consisted of five university students or students' spouses who had come to the Student Health Psychiatrist for therapy and had been deemed suitable for group therapy. The group met once a week for a total of 46 sessions. The therapeutic technique followed the group analytic psychotherapeutic approach set forth by Foulkes and Anthony.

While our future plans include careful physiological measures, we decided not to get involved in the technical problems of instrumentation until we could first assure ourselves that we were able to make reliable, valid and useful behavioral and subjective measurements to which to relate physiological measures. We did, however, measure pulse rate and blood pressure before and after each session as well as the amount of urine excretion during early sessions.

We focused our attention on the affects of anxiety, anger, and depression. We did this because they are the most clearly detectable, the ones upon which there was the greatest amount of previous work to relate our findings, and because we felt that changes, particularly in anxiety and depression, would be useful indicators of the course of therapy. In addition, we attempted to measure the level of arousal and the degree of social involvement.

In keeping with our conviction that in a study of affects it is necessary to measure both the subjective and behavioral state, we attempted to assess both. The subjective was measured by means of a 36-item questionnaire consisting of paired opposite adjectival statements rated on a seven point scale from minus three through zero to plus three. This is a substantial modification of a questionnaire used by us in psychopharmacologic studies which we adapted from one originally devised by Lasagna and co-workers. Items relating to each of the five dimensions under study are randomly scattered throughout the questionnaire. By taking the algebraic sum of all the items in each category a score could be obtained for each of the dimensions under study.

Examples of items in each category are as follows: *Depression* (Sad-Happy); *Anger* (I feel friendly-I feel angry); *Anxiety* (Nervous-Calm); *Arousal* (Peppy-Lethargic); *Social Involvement* (I feel lonely-I feel close to others). This questionnaire was administered immediately before and after each session, and in the later stages of the study, during each session.

Observable behavior was rated by the therapist and three to four observers watching from behind a one-way vision mirror. The ratings were based on a system developed by Hamburg and co-workers for rating a series of stressful interviews conducted by one of their colleagues. The same dimensions were rated by the observers as on the subjective questionnaire. The rating was done at the end of each session, and was a global estimation of the overall effect for that session. Scoring was difficult in instances where the subject verbalized minimally or not at all, or in instances where the subject had a brief period during which his affect was at marked variance with that of the rest of the session.

A sociometric instrument was also used. At the end of each session each subject wrote down the name of the subject he most liked, least liked, thought was making the most progress, and the least progress.

Time does not permit detailed discussion of the results. The subjective questionnaire gave evidence of reliability of items within a category. The different categories were clearly measuring different things. The clinical fit of the instrument was good. The observer ratings were somewhat difficult to evaluate. Frequently there were marked discrepancies in score. Discussion of these early in the study improved our agreement considerably and clarified our concepts. There remained, even at the end, differences of rating that were greater than we had hoped, but with strong affects there was good agreement. Both instruments are now being subjected to statistical analyses utilizing a UNIVAC computer.

The data obtained from these various instruments not only hung together meaningfully and provided quantitative scores of changing affect states but in several instances shed new light on the course of therapy. The details must wait for a later and more lengthy communication.

One of the chief questions we asked of this pilot group — namely, whether or not a therapeutic group would tolerate a variety of investigative techniques — was answered in the affirmative. Moreover, there was every indication that there was no significant disruption of therapy, and that the usual amount of therapeutic progress was made considering the types of problems dealt with and the amount of therapeutic time involved. Thus, we tentatively conclude that complex social-psychophysiologic studies of patients in group therapy can be carried on without disrupting the therapeutic process significantly.

This study suggests further that group psychotherapy can be used for research in a fashion relatively little exploited to date. It offers the possibility for repeated long-term study of individuals operating in an observable social situation which has intense and important meaning for them, and in which significant emotions and changes in accustomed patterns of behavior can be anticipated and measured.

AN EXPERIMENT IN GROUP-PLAY ANALYSIS WITH PRE-ADOLESCENT GIRLS RECEIVING SPECIAL EDUCATION IN WELFARE SCHOOL

by Maria Rita Mendes Leal

Adult groups are differentiated for therapeutic purposes by their activity, occupation or lack of occupation. In social groups, activity serves some therapeutic purpose. In psychotherapeutic groups, occupation is used as motive of reunion even though the inter-personal relation is considered the principal therapeutic agent in those gatherings. Group-analysis, on the other hand, is a process by which *free-floating verbal discussion or expression* takes the place of any group occupation. At the same time, it takes the place of *free* association, as found in psycho-analysis in the one to one relation.

In the same sense, we have found, one can differentiate between children's groups: Those with an activity serving recreational and instructional objectives; those *occupational groups* where free expression through play material or otherwise serves cathartic purposes, and "acting-out" is fully accepted in the situation serving psychotherapeutic objectives.

A third type of children's group appeared when play was not used as an occupation or, strictly, as a stimulus for socialization through action and inter-action in a permissive setting, but as a symbolic language.

501

THE INTERPERSONAL STABILIZATION OF AN INTRAPERSONAL PROBLEM

by Sheila Rouslin

How are problematic psychodynamics nurtured and sustained? The purpose of this paper is to describe the interpersonal group process through which intrapersonal problems become stabilized. The keystone of this process which takes place in various group situations in society, lies in the concept of reflected appraisals. These appraisals are incorporated by the individual in the development of the self early in life. The vehicle through which the reflected appraisals are incorporated is the nuclear family group. Later in life, the individual unwittingly seeks to maintain his particular system in his expanding group relationships. But why does a given group rise to the occasion and maintain a system of integration in the authority figure, even though it is pathological?

What seems to happen when a group is faced with a strong authority figure for its leadership is that the early family situation when the self was developing is recreated. The group as a whole acts as a receptacle for appraisals, which are then incorporated, just as each individual in the group had in the development of his self constellation. When the authority has intrapersonal difficulties, his relationship with the group is affected in light of the problems. This unwitting stabilization process is examined best by example and in operational form: 1. A strong authority figure has control over a given group; 2. His pathology is in the direction of a certain type, *e.g.* paranoid; 3. The group is dependent upon the authority figure for leadership, production or movement in production, rights, and privileges; 4. The authority figure communicates with the group in terms of his pathology, saying for example, "You are hostile — I know because I sense your hostility"; 5. The group responds predominantly with "nay" and in effect says, "We are open in the development of our opinion";

6. The authority figure repeatedly says, "You are hostile"; 7. The group moves from a climate of open-ness to one of indignance and anger at being falsely accused; 8. In addition, the authority figure does a variety of things designed to generate hostility in the group; 9. The group responds with hostility; 10. The authority figure has maintained his system of integration via the group response; the attribution is confirmed.

This stabilization process, then, is accountable to the original process of the development of the self via reflected appraisals from parental authority to child. This originally took place in a group situation — the family, and thus is touched off again or is potential in future group experiences. Furthermore, with any organized system or structure (personality, physical organism, social institution, group, or building) the aim is often to maintain its structure, since a change or intervening object would disturb the equilibrium and integrity of the existing structure. This tendency then, of the group to want to maintain its structure, and the authority's need to maintain his pathological organization form a kind of symbiotic integration by the familiar route of reflected appraisals. Both the "sustaining tendency" and the stabilizing process are illustrated in some of our great literature and political crises; both the tendency and the process have keen implications for the process of psychotherapeutic intervention.

GROUP PROCESS WITHIN THE
GROUP CONFIGURATION

by Cornelius Beukenkamp

A therapy group is a collection of "somebodies" who feel like "nobodies" and hope to be like nobody else but themselves. Their precariousness is not limited to their identity; it includes their existence. In using the word, existence, I refer to the psychological struggle for personal meaningfulness, not to the vegetative struggle for survival. A more definitive statement is: Group psychotherapy is a method of treating emotional disturbances, social maladjustments, and psychotic states in which two or more patients participate with each other and with one or more psychotherapists.

The small therapeutic group generally numbers five to eight, in addition to its leader. It has emerged for some as the most potent psychiatric environment available. Though group psychotherapy is a latecomer in the private practice of psychiatry, present results as well as portents of things to come, have made it the most exciting and gratifying form of psychotherapy currently practiced.

Had I been voicing my views a decade ago, I would have given indications and contraindications for the use of group psychotherapy in varied settings and with specific patients. This is no longer possible. For it is my conviction that anyone suitable for individual psychotherapy is also a candidate for a group.

The rationale behind this revision of my thinking is significant enough to state. Today's patient, with his increased free time, coming in for private psychiatric care from an opulent society, is not the same as his pre-World War II brother. Before the 1940's patients were more resistant and less open to treatment. Primarily, if not exclusively, they came to have their problems solved. The patient of today may actually enter the psychiatrist's office feeling that "it no longer makes sense" and "there is nothing to blame it on."

These present day patients may or may not be as ill as their pre-World War II counterparts, but what helped then, helps today. Perhaps this indicates that we have over-invested in diagnostic labels in the past. For regardless of what biochemicals wait in the vestibule, the problems in daily existence will remain in the living room, the kitchen, and the bedroom. Thus, dynamic psychotherapy will face a greater challenge not a lesser one. As man finds himself less paralyzed by his heredity and metabolism and the world becomes more involved in socio-economic crises, psychotherapy will have to keep pace. The therapist will require more than a deeper understanding of himself. He will be obliged to recognize that it is not enough to unscramble the complexes of a psyche in an isolated manner. If he does, his patients will remain as estranged from the world's climate as they were when the cause was their psychopathy.

There are those who claim that psychiatry as so practiced, invades the province of other disciplines. Though this may be true, the practitioner of group psychotherapy should recognize this challenge as having equal import with the untangling of an ensnarled psyche. No group therapist, especially in private practice, can claim he is treating his patients humanly if he regards the world's sociological state as foreign to the therapeutic process.

With this background, perhaps you will understand my belief that "who" shall be a group psychotherapy patient is no longer paramount; the question has changed to "when" and "with whom."

In considering "with whom" the patient will be placed in a group, the novice might observe certain values that have persisted from the past. For example, people suffering from the various addictions seem to do well, only at first, in homogeneous groups and later, with improvement, require heterogeneous groups. Those with physical stigmata such as blindness and deafness likewise need a homogeneous group at first and then a heterogeneous group. Men and women who seek psychic rehabilitation rather than psychological growth, such as many disabled paraplegics, are more often successfully treated when homogeneously grouped.

Patients whose problem is gender identification, such as women with strong aggressive drives, are often most beneficially treated in a group without male patients. The leader of such a group should be a man. When they become comfortable as women with women they can then be transferred to groups containing other men.

Individuals who have come in conflict with the law or who have spent time in correctional institutions apparently do better in their early treatment phases in a homogeneous grouping.

There is a growing belief that it is advisable to treat the overt homosexual in a mixed group, with or without the presence of other homosexuals of the same or the opposite gender.

The capacity to grow is not universal. In selecting patients for a group, the experienced therapist should be careful to avoid transgressing at the expense of either the gifted or the less gifted.

When one is forming a new group or considering a patient for an ongoing group, the concern with socio-economics, though important, can be over-emphasized. The most helpful guide is common sense. Children, adolescents and adults should not be placed together in a group unless they are members of the same family and are being treated by the technique of family group psychotherapy. Adults beyond the approximate age of sixty-five do poorly with patients who are considerably younger. Wide gaps in education can be difficult for patients to bridge. Economics seem least significant of all.

Husbands and wives can be treated successfully in the same or in separate groups. This subject, however, is so extensive that the limitations of this discussion prevent further elaboration. The same may be said for engaged couples in pre-marital panic.

One of the most satisfying results of modern group therapy is the benefits patients receive from one another. For example, those who have known despair and then seek psychological treatment are rarely detrimental to the growth of others. They often galvanize the enthusiasm for independence, beyond a mere vocal declaration.

Insofar as possible, I would refrain from placing people who know each other in the same group. Further, I would point out shortly after the commencement of a new group that conversations before and after sessions dilute the intensity that is necessary. I personally see no value in the alternate session with two possible exceptions. For individuals who are psychotic and for those who suffer acutely from emotional deprivation, the alternate session may provide a reassuring repressive effect. In other cases, the alternate session produces just the reverse and activates a subliminal malignancy. Thus it behooves the therapist to be familiar with primitive psycho-dynamics.

Now that I have enumerated "with whom", let me turn to

"when". To seek an optimum time is utopian. The sooner the group leader can say to the patient, "In my capacity as your therapist, I am prescribing group therapy", the better. Once the prescription has been issued, any and all material brought forth by the patient from that point on is related to the commencement of group therapy. This is true regardless of how topically remote the content may appear. The responsible group therapist will hear his patient's concerns, encourage him to experience his acute anxiety but remain consistent in the transactional process of therapy. It is pivotal that he view the onset of group treatment as merely one more event in the patient's therapeutic career. In other words, he should see it as just another step in an ongoing process.

Of course, it is easy enough for me to stand in front of you and state this. As you well know, it is a far different matter when it comes to the actual participation. Nonetheless, the principle remains sound. All other approaches which I have used or observed, ran a poor second to this process of prescribing group treatment. Our patients come to us to be treated. They are not competent to participate in our clinical judgment, nor did they seek us out originally with this in mind.

Questions referring to the prescription are not answered in subsequent individual sessions. Time, fees, and whatever instructions are necessary, should be thought out in advance by the therapist before facing the recipient of the prescription. It is preferable to lose a patient who did not intend to be treated in the first place, than to burden him with many weeks, months, or years of individual treatment while his therapist summons the courage to give his prescription or masters his countertransference which is placing both of them in jeopardy.

I am aware that the beginning group therapist may be rightfully insecure and find such guidance awesome; therefore, I would suggest that he obtain training, supervision, and any other help available before launching into this form of therapy. Where professionals are isolated and cannot avail themselves of these resources, the prescription stands little danger of failure since the non-clinical transference in the community will undoubtedly give sufficient authority to make up for his deficiency in the technique.

In my opinion, group therapy may be classified into two subdivisions: dynamic and non-dynamic. Non-dynamic, which is

507

sometimes called activity-directive group therapy, includes several subtypes. Inspirational-repressive and inspirational-authoritarian fall under this heading. Group guidance, group counselling, direct group discussion, text-book mediated group psychotherapy, recreational therapy, and activity group therapy also belong in this category, as do the didactic techniques such as the lecture method and the class method. I assume that these descriptive titles are self-explanatory. Activity group therapy may be an exception. This is a method often employed with children in which verbal communication is not relied upon as the principal mode of achieving results. In the presence of juvenile delinquency, the goal may be character molding. Here the technique is often one of rallying the individual and the group en toto to identify with a more mature ego ideal.

Dynamic group psychotherapy falls into two categories: these are analytic group psychotherapy and intensive experiential group psychotherapy. In this presentor's view, the latter form of treatment is the most desirable since it is the only one which leads to personal meaningfulness. It will be described in greater detail as I go on.

Now let us look again at analytic group therapy. This treatment modality utilizes psychoanalytic techniques and is not unlike individual psychotherapy in that it emphasizes psychodynamics and the reinforcement of transference. It enables the therapist to observe and point out distortions as they rise and fall on the testing ground of reality. However, in utilizing this technique, the therapist is dualistic. He entices the patient to reveal his unconscious, remains incompletely involved himself, and therapy becomes a somewhat obnoxious agent of reality.

In analytic group therapy, with its heavy emphasis on transference, there is often a re-creation of the family scene. Although much may be said for such a clinical development, it has its built-in limitations. For if this is the meaning of group therapy, then the individual group member cannot surpass the configuration and authority that is the original family. Thus, all those in the group, including the therapist, are denied a destiny which transcends family life.

Some writers have described the group therapeutic process as taking place in three stages. The first of these, the initial phase, is found almost in every form of group psychotherapy. Here the

508

orientation is verbal communication. The values of the therapist are exchanged unconsciously and sometimes consciously with the group members. In dynamic group psychotherapy, particularly, the therapist is chosen for his ego-ideal qualities. Unconsciously, he selects his patients for their desire to work toward similar values. This transference and countertransference, beyond its original definition, serves as the central rallying dynamic that triggers group action.

The so-called middle phase, which is not a real clinical entity, appears only in the dynamic forms of group therapy. It is characterized by patient-to-patient transference. Though the primary transference to the leader is still active, the group is less dependent upon its resolution for therapy.

During the terminal phase, a healthy adolescent behavior emerges. At this level of growth, the first two phases usually end. In other words, there has been a successful resolution of both the patient-therapist polarity which I have termed the primary polarity, and the secondary polarity, the patient-to-patient or sibling-to-sibling relationship.

Only in intensive experiential group therapy does this terminal stage go on into more adult behavior. During this phase, the group should be closed to new membership. Then the most exciting form of therapy this presentor has known can take place. For the group has attained psychological equivalence and may be reaching beyond the maturity of their culture. The individuals evolve creative ideas and imaginative judgments. They develop an adult sense of time, which includes an awareness that they will pass this way only once, as well as a healthy regretful acceptance of their own deaths. There is the feeling of being here in the world as it is now. Their problems and the world's daily problems are no longer in a state of separation. The therapist and his patients not only transcend their neuroses but reach the upper levels of their humanness and thereby attain personal meaningfulness. Indigenous to this experience is the penetration into the depth of the person to reactivate his authentic self, dormant up to this time. The self emerges through a mutation of the internalized "then and there" into the alive inner sense of "here and now". When the patient leaves therapy, his identity is intact and he is able to encounter experiences which are not only new to him but may be new to society as well. The healthy, non-rebellious pioneer feelings which

509

exist within him have been re-awakened. In such an emphasis, the group process is secondary to the internal process.

In my opinion, both types of dynamic group psychotherapy produce admirable results. However, personal meaningfulness, the most desirable outcome of therapy, cannot be reached through the use of any of the individual psychotherapies, psychoanalysis, or even analytic group psychotherapy. Though I recognize this statement is highly controversial, I would like to reiterate my position. Intensive experiential group psychotherapy is the only method which leads to personal meaningfulness.

SECTION 10: CULTURAL CONSTELLATIONS

A GROUP THERAPY PROGRAM FOR STUDENTS
OF VARYING NATIONAL BACKGROUNDS

by HAROLD KLEHR

The necessity of offering a variegated series of aide and services to students from foreign countries enrolled in colleges and universities within the U.S. has been widely accepted in our educational institutions. The author, a clinical psychologist, and Miss Laurette Kirstein (Foreign Student Advisor) instituted a group therapy program for students from foreign countries. The group's population consisted of students from various countries.

There were two assumptions underlying our intent to work with foreign students:

511

1) Students from other countries had problems of a personal nature which would benefit from the therapeutic approach. (Their therapeutic approach is here differentiated from social, vocational and educational guidance.)
2) Groups could be formed with students of differing countries of origin and such a heterogeneous group could function effectively.

Our central hypothesis was the evaluation of the feasibility of a group function with students of varying cultural backgrounds.

This is a report of the experience with 12 groups over a three year period. The groups (8 to 10 students in a group) were formed on a voluntary basis after each member received a written as well as verbal invitation. Each group was in operation for one semester (5 months). During this period there were approximately 15 sessions per group.

Method: Our overall view in regard to the group functioning was as follows: 1. The group is a free group in both discussion and behavior; 2. The therapists and other group members may aid in the understanding and solution of problems; 3. The tacit assumption that the group members have problems in adjustment; 4. The understanding of their situation (in a new country and with many adjustments to make) can be facilitated by discussion of feelings and attitudes about the past and present.

Group Performance Results: The groups' attitudes followed the usual pattern of group development: 1) resistance; 2) gradual discussion of problem situations; and 3) an acceptance of group interaction. The unusual aspect of the group was the rapidity of entering into group discussion. As a consequence of the students' need to adjust rather quickly to his environment as well as a kind of emotional need to relate to others, the group interaction process was heightened. The following describes some of the interactions: 1. The expression of loneliness of isolation was quickly discussed; 2. So called "deep" discussions of familiar attachment and dependency need became general group problems; 3. Morality and value structures were held up for contrast and evaluation; 4. Personal problems emerged spontaneously.

Certain problems could not be handled effectively in the group. These were: 1. Homesickness of home memories; 2. Nationalism and aspects related to this topic; 3. Emotional elements in American holidays, as contrasted to their own.

Summary: The group process with students from various countries was in general similar to expected group response. The group interaction was, however, heightened emotionally, and progress was rapid. Certain areas of discussion caused group immobilization. The group therapist should be alert to the freedom, intensity, and movement in such groups. The groups of students from differing countries of origin can relate effectively in a group situation.

CHANGING THE ATTITUDE OF CHRISTIAN
TOWARD JEW

A PSYCHOLOGICAL EXPERIMENT IN INTER-RELIGIOUS EDUCATION

by RABBI HENRY E. KAGAN

The reduction of intergroup conflict is the subject of intensive psychological investigation. This study, relating to Christian-Jewish relations, a matter of profound concern in our times, applies the principle of group dynamics to changing attitudes.

Empirical knowledge of anti-Semitism has been largely descriptive. By using opinion polls, scales for measuring attitudes, projective techniques for revealing personality structure and psychoanalytic case histories, these studies have been able to make quantitative measurements of the varying degrees of anti-Jewish prejudice and qualitative diagnoses of the emotional forces that produce the prejudiced person. They have correlated these measurements with a number of conditioning economic, political and social factors. These diagnostic studies are valuable for planning effective re-education and social action in the field of Christian-Jewish relations.

The scientific standards employed in *diagnosing* the case of anti-Jewish prejudice should now be applied to test the effectiveness of *therapeutic* measures. Do the programs employed to cure or at least reduce prejudice against the Jew work? Psychological measurements are being used to determine whether a specific intergroup activity does or does not change the attitudes of an in-group toward an out-group. Most of these studies in the United States have been conducted in the field of Negro-white relations. This study measures changes, if any, in the attitude of Christians toward Jews.

Without entering into debate on the specificity or generality of prejudice as such, there is this one consensus in the findings, namely, that there is no correlation between objective knowledge of fact and tolerance. Information does not reduce prejudice. This is significant, for it questions the value of much that is done to impart information on Judaism to Christians in order to reduce prejudice. This intellectual approach has included emphasizing the common religious ideals of Jew and Christian on the one hand and increasing an awareness of the Jewish foundations of Christianity on the other. Both approaches might conceivably increase resentment against Jews. As Kurt Lewin has pointed out, emphasizing common ideals may "merely heighten the discrepancy between the superego (the way one ought to feel) and the ego (the way one really feels) and thus give the individual a bad conscience. Such discrepancy can lead to a state of emotional tension but seldom to correct conduct." As for Jewish contributions to Christianity: Psychoanalytic theory declares that anti-Semitism functions as a needed dynamism for the release of repressed hostility because anti-Semitism is a displacement for subconscious rebellion against the moral restraints as well as altruistic goals of authoritarian Christianity, which are frustrating to a Christian. Therefore, knowledge of the *Jewish* origins of Christianity may boomerang and aggravate irrational hostility against Jews.

In intergroup re-education, other than the one between Christian and Jew, considerable scientific experimentation has proven that prejudice can be reduced *not* by information but by the use of emotional appeal, prestige symbols, equal status, and friendly contacts. A Rabbi has the advantage of these three additional influences when, for example, he is authorized by a Christian Church group to teach Bible to its members. In this religious frame of reference the Bible is more than informational; it possesses what Muzafer Sherif calls "emotional valence" which may be used to affect changes in attitudes. Do these advantages counterbalance the deeper psychic resistance which may be aroused in the Christian when he is taught the common ideals and Jewish contributions to Christianity?

This method of "dialogue" between a Rabbi and Christian groups is now in popular use in the United States. For the first time this method was tested when the writer applied psychological methods for measuring attitude changes of 97 Episcopalians from Connecticut and 380 Methodists from West Virginia. He was

515

invited officially by these national religious bodies to teach Bible to Christians for the express purpose of reducing anti-Jewish prejudice. The two groups represented two contrasting types in Protestantism and also in social background, since one came from the North and the other from the South. The average age was 17, an age level more readily influenced than older groups because religious doubts begin in this adolescent period and because the group is less set than older persons. At the same time, it is a critical period for the formation of anti-Jewish feelings as a compensation for adolescent frustrations. Reports indicate that overt dislike for Jews begins between the ages of 12 and 16. One-third of the students in five separate groups were subjected to two different teaching methods, the other two-thirds served as a control group. A scale of 16 items measuring attitude toward Jews was filled in anonymously before and after each course and again eight months later when the students returned to their separate communities. The scale satisfies the scientific criteria of reliability, validity and internal consistency and differentiates the least prejudiced from the most prejudiced. The initial tests showed that 27% were anti-Jewish, 26% pro-Jewish and 47% neutral.

The findings reveal that the method now popularly used does increase awareness of Jewish contributions to Christianity, but it does *not* decrease anti-Jewish prejudice. If it is any consolation, it may be noted that teaching common ideals and Jewish contributions to Christianity does not *increase* prejudice.

It should be observed that at no time in this popular approach is the Christian confronted directly with contemporary anti-Jewish prejudice, whether it be another's or his own. To say as little as possible about a specific conflict between groups, as is often advised, only diminishes the effectiveness of the effort to improve attitudes. Gordon Allport correctly observes that "lectures on the rights or virtues of minority groups accomplish very little. Because of the hostility of the listener, nothing new can come into his mind until something old comes out." Provision therefore, must be made for even a modest amount of free expression of hostility. This catharsis must be guided or it may merely reinforce self-justifications. The cathartic discussion technique used in groups has served as a talking cure by shocking listeners out of complacency or by exhausting pent-up hostility until they are receptive

516

to new facts. Only then does the reconstruction of attitudes begin. The individual must himself become actively *involved* in the inter-group problem, and he will accept new values if he considers them to be accepted by his own group.

Three classes in this study were subjected to this direct cathartic approach in which the same Biblical materials and information regarding common ideals and Jewish contributions presented in the other classes, were used, but this time as a springboard for a direct dynamic group participation in confronting contemporary anti-Jewish attitudes. The Christian students were encouraged to express their feelings about Jews and their personal experiences with Jews, and to examine them in the light of their own religious values. When the group evaluated its own expressed hostility, achieved insight into its stereotype thinking, and made its own decisions about the validity of its prejudgements, then the pre-judice of the individual members of the group was significantly reduced.

Since the growth or decline of anti-Semitism depends on whether the majority of Christians who are now neutrals will be affected by pro- or anti-Jewish influences, interfaith educational programs should adopt *tested* methods which *do* effectively reduce prejudice. Those who are frequently called upon to participate in these programs should become acquainted with the new techniques in group dynamics which offer a clearer diagnosis and a more effec-tive therapy in improving Christian-Jewish relations.

ASPECTS SOCIOTHERAPIQUES DU "NDOEP," CEREMONIE D'INITIATION A LA SOCIETE DES POSSEDES CHEZ LES LEBOU ET WOLOF DU SENEGAL

par H. Collomb, A. Zempleni et D. Sow

La communication que nous présentons ici puise ses éléments dans un travail plus vaste, effectué dans le Service neuropsychiatrique du Centre Hospitalier de FANN (DAKAR) au cours des années 1962 et 1963. Notre but est de montrer, sur un exemple précis, comment une société traditionnelle africaine a élaboré et utilisé certaines techniques psycho- et sociothérapiques que l'Occident possédait autrefois et qu'il a dû oublier pour y revenir au début de ce siècle, d'une manière consciente et sous une autre forme.

Avant de décrire la cérémonie elle-même, il est indispensable de dire quelques mots sur le système de représentations qui la sous-tend.

Le NDOEP est une cérémonie d'initiation à la société des possédés par les "rab." Les "rab" sont des esprits ancestraux et devaient faire partie d'un système "totémique" fortement dégradé de nos jours. "Rab" veut dire animal, en OUOLOF. Pour mieux situer les "rab" il nous semble justifié de les rapprocher des "Zar" éthiopiens (M. LEIRIS), et des "Folley" zerma (Dr. PIDOUX).

—Un rab, dans le sens originel du terme, est un esprit ancestral errant, qui est parti de Sangomar, l'île des morts. Si un rab est solidement attaché, grâce à un NDOEP, à une famille, un village ou une région, il devient "Tur" qui signifie "nom" (par exemple, Mame COUMBAM LAMB est le Tur de RUFISQUE). Dans ce cas, il protège la famille, le village ou la région et son nom sera toujours précédé du mot "mame" qui veut dire grand-mère ou grand-père. En fait, il s'agit plutôt de grand-mère car le Tur et le Rab s'héritent en lignée maternelle, de la grand-mère à la petite-fille ou de la mére à la fille, plus rarement de mère en fils.

518

—Les rab peuvent être des animaux ou des personnages humains. S'il s'agit d'animaux, on les distingue par leur espèce (lion, hyène . . .). S'il s'agit de personnages humains, on les distingue par leur nom, leur sexe, leur ethnie, leur religion (musulmane ou animiste) et, éventuellement, par d'autres caractères de moindre importance, profession, habillement, aspect extérieur. . . . Le contact avec la civilisation occidentale a entrainé l'apparition de certains rab très peu traditionnels: "Le rab policier," "le rab européen" . . . .

—Chaque "rab" a un "Bak" ou chant qui sert à l'évoquer et se compose d'une diziane de mots de louanges:

—*Mame guessou m'boul valina ragal bouka degué dao* (Mame Guessou de M'boul est arrivé; le peureux prend la fuite). *N'diaré n'diao abé toubab douka feyté kao* (N'diaré n'diao, L'Européen ne se mettra pas au-dessus de toi).

Ces chants peuvent être explicitement des louanges, comme on le voit ici. Mais un grand nombre d'entre eux ne s'explique que par l'histoire des sociétés Ouolof et Lébou:

—*M'boté m'botane mithi gouyegui lokaye doye, leke, lignour bakhoul lokaye doye leke.* (Qu'est- ce que vous allez faire avec la fleur du baobab; ce n'est pas mûr, ce n'est pas bon. Qu'allez-vous en faire? Manger.)

—Les "rab" ont de la famille, se marient, ont des enfants et peuvent agir les uns sur les autres en s'appuyant sur le statut qu'ils occupent dans leurs propres familles. Un Tur est toujours plus puissant qu'un rab.

—Au cours du NDOEP, le rab est identifié et fixé. On lui construit un autel domestique appelé "Khamb." Un "khamb" se compose d'une calebasse remplie d'eau dans laquelle flottent des racines d'arbre, d'un canaris renversé au fond duquel on a percé un petit trou, d'une pierre noire enfoncée dans la terre, d'un pilon cassé et piqué à côté de la calebasse, enfin de quelques objets accessoires qui symbolisent le rab particulier qui habite l'autel (par example, le "Khamb" de Mame YORO, le rab berger peulh, comporte une "guire" instrument pour remuer le lait, une "m'balka" baquet pour abreuver le bétail et une lance. Le khamb du "rab" européen comporte une petite table, des légumes et de la salade).

—Les "rab," malgré les confusions verbales, sont distingués très nettement des autres esprits comme les "Djinné" si repandus dans ce pays musulman. Les "rab" se nomment, se définissent, font partie d'un système. On se les attache par l'intermédiaire du NDOEP et des "khamb." Les "Djinné" sauf quelques exceptions, ne se momment pas, ne se fixent pas, ne forment pas un système, restent périphériques à la personne. On les exorcise.

Nous venons de décrire très sommairement ce que les Wolof et les Lébou du Sénégal entendent par "rab." *Mais qui devient possédé par un "rab" et comment?*

—Le premier cas, le plus simple, est la possession par voie d'héritage. La personne hérite du "rab" de sa mère ou de sa grand mère maternelle. Elle "a" ce "rab." Elle connaît son chant et elle est tenue de lui faire des offrandes périodiques de lait caillé et de "nak" (mil sucré et lait) sur le "khamb" que la mère ou grand'mère maternelle lui a légué. Cette personne se laissera occasionnellement prendre par son "rab" et fera une crise, mais son "rab" ne lui donnera jamais de maladies graves, excepté dans le cas où elle négligera d'une façon répétée le "khamb" familial. Les officiants du NDOEP se recrutent dans cette catégorie de possédés. Pour eux, on ne fait jamais de NDOEP.

—Un second cas se présente lorsque la personne hérite des "rab" appelés "at." Les "at" sont des jeunes "rab," fils ou filles du "rab" de la mère ou de la grand'mère. Pour ceux qui en sont possédés, on fait un NDOEP.

—Enfin, et c'est surtout cette dernière catégorie qui nous intéresse, n'importe quelle personne peut être prise par un "rab" si elle a offensé celui-ci ou, au contraire, si un "rab" s'est mis à l'aimer et désire habiter son corps. La présence du "rab" se révèle toujours par une maladie. La gamme des maladies imputées au "rab" est limitée. Les plus fréquentes sont: les affections gastro-intestinales, la stérilité, l'impuissance, les fausses-couches et surtout les troubles mentaux. Mais même parmi ces derniers, et nous allons voir comment, on opère une sélection. Les troubles d'origine organique qui sont particulièrement bien reconnaissables sont dès le début écartés et confiés au dispensaire ou à l'hôpital.

—La plupart des possédés sont des femmes. Comme l'ont démontré G. BALANDIER et R. MERCIER, dans la société Légou les femmes se sont chargées de la sauvegarde de la réligion traditionnelle, c'est-à-dire du culte des "rab," tandis que les hommes se sont tournés vers l'Islam qui réprouve la pratique du NDOEP. Néammoins, on rencontre quelques hommes initiés et la

520

ligne de démarcation n'est pas très nette entre l'Islam pratiqué et le culte des "rab."

—Les possédés forment une société qui impose à ses membres la participation à tout NDOEP qu'elle organise.

Ces remarques préliminaires ont été indispensables pour comprendre la cérémonie elle-même. Nous essayerons de la décrire dans son déroulement chronologique. On peut isoler sept phases successives: 1) *la Sete,* consultation d'un officiant de NDOEP. 2) *le Sadj,* commancement ou "Ray," caresses. 3) *les Nat,* mesures. 4) *le Boukotou,* danser autour. 5) *le Rey,* sacrifice. 6) *les Sampe,* construction de l'autel. 7) *la Danse.*

1) *La SETE* ou consultation d'un officiant de NDOEP. *Les pronostics positifs sont communiqués au malade* (par example, "il est pris par deux rab, l'un masculin, l'autre féminin, il pourra être guéri par NDOEP s'il tue la chèvre que les rab demandent"). Si le guérisseur lit que le malade est inguérissable, que ce n'est pas un "rab" qui est responsable de sa maladie, il l'envoie à l'hôpital ou chez un autre guérisseur. Si la nécessité du NDOEP est établie, pourtant, les pourparlers commencent aussitôt entre les officiants (le guérisseur en question plus ses co-équipiers, 7 personnes au total) et la famille du malade au sujet de la date, du lieu, de la durée (de trois à huit jours) et du prix du traitement. Dans l'intervalle le malade reçoit des médicaments fabriqués avec les racines que nous avons citées. Le jour convenu, en général le dimanche, officiants, anciens possédés et batteurs de tam-tam se réunissent vers neuf heures du soir. Les officiants mettent leurs habits de cérémonie (les hommes habillés en femme) et leurs innombrables gris-gris, (cornes, amulettes, colliers de perles) dont chacun des éléments a une histoire et une signification précises. Après que les griots aient accordé leurs tam-tam, tout le monde s'installe dans une pièce exiguë aux volets clos. Le "Ray" commence.

2) *Le SADJ* (commancement) ou le *"Ray"* (caresses). On commence par déshabiller le malade qui ne garde qu'un petit pagne autour des reins. Il s'asseoit dans la direction de l'est. Le chef des griots tape sept fois sur son tam-tam le rythme qui correspond au chant:

Sagui diambar regui moudiakhan mbara guidia (Sagui le brave le tue et le ranverse sur le dos l'animal de sacrifice).

Ensuite, tout le monde se met à chanter les "Bak" des 7 "tur" les plus importants: par example le chant de "Coumbam Lamb," "Tur de Rufisque":

Djiram coumba mame n'gondoye borom rire vi si dêbi (Djiram coumba, grand'mère de N'gondoye, le grondeur habitant dans le lac).

Ces chants sont accompagnés d'un battement de tam-tam lent et rythmé. C'est une "invitation" lancée aux grands "tur." On ne connaît pas encore le "rab" qui a pris le malade, on s'adresse donc aux "tur" que l'on connaît et qui sont susceptibles de lui commander.

Le rythme des tam-tam, les chants échauffent progressivement l'atmosphère. Tout d'un coup l'officiant principal fait arrêter les batteurs. On arrive au "Ray." Il prend du lait caillé dans sa bouche et le crache de toutes ses forces sur le dos du malade. Celui-ci sursaute et pousse un cris aigu. La même opération est répété sur sa poitrine, sur sa tête et sur ses flancs; mêmes cris et mêmes sursauts. Le malade est innondé de lait caillé lorsque les battements du tam-tam reprennent et les 7 officiants, à tour de rôle, se mettent à caresser, à masser le corps trempé du malade, de haut en bas, avec des gestes amples mais appuyés. Ceux qui sont inoccupés marchent autour et chantent:

Raye madé raye (Caresse, je te caresse).

Le "Ray" dure jusqu'à minuit; l'atmosphère de la pièce devient de plus en plus chaude, excitée. Les griots tapent avec force, quelques participants ébauchent des danses.

3) *Les NAT* (mesures). Le lendemain matin vers 9 heures, tous ceux qui ont participé au "Ray" se réunissent dans la même pièce. L'officiant principal fait asseoir le malade sur une natte et lui recouvre la tête, d'un morceau de percale blanche. Il lui souffle sur la tête, agite une corne de boeuf près de ses oreilles, et récite un verset. Cela recommence 5 fois; après chaque récitation on enlève la percale de la tête du malade et on l'agite. Ensuite on fait tendre les deux mains du malade vers l'avant, les paumes vers le haut. Les officiants agitent des clochettes aux oreilles du malade et on apporte un van sur lequel se trouvent des cornes de boeuf, des noix de cola, des racines, des billets de 100 frs. Puis on passe à ce qu'on appelle la "mesure." L'officiant met tous ces

objets dans les mains tendues du malade et y verse une grande quantité de mil. Le malade lâche tous les objets qui retombent sur le van et les griots se mettent brusquement à battre. Accompagné du son aigu des clochettes, du bruit assourdissant des tam-tam, cette opération est refaite plusieurs fois. Puis on "mesure" successivement le dos des mains, la tête de tous les côtés, la poitrine, les pieds. . . . Le protocole est toujours le même: on rapproche racines, noix de cola, cornes, billets de la partie à "mesurer," on verse du mil sur ces objets et on laisse retomber le tout sur le van. Dans les parties "mesurées," le "rab" ne pourra plus faire des dégâts car l'offrande le contentera et le mettra sous les ordres des "tur" puissants des officiants. Entretemps, on commence à chanter des "Bak"; le battement des tam-tam s'accélère, les clochettes sonnent de plus en plus fort, le rythme imprègne tous les gestes et mouvements des participants. Le moment est venu pour le malade de dire le nom de son "rab." Par toute une série de procédés (tintement insistant des clochettes, bruit assourdissant des tam-tam, secousses sur la tête du malade . . .) on amène le malade à un état d'épuisement; il crie, hurle, tremble, est tout en sueur. On lui demande alors le nom du "rab" qui le possède. L'officiant principal réitère sa demande en l'accompagnant de coups jusqu'à ce que le malade dise un nom. Si ce nom ne semble pas véridique, on recommence.

4) *Le BOUKOTOU* ou enterrement symbolique. Dans la cour, un grand espace couvert de sable est nettoyé. On conduit l'animal à sacrifier au milieu du cercle. Le malade se couche sur une grande natte et l'officiant principal fait coucher le beuf ou la chèvre ligoté à côté de lui. Le malade doit se serrer contre l'animal. Alors, on les recouvre de 7 percales et de 7 pagnes. Les officiants commencent à chanter des "Bak" et l'assistance, qui comprendra désormais des gens du quartier, non initiés, répond en choeur.

Puis, les 7 officiants se mettent en marche et tout en chantant contournent le tas. L'un d'entre eux tient à la main un coq rouge et un coq blanc; il les repasse à l'officiant principal qui se met à frôler les pagnes avec les deux animaux. Chacun des officiants répète, à tour de rôle, les mêmes gestes et on chante de nouveau: "caresse, je te caresse." Quelques minutes plus tard on ébauche un "Bak" adressé au "rab" du malade. Au bout d'un certain temps on s'aperçoit que celui-ci tremble. On retire les pagnes et les percales. Le malade surgit brusquement et, le visage épanoui, se met à danser. Les griots s'approchent. Au cours de la danse, le malade esquisse des gestes et des postures qui caractérisent son "rab" (si c'est Gaïdé, le lion, il gonflera sa bouche, se penchera les bras en avant, ouvrira de grands yeux, essayera d'avoir un air terrifiant et marchera de long en large comme s'il cherchait une proie). Les assistants et les officiants suivent ses mouvements et frappent des mains.

5) *Le REY* ou sacrifice. Dans l'enceinte où le "khamb" sera construit on fait couché l'animal ligoté. Le malade l'enjambe trois fois et s'asseoit par terre. On pose un récipient sous ses jambes et le griot principal égorge l'animal sur les genoux du malade. Le sang est récupéré dans le récipient et le malade en boit quelques gorgées. Puis on prend le coq blanc, utilisé pendant le "boukotou," on le pose sur la tête du malade et on lui tranche la gorge de façon à ce que le sang coule sur le front et le visage du malade.

6) *Le KHAMB* ou les *SAMPES*, construction de l'autel. Le malade assis dans l'enceinte enlève ses vêtements et s'enduit tout le corps du sang de l'animal sacrifié. L'officiant principal découpe les boyaux de l'animal et on attache quelques morceaux au cou, aux poignets et aux chevilles du malade. Puis, on passe à la construction du "khamb." C'est une opération fort compliquée. Le malade y participe activement. L'autel terminé comporte: la calebasse remplie d'eau et de racines, le pilon cassé, le canari renversé, une pierre noire des objets accessoires. Tout cela enduit de sang frais et de Nak. Le "rab" est désormais fixé, domestiqué, content. Le malade prend une première gorgée de l'eau de son "khamb" et se lave le visage. Dès ce moment, il pourra venir dans ce qu'on appelle "ses affaires" pour se soulager et pour faire des offrandes à son "rab" qui n'aura plus besoin de signaler son existence, de réclamer son dû, par les maladies, la stérilité, l'impuissance. . . .

7) *La DANSE*. Mais le Ndoep est loin d'être terminé avec la construction du "khamb." Nous n'en sommes qu'au deuxième jour. Désormais, on danse. Tous les jours vers cinq heures de l'après-midi, on dégage un grand espace au milieu de la concession ou dans une ruelle et les griots s'y installent pour "taper l'appel." Au bout d'une demie-heure, les gens du quartier, surtout femmes et enfants, commencent à arriver. Bientôt, une foule nombreuse, chaude, multicolore et excitée, entoure la scène. On attend l'ou-

verture de la danse. Tout d'un coup l'officiant principal apparaît à pas cadencés, en file indienne, au milieu de la scène. L'officiant ont revêtu la même robe et portent tous leurs gris-gris. Ils entrent à pas cadencés, en file indienne au milieu de la scène. L'officiant principal y plante ses instruments de culte et un des attributs du "rab" du malade (une lance, par ex.). Un autre officiant trace une ligne autour de la scène. Un troisième verse du lait caillé et de l'eau dans le sillon. Cette frontière ne pourra être dépassée qu'à pieds nus; c'est l'espace des "rab."

Ensuite, on appelle les grands "tur." L'officiant principal chante et toute la foule répond:

Mbeur hé mbeur hé Malikoum Simbogne dieulena savosse ngana (Malikoum Simbogne a pris le dessus sur la terre des maures).

Chacun des officiants ouvre la danse. Après un certain temps, c'est au malade de danser. On chante le "bak" de son "rab." Les griots accélèrent le rythme; toute l'assistance frappe des mains et sous la surveillence des officiants, il fait de son mieux pour danser et pour se compter à l'image de son "rab" (postures, mimiques, gestes).

Mais c'est juste le début. L'échauffement des hommes et des "rabs" demande beaucoup de temps. On reprend des "bak" moins connus, les tam-tam ne s'arrêtent pas un instant et peu à peu, anciene possédés et autres participants s'enhardissent pour sauter sur la scène et danser. N'importe qui peut entrer à la scène à condition qu'il soit pieds nus et qu'il danse. Lorsque l'officiant principal s'aperçoit que l'assistance ne participe pas suffisamment aux danses, il prend une boîte de conserve remplie d'eau et *arrose la foule*. Aussitôt, on se remet à chanter et à frapper des mains.

Le malade danse périodiquement. Quand il est fatigué, il s'asseoit au milieu des autres. Apparemment, personne ne fait attention à lui. Au bout d'une heure l'atmosphère est assez chaude pour les "chutes." On voit alors les comportements les plus variés. Telle femme, possédé par "Samb," le "rab" sévère, cultivateur, est en train de débroussailler ses champs à l'aide de sa Daba. Telle autre prise par le "rab" lion, se précipite sur un trou rempli d'eau et y boit quelques gorgées. Une troisième, prise par le "rab euro-péen" porte un casque sur la tête, une canne à la main et en se penchant de côté répète: "bonjour Monsieur, c'est très bien." Mais tout à coup, on voit quelqu'un qui se met à secouer violemment la tête et fait de grands gestes avec les bras. Le griot principal s'approche et bat très rapidement son tam-tam. La personne, d'abord debout, ensuite à genoux, se contorsionne, balance les bras et la tête, crie et tremble. Les officiants la tiennent par la ceinture. Elle s'agite de plus en plus, n'a plus l'air de savoir où elle est, ce qu'elle fait et finalement s'écroule, le visage dans le sable. Souvent, un orgasme se produit avant la "chute." Lorsqu'on la relève, elle garde les yeux fermés, elle est inerte. Quand elle se reprend, elle boit de grandes quantités d'eau et reste hagarde pendant toute la soirée.

Tôt ou tard, le malade aussi fait "une chute." Le déroulement de celle-ci ne diffère en rien de la précédente, sauf qu'elle est très attentivement suivie par tous les officiants.

Souvent, la séquence de comportements qui devrait normalement mener à la "chute" n'atteint pas son but. Alors, la personne se lève, marche sur la scène comme un somnambule, échange des invectives avec les autres (surtout ceux qui "ont le même rab") crie, bavarde, importune les griots, s'accroche aus autres, prend des postures et des gestes à caractère érotique. . . . Deux heures après le début, la scène est remplie de gens qui dansent, gesticulent et déambulent. Les assistants, acquis de tout leur corps au rythme des tam-tam, saluent les gestes, les danses, les chutes particulièrement bien réussis par des rires, des applaudissement et des cris. Il n'y a plus que des participants.

Le malade se comporte tout comme les autres. Au cours des danses successives, il fait l'apprentissage des mimiques, des gestes et des attitudes qui sont les deux attributs de son "rab."

La danse se termine vers huit heures du soir et recommence le lendemain après-midi.

THE CHURCH AND GROUP PSYCHOTHERAPY

by Allan N. Zacher

One group was composed of fourteen and fifteen-year-olds, the other group of sixteen and seventeen-year-olds. The psychodrama sessions were conducted on a twice-a-month basis. The young people in the group were from middle-class families in the northern Virginia area. The sessions were built around the problems that the young people themselves found the most pressing. Generally, the kind of situations presented were situations involving tension between the young people and their parents. During a period of discussion, or warm-up, one individual focused on a problem that the rest of the group thought was typical. Some of the problems presented included the choice of a girl a young man was dating; the time parents required their daughter to be in at night; the use of money; the use of the family car; or the relation of an adolescent to younger children in the family. Several things were apparent from the psychodramas presented. First, there was a great deal of anxiety in these young people about growing up, being able to date successfully, to marry, and earn a living. A good part of the tension between the young people and their parents was generated over the youths' concern that they might not be able to become functioning adults. It seemed to the adolescents that their parents were forcing them to remain children. Thus, much resentment was generated over parental restrictions. When a specific problem was described, the director moved the group to dramatize the problem. The young person who was taking the starring role would select other people in the group to take the parts of mother, father or siblings. The greatest amount of insight was generated when the star reversed roles with the parent. On a number of occasions, there was a dramatic development of insight. For example, a girl began to act her mother's part in a very realistic way. It was perfectly obvious to everyone in the group that she was identifying successfully with the mother's feelings. She understood why her mother had imposed certain restrictions upon her *and she also felt that she could do a good job of being a mother herself.* Thus, some of her anxiety about being able to take this role successfully was eliminated.

Some members of the group, particularly in the younger group, had a great deal of difficulty expressing the hostility they felt toward parental domination. This hostility was revealed by the use of auxiliary egos. In this technique, a member of the group stood behind the star, saying the things that the star felt, but was not able to verbalize. Sometimes, the auxiliary ego brought out resentments on the edge of consciousness. Often, the star began to identify with his auxiliary ego. The star was then able to verbalize resentments that had been repressed or hidden.

The second experience of group psychotherapy in a church setting involves the use of sociometric testing and grouping with twelve and thirteen-year-old boys at a two-week summer camp. There were forty-five in the group. The boys came from all over the state of Virginia. They belonged to many different Episcopal churches. Not more than one, or two, or three boys came from any one church, so that they did not know each other when the camp began. It might be of interest to add that this church camp near Richmond, Virginia, was racially integrated for the first time. The boys were assigned to three groups for one and one-half days. After this period of introduction, the campers were told that the group of forty-five boys was going to be re-divided into three groups of fifteen each, for the remainder of the camp period. They would be grouped on the basis of their choices. The boys were asked to list the three boys whom they would prefer to be with, and the three boys whom they would prefer not to be with. The boys' choices were plotted on a sociometric diagram.

SECTION 11: TEACHING AND

TRAINING METHODS

GROUP SUPERVISION AS A METHOD OF TRAINING
GROUP PSYCHOTHERAPISTS

by Beryce W. MacLennan

One very interesting type of experience we have noticed in supervisory groups is the re-creation of the climate or problem which is being described in relation to a therapy group. In this situation the therapist appears to play the part of the patient or group of patients in such a way that he stimulates reactions similar to his own with his group in the supervisory group. For instance, a therapist was describing how a group seemed to tantalize and to hold him off with isolationist obsessional mechanisms. They would complain, and then deny their reactions. As the supervisory group tried to help him explore this problem it became apparent that he was holding them off and refusing to reveal for them his real feelings, much in the same way that his patient group had dealt with him. The members of the supervisory group found themselves reacting as the therapist had done by feeling tantalized, helpless and angry with this shadow-boxing. After this interaction had been examined, the therapist was much better able to deal with himself and his patients in the therapy group.

In general, such supervisory groups should be kept small. When they are too large it is hard to develop sufficient trust and intimacy; and one does not have enough time to examine in detail what goes on in the therapy groups. I personally prefer — for groups that are being held once a week — a supervisory group of four therapists and a supervisor who meet for two hours each week. Each therapist has a group and we examine each group twice a month for an hour at a time. In order that everyone can keep track of the groups, we have brief summaries on each patient, and the therapists write processed reports of the meetings on which they will report, and summaries of the others, all of which are distributed and read before the supervisory sessions.

It is possible to set these groups up in different ways. They can be composed of:

1. Therapists who are all learning to work with the same type of group, such as analytically oriented group psychotherapy with neurotic patients or activity group therapy with children suffering from behavior problems.
2. Therapists who are working with different kinds of groups that are interconnected, such as parent and child groups.
3. Therapists who are using the same therapeutic method with patients who have different kinds of special problems, such as guidance groups for parents who have children with various types of handicaps.
4. Therapists who are working with groups where different therapeutic methods are being used experimentally with similar populations, such as counseling and psychoanalytic groups with adolescents.

Each of these arrangements has some special advantages from the point of view of a training experience.

In method 1 the therapists are able to quickly gain a wide

530

experience with a particular technique, problem or type of patient. For instance, four therapists, who were each conducting groups of unmarried mothers living in a shelter prior to giving birth to their babies, were supervised together. In comparing the four groups the therapists were struck by the similarity of the content and sequence, and additionally gained a very wide and speedy knowledge of the problems and decisions which the unmarried mother has to face.

Similarly, four therapists who were working with psychoanalytically oriented groups of neurotic couples working on their marital difficulties were impressed by the amount of pressure that each marital partner put on the group and on the therapist to try and get them on their side against the other. The therapists were able to share with each other the ways in which they dealt with this problem.

This method makes it easy to see how therapists can react differently to the same problem, and is helpful in overcoming resistance to looking at one's own difficulties. In one activity group the children expressed their defiance by not coming to the table for refreshments. The therapist understood their need to express their independence and remained relaxed and unconcerned. Very soon the children gave this up. In another group, however, the same problem arose; but this time the therapist was one who had had suppressed desires to act in this way as a child when angry, but who had not dared. She was threatened by her own present angry feelings, which she transferred to the children. They sensed that they had been able to get under her skin, so they continued to defy her. The therapist was able, with the assistance of her fellow therapists, to recognize her irrationally transferred feelings. This reduced her anxiety so that she was no longer upset by the children. Thus, the game of defying her lost its interest.

Interconnected groups are particularly useful in child guidance clinics. They enable therapists to gain an excellent picture of the ways in which different members of a family function, and to build up a realistic view of how parent-child problems mesh. If not all the parents and children are included in groups, we try to have them assigned for individual treatment within the same supervisory group constellation so that it is very easy for therapists to communicate and cooperate. This last is very important in large and busy clinics.

531

When therapists can examine the use of the same method with different kinds of patients or problems, they are able to gain an excellent idea of the flexibility and limitations of the method. They can learn what is basic to the method and what can be adapted. For instance, one can use well a psychoanalytically oriented approach with adolescents and adults, but one generally finds that it is necessary to be more active with the adolescent groups. The latter have a low tolerance of anxiety and silence, and often have great difficulty in staying with a problem for any length of time. A major factor in the adaptation of this method may be the degree of motivation. Highly motivated patients require less therapeutic intervention and less immediate gratification.

Finally, we can group together therapists who are working with similar patient groups but using different methods, for instance guidance and therapeutic groups of parents. This enables the therapists to understand something of the range of the different methods. They can compare the therapeutic activities which help a group learn how to function at a particular level, and can learn how to select more easily for different kinds of group therapy.

THE ABSENCE OF FACE TO FACE CONTACT IN TRAINING IN PSYCHOANALYSIS IN GROUPS

by Gerald J. McCarty, Irving A. Goldberg,
Emanuel K. Schwartz and Alexander Wolf

The ideas presented here are derived from a unique experience which the authors have undertaken for training in psychoanalysis in groups. As with most innovations, it was born of necessity. To date the experience has been one of a four-way phone supervisory conference once a week, wherein the supervisees talk face to face over a speaker phone to the supervisors, who are also together face to face.

The loss of visual cues in the hierarchical vector (that is, between supervisors and supervisees) brought about a heightened auditory sensitivity and fantasy compensation. The absence of such cues more quickly provoked, exposed, and brought to focus the transference, counter-transference and super-transference problems not only on the part of the trainees but also on the part of the supervisors. Another factor is the effect of the presence of visual cues in the horizontal vector (that is, between the two supervisees as well as between the two supervisors). This enabled the group to capture and focus on the qualities of the alternate session in group therapy in the regular phone supervisory sessions, because the trainees were together but remote from the teacher authorities. It also led to the development of clique behavior and the identification of the participants one with the other. The third factor is the parallelism between individual psychotherapy and individual supervision, as contrasted to the parallelism between psychotherapy in a group and training in a group. There was a repetition in the training process of the types of experiences which occur in therapy groups because of the similarity of underlying psychodynamics in the training situation. There was a shift from an initial concern with what is happening with patients of the

533

trainees (that is, patients' transference relationships and counter-transference problems of the therapists) to what we are doing with each other (an analysis of transference problems in the training situation).

As a result of our experiences, we have concluded that it is possible to significantly increase one's psychotherapeutic skills by training without visual or face to face contact on the hierarchical level. This enables many people to get high level training in specific therapeutic techniques where such training is not available on a local basis. Lines for further research in this training medium will be presented.

THE OBSERVATION GROUP:
A GROUP PSYCHOTHERAPY TRAINING TECHNIQUE

by Jack D. Krasner and Arlene Wolberg

This project originated in 1958 as an experimental procedure in a group psychotherapy training program under the direction of Asya L. Kadis. It was conducted at the Postgraduate Center for Psychotherapy, New York City. Each training session of this project comprised three hours. The first half was devoted to the therapeutic session of the "observation group." Observing the session afforded the trainee a non-participating, but direct, experience of the emotional interplay and reactions involving all individual patients and the leader. The remaining one and one-half hours were devoted to comment and instruction stimulated by observation of the therapeutic session. The duration of this project was nine months.

Those who observed the "observation group" will be hereafter referred to as "group of observers." This group comprised seven students — five males and two females — and a supervising instructor. With the exception of one female student, all of the students had prior experience as leaders in a psychotherapeutic group.

The participants in the discussion section of the training session (hereafter referred to as "instruction group") consisted of the "group of observers," the leader of the "observation group" and the supervising instructor.

The "observation group" comprised five persons — three females and two males, ranging in age from the early thirties to the early forties. Each patient was in conjoint therapy, *i.e.* being treated in individual therapy by a therapist other than the group leader. One of the females was Negro and had a Southern background (Pat — passive-aggressive personality). The remaining four persons were white and reared in the North: Bob (passive-aggressive personality with schizoid trends), Penny (phobic reactions in an

535

obsessive-compulsive), Ned (schizoid personality) and Ellen (passive-aggressive personality).

The methodology formulated for handling the group observation process was as follows: By way of the one-way screen, the "group of observers" watched the initial interviews at which time the members of the "observation group" were selected. During the first few sessions, the students were asked to make their observations in the following way: Two students would report on what they felt were the defenses operating in the "observation group"; two would report what they considered to be the counter-transference reactions of the therapist; two would give their impressions of how dream material was handled and what they conceived to be the group dynamics, and one student would report on the therapeutic techniques employed by the therapist. This procedure was modified after the fifth session (there were twenty sessions in all), so that each observer gave his total impressions of what went on in the "observation group" and discussed the aspects that appeared important to him. It was considered that this method would lead to a better understanding of what one should look for when analyzing a group session. The "group of observers" discussed the process while the therapeutic group was in session.

The instructor's orientation was in the direction of interpreting group processes, such as *interaction* and *sentiment,* in terms of *defenses* and the *feelings* associated with the defenses as experienced in the group. She encouraged the "group of observers" while they were watching the "observation group" to think in terms of defenses; to observe how these defenses worked and at what points they went into operation in the group session. As the session progressed, the instructor focused attention on the various types of defenses expressed by the different group members. The manifestations and the significance of the defenses were clarified in terms of psychodynamic and pathological material related to the individual problems of the members of the group. Various therapeutic techniques were pointed out that might be of value in making meaningful interventions, thereby enabling the patients to gain some insight into their defensive maneuvers. The interlocking defenses and their possible significance were also pointed out. Dreams of the group members were discussed in relationship to gaining information and understanding, as well as to when and how this material might be utilized by the patients in the group.

All members of the "instruction group" were experienced therapists. However, when confronted with certain group situations, some appeared to have difficulty in applying certain fundamentals of psychotherapy. Two significant problem areas were noted. One, it was felt by some of the observers that the verbalization of a problem and ensuing interpretation would result in the patient's gaining sufficient insight to prevent repetition of the same problem in the group. Two, difficulty was experienced in relationship to timing, appropriateness and level (intrapsychic, interpersonal or group behavioral) of interpretations. The significance of latent content and its relationship to repressed material was another focal point for discussion and arose as an outcome of the discussion on insight. Before interpretation of repressed material can lead to insight, the therapist must make sure that this material is in the pre-conscious and not too highly defended. In order to accomplish this, the therapist must pay close attention to the verbalizations of the patients.

As with most procedures, the one-way screen technique has possible hazards. The free discussion of different ideas and reactions tends to stimulate thinking. However, anxiety within the instruction group may result from transference, counter-transference, and/or identification reactions to the patients, and/or other members of the instruction group. No member of the instruction group is totally immune to these phenomena. These reactions, if not adequately handled, may result in intra-group hostility and a destruction of the training process.

An example of intra-group conflict focused by the supervisor was the following: During one training session, an intense competitive feeling was aroused. The instruction group's reaction tended to be severely critical to everything the therapist had done during the therapeutic session. The supervisor asked what techniques might have been used to bring about the results wanted by the observers. They found it difficult to make any positive suggestions. One members of the group focused a discussion on why the particular therapist was chosen rather than someone else. Other members joined the discussion, some defending, while others criticized the therapist. At this point, the supervisor asked for a clarification of this particular reaction. The discussion brought about that this same observer felt a great deal of competition with the therapist.

To prevent the discussion from turning into a therapy session, the supervisor circumscribed the problem to the existing situation. Using the information verbalized, she explained how well-trained analysts were capable of transference and counter-transference reactions. The aim of the supervisor was to clarify the existence of possible personal problems and conflicts, but not to assume the role of therapist for the group of observers. The group members were asked to consider their individual personal, conflictual involvement, and to try to work these out either on their own or through further personal analysis.

At the final session of the discussion group, this same observer again brought up his early conflictual feelings towards the therapist. He had given the matter a great deal of thought, and related it to a past personal experience: "I had mixed feelings about doing individual analysis in a group setting, and about handling the group as a whole. I remember that when I had my own observer, observing me as a therapist, I felt she was extremely critical of me. She would criticize me for doing individual analysis in a group setting. My observer knew a great deal about theory, but I am not sure how much she knew about practice. In this group, I felt the therapist knew a great deal about theory, but when it came to relating the theory with practice, I felt very uncomfortable and anxious as an observer because I often felt critical of the therapist. I felt especially critical about his way of handling the interlocking defenses — the group would seem to go into a group depression and it was necessary to bring them out of their boredom. I often felt the therapist was too passive in this respect and he helped to bring out this depressed reaction. It made me angry."

THE FUNCTION OF THE LEADER
IN DEVELOPING AND MAINTAINING
A WORKING PSYCHOTHERAPEUTIC GROUP

by Milton M. Berger

As a psychodynamically trained and practicing psychiatrist, it is my view that in individual and group psychotherapy the function of the therapist is pivotal in the patient(s)-therapist relationship. The key to the outcome of therapy lies in the therapist's personality, maturity, training and awareness of the significance of his function, as well as in his knowledge and ability to authentically fulfill his multiple responsibilities.

Training as a group psychotherapist usually takes place after or concurrently with training as an individual psychotherapist. However, because the task of the group leader has an artistic-intuitive basis which is at least as important as its scientific basis, increasing recognition is being given to the value of participation in a group experience for sensitivity training and growth in awareness of individual and group psychodynamics before traditional training in individual psychotherapy is undertaken.

Training for competency to lead a psychotherapy group whose goal is not just to relieve symptomatology, but also to bring about profound characterological change, is best based on a curriculum which includes: (1) Didactic lectures covering the history, theories, techniques and comparative practices of group psychotherapy; (2) Supervised opportunities to participate clinically as an observer and/or co-therapist and, most importantly, as a therapist of one or more groups; (3) Participation in a group experience for personal therapy and to increase awareness and sensitivity to individual and group processes.

This paper refers primarily to the function of the leader of a group of eight to ten adults who come for help for various reasons and for whom analytically oriented or analytic group psychotherapy has been prescribed for resolution of their psychopathology. It touches on: (A) Professional and administrative problems in the selection and preparation of patients; (B) Promoting group interaction and working through towards termination and the contrast between the therapist's functioning in the first sessions and in later meetings of the group; (C) Recognition and utilization of nonverbal communications; (D) The prevention and management of crises and emergencies; (E) The therapist's use of self; (F) Acting out; (G) The resistance of patients, therapist and the group as a whole.

A. *Selection and Preparation*

While Foulkes presents the function of the leader as analogous to that of the conductor of an orchestra, I picture the function of the leader of a psychotherapy group as being analogous to that of the captain of a training ship on which the crew is made up of sea cadets who will each one day captain a ship of his own.

Since early times, seasoned skippers have known the importance of being involved in the selection and cutting down and seasoning of the trees from which the keel and main members of their vessels would be structured. It is equally as important for a group psychotherapist to personally know the individuals who will comprise his group, not only from the viewpoint of their psychopathology and liabilities, but also of their past and present assets and future potential for self, for family and for the community-at-large. In many clinic settings patients are assigned to a group by an intake interviewer who will not be their therapist and who, all too often, also lacks the experience of having been a group psychotherapy patient or therapist and lacks belief in the value of group psychotherapy. Burdon and Ryan found "a definite relationship between continuation in group and the specific individual diagnostician who had performed the initial study and made the assignment to group." For patients to be placed in a group relatively at random because they have problems in relating with others is to make the task of the group even greater. It has been my experience that the development of a carefully selected group of patients who are strangers to each other and who predictably will be able to profit from interacting and being with each other is enhanced if

540

each has had a chance to have enough individual sessions with the therapist to have developed a positive trust and transference to the therapist. In addition, the therapist can better feel for suitability of "fit," feel for "balance" and "bounce," and assign patients to groups where the likelihood of successful psychotherapy is at its peak.

For me, such process concepts as "fit," "bounce" and "balance" are important considerations. These processes are at times more subjectively than objectively experienced by the therapist. While a self-effacing, injustice-collecting, suspicious, ruminating 37-year-old accountant who is functioning intrapsychically and interpersonally far below his potential at his work and in his marriage might be nosologically listed as borderline paranoid, he might "fit" quite well with a group of patients with character neuroses. However, another borderline paranoid patient, a 39-year-old unmarried male auto mechanic, who suffers from markedly unresolved fears of homosexuality, a history of being impulse ridden and of intermittent violent acting out and repeated fantasies of striking people, might not "fit" in the same group. For me, the humanistic factors are more important than the standard nosologic diagnostic ones. Frank states that "more important than diagnostic categories in guiding composition are the ways in which characteristics of the patients in a given group can be expected to interact. Thus one excessively aggressive patient in a group of timid ones may create an unworkable situation, but several may foster useful interaction."

We have increasing reports of patients formerly considered nonacceptable for group therapy participating successfully in a group experience with a therapist and a group who are "right for him" in a particular setting. A therapist who is "right for a patient" is able to understand the nature of the psychopathology of this patient and is competent enough to so modify his goals and techniques as to be able to utilize the group psychotherapeutic approach for this individual patient. A group which is "right for a patient," a group in which it is predicted that he will "fit," is one which offers him an opportunity to expose and work through his psychopathology by affording him people to identify with, to have transference reactions toward and to interact with in a spirit of mutuality as he becomes free enough to give up his neurotic way of life and to fulfill more of his potential.

If the group is composed of predominantly depressed patients

541

or predominantly resigned and alienated and withdrawn patients, it may never "get off the ground," may never "bounce" and become truly interacting. I have placed together in a heterogeneous group in private practice an overprotective, subtly and seductively dominating, guilt-provoking, intellectual, 54-year-old perfectionistic married mother of four children (R.N.), two of whom have required psychotherapy, and four younger married and unmarried individuals in their twenties whose emotional immaturity, self-effacement and dependency and approval needs are the result of having been raised by similarly driven mothers. In the same group I placed a financially successful, handsome, emotionally cold and alienated, compartmentalized, power-driven man who lives a shallow life with self-centered hedonistic values who may remind the patient R.N. of her husband and her mother. He entered therapy when his marriage moved toward dissolution. In addition, I placed in the group a "saintly," sensitive, compulsively-giving, seductively power seeking, divorced male therapist of 44 whose unspoken price for giving is that the recipients of his largesse love him and worship at his shrine. Such a selection of patients allows for "fit," "bounce" and "balance." Thus the members have a number of individuals toward whom they can project, transfer and express their neurotic, then healthy rebellion, can identify with, be jealous of, and can then gradually move beyond multidimensional transferences toward new ways of feeling, acting and being in the slice of life which a therapy group represents, as described by Beukenkamp.

Some patients who may be readily ruled out for admission to a specific group are those (a) prone to outbursts of uncontrolled violence or aggressivity, (b) overly hallucinating and, because of constant irrational productions, unreachable by other group members, (c) monopolizers who block group interaction, (d) unable to cope with their own or other people's anxiety-provoking conscious and unconscious productions, (e) whose real selves or egos are so fragile that they are hypersensitive to criticism, and (f) patients who are severely depressed and suicidal. However, even these may fit into another group in which they can be accepted, educated and conditioned or therapeutized until they fit. As Leopold has so succinctly stated it, the best approach in selection is one which considers the *relevance of the psychodynamics* of the patient and the psychologic impact of the group upon him, and vice versa, as the most important criteria for optimum results with a particular therapist in a particular setting.

Furst's research of homogeneous versus heterogeneous groups, with respect to diagnosis and psychopathology, in an analytically oriented private practice setting confirmed that both types of groups can be helped with group therapy. He concluded that heterogeneous groups are better than homogeneous ones for group psychoanalysis, interaction therapy or activity therapy and that interview therapy can be equally successful with both kinds of groups. Heterogeneous groups are more desirable for deep therapy, modification of character structure, when the training and experience of the therapist is adequate and when time and expense are less important.

Geller states that intense psychoanalytic therapy requires small groups of three to ten patients, that problem-centered groups of eight to fifteen are workable, and that repressive-inspirational, lecture and discussion groups can have thirty to one hundred or more people. The more superficial the approach to psychotherapy is, the larger the size can be. Sternlicht recommends ten to fourteen as an ideal group size for mental retardates because of their lack of verbal facility and the need for nonverbal cathartic techniques such as play therapy, finger painting, psychodrama and dramatizations.

In Burdon and Ryan's research project it was found in predicting group participation and group continuation, that the important clinical factors are: first, the patient's capacity to wait with his problem; second, to relate to other people hopefully; and third, to feel he is primarily responsible for his own well-being. In their study, 86% of those who continued in group psychotherapy also had a high capacity for mutual dependence.

Preparation for the group experience may vary from patient to patient even with the same therapist. For some, details of what is hoped for in group interaction are necessary, including some information about the other group members. For patients who are strongly motivated, little preparation is necessary because of their ability, strength and desire to risk joining a group of strangers in order to experience and explore in a voyage of mutual discovery what will happen intrapsychically and interpersonally. Beginning group therapists would do well to heed and attempt to work through direct evidence of resistance. Such expressions call for the person doing the preparing to patiently, kindly and empathetically — not patronizingly — respond with information to educate and relieve confusion and anxiety, as well as to constructively stimulate the patient to want to come because of the values the group has to offer which may be even greater for this patient than what individual therapy has to offer.

Before deciding to have a person in his group, a therapist should ask himself three important questions: Do I like this person? Can I help this person? Do I want to help this person? If the answer to *any* of these is "No," I believe it is important for the therapist, especially if he is relatively inexperienced, to attempt to work through his response before bringing the patient into the group; although his counter-transference response may be of some value to himself and to such a person if the therapist does work with him, even before resolving it.

As a final note regarding preparation of patients, I wish to add my belief in the value of the therapist's ability to communicate his belief not only in man's potential for constructivity and good, but also in the efficacy of group psychotherapy. His enthusiasm, hopefulness and optimism may be contagious and profoundly affect the outcome of therapy.

B. *Promoting Group Interaction and Working Through Toward Termination*

A group which is "right" gives its members an opportunity to test out in reality new and healthier ways of feeling, being and acting.

The writings of Ross, Mullan, Rosenbaum, Wolf, Leopold and others offer numerous suggestions to help maintain a working psychotherapy group. Education of each member for his role, by example as well as description, will do much to improve and maintain the working spirit and ability of the group and to stimulate group cohesiveness. Patients learn that through honest sharing, interacting and free associating with others they actually help themselves as well as others.

Whitaker and Malone emphasized that it is important for the therapist to understand and accept the fact that he is the essential dynamic in psychotherapy and must place high evaluation on the importance of "his feeling responses to the patient" and to be aware of and be able to utilize "the reciprocal quality of the relationship between the two persons who are called 'doctor' and 'patient.'"

Dividing the group process into three phases, for the sake of convenience, helps to point out some of the therapist's duties more specific to each phase, though the phases and functions overlap.

The Initial Phase. The therapist may state simple rules for the group: (a) mutual loyalty to keep within the group that which transpires within the group; (b) the mutual obligation to verbalize, rather than act out, as freely as possible during the group sessions what is thought, felt and experienced by each in relation to himself and the other group members including the therapist, particularly feelings of sexuality and rage. This can be spelled out to include free associations, fantasies and body sensations so that patients learn to use their total being for perception of what is going on both inside and outside themselves.

The therapist may use himself as an example at times to start the group ventilating and interacting. He may mention his own anxiety or confusion or a dream about the group. Nonverbal communications are always present to inform the alert observer about what is going on unconsciously as well as consciously in each individual as well as in the group as a whole. He can learn ways to ask questions about his tentative interpretations of such nonverbal phenomena, *e.g.* "Joe, you seem to have a lot going on in you right now. Could you share it with us?" This broad nonjudgmental, nonaccusatory question indicates awareness and interest in Joe. It implies he has something of value worth sharing which we can respect and attend to and which may be of significance to us. It also brings him from peripheral to more central involvement with his group. It helps him to sense that he, as a whole human being — psychologically, emotionally and physically — is received, just as he is, by the therapist. As Rogers puts it, the optimum situation is one in which the patient becomes aware implicitly that he is being understood empathetically as well as accepted. It is important that the patient experience this in order to feel a sense of safety and belonging and increasing capacity to trust in sharing what really goes on in him.

Ross and his associates emphasize that in the initial phase the individuals are finding a modus operandi in which learning about interpersonal reactions is facilitated by the group, rather than by one-to-one relationships with the leader or in other pairs. In this phase the leader may bring excessive dependency on himself into the open, thus reducing it and helping group members to find and respect the hidden resources in themselves. The leader may suddenly become aware he has been trapped into a one-to-one relationship with a group member who is addressing himself or herself visually and verbally only to him, seeking understanding, approval and help or advice. The therapist may then ask the group how they feel about being ignored, or he may deal with the situation nonverbally by turning his head and looking elsewhere until a change is brought about. He thus stimulates an increasing respect for the group as a whole — a significant microcosm of society with less rigid superego concepts than the patient had previously found in his family and other groups. He may then help mobilize the group's attention and efforts toward expressing its feelings toward monopolizers, help-rejecting complainers and injustice collectors and guide them toward finding ways of dealing constructively with such patients. He may open the road for increasing acceptance of such aspects of the human condition as pain, despair, failure, imperfection, weakness, helplessness, and finally even for trusting, helping, belonging and loving.

The therapist may actively elicit and point out evidence that amongst group members over-reactions and their oftentimes tragic interpersonal consequences are based on transference and over-identification. He may help members to feel the group as a family at times, a family more accepting, less judgmental, more aware and less likely to let him get away with irresponsibility toward self or others than his primary family.

It is suggested that the leader's activity be optimum between the Scylla of omnipotent domination and the Charybdis of passive frustration of all need for guidance. If the leader is too passive and non-directive initially, the frustration of dependency needs frequently leads to drop-outs or to too early emergence of one or more auxiliary leaders who are at times of paranoid or destructive bent and who may be followed in a non-therapeutic direction. I believe it is a mistake for therapists leading groups of psychotic or mentally retarded patients to pursue a non-directive passive role. It is an important leadership function to clarify for the group members the process of assuming responsibility for one's feelings and actions without self-blame and guilt; for the naturalness of being angry with parents as well as loving them, especially for psychotic patients whose schizophrenogenic backgrounds and double-binding parents have contributed to their being what they now are; to help patients understand that there is a value and a need for their symptoms, whether their symptoms be an expression of health and/or sickness.

Direct confrontation of the value to the patient of his delusional and hallucinatory productions can result in his developing insight and being able to give them up sooner than has been realized heretofore. O'Hearne views delusions as resulting from the emergence of primary process material due to loss of ego functioning. He believes we can help patients by working on both the level of strengthening ego functioning and directly with primary process material, although the latter "requires talents and tolerance that few of us have." O'Hearne finds it helpful for the therapist to regard the delusion as developing for the first time in the here and now of the group situation in which it is presented, and states that acute delusions often yield to a firm representation of reality by someone whose strong desire to help them is felt by the patients. O'Hearne presents an example "taken from the first five minutes of a new therapy group composed of eight male patients on a closed psychiatric ward. . . . As soon as the therapist had seated himself and looked at each one of the members and then introduced himself, one member, Alex, looked around the room, then back to the table in front of him and said, 'Well, I may as well tell you all right now, I'm the son of God.' The group members looked at him and waited. He was silent and kept his eyes down. Then all but Alex looked at the therapist."

O'Hearne goes on to state that "Some of the techniques available to the therapist follow: 1. Laissez faire. He could remain silent, look around, and wait for someone in the group to start the discussion. 2. Nonverbal communication. The therapist could look at another group member, raise an eyebrow and/or cock his head as if to ask, 'What do you think?' 3. He could note the reaction, verbal or nonverbal, of other group members, e.g., 'I notice you are frowning as Alex tells us he's the son of God.' 4. Invite the members to express their feelings about this, as: 'Do any of you have any feelings about what Alex just told us?' 5. Invite judgment. He could ask: 'Do you all agree: What do

547

you think about what just happened here?' 6. Direct attention to the process. He could quickly sum up the action, as in: 'Well, we meet as a group for the first time and Alex announces he's the son of God.' If there were no response to this, he might then ask if anyone saw any possible connection between coming to the first meeting of a new group and Alex's statement. If there were still no comment from the group, he might repeat this question to Alex; or he could ask Alex, 'I wonder what there is about coming to the first session of a new group that makes you feel like telling us that you are the son of God?' 7. Interpret the patient's feelings, e.g., 'You feel different from the rest of the group here.' 8. Question the perception, e.g. 'Do you men think he looks like the son of God?' or: 'You don't look like the pictures I've seen of the son of God.' 9. Question the reality of the belief. This can be done in several degrees of involvement with the patient. Some possibilities follow: (a) Can you people see how that would be? (b) Do you really believe that? (c) Do you honestly expect me to believe that? (d) Gee, you *are* sick. (e) Man, don't go telling things like that to people. They'll think you're crazy. (f) Please don't insult my intelligence by expecting me to believe something like that. (g) Now look, Alex, this group was formed to help its members get well enough to get out of the hospital and stay out. Do you honestly think that telling people you're the son of God will help you get well?

"There are some therapists who can establish strong relationships with a group even while using some of the latter examples. However, therapists not comfortable with such direct methods as (d, e, f, and g) above would do well to use other, perhaps less direct, techniques. In groups with some cohesiveness and some experience in working together, the first six items listed above usually suffice even when a still-believed delusion is introduced into the group. The same holds true for an actively delusional patient introduced into a group of patients convalescing from acute psychotic episodes. I am much less challenging to those chronically deluded patients who no longer doubt their delusions. In fact, if such a patient is introduced into a group which has considerable cohesiveness, I wait to see how the group members relate to him before questioning his delusion at all. To question such delusions usually results in increased anxiety.

"It seems to me that considerable benefit is to be derived from

548

helping the patient who has lost his delusion to gain some understanding of the circumstances under which this delusion developed and to see the purpose served by the delusion. In order to be effective, this understanding does not have to penetrate to the deepest layer of his unconscious. Rather, it can be done in simpler terms, as, for example: 'You felt so lonely I can see how you might like to hear some voices.' Or: 'You became afraid of the Communists about the same time that you felt that you just could not make the top grades your father demanded. Do you think it possible that you were more afraid of your own self and your father than you were of the Communists?'

"If humor fits the personality of the therapist, it is a very valuable tool to use in helping the patient recovering from delusions to gain further distance from his delusions and to integrate what he has learned from his psychosis."

The Middle Phase. In progressing toward the middle phase, the group leader may find it possible to function less verbally. A non-speaking leader or patient is not necessarily inactive. He may be communicating a great deal nonverbally which is helping to keep group interaction flowing therapeutically. The therapist may be able, through his looks and body movements, to serve as a catalyst for evoking additional reaction and interaction amongst individuals in the group as well as the group as a whole. For example, he may tap with his finger on the arm of his chair, or suddenly sigh deeply, or yawn and stretch his arms, or look bored and skeptical to indicate to those who are "tuned in" that he is feeling impatient, and thus regulate the group nonverbally. This may stimulate a group member to express his own sense of boredom or impatience with the stream of communications emanating from the person who is talking to impress rather than express or talking not to communicate but to lay a smokescreen over what is really going on.

There is never a clear demarcation between phases, as in the ongoing group process patients in the same group progress therapeutically at different rates. The extent of the middle phase differs according to the kind of therapy, its goals and its setting. In a psychiatric inpatient unit, where the stay is limited to six months or one year, this phase would be shorter in duration than in a long-term open-ended psychoanalytic group in private practice.

In the middle phase the multiple patient-to-patient, patient-to-group and patient-to-therapist transferences are intensified to the

549

point of maximum distortion, and irrational projective mechanisms are quite characteristic and overt. Patients are increasingly helpful to one another and, as a result, find their own egos and self-esteem markedly enhanced. The leader must be alert to discourage premature termination of members during this period when they are "feeling their oats."

The increasingly permissive, non-judgmental, accepting therapist in this phase activates and intensifies multidimensional transferences, promotes interaction by focusing on "what and how in the here and the now" phenomena, and undermines with and without the group's help the repetitive, compulsive, crippling distortions and over-reactions of the members and the group as a whole.

During all phases the group therapist may find it of value to intermittently give *brief* educative talks on the difference between guilt and responsibility, on the self-negating effects of absolute outdated concepts of right and wrong, on loneliness as contrasted to aloneness, on the disastrous consequences of *expecting what one only has a right to hope for,* on the value of listening to one's own inner voice in learning to make decisions based on wants instead of shoulds, on learning to accept *what is* without becoming apathetic, resigned, bitter, self-destructive, etc.

In the middle phase the leader can help to establish and maintain an atmosphere where regressive behavior can occur, be observed, identified with, analyzed and gradually given up. What is now becoming increasingly open to question and therapeutic "censure" is conventional behavior which is conpulsively fraudulent and non-conventional thoughts, feelings, free association or fantasies. Acting out is noticed, examined and increasingly understood during or immediately after its occurrence, with the group increasingly developing its own therapeutic potential and becoming less dependent on the therapist.

"Going around" is the therapist's (or member's) request for and the group's response, individual by individual, to an element in the behavior of a member, the therapist, or even, in rare instances, someone outside the group. It is quite unlimited in its frequency or scope and can be used to further the process of working through by examining behavior, fantasies, dreams, feelings for and against one another or the therapist. It is an extremely valuable technique for the leader to involve silent or peripheral members and to promote a feeling of worthwhileness in such

550

members as they learn that their contribution is really meaningful and therapeutic to others.

Another development during this phase which the leader helps to encourage or discourage is the "alternate" or "coordinate" session in which group members meet on their own at a place and time of their own making in between regular group meetings. While Kadis, Wolf, myself and others find much value in these meetings, some experienced therapists strongly oppose them on the ground that it dilutes the transference and group experience and encourages acting out. Coordinated meetings provide a climate for independent testing, exploring, and utilization of affective resources; for opening up with peers what cannot yet be revealed to the parental surrogate therapist. The risk of acting out is enhanced, but the therapist can encourage the group to join him in coordinating into the group therapeutic mainstream and working through what transpires during these extra meetings.

Interaction and working through which lead to closeness, warmth, catharsis, understanding and empathy are also promoted by (a) emphasis on immediate experience in the here and now rather than on reporting about what happened or on analysis of what transpired last week, (b) embracing of the paradoxes of life, (c) maintaining a loose unstructured informal structure, (d) the therapist's increasing participation as a real person and not just as a mirror, and (e) focusing on the "what" rather than the "why" regarding the nature of the interaction amongst the group members.

The Advanced and Terminal Phase: The therapist's continuing role in the third phase is to help group members to (1) become increasingly responsible for their lives without destructive guilt, (2) become aware of the difference between speaking and acting to express rather than to impress, (3) learn to compete to improve and not to prove, (4) give up expecting what they only have a right to hope for from self and others, (5) accept "what is" while learning that life is not automatically just or fair, (6) enjoy authentic emotional and bodly aliveness while giving up the spurious search for excitements to cover up inner deadness and emptiness which has previously plagued them, and (7) give up emotional illiteracy as they learn to own and "coagulate" their feelings, wants and wishes, instead of denying them.

Group members move toward termination as individuals in an open-ended analytic group and not as a group because some

551

progress more rapidly than others. Goals for termination must be individualized for each patient. Over-reactions in new healthier directions, especially excessive emerging aggressivity, must be spotted by the therapist and pointed out to be what they are. The leader must help clarify that the giving up of neurotic controls is to pave the way for healthy self-discipline and control and not for recklessness, *e.g.* to help patients learn the meaning of freedom with responsibility rather than with license.

It is up to the leader to evaluate and attest to a patient's improvement so that termination can be considered. He must disabuse patients of the notion of "graduating" if he believes growth goes on through life. The advanced patient will show less tendency to severe transference involvements; a greater capacity for mutuality and objectivity even with those who irrationally attack him because of their transferential distortions; increasing signs of capacity for self-direction, and independence without compulsive rebellion against authorities; increasing perception of his own and others' psychodynamics and communication processes; the strength to maintain a minority position while granting others the right to see things from their point of view; a marked decrease in egocentricity and compulsiveness and an increase in healthy feelings and consideration for others as well as self; a recognition and acceptance of the differences in people and their perceptions of life's experiences based on their differing points of view, as well as the paradoxes in life itself; a greater capacity to enjoy life and to express warmth, tenderness and love, as well as to receive such expressions without embarrassment, denial or feelings of unworthiness.

A good test to a member's readiness for discharge is to have the proposal evaluated by each member of the group. As the group reviews their peer member's progress, the extent of therapeutic gain is clarified and residual psychopathology pin-pointed. The leader may sum up their opinions and add his own, leading to the member settling back for a few more months of solid work with a significant sense of direction and accomplishment. Such a period is often allowed by another group evaluation and this time termination with congratulations as well as poignant sadness at the leavetaking of a close friend. There is a feeling such as occurs in crew-members who disband and say farewell after a series of stormy sea crises or naval battles.

C. *Recognition and Utilization of Nonverbal Communications*

The group psychotherapist is confronted at all times with non-verbalized expressions and communications of group morale, spirit, cohesiveness or divisiveness; of resistance of one or more members or the group as a whole to one or more other members, the therapist or the group as a whole; of transferential and countertransferential reactions to individuals or the group; of acting out; of attitudes of hostility, affection, prejudice, detachment, resignation, hopefulness, hopelessness, despair, helpfulness, etc.; of growth and new constructive behavior; of physical illness or health; of self images and many other aspects of the human condition.

To the degree the therapist's role includes a marked interest in recognizing and utilizing such nonverbal expressions and communications by bringing them into awareness or asking about them, the group members will learn to respect their importance too. This will bring about a decrease in verbiage used so often to conceal rather than to reveal the truth. The therapist too is revealed through his nonverbal communications, and he must be adequate enough to acknowledge authentically at appropriate times what he is told about himself if he knows it to be true. He is thus a prime agent in helping patients to know and own their identity as they try to validate their feelings, impressions and reactions in the group.

Neophyte psychotherapists are often afraid to comment on what is overtly being communicated nonverbally. Their concern that it may lead to disastrous consequences has been found to have little foundation in fact. The increasing experience of phenomenological therapists who dilute direct confrontation with tincture of tact and uncommonly good common sense and timing reveals that such confrontation constructively moves the therapeutic process directly into the "heart of the matter." It reduces the emotionally and financially costly "analyses interminable" in which patients know intellectually and with insight "all" about themselves and others but retain their crippling neurotic way of life.

As Kelman has so well pointed out, it has become axiomatic in psychotherapy that dreams reveal truthfully, artistically, precisely, concisely and economically what is going on in a person.

553

The therapist who approaches nonverbal communications with a similar belief will be well rewarded. Because he is present at the moment a nonverbal communication occurs and is therefore not only an observer but a participant, he can bring his own intuitive and experiential processes into the moment to expose it, clarify it and attempt to understand its meaning.

The therapist's and patient's awareness and increased utilization of nonverbal communication processes can help to cut through the familiar body-mind split and enable people to use and enjoy more of their total selves.

Birdwhistell and Scheflen's work points out that non-lexical, kinesic presentations serve not primarily to offer information but to establish, maintain and regulate relationships.

D. *Crises and Emergencies*

Crises and emergencies occur during the course of intensive analytic group psychotherapy as they do in life. The therapist needs to learn to differentiate between crises and emergencies, to recognize the signs of their development, and when to attempt to prevent them and when to bend with them and ride out the storm. He has to accept that his work is replete with risks. If the therapist cannot stand anxiety, then how can he help his patients live with it and grow through it? The values and sensitivity of the therapist and his knowledge of what helps people resolve their neuroses and become freer to grow stem from his life experiences, emotional maturity and from his theoretical and clinical training, and help him to determine which experiences are likely to be more constructive and which more destructive, and if, how and when he should intervene.

The therapist must learn the difference between therapeutic intervention and non-therapeutic interference. While some non-directive non-authoritative therapists refuse to show any active interest or support for fear this will be interfering, other therapists whose compulsive neurotic need to be "a helper" is unresolved may interfere too often because of their own low tolerance for anxiety or because they do not comprehend the significance and function of crises and emergencies in the growth process.

Crises and emergencies stimulate group binding and identification during psychotherapy and reduce isolation, pseudo-independence, prejudice and arrogance. The group therapist can help all the group members by bringing this out into the open and pointing out that awareness of an increasing capacity to survive pain and stress leads to a greater sense of self-adequacy and identity. A group therapist must prepare for medical psychiatric, intra-group or extra-group social crises and emergencies amongst his group patients. In general, I believe that patients with physical disorders of such a severe nature and degree (*e.g.* severe hypertension, gastric ulcer, prior coronary episodes, etc.) that we admit them to a psychotherapeutic group with reservations, should be in a group conducted by a medical therapist. In such situations it is advisable to inform the patient that his admission to the group is on a trial basis.

He must come to recognize "crisis-creators", *e.g.* those patients who stimulate emergency interest in themselves or others when they feel detached or depressed or who use crises to control and manipulate. They make dramatic last-minute presentations, and if the therapist and group reveal "real" interest and stay over-time, they temporarily come alive and feel some self-worth.

It is in the prevention of suicide that the group psychotherapist must assert his leadership role and accept that there is a time for analyzing, a time for experiencing, and a time for being more open, active and directive, and, most importantly, a time for functioning as a human being who is interested in and cares for another human being. At such times technique has to become secondary to humanity in the practice of the art as well as science of group psychotherapy. The prevention of suicide calls for reaching out to the patient who feels so isolated, alone, helpless and pained that he is considering suicide in order to kill off such feelings in himself. The key to dealing with threats to the integrity and continuity of the individual patients in the group and the group itself lies in communication. Shaskan, in his paper on panic, stated that it is axiomatic that anything like panic which threatens the existence of the vehicle of treatment, the group, should be avoided or dealt with as early and as effectively as possible so as to preserve the group structure. He states, "The three principles of panic prevention are 1) organization, 2) discipline and 3) morale; . . . communication is the means by which the structure of the group is related to its function."

Some situations which may provoke expected or unexpected crises and possibly emergencies are: (a) The admission of a new group member who stirs up stormy sibling arrival reactions. (b) The patient who door slams his stormy way out of the meeting room in anger or fear of for any other threatening reason. Leadership is called for, whether to encourage a peer group member to go after the person who has left or for the therapist to go if the group is still in its first phase or, if the group is in its second or third phase and is a cohesive more self-governing group, to sit with "masterful inactivity" while the group is trusted to mobilize its human resources and resolve the crisis. (c) The group member who goes into a homosexual panic. (d) The sexual acting-out which can occur in a mixed group. Frequently it is the attitude of the therapist which determines whether the situation becomes a crisis or emergency or not.

Generally, when a crisis or emergency occurs, the entire group focuses its active attention on the reality nature of the experience while evaluating whether it is occurring on an acting-out or transferential basis. If the members of a group do not move in with all their constructive energies and concern when crises occur, then individual group members may in fact become disillusioned. They may react intensely to the lack of interest evidenced by their peer group members. It is up to the therapist to lead the attention of the group to this so that together they can now look into the question of their lack of interest in others and the pervasive egocentricity of each group member.

E. The Therapist's Use of Self

The therapist's use of self is becoming of increasing interest and concern to students of the group psychotherapeutic process and others who are attempting to clarify what is curative. Most important in the therapist's increasing freedom to be and reveal more of himself is the admonition that he attempt to be as aware as possible of his own countertransference reactions, to work them through and not to burden patients with his own problems. However, it is, at times, very helpful for the therapist to share a real-life problem and to afford a model for identification through his capacity to come through such a problem period constructively.

Initially, patients want the therapist to be all-knowing, all-seeing and the purveyor of advice and direction which, without their having to change and give up their neurotic patterns, will magically lead them to a painless, happy and easy way of life in return for their confessing of their sins, their faults, their shortcomings and their secret dreams and aspirations. They give up this illusion slowly and with much reluctance and resistance as they learn to accept their own role in their own destiny. They learn to appreciate and emulate the therapist's capacity to identify and empathize with others without losing his own identity by over-identifying; his capacity to be warm, objective, analytical and non-judgmental, but not coldly clinical; his capacity to differ without being argumentative; his capacity to accept responsibility for his behavior without the kind of guilt which paralyzes and punishes self for human imperfection.

Each therapist can motivate patients through use of himself by (a) his affective and intellectual honesty and (b) his capacity for spontaneous unedited experiencing, creating and sharing of his free association. As the therapist can risk being himself, he provides a model for patients to incorporate so that they can now risk being real too.

In the middle or later phases, the therapist may sit back more often with an attitude of "masterful inactivity" similar to that of a good obstetrician who is not constantly rushing in with forceps. When the group members, individually or collectively, express their dissatisfaction and anger with him for not dealing with superficial monopolizers, reporters, help-rejecting complainers, repetitive crisis creators and other obstructionists, he can point out their continuing dependence on him and the value of their dealing directly with such interpersonal group problems. The therapist can remark in a provocative manner, "When I'm itchy I scratch myself. I wonder how come you still want me to scratch your itch?"

The studies of Whitehorn and Betz have pointed up and validated how different therapists had markedly different rates of success with similar patients. They indicated that the therapist who was more actively involved with his patients, sharing his enthusiasms, hope and expectations, achieved greater psychotherapeutic success than the therapist who was more mechanical, more inhibited, passive and deferential.

F. *Acting Out*

The therapist must help clarify the difference between acting out which refers to the compulsive repetition of early behavior patterns due to unresolved transference phenomena and new acting or behavior which the patient becomes free to risk during his group experience. For a group psychotherapist, acting out is not always *"persona non grata."* While acting out may at times be in the service of resistance, it does make available for working through that which has not previously been exposed in its raw state. If acting out is forbidden, it goes underground and becomes expressed in even more secretive patterns.

There is a realistic basis for concern about sexual acting out amongst members of a heterogeneous group. Whether such acting out leads to a crisis or emergency and then to a destructive dropout or premature termination, or whether it becomes part of the mainstream of therapy for the individuals directly involved and the other members too, depends primarily on the conscious and unconscious attitudes of the therapist.

To prevent an epidemic of acting out, it is of value for the therapist to remind the group at times of their obligation to verbalize, rather than act out, as frequently as possible what is thought, felt and experienced by each in relation to himself and the other group members including the therapist, particularly feelings of sexuality and rage.

G. *Resistance*

In some training and treatment centers, not only patients are *assigned* to group therapy and therefore resistive, but therapists in training are also *assigned* to do group psychotherapy. Some therapists in training not only do not believe in the merit of group psychotherapy as a first-class treatment modality, but have not had enough experience to even have confidence in the merit of individual psychotherapy. The unfortunate patients assigned to a group with such a therapist have not only their own resistance to contend with but also that of the therapist!

A therapist who is driven neurotically to be liked by everyone may resist leading the group's attention toward an unpopular subject, such as the hostility of one or more group members toward himself. His own resistance to moving into anxiety areas holds the group back and requires resolution through his involvement in supervision and in personal psychotherapeutic experience.

A therapist whose professional background has inculcated into him the concept that he must alleviate pain and suffering as soon as possible may be driven to shorten the immersion in pain, anxiety, conflict and other unpleasant experiencings which help boys become men and girls become women. He thus serves as a resistive force to the growth of each patient's real-self fulfillment. If a therapist has a compulsive urge to cure as a reflection of his therapeutic omnipotence, his pressure may lead the patient to feel coerced. The patient's over-reactions to coercion by authorities are stimulated and he may now move toward additional overt and covert attempts to maintain his neurotic status quo — to not be "pushed around" by the authorities as he believes he has been all his life. The patient may block and his counter-reactions may lead to even greater anxiety in the therapist who may then push harder and thus perpetuate the cycle of resistance and increase confusion as to what is going on. The therapist's resistance to the tides and currents of the patient's nature and therapeutic pace may help bring about a therapeutic impasse and possibly a failure in psychotherapy.

Freud's dictum to analyze the resistances and Horney's to undermine the blockages are the *sine qua non* for success in individual and group psychotherapy. Resistances and blockages are chameleon-like in character, assuming a new color and format as the seasons change in the course of the psychotherapeutic experience. Resistance can express itself through action or inaction, silence or words, feeling or non-feeling, overtly or covertly. The resistance of the therapist, individual patients and the group itself may occur simultaneously, consecutively or intermittently. Each may influence the development of the other. Those therapists whose personalities are marked by detachment, self-effacement, excessive fear of commitment, intense feelings and intense emotional involvement with others, are more likely to resist entering into or promoting in any way the values or the practice of group psychotherapy.

The resistance of the group as a whole or of the majority of members of the group may manifest itself in such different ways as: (a) prolonged and/or frequent silences, (b) a high rate of absenteeism, (c) tardiness, (d) tea party discussions about events and things outside the group, (e) nonpayment of fees amongst a high proportion of group members, (f) a decrease in the group's interactional patterns, (g) the non-presentation of dreams or fantasies for many meetings, etc.

559

Conclusion

The group is a laboratory of life for being and becoming in which each patient can be helped to move toward a clearer definition of himself, his potentials and his road toward self-fulfillment while contributing in the same vein to others.

It is imperative that the group leader be aware of his multiple responsibilities and attempt to fulfill them: (a) in helping the group to learn the nature of working together psychotherapeutically; (b) to be willing to take a position when it comes to prevention and utilization of crises and emergencies as well as acting out, to protect those individuals who are likely to become scapegoat victims or likely to be brainwashed by a group majority in its acting against the interests of an individual group member; (c) in being the prime mover toward bringing out the inarticulate, the inhibited and the withdrawn until other group members take over this responsibility as helpers; (d) in eliciting the latent, subliminal and unconscious into awareness whenever he believes it will be of value; and (e) to expand and clarify verbal and non-verbal communication processes which serve not only to inform but to establish, maintain and regulate relationships.

The function of a group leader in all its complex nuances can best be learned not by listening to lectures or reading the works of others, but rather by going through the experience. The personality of each group psychotherapist is unique. Therefore, there cannot be one way for all group psychotherapeutic practitioners to function. Unquestionably the most successful therapy is accomplished by those who can successfully integrate their capacities to function as leader and as participant appropriately. As Wolf stated it, "he must have adequate training, intuitive insight, a capacity for empathy . . ." "He must be strong enough to acknowledge his errors and secure enough to relinquish his leadership to the group or to a patient as the situation of the moment demands. It is distinctly no position for a practitioner who would evade the interpersonal give-and-take that is the very basis of group analysis. He must not approach the group with the missionary's urge to convert, with the supercilious spirit of the benevolent patron, or the oppressive dictatorship of the pedagogue. He cannot be pretentious, and any suggestion of pomposity will get short shrift from the group members, for he is a leader who at the same time must sit among his patients as an equal."

LE TRAVAIL EN GROUPE ET LA FORMATION PSYCHOLOGIQUE

par R. Canestrari et G. Minguzzi

Le problème de la préparation psychologique du médecin est aujourd'hui particulièrement urgent. Beaucoup de statistiques concordent que le 40% environ des patients ont des troubles émotifs, tandis que, d'autre part, sont connues les implications psychologiques d'une longue assistance thérapeutique aux malades chroniques. Les médecins, en constatant quotidiennement ces problèmes émotifs dans leur clients, ont pris conscience du besoin d'une formation psychologie sociale a demontré dépuis longtemps que l'utilité du traditionel n'est pas suffisant à satisfaire ce besoin, car il ne s'agit pas d'apprendre de nouvelles notions ou à développer l'esprit analytique, mais surtout d'apprendre à modeler son comportement, a mieux exploiter ses tendances en fonction des attitudes de celui que l'on a devant soi en tant que patient. Il s'agit donc de trouver une méthode qui puisse, plus qu'informer, former. La psychologie sociale a demontré dépuis longtemps l'utilité du travail en groupe comme méthode de formation, par exemple des cadres industriels.

Nous avons essayé d'appliquer cette technique pour la formation psychologique de jeunes diplomés en médecine: ils se réunissent une fois par sémaine en groupe de 6 à 8, sous la "direction" d'un psychologue, avec le but de discuter et analyser les cas par eux mêmes traités. Tous ceux qui ont fait de la formation connaissent les difficultés rencontrées par les moniteurs pour obtenir une atmosphère de vrai travail en groupe et non pas de "classe". Au début en effet on vient à la réunion non pas pour discuter mais pour avoir des conseils, tout en craignant les critiques des collègues et celles du "maître."

Il s'agit donc de réussir à transformer complètement l'atmosphère: d'un cours en faire une discussion. Si l'on veut aider le médecin à être plus sensible à ce qui se passe (consciemment ou inconsciemment) dans le patient, et dans soi — même, il faut qu'il arrive à exprimer, à rendre avec des mots, tout ce qu'il ressent chaque fois qu'il prend contact avec le patient. Or, l'exprimer son état d'esprit est en soi une chose difficile; plus difficile encore dans le rapport élève-enseignant. On peut espérer de surmonter, au moins en partie, cette difficulté en commençant par faire réfléchir les membres du groupe sur leurs attitudes dans le groupe même, en face d'un cas exposé par l'un d'entre eux.

Dans cette première phase on rencontre certains comportements caractéristiques (agressivité, trop grande confiance en soi, peur des critiques, etc.). Mais du comportement dans le groupe, l'analyse et la discussion doivent se déplacer bientôt au comportement en face du client. C'est le pas le plus difficile, qui exige une certaine familiarité entre les membres du groupe et le moniteur. Mais c'est justement à ce moment là que l'élève découvre des comportements qu'il n'avait jamais soupçonnés: le paternalisme, la peur des responsabilités, le commercialisme, etc. La decouverte de ces attitudes ne se fait pas sans crises, mais ces crises mêmes, une fois surmontées, peuvent devenir l'objet d'une discussion qui arrive à toucher les motivations profondes du comportement. Il est indéniable que, à travers cette technique ici à peine délinée, on arrive à une maturité affective complètement inconcévable dans un systême d'enseignement traditionel.

On dit que le travail en groupe met en cause l'autorité de l'enseignant puisque les "certitudes" sont discutées. En effet le "professeur" ne sorte pas indemne d'une expérience pareille: il n'est plus idealisé et admiré par le jeune médecin, comme le seul dépositaire de la science et de l'expérience.

Mais nous ne trouvons aucune raison de le regretter: au contraire, il nous semble que cela contribue à une plus grande maturité psychologique du futur practicien: il ne se sentira pas isolé, loin des milieux universitaires seules dépositaires de la science. Il verra au contraire les limitations de l'une et de l'autre situations, à savoir, il aura pris conscience de la réalité.

GROUP DYNAMICS IN A SUPERVISORY GROUP OF STUDENTS LEARNING PSYCHOTHERAPY

by H. H. Wolff

Theoretically, one could define two alternative aims of the supervisory group. The first would be to concentrate entirely on discussing the students' reports of the material produced by their patients and to help them to get a clearer view of the patients' problems and how to handle them. Such an approach would be largely didactic. The alternative is to concentrate on the students' reactions to their patients, and on their own anxieties and conflicts — stirred up as the result of their involvement with their patients. Supervisors differ in their emphasis, but in practice I have found it possible to combine both aims. The overt material discussed has usually been the material presented to the students by their patients, but by emphasizing throughout the emotional reactions between the student-therapist and his patient, transference and counter-transference phenomena soon become important topics of group discussion. No specific attempt was made to do psychotherapy on the individual students in the group or to make them speak in detail about their own problems or personality conflicts, but occasionally this happened spontaneously. The degree to which a student availed himself of this opportunity in the group was left entirely to him. This happens more often when students or postgraduate psychiatrists are being supervised individually. Frequently, however, problems that arose in the group were relevant to several of the student members individually, as well as to their patients. By making group interpretations, the supervisor could simultaneously give the students insight into their own problems and into those of their patients, thus combining both therapeutic and didactic aims. As supervisor, I find it essential to avoid assuming the role of the authoritarian teacher, and instead to maintain throughout a permissive, non-authoritarian attitude similar to that of the group-leader in a therapeutic group. This makes it easier for the students to speak without reserve. By identifying themselves with the supervisor, they learn to confront their patients in a similar tolerant and non-authoritarian manner.

TRAINING GROUP THERAPISTS: A REVIEW OF NINE YEARS' EXPERIENCE

by Eduardo Luis Cortesao

The needed improvements in training the author wishes to stress are mainly concerned with:

1. The utilization of the various University degrees, as for instance, the extension of medical and psychiatric qualifications.
2. The characteristics of personal (didactic) group-analytic training.
3. The supervision of trainees and qualified group-analysts themselves.
4. The post-graduate courses for group-analytic trainees.
5. The need for a "dialogue" with specialists using different theoretical orientations, trying to find a common denominator where encounter is feasible, and characterizing "variables" which apparently or really isolate them.
6. The need for an international organization of group therapists, probably with Sections constituted of professionals with well-established fields of action, common training, etc.

ZUM PROBLEM DER AUSBILDUNG VON GRUPPENPSYCHOTHERAPEUTEN

von Werner W. Kemper

I

Das Problem des sachgerechten Ausbildung in Gruppenpsychotherapie anzuschneiden ist eine ebenso delikate wie undankbare Aufgabe. Gilt es doch den rechten Ausgleich zu finden zwischen der Notwendigkeit einer gründlichen systematischen Ausbildung einerseits und den Verwirklichungsmöglichkeiten jeweils vordringlicher Erfordernisse andererseits. Zudem sind wir Guppentherapeuten uns bis heute nicht einmal darüber einig, wie weit oder eng das, was mit Recht Gruppenpsychotherapie genannt werden darf, zu umgrenzen ist. Diese Ungewissheit macht sich natürlich beim Aufstellen von Ausbildungsrichtlinien oder gar eines konkreten Ausbildungsplaneshöchst unangenehm bemerkbar. Noch bedenklicher wirkt sich ein weiteres, ein affektives Moment aus: die Tatsache, dass unsere wissenschaftlichen Auffassungen weit mehr, als wir uns klar sind, auch aus irrationalen Quellen gespeist werden und so vielfach zu blind verfochtenen Überzeugungsgewissheiten geworden sind, deren ideologischer Charakter — weniger freundlich ausgedrückt: deren Natur als Vorurteile — uns nicht bewusst ist.

Dies wurde mir mit meiner Übersiedlung von Berlin nach Rio de Janeiro besonders deutlich vor Augen geführt. In Südamerika, wo ich nun seit 15 Jahren in Rio de Janeiro als psychoanalytischer Lehrer der Freud'schen Schule tätig bin, zugleich aber die dortige Gesellschaft für analytische Gruppenpsychotherapie ins Leben gerufen habe, ist das mit der Gruppentherapie verknüpfte Gedankengut auf besonders fruchtbaren Boden gefallen. Ist doch ein lebhaftes Gruppenleben für den Südamerikaner von Kindesbeinen an die gewohnte Existenzform. Ich weiss nicht, wieweit Ihnen bekannt ist, dass es in Südamerika im Gegensatz zu fast allen Ländern gerade Psychoanalytiker, und zwar die der Freud'schen Gruppe sind, die die Gruppentherapie ins Leben gerufen haben und sie auch heute noch tragen.

Von diesen Erfahrungen möchte ich ausgehen, wobei ich zu berücksichtigen habe, dass sich die den dortigen Formen des sozialen Lebens angepasste und von lokalen Eigenheiten gefärbte *Praxis der Gruppentherapie* nicht uneingeschränkt in andersartige Verhältnisse übertragen lässt. In den *theoretischen Grundauffassungen* sollten die für die Gruppentherapie in aller Welt Verantwortlichen, die sich durch grosse, gemeinsam verfolgte Ziele verbunden fühlen, jedoch nach möglichst weitgehender Übereinstimmung bei Vermeidung von Einseitigkeit streben. Die gleich zu erörternden welt-weiten, für die Zukunft bedeutsamen Aufgaben, denen die Gruppentherapie verpflichtet ist, erfordern zielgerichtete Zusammenarbeit umfassend ausgebildeer Kräfte, die nur durch international verbindliche Ausbildungsrichtlinen gewährleistet wird.

Ein an ähnlichen Aufgaben schon erprobtes Modell existiert bereits: die Ausbildungsbestimmungen der Internationalen Psychoanalytischen Vereinigung. Wenn ich die in langen Jahren mit ihnen gewonnenen Erfahrungen auswerten und sie im folgenden zur Grundlage eines vorläufigen Entwurfs von Ausbildungsbestimmungen für Gruppenpsychotherapeuten machen werde, so handle ich zugleich im Sinne des — zugestandenermassen — bei mir vorliegenden wissenschaftlichen "Vorurteils", das nämlich die psychoanalytische Vertiefung jedweder Art von Psychiatrie, die sich unaufhaltsam in der ganzen Welt vollzieht, auch in der Gruppenpsychotherapie ihren Fortgang nimmt erfolgen muss.

Lassen Sie mich jedoch zunächst mit einem anderen Vorurteil aufräumen, das ich gewiss bei dem einen oder anderen von Ihnen durch meine Erklärung mobilisiert haben werde: die stillschweigende Annahme, dass alles, was mit Psychoanalyse zu tun habe, Privileg einer kleinen Zahl bevorzugter Einzelner sei und damit doch genau im Gegensatz zur Gruppentherapie stehe. Ich hoffe, Sie schon bald davon überzeugen zu können, dass gerade die mir besonders am Herzen liegende grosse Aufgabe einer die Massen erfassenden psychischen Hygiene am besten mittels einer *analytisch orientierten* Gruppentherapie anzugehen ist, eine Aufgabe, die ich für so dringlich und wichtig halte, dass sie unbedingt und von vornherein im Rahmen unserer Planung für die Ausbildung berücksichtigt werden sollte.

II

Alle bisherigen Ausführungen erfolgten um zu gewährleisten, dass unser eigentliches Thema, die Ausbildung in Gruppenpsychotherapie, von vornherein in der richtigen Weise angepackt werde. Es zeigte sich, dass es nicht nur um den Erwerb theoretischer Kenntnisse und praktisch-technischer Fertigkeiten zur Bewältigung der rein *therapeutischen* Aufgabe geht. Zugleich muss auch der *anthropologische* Aspekt im Hinblick auf die Forschungsaufgaben der Gruppentherapie im Studienplan berücksichtigt werden, und nicht minder zu beachten ist die *prophylaktische* Aufgabe, die der Gruppentherapie im Dienste einer allgemeinen seelischen Gesundheitsfürsorge zufällt.

Wie derart widerstrebende, ja z.T. gegensätzliche Dinge unter einen (Ausbildungs-) Hut bringen? Zunächst einmal hätte man zu untersuchen, ob dies noch im Rahmen *einer* für alle verbindlichen *einheitlichen Ausbildungsnorm* möglich ist, oder ob diese Vielfalt von Zielsetzungen *unterschiedliche Ausbildungskategorien* erforderlich macht. Falls ja, müssten diese abgegrenzt und sorgfältig aufeinander abgestimmt werden, gleich, ob sie nun nebeneinander als ranggleich vorgesehen werden, oder aber sich in eine Art "grosse" und "kleine" Ausbildung ausdifferenzieren, was dann wiederum die Festlegung einer gemeinsamen *Grundausbildung* erfordert. Schliesslich wäre das *Zulassungsproblem* zu klären: Welches Mindestmass an *Vorbildung* haben wir für die Zulassung zur Ausbildung in Gruppentherapie zu fordern? Falls sich verschiedenwertige Ausbildung skategorien ("grosse" und "kleine" Ausbildung) als erforderlich erweisen sollten, müssten auch die Zulassungsbedingungen entsprechend unterschiedlich sein.

Das hört sich alles einfach an. Aber schon beim ersten Punkt *(Aufgaben und Zielsetzungen)* prallen, wie schon eingangs angeführt, die gegensätzlichen Meinungen hart aufeinander. Daraus ergab sich betreffs Punkt zwei *(Ausbildungsgang)*, dass es bis heute so gut wie keine Norm, sondern nur mehr oder weniger örtliche oder schulgebundene Regelungen gibt. Und bei Punkt drei *(Zulassung zur Ausbildung in Gruppentherapie)* müssen wir obendrein noch ein heisses Eisen anpakken: die etwaige gruppentherapeutische Tätigkeit von Nichtärzten. Ohne in die Diskussion dieses heiklen Problems eintreten zu wollen, möchte ich hier nur feststellen: Die so oft gehörte, scheinbar zwingende und naheliegende Argumentierung, dass es sich um *Therapie* handele, wie ja schon die Bezeichnung "Gruppentherapie" besage, dass aber Therapie laut Gesetz in den meinsten Ländern dem Laien verboten und ausschliesslich dem Arzt vorbehalten sei, mag formal korrekt sein, geht aber am Kern des Problems durchaus vorbei. Ein Arzt, der nicht eine Sonderausbildung in Gruppenpsychotherapie durchgemacht hat, ist auf diesem Gebiet de facto mehr Laie als ein gründlich ausgebildeter Nichtarzt.

Ziehen wir nun die praktischen Folgerungen fuer unsere Ausbildungsvorschläge, und zwar zunächst betreffs.

A. *Aufgaben und Zielsetzungen*

1) Hauptanliegen der Gruppenpsychotherapie war bisher (und wird es wohl auch in Zukunft bleiben) die *Heilung von Kranken,* gleich ob die angewandte Methode rein analytisch ist oder mehr pädagogisch, suggestiv, kathartisch oder sonstwie. Gewiss sollte solche Tätigkeit im Prinzip dem für therapeutische Aufgaben speziell ausgebildeten Fachmann, dem Arzt, vorbehalten bleiben. Wo bleibt aber das Interesse der Arzteschaft für die Gruppentherapie? Und wieviele gruppentherapeutisch sachgerecht ausgebildete Arzte gibt es bis heute?

2) Anders steht es mit den *forscherischen* Aufgaben bzw. dem *anthropologischen Aspekt* der Gruppentherapie. Zweifellos erweist sich die heute uebliche naturwissenschaftliche Fachausbildung bei der Ausübung des ärztlichen Berufes als ein grosser Vorteil. Die Überlegenheit des Fachmannes ist jedoch bei allen Spezialisten unvermeidbar mit der Gefahr einer bestimmten Festgelegtheit und Einschränkung des Weltbildes verbunden. Darin ist ja die (nur anfangs überraschende) bekannte Erfahrung begründet, dass auf den verschiedensten Fachgebieten in Wissenschaft, Technik und Kunst entscheidende Anstösse zu neuen Entwicklungen vielfach von Aussenseitern erfolgt sind. Deshalb sollten wir, zumindest in begrenzter Zahl, auch begabten "Aussenseitern" aus Nachbargebieten (Soziologen, Pädagogen, Jugendpflegern, Richtern und ähnlichen Berufen) den Zugang zur Gruppentherapie nicht grundsätzlich verschliessen. Zum mindesten nicht, soweit es sich um die Forschung handelt. Vielleicht aber in besonderen Fällen auch für andere Aufgaben. Nun lässt sich aber auch hier die für solche

Forschungstätigkeit nun einmal notwendige Vertrautheit mit der Materie nicht mit bloss theoretischen Studien erwerben. Selbst erlebte Erfahrung ist auch hier unerlässlich. Diese Eigenerfahrung wird dann rückwirkend jene Nichtärzte in ihrer eigenen beruflichen Tätigkeit bereichern; dafür werden sie umgekehrt der Gruppentherapie, die sie unter einem anderen Blickwinkel ins Auge fassen, fruchtbare Anregungen geben.

3) Und schliesslich die *prophylaktische Aufgabe*: die Gruppentherapie als das spezifisch geeignete Instrument, die schon von *Freud* geforderte breite "Aufklärung der Massen" im Sinne einer allgemeinen Neurosenprophylaxe in grossem Mabstab durchzuführen. Wenn diese Arbeit auch von gruppentherapeutisch geschulten Arzten geplant und in ihren grossen Linien organisiert werden muss, so sind zu ihrer praktischen Durchführung im einzelnen doch tausend und abertausend Kräfte notwendig, weit mehr, als wir Arzte allein stellen könnten. Ohne breiteste Mithilfe von Nichtärzten (Sozialfürsorger, Lehrer etc.) ist es nicht zu schaffen. Aber auch sie können diese besondere Aufgabe nicht mit nur theoretischen Kenntnissen bewältigen. Praktische Gruppenerfahrung ist auch hier unerlässlich, wenngleich in der Regel eine "kleine" Ausbildung ausreichen dürfte.

B. *Die Eigentliche Ausbildung*

Das nun folgende Ausbildungsschema ist, wie schon gesagt, an den fast 50 Jahre erprobten, international verbindlichen Richtlinien für die Ausbildung von Psychoanalytikern orientiert. Die Erfahrung muss lehren, welche Abänderungen erforderlich sind.

1) *Didaktische gruppentherapeutische Eigenerfahrung ("Lehranalyse")*. Bekanntlich geht die Psychoanalyse von dem Grundsatz aus, dass nur das Erlebnis der eigenen Analyse den künftigen Analytiker befähige, später mit seinen Patienten sachgerecht Analysen durchführen zu können. Deshalb steht unter den drei Kernstücken der psychoanalytischen Ausbildung (Lehranalyse, theoretische Ausbildung, Kontrollanalysen) die Lehranalyse nicht nur zeitlich, sondern auch rangmässig an erster Stelle. Auch für die Ausbildung in Gruppenpsychotherapie möchte ich eine obligatorische gruppentherapeutische Eigenerfahrung für unerlässlich halten. Man kann sie nur als regelrecht eingereihtes Mitglied in

einer Gruppe erwerben, der man vom Beginn bis zum Ende angehört. Es genügt nicht, dass man als Beobachter anwesend ist, ja nicht einmal, dass man als Gruppenleiter teilnimmt. Die Zeitspanne der eigenen Gruppenerfahrung des Ausbildungskandidaten hinge von der Dauer der betreffenden Gruppe ab und dürfte bei mindestens einer Doppelstunde in der Woche (oder 2 wöchentlichen Sitzungen von je 1-1½ Stunden) im Durchschnitt 1½-2 Jahre betragen. Zu klären wäre noch, ob man Sondergruppen, die nur aus Ausbildungsanwärtern bestehen, zusammenstellen sollte, oder ob es nicht besser sein würde, die künftigen Gruppentherapeuten möglichst einzeln auf therapeutische Gruppen zu verteilen.

2) *Theoretische Ausbildung.* Um das Erleben der Gruppenanalyse nicht in seiner Spontaneität zu beeinträchtigen, sollte man mit der theoretischen Ausbildung erst ein halbes bis ein Jahr später beginnen. Sie erfolgt in Form von Vorlesungen, Seminaren und Arbeitsgruppen, die nicht nur Kenntnisse auf dem engeren Arbeitsfelde der Gruppentherapie vermitteln sollen, sondern einen so weiten Raum umspannen müssen, dass der Lernende die grossen kulturgeschichtlichen Zusammenhänge erfasst, in die die Gruppentherapie eingebettet ist. Das hiesse also, dass als Studienfächer vertreten sein müssten zunächst einmal Anthropologie, Soziologie, Psychologie, Psychosomatik, Psychotherapie (in allen ihren Formen) usw. einschliesslich Sonderthemen wie Traum, Mythos, Symbolik etc. und dann erst das Studium der eigentlichen Gruppentherapie im engeren Sinne das sich so auf diesen Grundlagen aufbauen würde. Auch hier müssten die verschiedenen Richtungen, Strömungen und Methoden sachgerecht dargestellt und gewürdigt werden, bevor der Schwerpunkt auf *die* Schule verlegt wird, der das betreffende Ausbildungsinstitut wissenschaftlich verpflichtet ist. Seminare über therapeutische Technik sollten erst später folgen.

3) *Kontrollgruppen und technische Seminare.* Hat ein Kandidat nach dem Urteil seiner Ausbilder den Reifegrad erreicht, dass er an einer Gruppe als sogenannter Beobachter teilnehmen darf und kann ihm, noch später, auch schon die Leitung einer Gruppe anvertraut werden, so sollen ihm Kontrollen und technische Seminare die Möglichkeit bieten, seine neue Tätigkeit zunächst unter Aufsicht auszüüben. Dies geschieht in der Form, dass der Kandidat seinem Kontrollausbilder von seiner neuen Tätigkeit einen detaillierten Bericht über den Verlauf einer jeden Sitzung erstattet, der Gelegenheit zu Meinungsaustausch und etwa notwendigen Ergänzungen

und Richtigstellungen gibt. Neben einer solchen *Einzel*kontrolle, die mit der nächsten Gruppe zwecks Erweiterung der Erfahrung bei einem anderen Kontrollausbilder gemacht werden kann, finden auch *kollektive* Kontrollen in Seminarform statt, in denen sich ergebende Probleme aufgezeigt und behandelt werden. Diese vorwiegend praktischen Übungen werden ergänzt durch mehr theoretische Seminare über spezielle Probleme der therapeutischen Technik.

C. *Zulassung zur Ausbildung*

Die Folgerungen für die Zulassung zur Ausbildung in Gruppentherapie ergeben sich aus unseren Ausführungen eigentlich von selbst. Im Regelfall sollte die "grosse" Ausbildung nur Arzten und Personen mit einer gleichwertigen Vorbildung offenstehen, gleich ob sie nun praktizierende Gruppentherapeuten werden wollen, oder die erworbenen Erfahrungen und Kenntnisse zur Erweiterung der Wirkungsmöglichkeiten in den eigenen Berufen oder zu wissenschaftlichen Zwecken zu verwenden gedenken.

Anderen Personen sollte die "grosse" Ausbildung nur in Ausnahmefällen, d.h., bei besonderer Begabung und Bewährung offenstehen. Genauere Angaben finden sich in meinem lateinamerikanischen offiziellen Kongressreferat, dem ein bis in alle Einzelheiten ausgearbeitetes synoptisches Schema der verschiedenen Ausbildungskategorien beigefügt ist.

Soweit unsere konkreten Vorschläge. Die korrekte Durchführung solcher Planungen setzt die Existenz von gut organisierten Institutionen voraus, seien es nun Kliniken, wissenschaftliche Institute oder Gesellschaften, die die nötige Mitgliederzahl erfahrener Gruppentherapeuten aufweisen und satzungsgemäss über die erforderliche Autorität verfügen, um die Einführung und Einhaltung verbindlicher Normen zu gewährleisten. Soweit noch nicht vorhanden, müssten diese Institutionen zunächst einmal geschaffen werden. Die einzelnen Ausbildungszentren, die sich auf die gleichen Ausbildungsrichtlinien festgelegt haben, müssten sich dann in jedem Land und Kontinent zusammenschliessen. Durch Koordinierung gleichsinniger Bemühungen werden Unverantwortlichkeit und Willkür und die daraus mancherorts erwachsenden Misstände allmählich überwunden und ausgemerzt werden.

Gestützt auf die von uns ausgearbeiteten Ausbildungsnormen,

müssten wir dann in jedem Lande Kontakt mit den für Gesetzgebung und Berufsordnung zuständigen Instanzen aufnehmen. Sonst könnten diese Instanzen sich veranlasst sehen, von sich aus regelnd einzugreifen, wobei wir Gefahr laufen, dass die dann in bester Absicht getroffenen und verwaltungstechnisch wahrscheinlich vorzüglichen Massnahmen existenzielle Belange der Gruppentherapie unberücksichtigt lassen. Deshalb: schnelles Handeln tut not!

SECTION 12: SELECTION METHODS AND SOCIOMETRIC GROUP FORMATION

ARE THERE INDIVIDUAL DIFFERENCES IN SOCIAL POTENTIAL?

by MARY L. NORTHWAY

Introduction. Sociometric status scores have shown remarkable consistency. Why should this be so? There have been many speculations. My own guess is that constancy of an individual's status may be due to inner differences of social potential. Evidence to support this contention emerged spectacularly from a study we have recently completed. I shall describe this study very briefly here and report on only one of the several findings; a detailed and complete account is in preparation for later publication.

The Study. This study was a longitudinal and *microscopic* investigation of children's sociometric relationships over a four year period. The design for it was reported in the Sociometric Journal for 1954: *"A Plan for Sociometric Studies in a Longitudinal Program of Research in Child Development."* The three criteria-three choice sociometric test (described by Northway and Weld in *Sociometric Testing: a guide for teachers)* was given each spring and fall throughout the schools of the Institute of Child Study, University of Toronto, from Junior Nursery to Grade Six. After four years, an analysis was made of the results of the eight tests in which ten children, who had started together in Kindergarten and continued with one another until Grade Three, had participated. While our interest is in the ten children who continued throughout the four years, it should be noted that at no time had these ten made up the complete classroom group.

In Kindergarten there were 21 children; in Grade One, 17; in Grade Two, 15; and in Grade Three, 15. It was, of course, on the total classroom group that the original sociometric data had been obtained.

To study the 10 permanent children, we first listed their scores obtained on the eight tests from choices made to them in the total classroom group. Secondly, we extracted the choices given and received by the ten children and re-scored the sociometric data on these. These were called the *core* group scores. Similarly, we scored these 10 on choices received from the "comers and goers," this being known as the *fringe* group scores. Therefore, there are three sets of sociometric scores for these ten children: (1) scores from the *total* group, (2) scores from the *core* group, and (3) scores from the *fringe* group.

Analysis. To ascertain the constancy of sociometric status, rank correlations between scores on each of the eight tests were obtained — 84 correlations in all: 28 between scores from the *total* group; 28 from the *core* group; and 28 from the *fringe* group.

Results. Of these 84 correlations, all but two were positive. Of the correlations between scores from the *fringe* group, four were significant at the 1% level, and four at the 5% level; that is, there were eight significant correlations.

Of the correlations between scores received from the *core* group, five were significant beyond the 1% level, and nine beyond the 5% level; that is, 14 of the 28 correlations were statistically signif-

574

icant. Of the correlations between scores received by the 10 subjects from choices made by the *total* group, 10 were significant beyond the 1% level and 13 beyond the 5% level; that is, 23 of the 28 correlations were statistically significant. The remaining five approached the 5% level.

The rank correlation between the scores on these two occasions, four years apart and with the personnel of the fringe group completely changed, is + .88.

The fact that the status of the 10 children obtained from choices in the total group shows such high consistency demonstrates that individuals maintain their particular level in a group situation, despite changes in the personnel making up the group. This I attribute to inner differences in social potential.

To examine further the consistency of status despite group changes we did two things: *First,* we compared correlations between fall-spring tests and spring-fall tests for this group of 10. The fall-spring tests are given in the same school year, during which there is no change in the composition of the classroom group. The spring-fall tests are separated by the long summer vacation, during which some children leave the group and others are registered. If sociometric status is a function of the particular group personnel, there should be lower correlations between spring-fall tests because of the separation of children from one another and also the change in the members. However, the correlations obtained on fall-spring tests and spring-fall tests were almost identical. *Second,* in the year following the completion of this four year study we examined sociometric results obtained on all classroom groups. Correlations were obtained between the children's scores in the spring in each grade and their scores the following fall in the next higher grade. The results showed that all the correlations between successive grades from Senior Nursery to Grade Six were positive and at the 2% level of significance or better; that is, from one grade to the next year by year, children's sociometric status remained highly consistent.

To verify our contention of differences in social potential, this study should undoubtedly be repeated with larger groups over longer periods of time. Our own investigation at least offers a method by which this may be done. Also, studies should be made to examine individuals' sociometric status in the various and different groups to which they belong.

575

Conclusion. If our indication of the consistency of sociometric status over four years, despite changes in the group, is supported by further studies, then we may verify the fact of real differences in individuals in their social potential. If this is verified through further research, two questions emerge: *One,* in what is social potential based? Heredity? Early parent-child relationships? Initial group experiences? *Two,* in what way are our goals in group supervision and guidance affected?

CONTROL SOCIOMETRICO ESTADISTICO
EN PSICOTERAPIA DE GRUPO

por J. L. Marti Tusquets

El desarrollo de las técnicas psicológicas en Psicoterapia de Grupo, determina que como ocurren en todas las ciencias debe plantearse el problema de la comprobación científica y experimental de los fenómenos que surgen y se producen en dicha dinámica de grupo.

Para ello consideramos que puede ser de gran valor la aplicación de métodos estadísticos y sociométricos tendientes a poner de relieve la realidad de la problemática fenomenológica y psicodinámica que se encuentra siempre latente en toda interacción que se produce en el grupo.

La metodología que hemos seguido para ello, consiste en aplicar un cuestionario de estimación sociométrica para Psicoterapia de Grupo, en dos aplicaciones separadas con un intervalo de 6 meses en la vida del grupo a estudiar.

Los datos recogidos en estas dos investigaciones sociométricas han sido estudiados estadísticamente intentando encontrar el trasfondo de la motivación original de las correspondientes elecciones entre los miembros del grupo.

Elaboración Estadística de los Datos Obtenidos en la Investigación Sociométrica

Computamos las elecciones que en cada uno de los "items" ha recibido cada uno de los individuos teniendo en cuenta para este cálculo las dos distintas aplicaciones y la suma de ambas en total.

Obtenemos así tres series de datos para cada una de las preguntas, "items," del cuestionario. Calculamos la media aritmética aproximándola al valor entero más cercano y a continuación reali-

577

zamos el estudio de las desviaciones que ofrece cada individuo con respecto a la media del grupo.

Con objeto de hallar las desviaciones standard y las correspondientes correlaciones calculamos las sumas de los cuadrados de las desviaciones anteriores.

El estudio de las correlaciones se ha desarrollado mediante la aplicación de la fórmula de Bravais-Pearson entre cada pregunta, "item," del cuestionario con cada una de las 49 restantes. De la complejidad de este estudio dará idea el que este cálculo de correlaciones ha debido efectuarse por tres veces con los distintos datos obtenidos en la 1ª aplicación, en la 2ª y en el total.

Análisis Factorial

Tomando como punto de partida los coeficientes de correlación entre todas las parejas, posibles items, pasamos al análisis factorial. Las condiciones experimentales las consideramos fijadas automáticamente en el hecho de las correlaciones obtenidas, que por sí solas nos muestran las relaciones que ligan entre sí todos los items. Y el problema lo creemos fijado en la pregunta que nos hacemos al pretender "determinar experimentalmente las unidades funcionales que operan en la conducta empírica" es decir, al pretender investigar *cuáles son los factores determinantes o motivacionales que producen las elecciones en los individuos.*

El segundo paso consiste en "averiguar cuántos factores comunes es preciso admitir para explicar los datos experimentales," e intentamos descubrir el número de factores comunes y distintos que precisamos para explicar sicológicamente el conjunto de items de que está constituído el cuestionario en el estudio empírico. Para ello factorizamos la matriz que forman el conjunto de correlaciones. El método seguido es el centroide o de Burt.

Al calcular el noveno factor centroide nos encontramos con que los valores máximos, positivos o negativos, no alcanzan a 0,3, por lo cual despreciamos ese factor noveno y nos quedamos solamente con los primeros ocho factores como significativos en la comunalidad estudiada en la presente tabla de intercorrelaciones. Los restantes serán interpretados en función de su especificidad.

La tercera fase en el desarrollo del estudio factorial, consiste en preguntarnos "cuáles son las relaciones entre estos factores y las pruebas sicológicas." Intentamos saber *qué son* estos factores.

578

Recordamos que el resultado de la factorización anterior es arbitrario, dependiendo sustantivamente del método seguido. Pero por eso, porque hay muchas soluciones correctas, el problema factorial queda indeterminado al final de la factorización. El objeto principal del análisis factorial, considerado como método de investigación en sicología, es llegar a ciertos factores interpretables sicológicamente. La interpretación de los factores se hace en función de los coeficientes que en ellos tienen los diversos tests.

Pero estos coeficientes dependen de la posición de los ejes. Como esta posición es fijada arbitrariamente en la factorización, no es razonable esperar que estos ejes representen factores significativos desde el punto de vista sicológico. (Yela.)

Para ello procedemos a la rotación de los ejes hasta una posición en la que, por razones suficientes, aparezca una posible interpretación sicológica.

Finalmente pasamos a interpretar los resultados obtenidos, a la luz de los coeficientes que cada uno de los items tenga, en cada uno de los factores estudiados.

Interpretación de los Resultados del Análisis Factorial

En el estudio anterior han quedado determinados unos factores que consideramos como motivacionales en la elección del grupo. El primero de dichos factores tiene una gran influencia por la saturación de la mayoría de los items del cuestionario de tal forma que casi es decisivo como determinante de la elección. Los restantes factores tienen una importancia mucho menor como determinantes de las decisiones de los individuos en el grupo.

SOZIOMETRISCHE GRUPPIERUNG ZWECKS SOZIOTHERAPIE UND GRUPPENLEBEN IN EINER PSYCHIATRISCHEN KRANKENHAUSABTEILUNG

von Horst Flegel und Helge Riemenschneider

Problemstellung

Welche sozial-therapeutischen Möglichkeiten zeichnen sich ab, wenn man die Kranken einer psychiatrischen Abteilung günstig gruppiert? Nach welchen Merkmalen müsste sich eine therapeutisch wirksame Gruppierung richten? Wie findet man solche Merkmale heraus? Was sind die Wirkungen einer erfolgreichen Gruppierung im einzelnen? Auf welcher Ebene des Gemeinschaftslebens sind die sozialen Gegebenheiten am leichtesten zu erkennen undzu handhaben?

Diese Fragen veranlassten eine Reihe von Untersuchungen auf einer Frauenabteilung für subchronisch und chronisch Gemütskranke im Psychiatrischen Krankenhaus Düsseldorf, Psychiatrische Klinik der Medizinischen Akademie Düsseldorf. Der Versuch wurde anlässlich der Verlegung einer ganzen Abteilung mit 66 Patientinnen in einen neuen Pavillon, als Mehrzweck-Wechselkrankenhaus strukturiert, vorgenommen und zentriert sich um zwei Verfahrensweisen.

Verfahren

Die Patientinnen hatten Kenntnis von der Verlegung und der Absicht, sie auf der neuen Station nach ihren Wünschen zu gruppieren. Man konnte daher laut Moreno erwarten, dab sie eine entsprechende *Befragungsaktion* ernst nehmen würden. Sie konnten auf Fragebögen ihre Vorlieben und Abneigungen angeben, jeweils höchstens 3, zumal vorwiegend Vierergruppen gebildet werden sollten.

Auf der neuen Abteilung wurden die Kranken weitgehend nach Massgabe ihrer Antworten gruppiert. Ergänzt wurde das Antwortenmaterial durch die Kenntnisse, die das Pflegepersonal von den interpersonellen Beziehungen und informellen Gruppenbildungen hatte.

Von den neuen Gruppen wurden Soziogramme mittels "teilnehmender Beobachtung" erstellt. Das Gruppenverhalten wurde während eines Gesprächs von 20 Minuten Dauer registriert. Dabei wurde besonders auf spontane Anrede, Aufforderung, Fragen, Antworten, Zustimmung, Ablehnung, Vorbeireden und Blickkontakt geachtet und entsprechend signiert. Subjekt und Objekt (Ausgang und Ziel) der Interaktion wurden jeweils mit erfasst.

Trotz gezielter Plazierung erwiesen sich einige Gruppen als "gestört." Ihrer "Entstörung" diente eine z w e i t e G r u p p i e - r u n g, eine Umbesetzung. Wer sich beispielsweise nach den Soziogrammen als "Randsteher" erwies, es m.a.W. allzusehr an Kontakt fehlen lieb, kam durch die Umbesetzung in eine besonders aktive Gruppe. Sehr Unbeliebte wurden notorisch Toleranten zugewiesen oder abgesondert. 4 Gruppen wurden als K o n t r o l l g r u p p e n konstant gehalten. Die Anzahl der V e r s u c h s g r u p p e n belief sich auf 9. Sie waren bei Versuchsende sämtlich umbesetzt. Es sind die veränderlichen Gruppen. Deswegen zählen sie doppelt, so dass insgesamt 18 Gruppen resultieren. Darunter sind 11 Vierergruppen, 3 Fünfergruppen, 4 Sechsergruppen. Immer handelt es sich um Tischgruppen.

Ergebnisse

Die Soziogramme vor und nach der Umbesetzung wurden miteinander verglichen. Wie sich ergab, hatte die erste Gruppierung —orientiert an den Befragungsergebnissen und den Personalerfahrungen— offenbar nicht alle Harmonisierungsmöglichkeiten erschöpft. 5 Versuchsgruppen der ersten Gruppierung enthielten insgesamt 19 *Ablehnungen.* Diese Zahl verringerte sich auf 2, nachdem das zweite Mal gruppiert worden war.

Eine weitere Abweichung zeitigte der Vergleich zwischen den Gestörten und den übrigen Versuchs-Gruppen, indem "spontane Rede" nach der "Entstörung," also nach der zweiten Gruppierung, häufiger vorgekommen war als vorher.: Die Umbesestzung von 2

Gruppen hatte bewirkt, dab sich *Spontansprechen* um 1/3 gehäuft hat (32- vorher 24). Diese Berechnung ist anders zustande gekommen als die der Ablehnungen. Die Spontaneitätszunahme wird in dem genannten Ausmab erst sichtbar, wenn man sich auf die k o n s t a n t e n Gruppenglieder der umbesetzten Gruppen beschränkt. Dann bekommt man nämlich in den Blick, welchen Einfluss der Austausch eines Gruppenglieds auf die Interaktionen der R e s t g r u p p e ausübt. So erweist sich dass man die Restgruppe durch die Neueinführung eines Gliedes an der Leerstelle des herausgezogenen a k t i v i e r e n kann. Dabei ist noch nicht berücksichtigt, was der "Neuling" seinerseits mit den Restgliedern an Kontakt aufnimmt. Das wird erst belangvoll, wenn man die umbesetzte Gruppe als neue Gesamtheit betrachtet. Dann ist der Unterschied zwischen den Versuchsgruppen vor und nach der Umbesetzung nicht so deutlich (34-vorher 29).

Die Anteile der verschiedenen K r a n k h e i t e n gliedern sich wie folgt: Schizophrene 3/5, Schwachsinnige 1/5. Der Rest entfällt auf Depressive, Epileptische und Psychoorganische. Dieses Verhältnis hat sich nicht geändert, obwohl nicht verhindert werden konnte, dass während der Untersuchungen einige Kranke entlassen und ihre Plätze neu besetzt werden mussten. Die Untersuchungen dauerten 4 Wochen, von der vorgeschalteten Befragungsaktion abgesehen. Die Diagnosenverteilung der entstörten Gruppen weicht nicht wesentlich von derjenigen der gestörten ab.

Eine kleine Verschiebung zeigt sich, wenn man die verschieden langen Zeiten des A u f e n t h a l t e s auf der Station vor und nach der "Entstörung" der Gruppen miteinander vergleicht. Durch die Umbesetzung ist der Anteil des 2.Quartals von 1/3 auf 1/7 gesunken. Wegen der kleinen absoluten Zahlen ist eine Verallgemeinerung nicht möglich. Die übrigen Aufenthaltszeiten bleiben annähernd gleich verteilt.

Diskussion

Mit den Kontrollgruppen sollten die Merkmale auf ihre Zuverlässigkeit geprüft werden. Innerhalb der Kontrollen zeigten sich bei der zweiten Registrierung keine wesentlichen Unterschiede gegenüber der ersten. Daraus darf man schliessen, dass einigermassen konstante Interaktionen erfasst worden sind; die erfassten Interaktionen repräsentieren offenbar etwas, das nicht wahllos schwankt, sondern die jeweilige Gruppe kennzeichnet.

Von den Versuchsgruppen wurden 5 durch die zweite Gruppierung, die Umbesetzung, günstig beeinflusst ("entstört"); die Interaktionen der vier restlichen Versuchsgruppen waren — ähnlich den Kontrollgruppen — verhältnismässig k o n s t a n t, o b w o h l sie — im Gegensatz zu den personell konstant gehaltenen Kontrollgruppen — u m b e s e t z t worden waren.

Die Alterszusammensetzung der "entstörten" Gruppen ist an der Gesamtheit der übrigen Versuchsgruppen gemessen, d.h. an den "gestörten" und den trotz Umbesetzung in ganzen unverändert gebliebenen Gruppen. Das sind zunächst die nachmals 'entstörten' Gruppen, bevor sie umbesetzt wurden. Hinzu kommen die Versuchsgruppen, deren Interaktionennetz trotz Umbesetzung keine wesentliche Umstrukturierung erfahren hat. Dadurch sind die maBgebenden Vergleichsgruppen zahlreicher als die "entstörten" Gruppen, deren Strukturveränderung vor dem Hintergrund der übrigen Gruppen möglichst sinnfällig hervortreten soll. Das Material enthält zu wenig "entstörte" Gruppen, um zuverlässige Verallgemeinerungen zu gestatten.

Die Verteilung der Krankheiten vor und nach der Umbesetzung interessiert im Hinblick auf die 5 Versuchsgruppen, deren Interaktionen-Struktur nach der Umbesetzung günstiger geworden war. Daraufhin durchmustert und verglichen wurden also die Strukturbilder vor und nach der Umbesetzung.

Vor der "teilnehmenden Beobachtung" waren die Kranken befragt worden. Nach dem Befragungsergebnis richtete sich die erate Gruppierung. Infolgedessen war die Ausgangskonstellation der Gruppen offenbar schon verhältnismässig günstig. Trotzdem konnten einige Grupen durch Umbesetzung anhand der ersten Soziogrammserie harmonisiert und aktiviert werden. Dieser Effekt trifft letzlich einzelne besonders Behandlungsbedürftige, um deren Therapie es dem Arzt vornehmlich zu tun ist. Mit dem soziotherapeutischen Effekt konkurriert mitunter eine arzneibedingte Besserung. Gelegentlich wird man ihr den Einflus zuschreiben müssen, den sonst der Ersatz eines unliebsamen Gruppengliedes durch ein sympathisches bzw. kontaktfreudiges ausüben mag. Die Arzneitherapie bewirkt dann so etwas wie einen f u n k t i o n e l l e n P a r t n e r a u s t a u s c h.

Was ausserhalb der Gruppengliederung für den psychiatrischen Aspekt sonst noch aus den Befragungen und Soziogrammen resultiert, soll an anderer Stelle dargelegt werden.

SOZIOMETRISCHE NUANCIERUNG THERAPEUTISCHER METHODIK BEI MANNER-UND FRAUENGRUPPEN

von A. PLOEGER

Es ergab sich im Verlaufe gruppentherapeutischer Arbeit in der Klinik bei homogenen Männer — bzw. Frauengruppen die Notwendigkeit, die Methodik im Vergleich beider in gewissen Punkten zu variieren. Diese Unterschiedlichkeiten werden notwendig aus der geschlechtsspezifischen Wesenseigentümlichkeit, welche zu einem anderen Gruppengefühl in geschlossenen Männer — bzw. Frauengruppen führt. Die Männergruppe entspricht der der "Miniaturgesellschaft" (Moreno) die Frauengruppe eher dem "Familienmuster" (W. Schindler). Hieraus resultiert auch eine unterschiedliche Stellung des Arztes: In der Männergruppe wird er als Kameradschaftlicher Helfer auf gleicher Ebene akzeptiert, in der Frauengruppe dagegen wird auf ihn häufiger ein Vaterbild projiziert, dessen vermeintliche Autoritat bei den Patientinnen Hemmungen schafft und dem Arzt eine Aussenseiterposition in der Gruppe gibt. Gefahren und Vorzüge beiden Positionen und daraus resultierendenmethodische Unterschiede werden diskutiert.

Eine je 1 1/2-jährige Tätigkeit in einer klinisch stationären Männer — und einer Frauengruppe liess aus der Sicht eines männlichen Therapeuten verschiedene Unterschiedlichkeiten in den gruppenpsychologischen Bedingungen und daraus resultierendem therapeutischen Vorgehen erkennen, die wir in der Dynamik, der Gruppenatmosphäre, den Gruppengesprächen und der Stellung des Arztes innerhalb der Gruppe aufsuchen wollen.

Bei der Dynamik ergab sich die Notwendigkeit, die *äussere*, d.h. im unmittelbaren Eindruck des Stationslebens und im Zuge des Tagesablaufs erkenntliche und die *innere* Dynamik, welche der Anderung der "inoffiziellen Struktur" entspricht, zu unterscheiden. Denn das äussere Gruppenleben wie es sich in Initiative, Spontaneität, Unternehmungslust und Aktivität beim Sport, gemeinsamen

584

Unternehmungen und den gruppenpsychotherapeutischen Sitzungen zeigte, war in der Männergruppe wesentlich lebhafter, in der Frauengruppe dagegen beharrlicher mit Neigung zu bestimmten Gewohnheiten. Umgekehrt stellte sich aber die innere Gruppendynamik beim fortlaufenden Vergleich wöchentlicher Soziogramme dar: Der Positionswechsel war hier in der Frauengruppe wesentlich häufiger und extremer als bei den Männern. Die inoffizielle Gruppenstruktur muss daher bei den Männern als vorwiegend stabil, bei den Frauen als labil bezeichnet werden. Mit anderen Worten: Die äuBere Gruppendynamik war auf der Männerseite, die innere in der Frauengruppe grösser.

Die Gruppenatmosphäre, d.h. die Art des zwischenmenschlichen Fluidums, die aus der Gesamtheit aller emotional-affektiven Regungen und vorherrschenden Stimmungsgehalte in der Gruppe resultiert und wesentlich mitbedingt wird durch das Verhältnis von Kohäsion zu Gruppenspannung, schwankte auf der Frauenseite erheblich stärker und schneller. Sie war von dem störenden Verhalten einzelner Mitglieder abhängig. Intrigen, Geheimnistuereien und latente Opposition verbanden sich des öfteren mit Untergruppenbildung. Das Gefühl der Mitverantwortung war auf einzelne Mitpatientinnen beschränkt, doch umso intensiver. Die Übertragungen waren lebhafter und wechselten schneller, die soziale Distanz war sehr unterschiedlich und änderte sich schnell. — Der Frauengruppe schien in dieser nur geringen Kohärenz ein intensiver Drang nach Strukturierung auf eine schutzgewährende, vertrauenswürdige und Autorität verkörpernde Instanz innezuwohnen. Vater —und Mutterübertragungen auf den Arzt, die Stationsschwester oder eine Patientin, die spontan die Funktion einer "Stationsmutter" übernahm, waren daher häufig. Die Frauengruppe hatte ein deutliches Bedürfnis nach solcher Ausrichtung im Sinne des F a m i l i e n m u s t e r s. Trat dieser Zustand ein, wurden die Interaktionen allgemein stimuliert, die Gruppenidentifikation wuchs, die soziale Distanz innerhalb der Gruppe nahm insgesamt ab. Gleichgültigkeit wurde durch Interessenehmen und Ablehnung durch Geschwisterrivalität ersetzt.

Dieser Tendenz zur Familienbildung lag einerseits die bei unserem Patientengut häufig stark ausgeprägte Regression und das damit verbundene Bedürfnis nach Geborgenheit und Befreiung von Verantwortung, andererseits das weibliche Streben nach mütterlich-liebender Zuwendung zugrunde, welches häufiger zum Durchbruch

585

kam. Beide Haltungen ergänzen sich gegenseitig, sodass die Frauenstation von einer Atmosphäre des Helfens und Helfenlassens durchpulst werden kann, wie sie in der Männerstation niemals aufkommen würde. Bei mangelnder Überwindung der infantilregressiven Haltung waren des in der Frauengruppe vorherrschenden Gefühls des Behütetseins wegen Entlassungsreaktionen in Form einer Verschlechterung der Symptomatik vor dem geplanten Entlassungstermin mit der Tendenz zum "In-der-Familie-bleiben-Dürfen" häufiger als in der Männerstation. Lag somit in der Frauengruppe eine grössere "Hospitalisierungsgefahr", so war andererseits in der Möglichkeit zur Entfaltung spezifisch weiblichen Wesens ein günstiger therapeutischer Vorzug gegeben.

In der Männergruppe war dagegen die Atmosphäre insgesamt ausgeglichener, die Kontakte der Mitglieder untereinander waren überwiegend sachlich bestimmt, primäre Sympathie und Antipathie traten hinter der Verbindung durch gemeinsame Interessen zurück und wurden erst durch diese konstituiert. Da dieses Interesse in der Krankenrolle im Gesundwerden liegt, gerieten Patienten, die dieses Interesse nicht teilten, weil ihr Krankheitsgewinn (z.B. eine Rente) grösser war, sehr schnell in eine Omega-Position. — Die Übertragungen waren in der Männergruppe weniger intensiv, dafür aber stetiger. Die aus ihnen resultierende Affektivität und Antriebsimpulse waren durch die beim Manne stärkere rationale Überformung der endothymen Regungen gedämpft, die Interaktionen dadurch einheitlicher verteilt. Die Atmosphäre erschien versachlicht, gegenseitige Hilfestellung aus der Einsicht zu entstammten: "Wir sitzen im gleichen Boot". Die Identifikationen mit der Gruppe waren allgemeiner als bei den Frauen und zeitweise derart intensiv, dass geradezu ein Corpsgeist entstand. Lag die Skala der Gefühlsregungen in der Frauengruppe zwischen Liebe und Hass, so hier zwischen Achtung und Verachtung. Die Gefühle für die Mitpatienten entstammten weniger der "Innerlichkeit des Erlebens" (Lersch) als einer objektivierenden Stellungnahme den Werten oder Unwerten des anderen gegenüber. Dadurch konnten Enttäuschung und Begeisterung für Mitpatienten niemals in der Heftigkeit Platz greifen, wie in der Frauenstation, wo die mütterlich-liebende bzw. geliebtwerdende Regung die vorherrschenden Gefühlsqualitäten waren. — Auch deswegen war die Männergruppe stabiler. Sie entsprach mehr einer "Miniaturgesellschaft" (Moreno). Störungen durch einzelne Gruppenmitglieder traten sehr viel weniger auf.

Schien somit die Atmosphäre der Männergruppe auf den ersten Blick eine günstige Voraussetzung zur Gruppenpsychotherapie zu sein, war dies bei näherem Hinsehen doch wiederum zweifelhaft. Sicher ist es ein Vorzug, dass der männliche Therapeut besser als in der Frauengruppe als Kamerad und partnerschaftlicher Helfer auf gleicher Ebene integriert wird. Doch war seine Einflussnahme daduch wiederum beeinträchtigt, dass in dem festen, männlichen Gruppengefüge weniger persönlicher Konflikt — und Erlebnisstoff frei wurde, um einer auf die Behandlung des Eizelnen gerichteten Psychotherapie Nahrung zu geben. Die Ausrichtung auf ein gemeinsam interessierendes Ziel, die sich häufig mit einem gewissen Leistungesehrgeiz verband, waren der therapeutischen Einflussnahm auf den Einzelnen abträglich, da sie die hierzu notwendige reflexive Haltung beeinträchtigten.

Lag also die Schwierigkeit bei der Frauengruppe in der Herstellung von Geschlossenheit, so hier in der individuellen Vertiefung therapeutischen Wirkens. — Schien die Stabilität der Männergrupe anfangs ihrer Immunität gegen äussere und innere Beeinträchtigungen wegen den Vorrang zu haben, so stand sie bei näherer Prüfung in Gefahr, zur Starrheit mit der Verpflichtung an eine Norm zu entarten, welche nichts unmittelbar Persönliches mehr gestattet.

Im Gruppengespräch spiegelten sich diese Eigentümlichkeiten auf der Männerseite in einem grösseren Verantwortungsgefühl fur den Ablauf, während die Frauen die Verantwortung hierfür dem Arzt überliessen. In der Männergruppe war das Gespräch daher meist flüssig und störungsfrei, doch konnte man sich hier häufig des Eindrucks einer unverbindlich-glatten Fassade nicht erwehren. In der Frauengruppe dagegen war es von langen Schweigepausen unterbrochen, durch flüsternde Nebengespräche einzelner Patientinnen gestört. Das Erscheinen oder Verschwinden des Arztes setzte eine Zäsur, welche auf die autoritäre Vaterübertragung der Gruppe auf ihn zurückgeführt werden musste und nur schwer zu beheben war. Die "inoffiziellen Gruppengespräche" im Zusammenleben auf der Station waren somit, da unabhängig vom Arzt, viel häufiger als bei den Männern. Das Schweigen in Anwesenheit des Arztes musste als Widerstandssymptom verstanden werden. Der Widerstand im männlichen Gruppengespräch dagegen zeigte sich in der Wahl unpersönlicher, technischer oder wissenschaftlich-abstrakter Themen.

Die Folgerungen aus dieser unterschiedlichen Bedingung in Männer — und Frauengruppen für die Stellung des Arztes sind vor allem unter dem Aspekt der Autorität zu sehen: Er steht in der Frauengruppe in der Gefahr, in eine autoritative Haltung gedrängt zu werden. Diese würde aber kindliche Angste wachrufen, welche die Entfaltung des Selbstgefühls und damit die erste Voraussetzung zu Reife und Selbstverwirklichung und zur Übernahme von Verantwortung behindern würden. Autorität im Sinne einer bindenden Einflussnahme, die von der Gruppe als einer Wertverkörperung selbst ausgeht, ist aber nicht zu umgehen und sogar zu fordern. Der Arzt hat also möglichst die ihm zugeschriebene Autorität von sich auf die Gruppe selbst zu verlagern. Er sollte nicht autoritativ-aktiv, sondern fermentativ-aktivierend wirken, da er sonst in Gefahr gerät, in die "Gegnerstellung" zur Gruppe zu geraten, aus der Psychotherapie kaum möglich ist.

In der Männergruppe besteht diese Gefahr kaum, da er in deren Corpsgeist einbezogen wird, wenn er sich dem nur stellt. Er hat hier seine Autorität vielmehr gelegentlich sogar zu unterstreichen, doch sollte dies nur immer gegenüber Einzelnen und in Vertretung der Gruppennautorität geschhen, wenn diese missachtet wurde, da sich sonst sofort eine ihn ausschliessende Front bilden würde.

SOZIOMETRISCHE UNTERSUCHUNGEN VON KRANKEN MIT ULCUS DUODENI UND ULCUS VENTRICULI

von A. Bonzi und D. Kieser

140 auslesefreie Ulcuskranke, die in den Jahren 1956 bis 1962 in den beiden Inneren Universitäts Kliniken der Berliner Charite behandelt wurden, ihre Entwicklung, Persönlichkeit, Konflikte, besonders aber ihr Sozialbereich werden geschildert.

Die Spannweite der gefundenen Persönlichkeitsformen und das hierdurch bedingte besondere Sozialverhalten werden dargestellt. Weit überwiegend neigen die Patienten nich zur Normierung von Meinungen. Das Nichtzusammenpassen der eigenen Normen mit den sozial anerkannten Normen und Wertmasstaben fuhrt zu Fehlanpassungen in den eigenen Gruppen, besonders wenn man diesen räumlich und erlebnismassig nicht ausweichen kann. Bereits von der Erkrankung fehlt den Menschen Anerkennung und Wertung in den für sie erlebnismassig intensivsten Sozialen Feldern. Sie fühlen sich vorwiegend von ihrem Sozialbereich subjektiv enttäuscht. Eine absichtliche Isolierung vom Sozialbereich wird vor der Erkrankung von den Patienten in keinem Fall vorgenommen.

Diese Angaben werden statistisch und kasuistisch belegt.

SOCIOMETRIC INVESTIGATIONS AS SELECTION PRINCIPLE IN FORMING THERAPEUTIC GROUPS AMONG HOSPITALIZED ALCOHOLICS

by C. Sacchi, A. Maddedu and E. Jannaccaro

In order to choose the subjects suitable for a group therapy, we have applied sociometric investigations to a section of hospitalized alcoholics and have been able to determine some particular characteristics of this nosological entity.

From a comparison of our results with those obtained by Melandri and Simonazzi in a Psychiatric Hospital, we have found that our group of alcoholics is the most similar to the dysthymic group, inasmuch as the attitude of participation in the group, and the tendency to social expansion and to new social ties, are common characteristics to both groups.

The proper characteristics of alcoholics are the following: dilution of leadership, generical and superficial sociability, greater number of isolated. These isolated have an extroverted attitude towards the group but are not reciprocated, and are sometimes also despised and refused by the group. The isolated persons are those who strive to be accepted by the group, whereas those who have already been accepted have a centripetal and passive attitude.

In general, the results of our investigation emphasize the tendency, in alcoholics, to refuse the "super-active" and "productive" members and to accept the subjects having a centripetal and passive attitude.

THERAPIEKONTROLLE DURCH DAS SOZIOGRAMM

von A. Bonzi und D. Kieser

Es handelt sich um eine Untersuchung an vorläufig 70 Patienten, welche in stationärer, klinischer Behandlung standen. Neben Einzelbehandlung und Gruppenpsychotherapie u.a. wurde wochentlich einmal ein Soziogramm ähnlich in der von Moreno angegebenen Form durchgefuhrt. Die Patienten wurden gebeten den ihnen am meisten und am wenigsten sympathischen der Mitpatienten zu notieren. Dabei ergaben sich bei fortlaufender Registrierung postive Korrelationen zwischen der Änderung der soziographischen Stellung im Laufe der durchschnittlich sieben Behandlungswochen mit dem Erfolg der Psychotherapie. Bei 44 von 40 Patienten zeigte sich eine vollkommene Parallelität bei 21 eine massige und bei 5 Patienten von 70 keine Übereinstimmung.

SECTION 13: GROUP PSYCHOTHERAPY WITH ALCOHOLICS AND DRUG ADDICTS

A GROUP PSYCHOTHERAPY EXPERIENCE WITH MARRIED ALCOHOLIC COUPLES

by RACHEL B. BROSS

Introduction. With all the existing theories concerning alcoholic addiction, the etiology of chronic alcoholism remains an open question. The generally accepted view of alcoholism as a disease entity still confines psychotherapy to the problem of drinking with sobriety as the ultimate goal. Those investigators who see chronic alcoholism as an attempt to adjust and adapt to difficult environmental stresses urge the evaluation of the psychopathology underlying alcoholism and strongly suggest "to treat the patient and not the symptom."

The hypothesis advanced in this paper is: as detrimental as it may be, alcoholism serves a useful purpose for the drinker; *i.e.* heavy drinking protects his healthy ego potentials from exposure to the distortions and thwartings that take place under the assault of adverse and intolerable life experiences. The fact that many alcoholics learned to drink after their formative years may very well indicate that the ego potentials do remain dormant and intact. Therefore, dealing psychotherapeutically with alcoholics, the emphasis is not to be placed on the underlying psychopathology (which nevertheless should be scrutinized and evaluated) but on the search for these healthy potentials.

In a permissive, all accepting emotional atmosphere created by a positive Dr.-Pt. relationship, sobriety is sought not as an end result of the psychotherapeutic effort but as an essential and indispensable tool for the development in the alcoholic patient of a System of Self-Values — of self-respect, self-esteem, self-confidence, and self-realization.

The review of current literature on psychotherapy in chronic alcoholism indicates a preference for group psychotherapy with married couples as compared with individual or conjoint. As reported by the investigators, the group psychotherapy sessions were conducted with the spouses in separate groups for the wives and the husbands. In our experience both were treated simultaneously in a group of married couples with similar problems. This paper is a report on the first of three groups of alcoholic couples treated in this manner during the last three years at the U.C.L.A. Research Alcoholism Clinic, each of one year duration. (The first group lasted from Nov. 1960-Nov. 1961; the second group from Nov. 1961-Nov. 1962. The third group is at present in psychotherapy.) Each session was recorded and later translated by Mrs. Doris Boyd, a volunteer social worker to whom I am expressing my gratitude for a job excellently and thoroughly done.

Screening and selection of patients. This was accomplished through: (1) the initial intake of the psychiatric social worker; (2) individual interviews with the psychiatrist; and (3) scrutiny and evaluation of obtained historical data and of the dynamic material.

Structuring the group. A psychotherapeutic group structured on democratic principles in a permissive non-threatening, yet challenging, atmosphere provides the necessary tools for dealing realistically with frustrations, dependency needs, and character defenses brought into play in day-to-day living. The presence in the group of the non-drinking spouse made the task of psycho-therapy more meaningful to the members of the group. It was their group initiated by them and conducted as they desired within certain limitations of acting-out. The patients drew support from each other. Spontaneous remissions in one drinking participant, or even a short attempt to combat drinking, would be followed by a period of sobriety of other group members.

Group composition. The group was composed of five married couples: Mr. and Mrs. J., Mr. and Mrs. L., Mr. and Mrs. R., Mr. and Mrs. D., and Dr. and Mrs. S. Mrs. S. was the alcoholic patient, sent to the clinic by court order. Dr. S., himself in the past a skid row alcoholic and drug addict, in and out of jail and mental institutions, now "dry" for the past four and a half years, brought charges against his wife, who resented the implication that she was an alcoholic. The ages ranged between 32-35; education, from the 11th grade to college graduate. One of the wives was attending psychology courses at U.C.L.A., aiming at an M.A. degree. Common to all these couples was their symbiotic attach-ment to each other. Most of the alcoholic men were passive indi-viduals, letting their wives live their lives for them, but rebelling and demanding. They all came to the clinic because the wives threatened with divorce; there was little motivation in any of them.

Psychotherapy with the married alcoholic couples. Our main goal in treating the alcoholic married couples was to help them attain a degree of emotional maturity through group participation and collective strength of ego development. The purpose of group psychotherapy for the individual patient within the group was to help the alcoholics recognize the kind of problems they were all having, to give them the tools and show them the way to deal with their problems without resorting to alcoholic oblivion. It is an accepted fact that because of drinking, the alcoholic is unable to establish satisfactory interpersonal relationships, whether with an individual or with a group, mostly due to the negative image he has created about himself.

To convince the alcoholic that drinking is not only an escape from anxiety and tension, but also an overt expression of the turmoil that unfulfilled deep-seated emotional needs stirred up within him is not an easy matter. The alcoholic refuses to see himself as a sick man, and yet the motivation for getting well

595

is most crucial for successful psychotherapy. The patient is the one to want to sacrifice some of himself in order to attain complete abstinence.

Unfortunately, most of the alcoholics came to the clinic under duress, totally unprepared to accept psychotherapy on our terms, though several of them did have psychotherapy before. The denial by the patient of the significance of imbibing, and his conviction that if he wishes to, he could stop drinking by will, were most frustrating and disheartening to the therapist.

Almost all of the alcoholics in our group abstained from liquor at the beginning, some for weeks, others for a few months. Now, they said, they proved to themselves their will power, now they would test their ability to quit after but one or two drinks, only to start the cycle all over again. It was the task of the therapist to convince the patients that their belief was false.

In the very first contact with the patient, the therapist's personality assumes a primary importance. It is the therapist who must relate to the patient and not vice versa, especially if the patient is the disillusioned, mistrusting alcoholic.

The first step in psychotherapy is the establishment of a positive Dr.-Pt. relationship; warm, interested, and understanding of the patient's problems. A sincere and direct approach on the part of the therapist furnishes the foundation for such a relationship. In our experience, the patients continued to test the therapist; will she let them down? is she worthy of their trust? will she accept them just the way they are? and without undue expectations or demands?

Anguish and low frustration tolerance leaves the alcoholic with a desperate feeling of aloneness. This initial Dr.-Pt. relationship should pace the way to group relationship and later to a change in husband-wife relationship.

Our aim was to bring about in both spouses a change in attitudes towards themselves and each other, a change in the values of living, and an effort to assume more responsibility for their uncontrolled behavior. The personality of the alcoholic is a complex one, and the unique difficulties in his personality have to be determined, his capacities and limitations continually re-evaluated; his ego strength has to be ascertained and used as a guide in the treatment.

For successful therapy, it was essential that all three, the alcoholic, his spouse, and the therapist, should coincide in their approach to the problems at hand. Here, the personality of the therapist gains its importance, when dealing with the alcoholic's character defenses, his attitudes and sentiments. To reach out, to recognize and evaluate the healthy attributes of his fragile, vulnerable, quivering ego, requires not only therapeutic skill, but the willingness of the alcoholic to be "manipulated" (not a nice word!).

A sincere desire and determination for the reconstruction of the family stability and family relationships, so rudely disrupted by his drinking, was offered to the drinker as a highly gratifying incentive. The reorganized family would provide a rightful place for the father.

The permissive, supportive, and stimulating group atmosphere was conducive to the development of the patient's Self-Value System (*i.e.* of self-esteem, self-respect, self-confidence, and self-realization). In a hopelessly discouraged alcoholic, the rekindling of self-respect and self-esteem is the first step to recovery. This was borne out in our groups. The stigma attached to the label "alcoholic" was removed with the non-judgmental, non-moralistic attitude on the part of the therapist. The label "chronic alcoholic" became a descriptive term instead of a swear word.

The role of the therapist in our group was one of an active listener and catalyst at the same time. She led and channelized the discussions, interpreting and clarifying dynamic material. Directive or non-directive, as the group interaction warranted at the moment, and at times provocative, she would involve the silent members in controversies with their spouses, stirring up feelings of hostility or compassion. The incentive of family reconstruction was constantly kept before the group. The group atmosphere allowed for reality testing. There were incidents when the therapist had to serve as a social worker, in arranging for child guidance or hospital placement for other members of the patient's family. To fulfill the function of a marriage counselor, or even referee, was not new to her. One of the most trying episodes during the period of psychotherapy was the handling of a transference relationship of Mr. D., who felt rejected by the therapist and made two suicidal attempts only to be discovered and saved in the nick of time. As peacemaker the therapist would attenuate anxiety and tension that would result from direct attacks and counter-attacks between the spouses. It goes without saying that the therapist had to be cognizant of her own countertransference reactions and of the frustrations and annoyances that the patient's repetitious lack of cooperation generated in her. She dealt with these feelings openly in the group, as she expected the patients to do.

Progress. The progress in psychotherapy within our group was judged according to: (1) The degree of resolution of marital problems; (2) The change in the patterns of drinking, amount of liquor consumed, and the length of intervals between sobriety and drinking; and (3) The broadening of family interests and the strivings for a closer and more satisfying family relationship. Group psychotherapy did prove the therapy of choice for our patients. In the group they frequently saw their problems as highly exaggerated in comparison with the tragedies revealed in the lives of other group members, and the importance of their own problems would be reduced to a minimum, allaying anxiety and tension.

The need for the group as a medium for self-expression and emotional nourishment rendered the sessions meaningful to the individual members. The patients seemed to find in the group a response to their need for "mutuality," in "belonging," to be "wanted" and "accepted". Sustained interest in the group activities was demonstrated by consistent and regular attendance (over 85%). Mr. L. and Mr. R. would make special trips from Seattle to Los Angeles so that they would not miss the group meetings. None of our alcoholic patients were especially motivated to give up drinking when first seen in the clinic. At first, some of the patients tried to use the group as a "giving mother"; Mr. D. blamed the clinic and the group for not helping him to obtain a job when his idleness stretched out for months. Yet he continued to attend the group meetings because, he said, he liked the people and enjoyed the sessions.

The problem of communication between the spouses gradually ameliorated as time went on. At first, the wives tried to monopolize the sessions, dominating, aggressive, anticipating almost a magical change in their husbands to suit their personal neurotic needs. Group interaction enabled the non-drinking spouse to become aware of her emotional needs and distortions. Together with her husband she learned to deal with her unrealistic expectations. A change was observed in the way the spouses learned to listen to each other, in their attempt to understand the meaning of what was said, instead of reading in their own feelings, thinking and forming conclusions about the other person's remarks.

598

Their defenses were considerably dented by group interaction and the therapist's interpretations of character distortions. The sensitivity about "cutting remarks" gave way to a better evaluation of their marital relationships. The group learned to regard this "reading in" as a destructive device in order to preserve one's self-righteousness and resolve, or rather to project feelings of guilt. Since guilt was experienced by all group members, it was universalized and considerably diluted, and there was no longer reason to project.

The patients learned to manage their mood changes, instead of displacing their anger upon each other. They were willing to assure their respective spouses that they had nothing to do with their isolation and pouting. Most of the time they would admit that they did not know even what they were unhappy about, but unhappiness was a sufficient reason for getting drunk. They learned what it means to speak to each other without "a chip on the shoulder" and they gradually became aware of the fact that their feelings of being hurt and bitter were carried over from the original family interrelationships. The significance of the mechanisms of inhibition, projection, repression, reaction formation, and other exaggerated mental mechanisms of defense were frequent topics of discussion that followed abreaction of feelings and reality testing. Energies freed from the "emotional strait jacket" would, at the end, be used for mobilizing anxiety and constructive psychotherapeutic work.

To the therapist these results appeared gratifying, considering the depths of the psychopathology in each and every group member. Due credit was given to the "co-therapist at home" — the non-alcoholic (in our case, the wife). The final results may appear not too spectacular, nor even too promising because of the therapist's wishful thinking, but at any rate, we did have one case of 100% improvement. This was Mr. J. When first seen, Mr. J. appeared tearful at the least provocation, dejected, depressed, like a small frightened child fearing abandonment by his mother. He quit drinking at the beginning of the therapy just to see "what it was all about," and has not resumed drinking since — two and a half years after. Also, the L.s became reconciled. Mr. L. tried to quit drinking, but he was one of those who would get over-confident and test himself time and again whether he could drink normally, only to start the vicious cycle all over again. The change was in Mrs.

L. — she found outside interests when Mr. L. was away on business trips, while before, she would stay in the house and wait for her husband's call. Her attitude towards his drinking changed for the better. Mr. and Mrs. R. could not be reached. During therapy Mr. R. became the "big brother" for the less strong members of the group. Dr. and Mrs. S. left the group after about five months of therapy. Mrs. S. relinquished her drinking, but the group began to probe into Dr. S.'s defenses, which apparently frightened him away.

A THERAPEUTIC APPROACH TO THE ALCOHOLIC AND HIS NON-ALCOHOLIC SPOUSE IN GROUP PSYCHOTHERAPY

by Howard E. Mitchell

In this project we have sought to better understand the relationship of the alcoholic husband to his most intimate interpersonal associate, his wife. Our experience has demonstrated that the relationship between the alcoholic and his family is two-way. Not only does the alcoholic and his drinking affect the behavior and attitudes of family members toward him, the community and themselves, but the family may in turn contribute to the alleviation or persistence of the alcoholism. In some instances the very existence of family ties appears to be related to recovery from alcoholism. On the one hand, some families are successful in recognizing the alcoholic's need for help and are supportive with treatment efforts. Yet other types of families may consciously or unconsciously discourage the alcoholic from seeking treatment and may actually reinforce the alcoholic behavior. These facts, as well as theoretical issues mentioned later in this paper, have led to the conclusion that the most successful treatment for alcoholism of a family member involves helping both the alcoholic and his spouse. If our primary interest is in assisting both spouses to better understand and come to some decision about the difficulties existing between them in their family life, we should simultaneously approach both marriage partners and engage them in the therapeutic effort.

In the first few years of this project we counseled the alcoholic and his spouse individually. Then we questioned whether a group counseling approach might be more advantageous. During this period we were impressed by the steady accumulation of reports concerned with treatment of alcoholics in group settings. For example, we appreciated, from the history of the A. A. movement, how many alcoholics achieve sobriety through a spiritual reawakening in the group atmosphere with fellow alcoholics. However, from the researcher's point of view, little is known of what happens intrapsychically and interpersonally in these groups to bring about such dramatic behavioral changes.

Furthermore, considering the psychological significance of excessive drinking *per se,* we know that one pathological sign that differentiates social drinking from the obsessive-compulsive drinking of the alcoholic is associated with the individual's drinking alone or in relationship with others. In spite of evidence to the contrary, once the individual begins to drink alone, we begin to suspect and label his behavior as clinically alcoholic.

We maintain that in order to more fully understand and counsel this type of troubled marriage — in which the alcoholic husband has been turbulently married to his non-alcoholic spouse for a protracted period — both need to be approached simultaneously and engaged in the therapeutic enterprise. We do not primarily treat the individual symptoms shown by the alcoholic or his partner. Instead, therapeutic energies are directed at supporting the dependent attitudes of both spouses with the alcoholic's symptoms being viewed as a barometer of his condition *vis a vis* his relationship with others. The goal is to assist both spouses to understand better and to come to some decision about the difficulties existing between them in their family life.

Our experience suggests that this goal is best achieved in group psychotherapy with such couples than in individual or joint marital counseling. The kind of alter-ego role played by other spouses often develops in the group setting of alcoholic husbands and their non-alcoholic wives and is of therapeutic value.

THE SIGNIFICANCE OF TREATMENT IN PRIVATE PRACTICE OF BOTH MARITAL PARTNERS — PARTICULARLY WHERE GROUP THERAPY OF ALCOHOLICS IS CONCERNED

by O. Martensen-Larsen

Group psychotherapy has now been employed for over eleven years in private psychiatric practice and plays a considerable part in the active treatment.

First, a short description of the present practical system: Three evening group therapy sessions are held weekly, each lasting for two hours. The number of participants is between four and seven. Both sexes are represented in each group. Patients start with two to three sessions weekly and later only one session weekly (preferably combined with weekly private interviews). As a rule, two parallel group sessions are held in separate rooms. One of the groups is first led by the author himself, and the other by a female group therapist. After approximately an hour, the therapists change places. In this manner, all of the participants obtain contact with both the male and female therapist, with the resulting possibilities for different adjustments and identifications. The two-therapist system permits the one therapist to be more provoking and activating in contrast with the method most usually employed, while the other is more "accepting". In the groups, both male and female patients suffering from different psychic conditions take part, but the object is to get their partners also to participate, as these are treated, in principle, as patients! The couples are separated and placed each in a group, possibly in parallel groups.

The wives of male alcoholics showed particular enthusiasm in the therapy. The men were always pleased that their wives participated. Only one instance can be brought to mind in which a male patient sabotaged his wife's participation (*this* particular marriage ended in divorce).

The progress made by the patients is frequently proportional to the participation of the partner. It is stressed that the aim of therapy of the marital partners is to make them realize *their own* neurotic need for a *sick* partner. Wives of male alcoholics who commenced group therapy at a later date than their husbands have frequently reported the jealousy they experienced when *he* came home filled with impressions and fortified by the group therapy. Group therapy of both partners gives the partners a *new* common interest which frequently is manifest, for example, in the subsequent private two person group at home, which may continue until far into the night. Simultaneously, they come out of the entrenched positions into which they have dug themselves, perhaps for years, and face one another directly. "The ice is broken!"

SECTION 14: GROUP PSYCHOTHERAPY
AND EXISTENTIALISM

GROUP THERAPY FROM THE EXISTENTIAL
POINT OF VIEW

by Robert Meigniez

Goals Of Perception And Of Change

By "Group-Centered Group" we refer to the meeting of a limited number of persons (say, six to fifteen) who have as their acknowledged purpose the attainment, within a certain number of sessions, *of an improved perception of their existential relation to the group.* This relation integrates what I project myself to be for others, what I *project* others *to be* for me, what I *project* myself *to be* for the group and what I *project* the group *to be* for

605

me in terms of the total situation. Needless to insist, in such a group the inter-action of these projects is necessarily involved with my own perception of the corresponding projects of others, and with that which constitutes the reality of the total situation. Also, the existential relation to the group of any one member of the group contributes, of its nature, to the make-up of all the elements of the groupal field.

Thus, it is clear that the realization of a more adequate perception of their existential relation to the group by the individual members implies *a change* in the group; that is, where the members of a group perceive more clearly their relation to the group as a whole, this group is different, *not only in knowledge but also and above all in existence,* from the group where this relation is often distorted. This means that those group processes which involve a raising to consciousness are simultaneously processes which involve change.

Therefore, being willing to accept an improvement in the perception of their existential relation to the group, the members come to see more or less implicitly that they are accepting a certain new perspective of self, and/or of others. This perspective, however, can be neutralized by an even greater resistance to change.

The Technical Function In The Group

Generally speaking, one or several technicians of the group-centered-group, whom we will call *"monitors,"* are present at all, some or part of the meetings. Their function is to help the group progress toward their objectives as defined above. Hence, they may not, while striving to have the members promote groupal and existential relations, use methods of intervention, nor procedures that are by their very nature alienating and reifying. Specifically, they may not use the argument of authority, they may not pass moral judgment on the activity and success of the group and its members, they may not propose values to be discarded and adopted, nor suggest procedures to follow. *Their task is to help the group accept the recognition of its own existential reality.* They aim, then, to recommunicate to the group the concrete picture of its total situation, at the very moment when the picture, as recommunicated, coincides with the situation of the group, i.e., the "on the spot" analysis of the monitor. This analytical function to particular elements in the situation (for example, to such and such a member

606

whose activity is being "analyzed") would tend to alienate or reify the activity of the group. It should be clearly noted that the monitors cannot intervene in the group discussions without the risk of alienating the *being* of the group which underlies the *"opinions"* of the group. *However, the monitors must invest themselves in the group at the level of their function,* i.e., at the level of their desire to see the group take possession of its proper being. They should then reveal themselves with all the affective content which is awakened in them by their situation as monitors; if not, they will tend to deepen the state of the groupal alienation.

Basic Focus on the Group Itself

All of the elements mentioned thus far appear to us to be secondary compared to the fact that *the group is basically centered on the group.* That is to say, the behavior of the group *tends* towards the following characteristics: a) the members make known to the group their feelings and perceptions *hic et nunc,* that is, as they arise, and as they concern the group situation itself; b) the members avoid focusing their attention on situations or problems extraneous to the group, or on "group process" and psychological phenomena in general, or on the individual psychology of member X or Y; c) the members attempt to tie in their own feelings and perceptions with the group situation taken as a whole, to clarify them in the light of this total situation, and to clarify the total situation in the light of their own individual feelings and perceptions; d) finally, as a result of this common activity, grounded on common and anti-reductive bases (or de-reifying ones), the members aim at attaining among themselves a profound level of *communication.*

The essential characteristics of the activities of the group-centered-group are never acquired once and for all. They represent a direction which the action of the monitors aims to preserve and develop. They tend to be denied by the individual and collective resistances which, *under all their forms,* stem from the refusal to incorporate the process *a* through *d,* that is, to avoid that the group be centered on the group itself.

Distinctiveness of the Group-Centered Group

The characteristics *a* through *d* above constitute the **boundary**

607

lines which distinguish in a definitive manner the group-centered group from every other kind of group technique.

The Fundamental Rule

The only rule given to the members in the situation of the group-centered group is that they should *verbalize exclusively their perceptions and feelings relative to the situation hic et nunc.* Experience shows that this rule "works"; that is to say, that the members do succeed in feeling acutely the difference between what pertains to "elsewhere, formerly, later or never and always" and what pertains to "here and now," the pregnant microcosm of the situation of the group. But this distinction is not understood at the outset by the group; it has to be mastered. Once the rule is declared impossible to observe, we are generally faced with a resistance to analysis. Conversely, the observance of the fundamental rule by the group marks a progress by the group. In fact, the sole explicit objective which can be set before the group is the application of the rule. The function of the monitor is not, however, to impose the rule because it is the rule, but to interpret, in terms of the concrete situations of the group, the significance of the non-observance of the rule.

It is certain that the group may at first interpret this fact — that the application of the rule is the goal of the situation — as the manifestation of a system of constraint (we must obey the Law because it is the Law). Actually, the group makes this interpretation by projecting upon the monitor the image of an exacting authority. But what ensues, through a series of "crises" of the group, is that all the resistances to the internal acquisition of the rule by the group are objectified and mobilized through a confrontation by the group with the image of the all-powerful monitor which the group itself has created. This confrontation results in rites of introjection of the all-powerfulness of the monitor by the group (*e.g.*, "cannibal meal"), and finally in the internal acquisition of the rule by the group.

Thus it is advisable to emphasize that the rule is *not just any rule.* It is a rule whose application calls once more into question the structure of authority and dependence, thereby including the authority of the rule and the dependence to the rule. It is, if we dare call it so, an "anti-rule."

608

EXISTENTIAL GROUP ANALYSIS

by Herbert Holt

In the early 1950's, it became apparent to many practitioners in group psychotherapy that a new way of looking at man was needed to make communication possible. Existential analysis, which had flourished in Europe, especially Switzerland, since the early 1930's, particularly under the influence of Ludwig Binswanger, made its impact upon the intellectual climate of the United States. A new humanistic point of view developed and its vocabulary made possible communications between therapist and patient and between therapist and therapist. This new concept of 'being in the world' and the new emphasis on existence made this possible. Gone was the mechanistic view of man and the stress was no longer on scientific understanding of mechanisms, nor upon social engineering that would change the values and behavior of individuals and groups toward a provincial view of adjustment and mental health. Instead, stress shifted towards liberty and the right of the individual to evaluate himself and his world from a critical, rational point of view; thus, moral, philosophical, religious, and political values became important once more. This new focus in group analysis was not easily acceptable to people entrenched in their institutes; they became controlling political forces who wanted to sell their own brands of ideas to the psychotherapeutic professions. And so individual psychotherapists who wished to communicate their experiences in existential analysis to one another had to form new organizations, such as the New York Ontoanalytic Society and the New York Institute of Existential Analysis.

In this way, a new basis was laid for the free communication of ideas in the field of individual and group existential analysis from a clinical point of view. However, one may well ask in what way existential analysis of groups differs from other forms of group psychoanalysis. The major difference is that existential psychoanalysis focuses on 'being in this world.' It is based on the relationship of one man or woman to others and on the emotional and intellectual climates they create spontaneously with each other in the short time they are together. Each participant in group analysis brings his own personality, character structure, and style of life to the group. Since existential analysis is based on the assumption that individuality is an expression of relationships to other human beings, it is self-evident that each one — to the degree that he *voluntarily* contributes himself or does not contribute himself — can reach more or less authenticity of himself and increased awareness of himself. His relation to others is therefore guided by the principle of voluntarism, as opposed to coercion. Although he is encouraged to communicate — verbally or otherwise — he is not forced to say whatever is on his mind. Nonverbal communications, it is assumed, are an unconscious body language which, if properly understood, will reveal as much as content communication.

This idea of a noncoercive, voluntary group that meets and focuses on spontaneous verbal or nonverbal communication is based on the concept of existence as a form of liberty of the individual. Since individuality can be communicated more or less authentically, depending on mutual respect and responsibility toward self and other, physical acting-out is by definition not possible, because it would be experienced as coercive by the group. Since this respect for individual liberty of being is seen as a group phenomenon, each group creates and re-creates its own climate each time it meets. Also, since there is no limit put on the form of communication, dreams, daydreams, fantasies, and hallucinations are empathically shared and responded to. The underlying emphasis on the similarity of the condition of being human and the diversity of individual expression became apparent to each group member. In time, the participants become aware of their attitudes toward interpersonal space and the emotional experience of time, and these become two modalities in which the individual self can be experienced as a unique entity interrelated to others. The distortion of awareness of the self in its relation to experienced time, space, and other individuals comes to be seen more acutely.

As a group member, the existential analyst fulfills a particular role from this point of view. He does not use the group as a psychotherapeutic vehicle for himself nor does he feel that he makes a major contribution to the group climate by sharing his own dreams, fantasies, hopes, wishes, and fears with them. This kind of 'chumminess' is frowned on by most of the group members, who consider it inconsistent to pay a friend for the time they spend with him. In fact, the concept of friendship is seen in a new light in a therapeutic group. The therapist is seen to be making his contribution by being himself as fully as he can — in the sense of relating emotionally, rationally, and nonverbally in the full range of his expression without burdening the group with the content of his own fantasy life. Also, he does not function as a withdrawn, blank-faced, suppressed therapist who rationalizes his detached and alienated behavior and the conscious suppression of his thoughts and emotions as beneficial for the group members for the supposedly therapeutic motives of motivating their projected anxieties and hostilities.

In fact, existential group therapists engage in a form of communication for the purpose of 'setting up' other participants. The therapist often does this by playing the counter-roles and historical roles they have communicated to the group; his purpose is to help the other group members, if they want to, to bring out into the open the feelings and attitudes that they have never dared experience or be aware of without terrible guilt and fear. These 'setting up' exercises can become very dramatic and can then stimulate spontaneously in other members the memories that otherwise would not be available to them for inspection. This work of the group therapist helps to mobilize and to bring into consciousness the forgotten fantasies that motivate the group members. These fantasies have created in the patient a false image of himself and his world by his unconscious identification with these fantasies; such communication can best be shared in an existential group since everyone can voluntarily and spontaneously decide to participate or not in the fantasy communication. By expressing these fantasies in the interpersonal field of the group, they are made real, can be examined as shared experiences, and evaluated by group members as to their appropriateness, adequacy, and timeliness. The evaluation of each group member relates to the way he sees himself today and tomorrow, not just a compulsive, repetitive pattern from the past. A brand-new modality of choice or no choice, decision or no decision, of voluntarism, has been added.

Patients often become aware for the first time that they are not trapped in certain attitudes in which they saw themselves in the past but can now re-experience themselves as new and see themselves from a new perspective and point of view. This shift of self-perspective and point of view is only possible when the old values which often underlie their emotions, behavior, and thoughts are brought into the open, shared again and again and again, until finally a new pattern of thinking and feeling, of moral and religious values — and often of political values — is created. These new values are not based on fatalistic acceptance of instinctual values or on provincial adjustment values. Each person begins to see himself as a unique human being who can make voluntary decisions to the degree that is possible in the environment in which he lives, or recognizes the limits that are put on his human choices not only by other group members but also by the pressures of living in an advanced industrial society where the total environment is organized to encourage conformity to a local ideal. He therefore can learn to stand up and be counted as a person with the more or less full awareness of his identity, with its limits, aspirations, capacities, and potentials, in reference to other people and to his social group. A new optimism about the possibility of even limited personal lives develops.

It is true that in our time, age, and circumstances only a few people can live predominantly authentic lives. In the history of man such times have been rare and short. Most men live in quiet desperation since their need for survival has precedence over their need for authenticity (by which I mean self-realization of innate potentials with a feeling of dignity and respect, a capacity for taking the responsibility for making one's own decisions and directing one's self in a relatively friendly environment). Since most people must lead nonauthentic lives with the accompanying manifestations of neurotic, sociopathic, and psychotic reaction patterns, the ideal of authenticity can often show itself only in the hopes, wishes, and dreams of individual liberty of persons who are not completely damaged in their interrelationships with other human beings. The group therapist, therefore, can try to help them towards more self-fulfilling lives by sharing and participating in their fears, wishes, and fantasies and by guidance, illumination, and interpretation of their existential situations.

AN EXISTENTIAL APPROACH TO GROUP THERAPY PROCEDURES (IN WORKING WITH MEMBERS OF THE "HELPING PROFESSION" FOR MENTAL HEALTH PURPOSES)

by Frank M. Buckley

I. A brief resume of certain fundamental points of agreement and principles of operation in existential and phenomenological thought include:
1) its awareness of the *depersonalizing* and *alienating* forces of modern technological thought and society.
2) its emphasis on *understanding* man as distinguished from *explaining* him.
3) its starting point of *everyday human experience.*
4) its insistence on ever seeing man in *his situation* (in time and place-Dasein) and that situation always *in its totality.*
5) its core emphasis on what constitutes the vitally *human,* and the primary place of *meaning* in human existence, as *each individual* struggles to grasp this meaning *for himself.*

A brief indication of the congruence of these principles with commonly accepted psychodynamic principles as found in the primary general objective of comprehending: a) the *response patterns;* b) of *the person;* c) within a *situational context.*

II. A concise description of the several *specific goals* derived from an existential approach to group psychotherapy. These would include:
The gradual development within the group member of such internalized "psychological convictions" (held in a consistent and durable manner) as:
Recognition and acceptance that *fundamentally what is,* or *what is human*

613

—is always particular, *situational,* hence changing.
—is always individual, *unique,* hence not generalizable.
—is spontaneous, creative, free.

The gradual concomitant development within the group member of such *modifications* of 1) *attitudes* and 2) *behavior* as reveal a strengthening of the capacity (ies):

a) to live meaningfully in *the present;* deal with the *here and now,* in terms of satisfying love and work and in terms of future oriented meanings and goals.

b) to more truly *communicate* with oneself and others; i.e., to be able to *express* oneself (to *be* oneself) and to *listen* to others (to let others *be* themselves).

c) to *participate;* to more truly share, to experience an abiding *sense of equality* as a person, give and receive; to love.

d) to live *with problems* (*i.e.* without undue accompanying feelings of frustration, anger or anxiety).

e) to live *with* human anxiety (Die Angst der Kreatur) *i.e.* to *accept limitations* (of all kinds) as an integral part of being human.

f) to *accept suffering* itself, when inescapable, *e.g.* boredom, depression, fatigue, as an authentic component of human existence and, hence, as of value.

g) to become "engaged," accepting *responsibility* for one's action (not *blaming* other persons or events) to achieve commitment to value and purpose.

III. A description of the group therapeutic process through which the above specific goals may be pursued: (In a group of a limited number of persons [six to twelve, no more than fifteen], meeting a limited number of times once a week for approximately fifteen to thirty weeks).

a) based on contemporary knowledge of psychodynamics of groups.

b) careful consideration of what may be called *the fundamental rule,* in this existential approach (consistently borne in mind by the leader and given to the members of the group from the outset), that they are *to verbalize only those thoughts, feelings and reactions that are related to the situation here and now.*

614

—indications, from experience, that this "rule" works, and *how* it works, by moving through:

1) resistance, declaring it impossible, etc.
2) gradually exploring this resistance, or "refusal," in existential terms — pointing up, at appropriate times, how the group strives to remain on the "conversational" or intellectual level in order to prevent reaching the level of its "being," or the existential level.
3) Promoting on the part of each member what may be called an *improved perception of one's existential relation to the group.*
4) Consistently focusing on the analysis *of the total situation of the group* (rather than on the particular problems of individuals) at the very time it is being experienced.
5) Investing oneself, as the leader, *in the group in an affective and human manner,* and avoiding all methods which of their nature tend to be *"alienating"* or *"reifying."*

IV. Brief illustrations, derived from records of actual sessions with groups composed of members from the "helping" professions (such as psychologists, nurses, educators), can be introduced to concretize the above described processes in operation, if thought desirable.

V. Reference will be made to the availability of observations and data which indicate the presence of certain group phases and certain group themes, and which provide a limited attempt to evaluate group outcomes. These would constitute the work of another study.

615

EXISTENTIALISM AND PEACE

by Thomas F. Graham

This essay defines and discusses a non-violent approach to international relations in the nuclear age. It begins by asking: Is all of this just a theory of peace, a dream, a fantasy? Has non-violence gone out of style? Is a hard-headed policy of might in vogue? Is this the only realism? If answers to these questions are affirmative, then historians must be prepared to record the murderous vengeance of nations on the largest scale since man was born. If answers to these questions are negative, then something must be done now before it is too late. All about us are the angry symptoms that the world dare no longer ignore. The time is long overdue to see above the vested interests and the national rivalries and to do something more than talk about peace.

It is often expedient to pause from time to time on the diverse aspects of evolution in a given field of inquiry. The traditional slow pace in mental health has been accelerated somewhat by a flurry of papers and research that have rolled back the frontier of theory, methods and therapy. Psychotherapy, in general, and Existentialism, in particular are emerging as techniques that promise to have far-reaching effect on mental health — especially in the area of prevention. Existentialism is selected here for discussion because of its international appeal and because of its wide range or flexibility.

The first part of this essay deals with the "Basic Concepts of Existentialism." Herein, Existentialism is described as a philosophy — a very old and yet a very new system. Its history is briefly traced from Kierkegaard to Heidegger. Its meaning of self and personal freedom as highly valued concepts is clarified. Its application by Jean-Paul Sartre is reviewed.

The second part covers "Implications for Mental Health." Sartrian variety is examined in respect to self-deception and personal freedom. Camus' Existentialism is mentioned as it portrayed not only the dynamics of the individual man — alienated from himself — but also as a social being — caught in the icy currents of a cold war. The story of Camus' Everyman has a familiar ring to clinical ears. He is a sick man dimly aware of his paranoid nature in a paranoid world.

The third part, "Disarmament or Destruction," reveals the schizoid-paranoid process operating in Everyman on both sides of the Berlin Wall with a compelling need to be equal. It is a process that combines suspicion with tortuosity and depicts Eastern and Western man as being dishonest, when both may be scrupulously honest.

The fourth part studies the "Personality of the Politician." People in every land must eventually come to realize that their very existence is dependent ever so much on the mental health of their leaders. Lest we forget, political leaders do not always accept even the best-intended blueprints for peace; but being humans with a high power value, they often consult their own variable moods. These same variable moods may not be influenced easily unless the citizens have some basic knowledge of how the politician's mind works and he, the politician, is aware of this fact.

The fifth part outlines "Existential Equivalents for War." It must be faced that war has a psychological attraction for many men. In war, needs for adventure, heroism, self-sacrifice and group solidarity may be reduced. This section recommends an imaginative pursuance of academic, scientific and cultural contacts between East and West which could redirect much of the psychic energy that is now expended on military programs.

617

SECTION 15: GROUP PSYCHOTHERAPY
IN EDUCATION

SEPARATION PROBLEMS IN COLLEGE STUDENTS

by SAMUEL SLIPP and MADGE K. LEWIS

This paper deals with the process of intrapsychic and physical separation of a group of college students from their parents. The group therapy in which Dr. Lewis and I were co-leaders took place in the Counseling Center of San Francisco State College, an institution of about 14,000 students located in metropolitan San Francisco, California. This group has a history of two years. There are both male and female students, generally coming from a middle class socioeconomic background. All sessions were taped, including a brief analysis of each session immediately following. The group has been open, with students coming and leaving from time to time; however there has been a generally consistent core of about five. As we studied our group, we came to realize that certain patterns of self concept and ways of relating to others appeared, in which self worth was still greatly dependent on performing a role which had been determined within the family interaction.

It was our hope that the students, given new experiences in a therapeutic group with a leader of each sex, could achieve perspective and growth with the support of a new group unlike their own family group, and thus at least begin to find a new and separate identity with their own value systems concerning themselves and their environment. We hoped that they would be freed from seeing themselves and their world *only* through their parents' eyes or in terms of the role that had been prescribed for them in their family symbiosis.

We asked ourselves the question, why had not individuation occurred in the home during adolescence as a natural process in resolving this family symbiosis? We speculated that the parents themselves had not individuated and were perpetuating the symbiosis probably, in most cases, out of unconscious needs. With this viewpoint in mind, we attempted to differentiate what seemed to be certain types of family interactions that were brought out in the group. Generally, these parents seemed to be caught in a conflict of still emotionally adhering to traditional patriarchal standards concerning roles and sexual attitudes, while intellectually trying to conform to modern, equalitarian attitudes. This state of cultural transition, of which a great deal has been written in the literature, has created considerable instability in family relationships because of the conflict of simultaneously accepting and rejecting old and new roles. We were interested in finding that this conflict had even effected Zulu women in Africa. This was documented in a lecture given by Professor G. M. Carstairs of the University of Edinburgh, on the "New Role of Women." What does this conflict mean descriptively with our group? From the students' verbalizations, it appeared that their parents' own upbringing had largely been along traditional lines, with the roles of the husband-wife relationship characterized as husband autocracy and wife submissiveness. This has become a part of *their* ego identity; and in order for these parents to value themselves, they could not relinquish this family group identity since their self worth is so involved.

On the other hand because of a multitude of changes in our societal structure, especially since World War II, such as the break-down of primary group controls, the Industrial Revolution, mobility of the population, economic opportunities for women, modern mass communication, urbanization, and probably even the nuclear war threat, different concepts of husband, wife, and family relationships have evolved. On the one hand the parents seem to need to cling rigidly to old standards which have meant security for them in the past, and yet on the other hand they are aware of new opportunities and conditions and are disillusioned with the old ways. What effect does this transition have on the family interaction? We have attempted to tease out the different types, as observed in our group, and will list our findings.

In the most conservative type, which we have called type one, we have observed that both parents join hands in their attempt to dominate the child and force him into a role that they have chosen for him. Thus they are enacting the old, traditional idea that the child is subjugated to the will of the parents for the gift of life they have bestowed on him. The identity of the child, then, is a narcissistic extension of the family identity, and therefore is subject to exploitation as an object or the purpose of the family's needs. Attempts on the part of the child toward a separate identity are seen as defiance and are blocked by parental threats of loss of love, which at a deeper level mean abandonment, starvation, and death. In this type, the child constantly has to prove himself by achieving, and is denied the right of indecision or lack of success since it reflects on the family.

Type two are the dependent parents, often a single parent as a result of divorce, death, or physical or emotional desertion. These parents may be attempting to be the perfect, modern parents frequently described in ladies' magazines, glued together by togetherness, the 'buddy'; in other words, a sibling rather than a parent. There may be an over-evaluation of the parental role and its responsibilities for the benefit of the parents' self esteem. This is especially seen in the mothers. The parents have placed great emphasis upon conformity to ideal child-rearing practices at the expense of themselves and spouses, thus placing a large burden of guilt on the children. This seems to be one of the side effects of the so-called modern child-centered family. The young adult's attempt to deal with this masochistic and guilt-provoking goodness and selflessness on the part of the parents causes difficulties in separating and finding his own self-fulfillment and happiness. These parents frequently become very dependent on the favorable responses of feedback from the child in order to validate their self esteem. This continues the symbiosis by placing the child in a position of unusual power since he can withhold the validation, or act out. In this situation the child becomes the controller and manipulator of the parent, one who can exploit them because of their excessive feelings of responsibility. Another factor contributing to this dependence may be the fact that the child symbolically represents the new way of behaving. This was most evident in the relation of immigrant parents to their native born children. The parents are trying to learn a new culture, and the children are a communication agent with it. In a sense they are a bridge from the parents' ego to the culture.

The third type is the parent who vaccilates between both the traditional dominant and modern permissive attitudes. This leads to inconsistent responses: at times authoritarian and at other times equalitarian. Learning theory shows that this type of intermittent reinforcement results in confusion and heightened tension in the child. A parent may consciously ascribe to patriarchal authority yet unconsciously encourage the child to rebellion. Since we have not had any schizophrenic students in the group, we have not had any double bind phenomena (as Don Jackson and Gregory Bateson have described this), in which there are simultaneous and conflicting messages. We have observed also a split between the parents in which one parent represents the more traditional values, and the other the more modern; so there is inconsistency between the two parents.

In type four we have observed the results of alienation and conflict between the parents, in which the child is trapped into taking sides. The most clearcut example is the traditional pattern which is still in effect. The mother feels weak, ineffectual, less important than the man, and submerged by her role. In her attempt to gain power, she involves her children as allies; and to gain self esteem she degrades the husband. She does this by portraying him as selfish, or as a failure as a provider. The mother portrays herself to her children as self-sacrificing, innocently injured, a helpless victim of the father's failures and weaknesses, in essence, a martyr. She does not take responsibility for her aggression, and it comes out in these indirect, manipulative ways. The victim thus controls and devours. She encourages her children to identify with her in her martyred role by using the child's dependency on her, and in the case of the boy by using unconsciously the Oedipal situation. In the boy's case, he enjoys the intimacy emotionally, sharing secrets, and feeling victorious over the father. This traps the child into being a narcissistic extension of the mother. He thereby loses his individuality and freedom of choice. It also robs him of being able to identify with the father. He feels a sense of guilt at being a contributing factor in the destruction of the father, and the guilt over the secrets he shares with the mother creates a barrier to closeness with the father. The son frequently feels obliged to achieve for the mother and make up for father's failures. He is expected to be the man that his father is not. The result is that the child who can not attain this goal is robbed of his masculine identification, is passive and controlled by guilt, and is fearful of closeness and dependency since he expects to be exploited. The child empathically responds, probably unconsciously, to the pain in the parents, is unable to tolerate this, and is seduced into wanting the correct and change the parents' relationship so that he can consolidate his own identification with them as suitable models and resolve his guilt by separating from them as an individual and in having a life of his own. He needs his parents to be models for identification of success and strength. His is still a symbiotic relationship; he needs *them* to change so that *he* can change, since he still feels part of them. His failure in being able to help his parents to change robs him further of ego strength. He fails to see the neurotic equilibrium in his parents — that they cannot really change. His efforts probably will only meet with hostility and be regarded as interference. Some of these children physically move away to get away from the pain and their own inability to effect any change; but they are still trapped by identification with the family tragedy; namely, they carry a myth that they are also doomed to failure, since their parents have failed.

The fifth type might be termed the withholding parent who never emotionally gives affection or approval to the child. This results in the child's never gaining a feeling of personal value. He never obtains any kind of measuring stick on which to gauge approval. This results in a feeling of impotence and apathy.

We have probably not exhausted all the types of parental pa-

623

thology. However, these have emerged from our observation of this particular group.

How were the students attempting to cope with their situation and maintain some sort of ego integrity before they came into therapy? One way is flight into random casual sexual relations in a search for closeness and some feeling of worth. Since there is exploitation on both sides, the affairs resulted in considerable guilt which only compounded the problem. Another way is through withdrawal into a world of intellectuality. A good example of this in literature is Sartre's young intellectual in his play, *Dirty Hands*. There is no real emotional rapport with people; instead they hide behind words and attempt to control the group and make *it* also a world of cold ideas without feelings.

One means of coping is through putting actual physical distance between themselves and their parents in an attempt to gain psychological distance. This only results in guilt and a continuation of the same fears in other relationships. Isolation and withdrawal is another way used by some. They are affectless, depressed, and fearful of closeness, yet long for it. Still another way is by identifying with the role of helper, the role they had in the family. Having achieved this identification in the family, they continue to use this in the group, becoming a pseudo-leader, thus unable to seek help themselves, seduced into overgenerosity and an excess of responsibility. Teasing and sarcasm is a direct way of hitting back, a form of self-assertion towards the parents. Another way is negativism and acting out in direct opposition to parents' wishes and expectations. Still another is nonconformity.

What are the goals of the clients and how is the group experience helping them to attain these goals? First of all, the goals emerge during therapy. They discover, for example, that masculine self-assertiveness and independence are not hurtful, and that the woman does not have to be weak, passive, and ineffectual. In the Victorian era, some women were infantilized and had to mould their identity according to masculine wishes. This is a theme that Simone de Beauvoir uses in *Second Sex* and Ibsen in *A Doll's House*. Among the better adjusted, all proponents of the personality are allowed to come out. Man can be *all* he is, and woman can be *all* she is. Masculine and feminine elements in each can be present. Both the man and the woman in the family can be individuals, assuming their own responsibility and interacting in a healthy, mutually enhancing way. The traditional situation was a symbiotic relationship in which the woman gave up management of herself in a dependent way. She was submerged, and her aggression came out in indirect ways towards her husband and children. The Victorian roles tend to be quite static and rigid so that a person's whole nature did not come out healthily. The girl was afraid to be more aggressive, and the boy afraid to be tender and feeling.

The group offers the student: 1. support and strength while attempting to avoid pressure and excessive demands; 2. an opportunity to gain perspective by looking at present values obtained from parents, re-evaluating them, and finding their own values; 3. understanding of their feelings; 4. support in their ability to trust their own values; 5. the opportunity to observe the therapists, who are of opposite sexes, who respond differently, yet without rejection or domination of each other; 6. new ways of perceiving and coping with problems. Hence, the group serves as a stepping stone for these college students from the family symbiosis to a new and separate identity.

GROUP THERAPY IN A SCHOOL
BY THE SCHOOL PHYSICIAN, IN ISRAEL

by E. CHIGIER

In order to focus on the essentials of my subject, I propose to relate a "psychodramatic" story, which will include the following points: a) the setting; b) the participants; c) development; d) themes; e) conclusions.

The setting. This is a primary (or grammar) school in the city of Tel Aviv. It is an old building, badly in need of repair. in a poorer section of the city, with 1300 pupils. The vast majority of the parents are immigrants who have come to Israel from 53 countries of the Eastern and Western World, since the establishment of the state in 1948. The parents of the children involved in the project come from Syria, Israel, Poland, Greece, Egypt, Rumania and Turkey.

The participants. The participants are 9 children (5 boys and 4 girls) aged 11-13, in the sixth grade at the school. They are part of a special class of children with educational difficulties. Five of them had been in individual therapy, but failed to continue. They were disturbed and disturbing, the "worst of a bad lot," and had driven their capable and conscientious male teacher to a state of despair and hopelessness, preventing any progress of the class as a whole. All were backward in academic work, restless or talkative. One boy was over-aggressive and had upset a table over a teacher; one was the clown of the class, two wandered around in the classroom. One lay on the floor when he felt like it; one boy would go into hysterical faints regularly when he felt insulted; one girl gave gifts to others, including a gold ring which she had "stolen" in order to give it to the sympathetic school nurse. These are the characters of our story.

Development. With nothing to lose, I proposed as an experiment

626

to take these children into group therapy, with the school nurse as co-therapist. The group was organized as a "social circle," to meet for one lesson (one hour) a week, during school, to discuss matters of topical interest. Maximum co-operation of headmaster and schoolteacher encouraged good attendance at the start. Later, no encouragement was necessary.

The group sat around in a circle of chairs, with free expression, opportunity to move around or leave the room if anyone so desired. The nurse acted as a disciplinary restraint only in order to avoid damage to property or person. Some themes were elaborated or introduced by the therapist, but very soon the group became group-centered and almost "forgot" the presence of adult therapists.

After two good sessions, we ran into trouble. The children refused to continue, since other children in the class and in the school maintained that this was a group for "daft kids" or "nuts," and that the doctor was out to do some "brain-washing." Persuasion on all sides was of no avail. To overcome this resistance, it was decided to have two "visitors," in rotation, from the class, who could come along and be convinced that "brain-washing" was not on the program. This measure succeeded beyond all expectations, and created another kind of problem. The visitors were fascinated by the free expression atmosphere, and wanted to continue to attend meetings of the group. The intense pressure of visitors led to arguments as to whose turn it was, and required physical efforts to prevent the group turning into a social rather than a therapeutic medium. Two mentally healthy children, who seemed to have a good influence, were incorporated as members, and could be regarded as auxiliary therapists.

Themes. The group has met for almost a year (up to now 23 meetings), and will continue for another two years until these children finish primary school. What did we discuss? Movies; topical newspaper events; topical items about the neighborhood; school events; personal items.

Conclusions. At this stage, one boy is an off-and-on-attendant. One has moved up a grade and has stopped clowning. The hysterical faints have ceased, the one girl has stopped her compulsive giving of gifts. Academic progress has not been evident. The group is an accepted part of the school milieu, has a high status,

627

plans excursions, runs smoothly, and its continuation is taken for granted.

I believe that this experimental period has demonstrated the following points:

(1) Individual therapy demands experts, who are in short-demand, and an artificial face-to-face atmosphere in a clinic removed from the child's background. It is not surprising that there is resistance to going to a psychiatrist, demands for compliance on child and parent and a severe problem of continuity in regard to treatment. The alternative set up described has the advantage of a natural atmosphere (a group of peers), a natural habitat (the school), and a natural setting (school lesson on social themes), with no problems about continuity since all children attend school and will continue to do so until the age of fourteen. The school nurse is in daily touch with teachers, children and parents, while the doctor is at the school twice a week. The use of a school physician with psychiatric training eliminates the stigma of treatment and the resistance to psychotherapy.

(2) Mixing of early adolescents of both sexes has not been detrimental and has allowed a certain measure of healthy sex attitude to develop.

(3) The use of mentally healthy peers as auxiliary therapists has been beneficial, and is a trend which could be developed further.

(4) The resultant free discussion has been instrumental in giving the therapist an intimate understanding of the cultural background, which up till then was completely alien, and remains alien to the vast majority of "western", middle-class psychotherapists, teachers, nurses and social workers.

(5) The carrying-out of a project of this nature, right in the middle of the school, has focused practical attention on mental health problems of school children on the part of teachers and school nurses, and for this alone the project is worthwhile.

In conclusion: Group therapy is a valuable tool for achieving mental health. The more who learn to use it, the more valuable will the tool become.

THE USE OF CLASSROOM DISCUSSION AS A SPECIAL TECHNIQUE FOR THE PROMOTION OF PERSONALITY GROWTH OF STUDENTS

by Josef Ernest Garai

With our vastly increased knowledge of unconscious motivation, our methods of teaching are bound to undergo profound changes. New methods of instruction must be developed which will utilize the insights of psychoanalysis in the promotion of personality growth. The technique described in this article relies heavily upon the clarification of unconscious motives, the investigation of ego-defense mechanisms, and the working through of unconscious conflicts. In general, its main purpose can be defined as providing the individual student with a more profound insight into his own unconscious motives, enabling him to face himself and to become an emotionally mature and self-reliant individual who establishes his own goals in life. Its ultimate aim is self-actualization. Its basic method is a ceaseless search for release from emotional blocks through a dauntless exploration of unconscious forces.

In the social sciences the presentation of case history material may frequently serve as an excellent opening for fruitful classroom discussion. Thus, for instance, in the discussion of the causes of the high divorce rate in the United States in an introductory sociology course, the teacher pointed out that people often marry for the "wrong" reasons or in order to satisfy certain neurotic needs. The case of a girl who was, on one hand, afraid of breaking away from her mother, while, on the other hand, greatly resenting her dependence on her mother, was used to demonstrate one of these neurotic needs. Her case history was presented to the class.

Then one student mentioned the experience of his brother who had married a girl, with whom he was not even in love, for the

629

sole purpose of getting out of an unhappy home environment. The parents of the girl offered him a chance to enter their shoe manufacturing business and to be settled comfortably in a newly built house in a fashionable suburb. But he soon became even more dependent on his in-laws than on his own parents, with the result that he resented their "charity". Nevertheless, he was still unable to become financially self-supporting, let alone to provide for his family.

From the experience of his brother, the student drew the conclusion that his brother's dependency prevented him from gaining the emotional maturity necessary for the enactment of the husband-role. In the ensuing discussion, a student summarized the problem in the following manner: "Both case histories demonstrate the necessity of solving one's own dependency problems before one embarks upon a marital relationship." Several students emphasized the fact that certain dependency needs should be recognized and fulfilled in a marriage, especially in times of crises, when a husband may need his wife as a mother-substitute or a wife her husband as a father-substitute. The general consensus of the group, however, stressed the preponderance of independence and self-reliance of the spouses, while it relegated the fulfillment of dependency needs to a secondary and more temporary role.

It should be pointed out that the main purpose of this novel technique of group discussion consists in the establishment of a group atmosphere which is free from the traditionally imposed superego restraints. As soon as the students are aware of the fact that they are permitted to give free verbal expression to any and all feelings and emotions in the classroom, they gain courage to investigate their own unconscious drives and impulses. They learn to acknowledge their own positive and negative emotions and to cope with their erotic and hostile impulses. Students who feel that they cannot solve their problems without professional help are encouraged to seek assistance. I was able to refer thirteen students to competent psychotherapists for individual treatment within a single year. Other students are enabled to work through their problems either through direct participation in the group discussion or through identification with the problems brought up by fellow students. It is especially gratifying for a teacher to witness the accumulating evidence of steady personality growth experienced by certain students, and a not infrequent concomitant of such personality development in the removal of blocks to the road of scholastic achievement. It gives us pause to think whether the harrowing problem of school dropouts should not rather be attacked from the emotional, than from the intellectual, viewpoint. The technique described in this paper may yet prove to be an invaluable tool in the reduction of academic attrition on all levels.

THE PROBLEM OF TEACHING GROUP DYNAMICS
IN A UNIVERSITY SETTING

by Samuel Tenenbaum

To teach group dynamics in a university setting presents many problems which appear at times insoluble. This article is an attempt to discuss some of these problems. At the university where I teach, group dynamics is a graduate three-credit course and the instructor is required by university regulations to give students a midterm, a final examination, a term paper and, at the end of the semester, a grade.

At best, this teacher-grading role is hard on me since I am by philosophy non-directive and non-judgmental. But when giving a course like group dynamics, even if one felt otherwise, if one were authoritarian and directive, it would be difficult to pursue this approach. In a course like group dynamics, there is the process itself; and, two, there is the body of content, the intellectual portion, that supports the process. I raise the question: What better way is there to learn group dynamics than to experience it, to feel it, to eat of it, to live it? Can anyone learn to be part of a group in any other way?

I myself came to teaching from the practice of psychotherapy. I believe — perhaps I am biased — that for this type of course, this orientation is still the best. Group psychotherapy has contributed the most to the field of group dynamics; this approach has touched people in the most profound and deepest way. Here is a group of human beings facing one another, confronting one another; human beings every day dying a little bit, meanwhile trying to fulfill themselves, trying to become what they were meant to become, hoping, suffering, disappointed, and, as Freud said, with moments of exaltation, and then more suffering.

As one who has been strongly influenced by Carl Rogers, I believe that as you give a person acceptance, regard, compassion,

632

understanding, he is more apt to muster the courage to articulate his problems, to try to cope with them, to face them. In this confrontation there is always the hope that he will develop the courage to be.

Normally, a person joins a therapy group with these attitudes, expressed or implied: "I don't like myself. I want to be different. I want help. I need help." He may not use these words or say them but the implications are there. The best learnings take place under such conditions — when a person says: "I do not like myself. I want to change." Further, in group psychotherapy nothing is demanded of the member. The group nor he need do nothing, achieve nothing. They have no program, no task to complete; they need do nothing, nothing outside of being themselves. In our dynamic, purposeful, driving culture, can you conceive even in imagination the existence of such a group — there for no purpose but to be? Even as I write this, burden and anxieties seem to fall off me.

In this non-judgmental atmosphere, what is good in group psychotherapy appears. If the process works, if the group jells, there is warmth engendered, there is closeness. I have come to believe that the first sign of emotional illness is the impairment of human relationships. One of the signs of good health, I have come to believe, is the ability to give affection and to receive affection, to give warmth and to receive warmth from others, to sacrifice for and to be sacrificed for. In our society the great tragedy is that so many want to be loved and so many cannot love. This is the wonder of the group, for in the group there is the possibility to learn to give and take, to learn to become a giving and receiving individual; and this is why I believe in the group.

Now to return to my university. When giving the course in group dynamics, I am always in a dilemma. Shall I lecture? How much? If I do, don't I structure the course? Instead of the feelings and the emotions of the group and each of the members coming forth, flowing freely, like a brook, unendingly, students will come forth with intellectual matter, with the contents of a text: as persons, they will attempt to please, conforming to what they think the instructor wants them to say and think; or if rebellious, they will dispute and contend. And yet I have to remember that the persons in this group before me may become counselors,

633

leaders themselves of groups, and, perhaps, therapists. And there is an intellectual content which attempts to understand the process.

Further, for many students what is expected from them in the group is strange. They're used to a body of content; they're used to regurgitating the content; and for this, they get a grade; and if it is a good grade, they feel they licked the course and they know what they have to know. But in group dynamics, the whole process is open, unstructured. And some are frightened. "How do I know I am doing it right? What shall I say to the group? What answers shall I make? Am I right? How will you mark me if I am quiet?" They seek — many want — an authority, a text.

Some are resentful of the whole process. They feel they got stuck with something. It's so strange. They're used to having the instructor say: "The four reasons for this are . . ." "The results are . . ." You memorize it and you have the stuff licked. But the process of group dynamics revolves around an endless flowing and at times you seem to get nowhere.

In a clinical setting, if a member is unhappy, he drops out. He comes voluntarily and he has the right to leave whenever it pleases him. But here at the university I have, more or less, a captive audience. Even if a member doesn't like what is happening, he doesn't drop out. What about the hostile member who is destroying the group? In an actual therapeutic setting, he is selected by the therapist as a likely member, and if the therapist's judgment proves wrong, the member is asked to leave. But you can't do that in a university course. The same as the student feels captive, you, as the instructor, feel captive as well.

You can make the course intellectual. You can take your text, lecture on it, examine students on it, have students make reports. But wouldn't it be like killing the goose to get at the eggs? Like teaching someone to swim from a text book? The story is told of Lord Chesterfield who had a natural son of whom he was extremely fond. On this natural son, he lavished much affection, sending him an avalanche of long, detailed letters, giving him precise and detailed directions as to how to act and behave and speak in all possible circumstances. Helped along by the good Lord Chesterfield himself who purchased the seat, his natural son was selected for Parliament. We can imagine how careful and precise were Lord Chesterfield's instructions to his natural son when the great moment came for him to make his maiden speech in Parliament. The young

634

man arose, looked around in dismay, tongue-tied, and then after the longest while started spluttering and stuttering, and eventually left that august body in fright and terror.

The way to learn how to make speeches, it seems to me, is to make speeches, not read letters. The way to teach group dynamics, it seems to me, is to have the students experience the process, eat of it, touch it, live it. You can't understand the textbook, the intellectual part, without that. There is no other way. And to do that you can't introduce examinations, term papers, grades, and, yes, intellectualizing, for then you forget the process — the human beings gathered together in a group, in all the wonder, the agony and the beauty of being human beings. But omnipresent, always there, is the university with its demands for examinations, term papers, grades and all the harsh judgments that go with grades. How can the two be reconciled?

SECTION 16: GROUP PSYCHOTHERAPY IN PRISONS AND REFORMATORIES

GROUP PSYCHOTHERAPY WITH MENTALLY ILL OFFENDERS

by Joseph Andriola

California's Atascadero State Hospital provides treatment both for non-psychotic sex offenders and for the criminally insane. Although chemotherapy, electroshock therapy, and occupational therapy are provided, group therapy rather than classical individual psychotherapy is the major psychotherapeutic method employed. Approximately 1,400 patients attend one or two group therapy sessions per week. Eight hundred of these patients receive group therapy from 14 social workers, the remaining 600 receive group therapy from the eight psychologists and 15 psychiatrists on the staff. Each therapy group has 10-15 patients. Virtually all patients also participate in weekly ward meetings at which about 50 patients and five or six members of the ward team are present. Since the hospital opened in 1954, there has been experimentation with a variety of methods of group therapy such as the inspirational method, didactic-lecture method, activity group therapy, non-directive therapy, "hot seat" therapy, psychoanalytically-oriented therapy, and an eclectic approach. Until recently, no systematic attempt had been made to utilize the techniques of psychodrama. Because of my ignorance of group psychotherapy (despite the fact that I spent many hours perusing the literature) I tried to keep an open mind and during the last five years have developed an essentially eclectic approach, derived primarily from the philosophical orientation of the field of social work.

One of the "canons" of social work philosophy in the United States is that the integrity, self respect, confidentiality, and *self determination* of the patient or client must be respected at all times. Professionally trained social workers generally do not do things for people or to people. We do not give moral lectures, prescriptions or other types of orders or advice. Rather, we try to encourage the adult client or patient to help himself solve his own problems.

As a social worker, my training and experience had been almost exclusively in the one-to-one approach — namely, in the casework method. Consequently, when I began to try to do group psychotherapy in 1957, I had much to learn and many biases to overcome. In addition to thinking of patients as specific individuals or as members of a family, I also had to develop the concept that they were members of a new organismic whole, namely — the therapy group. Furthermore, I had to divest myself of the tendency to get involved in a one-to-one relationship with designated patients in the group and to learn how to mobilize both the conscious and unconscious variables in the group situation so that the focus was on the group process *per se* rather than the individual or casework process which I had utilized for almost 20 years. During the past two years, continuous study, the responsibility of conducting a staff seminar in group psychotherapy, and constant evaluation of my own work by myself and others, have helped me to evolve a philosophy and a methodology of group

638

psychotherapy which seems to work effectively in this kind of setting and with which I can feel comfortable.

Besides my basic orientation as a social worker with a strong, but somewhat jaundiced, Freudian point of view, I have been influenced by the ideas of many other leaders in the helping professions. But in the final analysis, what I do as a therapist and the way I do it can be discussed under the following headings: (1) Do not be friendly with patients; (2) do not answer questions; (3) do not give advice; (4) do not interpret "dynamics" or other "unconscious" behavior. In addition to these four negative statements, the following four items will also be discussed: (5) Personal warmth; (6) honesty and candor; (7) open-mindedness; (8) sense of humor. The first four statements may sound like arbitrary admonitions and, therefore, require some elaboration; the second four statements will be discussed more briefly. All eight statements are derived from certain empirical as well as theoretical considerations.

(1) *Do not be friendly*

This admonition certainly seems to go against the teachings, customs and ideology of much of the Western Christian world. However, a group psychotherapy session is not a social, political or business gathering. It is for people who are sick or who think they are sick and who come to the session ostensibly to receive some treatment for their sickness. Hence friendliness, in the usual sense of the term, is out of place in a therapy session.

(2) *Do not answer questions*

The temptation to answer direct or indirect questions is a great one as everybody engaged in this work knows too well. All patients like to invest their therapist with god-like halos and many therapists may, at times, be willing to accept such halos. It is obvious that, among other things, answering questions tends to keep patients dependent upon the therapist and hence does not help them to grow up and figure out the answers or alternatives for themselves.

(3) *Do not give advice*

Much has been written and discussed about the giving of advice. Although there may be a time when a therapist giving advice may actually have the momentary insight which enables him to give sound advice, this is an unlikely situation. There may also be a time when a patient is actually willing and able to take advice. The combination, however, of a therapist giving sound advice and of a patient ready and willing to accept it, is a rare phenomenon. Although, in general, giving advice may be harmless, it should be avoided for two major reasons: it does not benefit the patient and it wastes the valuable time of both patient and therapist.

(4) *Do not interpret*

One of the greatest hazards for any therapist from any school or discipline is to communicate by words, gestures, posture or facial expression, "ah-ha!" Ah-ha, means of course that you are ready, willing and eager to interpret to the patient what went on in the interchange. When the therapist says, "ah-ha", even when he may appear to be involved in clarification, what is really going on may be quite different. But the fact that he is saying this indirectly, under the guise of a therapeutic maneuver, suggests that he is involved in a dishonest gesture, which automatically makes it anti-therapeutic.

(5) *Personal warmth*

I have become increasingly convinced that regardless of technical skills, the therapist who lacks what may be called "personal warmth" generally is less effective than the therapist who has this quality but whose technical knowledge and training are more limited. Since many of my colleagues seem to agree with this opinion, I will not belabor it here.

(6) *Honesty and candor*

There are two groups that one cannot fool very easily: children and mental patients. Although at times it may be necessary to lie to a patient, in general, in order to be effective as a group therapist, honesty and candor on the part of the therapist are imperative. This does not mean, of course, that one must be "brutally frank" at all times. Persons who behave in such a manner usually do not help patients although they may help themselves by using such "honesty" as a release for their own aggressions.

640

(7) *Open-mindedness*

This is a very important requisite. Although some therapists who are orthodox Freudians, or orthodox Jungians, or Adlerians, and so on, may be quite effective with many patients, my own impression is that orthodoxy of any kind can stifle creative therapeutic endeavors. At worst, of course, orthodoxy in psychotherapy leads to cultism which is in close proximity to quackery. Therefore, I am inclined to believe that the effective therapist is one who has a good background of education and experience in one or more of the helping professions and whose ideas and techniques are not ossified. Most important of all, the effective therapist is the one who continues to learn about psychotherapy from his patients.

(8) *Sense of humor*

When all else fails, the therapist who has a sense of humor — particularly the one who can laugh at himself — will usually be able to maintain his sanity and help his patients regain theirs. Consequently, although one should be serious about one's work, one should not take oneself too seriously. In my own case I find that when I take myself very seriously I lose my sense of humor and when that happens I am in trouble both with myself and with the patients.

GRUPPENPSYCHOTHERAPIE IM ZUCHTHAUS

vonLISELOTTE MEIER

In meinem Vortrag soll im Rückblick über den Veruch einer analytisch-psychotherapeutischen Gruppenpsychotherapie im Zuchthaus selbst dargestellt und diskutiert werden.

Zuerst wird herausgestellt, dass durch das Milieu im Zuchthaus selbst vollkommen andere Bedingungen gegeben sind als bei einer psychotherapeutischen Gruppe in einer für diese Methode aufgeschlossenen Klinik oder bei einer Gruppe von Schizophrenen in einer Anstalt.

Das Milieu in einem Zuchthaus ist psychologisch gesehen folgendes: Die Gefangenen sind hier in Zürich zusammengewürfelt aus Delinquenten, die eine Zuchthaus-oder eine Gefängnisstrafe verbüssen und aus Verwahrungsgefangenen. Sie werden hier nicht in verschiedenen Abteilungen untergebracht. Ebenfalls sind diese Gefangenen nicht in jugendliche Abteilungen und solche für ältere Gefangene unterteilt. Ausserdem hat man keine Aufteilung nach Delikten wie schwer aggressive Mörder, rückfällige Zuhälter und rückfällige Betrüger. Dies erschwert naturlich die Arbeit bei dieser spezifischen Psychotherapie mit Sexual-delinquenten.

In den folgenden Ausführungen soll der Versuch einer analytischen Psychotherapie bei Sexualdelinquenten herausgestell werden.

Nach Erfahrungen, die ich bei Psychotherapie einzelner Sexualdelinquenten gemacht habe, d.h. ich behandelte einen Exhibitionisten und einen Lehrer, der sexuell sich an jugendlichen Schülern vergriffen hatte. Durch den Erfolg dieser Behandlungen machte ich mich daran, die übrigen Sexualdeliquenten in unserem hiesigen Zuchthaus zu betrachten. Ich stellte fest, dass mehr als ein Drittel (d.h. von 300 Strafgefangenen ca. 100 wegen eines Sexualdeliktes dort ihre Strafe verbüssen). An einem Stichtag machte ich mir Aufzeichnungen über diese Deliquenten und teilte diese mir in Bezug auf meine Gruppenpsychotherapie folgendermassen auf:

642

1. nach Alter; 2. nach Beruf; 3. nach den spezifischen Sexualdeliquenten; 4. nach gewissen psychiatrischen Ueberlegungen, d.h. ich schloss Aterosklerosen, Demente, Debile, Imbezille und Grenzfälle von Schizophrenien aus. Natürlich nahm ich schizoide Charakterstrukturen in meine Gruppe.

Zu jedem dieser Deliquenten lag selbstwerständlich ein psychiatrisches Gutachten vor, das ich ebenfalls in meiner Auslese miteinbezog, doch waren diese Gutachten für ihr Delikt hauptsächlich nur auf die spezifische Zurechnungsfähigkeit abgestellt.

Da nach meinen Erfahrungen bei den Sexualdeliquenten die tiefe *Kontaktstörung zur Mutter* im Zentrum ihrer deliktischen Fehlhandlungen steht, was m.E. vom analytischen Standpunkt aus betrachtet die prä-ödipale Entwicklungsstufe nicht überwunden worden ist, setzte *ich* mich als *Mutterfigur-Symbol* in die Gruppe. Somit sollten die Deliquenten an mir als neuer Mutterfigur die Möglichkeit gegeben werden, diese nicht verarbeitete Stufe zu überwinden.

THREE YEARS OF GROUP PSYCHOTHERAPY
WITH OFFENDERS

by Nicholas S. Ionedes

The total cost of crime in the United States runs into the billions each year. In 1961, the United States Federal Bureau of Investigation estimated that the total annual cost of crime in the United States was about twenty-two billion dollars. I am sure that the situation is similar in every country. The cost, however, in terms of misery, misunderstanding and general unhappiness of the people is immeasurable.

It is not easy to find therapists, mainly psychiatrists, to work in correctional institutions. It is not because these institutions do not pay enough; the main reason is that the majority of the therapists believe that the criminal cannot change. Pessimism, ignorance, and misunderstanding still exist about the treatability of the offender. Some therapists may accept individual counseling for the offender, but group psychotherapy is, most of the time, out of the question.

My actual experience with offenders stems from my former position as Chief of Legal Psychiatric Services, Washington, D.C., from May, 1960, to February, 1963. For three years I saw about 60 patients in two groups. I do not say that it was an easy endeavor. I learned, however, certain important points that are not so discouraging, and that I summarize in the following.

The Personality Of The Offender

It is known that offenders suffer from a personality disorder that is nothing but a form of mental illness. Offenders are very disturbed individuals who are basically very unhappy and anxious, and who express their feelings in an antisocial way. They project

644

their anxieties on society. They are different from the schizophrenics, who express their anxieties by creating a world of their own, and the psychoneurotics, who cover up their anxieties with obsessive ideas, physical symptoms, depressions, etc. Offenders are not born in this way. Their patterns of behavior are what they learn from the very beginning of their lives — how to fight society and socially accepted ideas. If you examine the backgrounds of these people you can see that they do not have anyone to guide them and to show them the correct way from the very beginning; to give them encouragement to face the problems of life. One of my patients is divorced and going steady with a lady who was married three times before. His mother is divorced three or four times, and is married to another person who was married several times before. His sister is an alcoholic who spent time in different institutions.

Offenders are not so mentally deficient as many people may think. It takes intelligence to make a key which opens all the doors in the city. Many of them are intelligent, but they use their intelligence in the wrong way. Offenders may appear courageous and tough superficially, but basically they are scared. Many of these people actually do not want to leave jail; they want to stay where they feel they have a place, and where they belong. I will never forget a 23 year old male patient who spent most of his life in jail. He was in therapy with me for six months. The last month before his release he could not sleep or relax, and finally he admitted his problem — he was afraid of going out because he did not know if anyone would accept him. This man, by the way, was released. He came to see me immediately after his release, but unfortunately I could not see him at that time. He thought that I was rejecting him, hence, he stole a car the same day from a policeman so that he could be sent back to jail, where he felt he belonged. Another one of my patients was eligible for parole, but he did not dare ask for parole because he was afraid of going out. Finally, I persuaded him to ask for parole. When he was ready to leave the institution he was so upset that he decided to have a hernia operation that he had postponed for many years, so that he could further his stay in jail. Many patients express their fear and inadequacy of going out into the society by saying, "You know, in jail at least you have three meals and a roof over your head."

645

It is very interesting to observe the mentality of the criminal about society. According to them, society is made up of terrible people, and they, themselves, are its victims. They are full of hostility and anxiety against society, which means that they have the same ideas about us as we have about them.

Group Psychotherapy With Offenders Can Work

As I mentioned before, I saw 60 patients during the three years of my service. I had two groups, one in jail, and one on the outside. I preferred to have people in my jail group who were scheduled to leave jail in six months or less. The purpose was to prepare them so that they could follow therapy on the outside on an outpatient basis. I accepted anyone who wanted to join my group. I never asked them about their offenses or about why they were in jail. The only thing I wanted from them was their acceptance of the idea of joining my group. I spent most of my time trying to improve my relationship with them, talking about every subject. I wanted to convey to them the idea that I was their friend; that I would be honest with them, and that I was objective in their conflict with society. I tried to make them understand that jail was not for them and that they could do better. I tried to make them understand that their ideas about society were based on their own private logic. I sympathized with them and blamed the society for some of the injustices done, but I blamed them also. I tried to change their self-image and to give them hope for the future. Every technique was used to make them trust me and form some insight into their situation. Cases were presented to them on every type of mental illness to help them form some insight. In my group on the outside, probation and parole officers had to be used to force them to come to the group. I explained to them that I was using the probation and parole officers because I wanted to help them; that it was for their own good that I did this; and that I was interested in their welfare. Finally, after some time — about three to four months of therapy which had as its purpose the improvement of our relationship and insight — many finally wanted to talk to me about themselves and their problems. Some of them accepted a complete evaluation of their personality, based on my Adlerian orientation. They were explained their life style and their goals,

646

and they were encouraged to do something about their situation. Education and responsibility were stressed continuously. Out of these 60 patients, only one violated his probation; the rest did not get into trouble with the law or violate their probation or parole. The one who violated his probation was the patient who stole the car from the policeman. Not one was a problem in the institution. Six of them are now in college; one of them, a homosexual, works with I.B.M. machines; another is studying to become a newspaper man; and two others are studying to become lab technicians.

SECTION 17: GROUP PSYCHOTHERAPY WITH DELINQUENTS

PRINCIPLES OF INTERPERSONAL THERAPY AS APPLIED TO TREATMENT OF CHRONIC DELINQUENTS

by ROBERT R. BENSON

In over a decade of experience in the area of clinical psychology as applied to the field of corrections, I have found that those chronic "acting outers" who either could or would verbalize directly their need for help have been rare. They refuse to be humbled or to kneel symbolically at the feet of authority. They not infrequently are defensive of their behavior, and their comments indicate that they desire to cling to their dissocial orientation in an effort to maintain at least some degree of self esteem. In many instances, their patterns of behavior are simply those which their own family, sub-culture, or community, have directly or indirectly taught them. Many have learned the lessons taught by their parents and by their dissocial environment all too well —to the dismay of a society that has offered them but little. This appears to be the case whether the client is one seen in the Juvenile Court setting or in private practice. In Juvenile Court, the psychologist is in an authoritarian situation where he can utilize his special sensitivities and skills involved in a dynamic appraisal of personality functioning. The diagnostic study, with its own forthrightness, which the demeanor and general attitude of the court psychologist should call forth from even the most recalcitrant delinquent, more often than not serves as fertile soil for a continuing therapeutic relationship. It is axiomatic that to the extent to which the diagnostician or therapist understands the fantasies and feelings in his client—to this extent will he be able to actually understand his client. Fromm has repeatedly raised questions as regards the therapist-client relationship. How can the specialist in human relations understand the fantasies and feelings in his client unless he senses them in himself? He may talk clearly and be intelligent. He may have read all of the theoretical books and given correct interpretations. But what does he actually know of the innermost thoughts and feelings of the client? The client knows whether the therapist speaks from experience, understanding, or simply from theory. He knows whether he is being respected as a human being or whether he is being treated simply as an object to be interrogated in an aseptic atmosphere. One speaks from experience or understanding only if one has experienced or sensed within oneself the very same thoughts and emotions that the client experiences.

Striking similarities exist in the relationship between parent and child, teacher and pupil, counselor and client, therapist and patient. In each, we find elements of authority or "expertness" in relation to dependence, weakness, or feelings of inadequacy. In my own practice, I attempt to cause the delinquent to speak freely, to know that I do accept him as a person and that I know something about his delinquencies. Not infrequently, the diagnostic session begins with an appropriately emotional tone: "To the extent that you can cause me to see things as you see them, to

650

feel about your situation as you do . . . to this extent can I really come to know you and to make recommendations to the court that will be more nearly in keeping with how you might like things to go. . . ." These comments pinpoint reality. I then share with the adolescent those essentials that I know regarding his particular situation in order that he may feel I am being honest with him and I am interested enough in him to have taken time to know a little something about why he is before the court. Realistically, there is little point in his being deceptive.

One such youngster may serve as an example of what I am trying to illustrate: Jeff, a small pugnacious, W-M-17 year old of average mentality had lived with a crippled father in a shack in the "Dog Patch" area of a midwest metropolis. His mother had died when he was quite young; a somewhat older brother was diagnosed as a Paranoid Schizophrenic and was institutionalized. Jeff's social adjustment had been one of "every man for himself" from his earliest years — his mode of relating, highly narcissistic, competitive. Academically, he was grossly retarded; he harbored a bitter hatred toward school because of its authority and rules, to which he felt unjustly subjected. The school situation had, over the years, only served to heighten Jeff's sense of inadequacy and deprivation. It was easy for him to become aligned against a society which had given him nothing but a hard time; a society which demanded, but never gave. Juvenile Court had permitted Jeff to remain in his home, notwithstanding numerous delinquencies. Then came the day when Jeff, along with several other co-delinquents, was referred to Juvenile Court for having been involved in a "gang bang" episode with a defective 12 year old girl. All of the boys admitted to the complaint; dispositions varied in accordance with the merits in the individual cases. The million dollar question was what disposition should the Court order in the case of Jeff. To commit him to the State Industrial School would have undoubtedly necessitated some type of institutional placement for the hopelessly crippled father — a father for whom Jeff has cared, and in fact, for whom he had stolen food and coal. All of this notwithstanding his delinquencies and dissocial adjustment. Jeff was seen in Sullivanian oriented therapeutic interviews "for whatever gains could be made". Movement in therapy over the months took the form of Jeff's coming to the office in self laundered dungarees, a home-style hair cut, and increased body

651

cleanliness. Grades at school rose to barely passing, as contrasted with previous failures. Jeff did develop a therapeutic dependence upon the therapist in spite of his "toughie" facade. Ultimately, he became so "socialized" that he began asking to be removed from the environs of "Dog Patch", to have an opportunity to live like others of his age, and most of all to have a real home. For obvious reasons, it was impossible to fulfill the desires. The purpose of "therapy" had overshot its mark! In essence, what had occurred was that the movement was not consistent with the reality of the situation! A kind of retracting had to be accomplished, *i.e.* to assist Jeff in once again accepting his dissocial sub-culture, and yet at the same time, to help him retain some of the more cooperative approaches he had begun to inculcate on the interpersonal level — especially in relation to authority. Therapy was terminated after approximately 1½ years, at which time the therapist relocated. Follow-up over a seven year period indicates that Jeff is still living with his invalid father, experiencing fewer "scrapes" with the law, but still maintaining a dissocial adjustment with occasional minor crimes for which he has not as yet been apprehended.

Let us take a look at the positive results that *can be* achieved in the treatment of sociopathic-like adolescents via a Sullivanian interpersonally oriented approach: Rick, a W-M-15 year old of average or better mental abilities came to the attention of Juvenile Court on a complaint of over 40 "lone-wolf" burglaries! Overt behavior was characterized by a sullen, aloof, distrustful "nervous" quality. In view of the nature of the complaints and previous history of delinquent acts against person and property, the Court was justifiably concerned with regard to the course planning should take. Full scale psychological study and social history work-up by a Probation Counselor were ordered. On the eve of Rick's official final hearing, the psychologist had Rick brought from Detention Services to his office. As he awaited Rick's arrival, the psychologist reviewed his diagnostic impressions: "Emotionally unstable personality; a very anxious, impulse ridden youngster; feelings of inadequacy and inferiority very strong; acting out believed to be compensatory in nature; insight and sense of guilt minimal, if any . . ." Probation Counselor's summary: ". . . of somewhat below average income; no evidence of rivalry in relation to his sister who is 3 years older than himself; parents feel that Rick is not the model boy they had expected; mother, highly nervous; father, passive except when he is angered and then he severely whips the boy; parents verbalize interest in their son — they are at a loss as to how to explain his delinquencies or to cope with his incorrigible behavior . . ." In the final session preparatory to formulating recommendations to the Court, every opportunity was given Rick to reveal, either by word or feeling, some regret for his delinquencies, or at least a degree of dissatisfaction with his overt behavior and its self defeating results. Such expressions did not come. Of course, he desired to be returned to the home of his parents. Asked in what way he felt that things might be different either in himself or in his home situation in the event he were permitted to return home, he gave an affectless enumeration. At this point, the psychologist offered very direct interpretation — friendly, but firmly: "You are fearful of being locked up forever. I will share my opinion with you — you feel frightened, afraid, angry; you hate school, your parents, and all others who get in your way; you aren't just sure of me either, yet you know that I have been honest with you and that I am genuinely interested in you, otherwise, why would I have taken of my own time to see you this evening? You don't know whether to take a chance on me or not, yet what do you have to lose?" Rick looked stunned, his eyes watered, he hung his head. He was asked to comment upon the interpretations which the psychologist had offered. All he could muster was a barely audible, "you are absolutely right." This provided the opportunity to get across the idea that the greatest freedom he has, and which no living individual can ever take away, is the freedom to think and to feel as he chooses, and hence, what was the need to fight and rebel in relation to that which he already possessed? Such an idea had never crossed his mind! Recommendation was for probation with concomitant therapeutic interviews either with a private practitioner or with the local Child Guidance Center. The Court was extremely skeptical of such planning, but did give Rick "one last opportunity" to prove that he could get along in the community. Doors for treatment of such individuals are difficult to open. Rick's case was no exception — lack of funds to defray the cost of private psychotherapy, "poor risk", etc. Arrangements were ultimately made for Rick to be seen in out-patient therapeutic interviews by the Court Psychologist. Therapeutic interviews were scheduled on a one hour a week basis, with clear understanding that the psychologist would also be available at other times should the need arise. A casework approach was initiated by the Probation Counselor in relation to the parents. Rick knew that the therapist would lend assistance at any hour of the day or night. This privilege has not been abused. Ability to communicate improved as Rick began to sense within himself that the therapist was genuinely interested in him, and as doubts relative to any "trickery" were removed. He was able to accept benevolent but directive therapy, and to follow through even when he was not certain, or else doubted the wisdom, of the prescribed action. For example, the therapist suggested patterns of behavior in little dosages which might ease the pressures at home, at school, and in relation to peers. Every opportunity was seized upon to enhance Rick's self esteem on a realistic basis — to assist him in developing a realistic command of himself. He began to take pride in his improved school grades, notwithstanding the skeptical comments in the beginning from some of his teachers. These comments suggested that perhaps Rick's higher marks were not honestly earned. In time, however, even these doubters were won over. The dependency relationship between client and therapist deepened, and through this relationship Rick grew to have increased self-confidence, became more trusting of others, and became better able to effect a more comfortable adaptation in relation to authority, along with increased self-control. Interpretations dealt with the immediate and future situations and rarely with the past. The nature of the client-therapist relationship was frequently a focus of attention with accompanying generalizations. This young man was seen for over 47 therapy hours extending over a period of 15 months. No serious "legal" problems arose during this time. The last three grading periods reflected a B— average. Probation is now terminated, and as evaluated by others, including his parents, teachers, and probation counselor, Rick is a "changed boy". His relationships with others have markedly improved, and he is obviously a much happier adolescent. Considering the earlier descriptive data, and the Sullivanian orientation of the therapist, the personality growth that took place in Rick was amazing.

The case of Rick has been, and is continuing to be duplicated in many instances within the framework of out-patient psychotherapy in the Montgomery County Ohio Juvenile Court's Psychological Services, as well as in the author's private clinical practice. Such service is very much needed in behalf of those adolescents in whom society, and the home, ofttimes have fanned the flame of "normal" rebellion. "Social illness" is not hopeless; perhaps, *it is only our dulled sensitivity and underdeveloped techniques which make it seem so.*

PEDAGOGIC ASPECTS OF GROUP PSYCHOTHERAPY WITH DELINQUENTS

by GERARDINA L. VAN DALFSEN

Some countries now use group psychotherapy within the setting of prisons and as a means of curing offenders who committed their offenses because of neurotic disturbances. Where this is the case, psychotherapy and punishment, or at best re-education, follow their own parallel courses without any therapeutic interaction being consciously sought. This is the aim of the small psychotherapeutic community in the Netherlands known as "Groot Batelaar", and one which to a large extent it manages to achieve.

It is a semi-state Salvation Army institution founded in 1953. Psychiatrists, educational therapists, psychologists and other therapeutic personnel are paid by the State, while premises and administration are provided by the Salvation Army. Juridically speaking the inmates are so-called psychopaths, while according to their psychological diagnosis they are psychopathized neurotics. All are males, aged 20 to 40.

Uncovering group psychotherapy according to the methods of Rogers and Bach is the core of the therapies in this institution, which is also rooted in Adler's psychology. Organizationally, the group psychotherapeutic units are also the core of the therapeutic community as a whole. The idea behind this structure is the conception that human life as such expands in concentric circles, the smallest circle being that of the mother and newborn child. It is the task of the mother to direct the attention of the growing child towards the wider circle of father and siblings, while later on the growing adolescent learns to encompass the school, the village or town, the nation and ultimately humanity as a whole. When a child gets into trouble while expanding to the wider circle of the school it has to rely for consolation and encouragement on the smaller circle of the family until its power for further expansion is renewed. But if the smaller inner circles happen to have been impaired, the same impairment will occur in the expanding circles as early traumatic experiences tend to be repeated in later life. As the inmates of Groot Batelaar belong to those who were seriously disturbed in their early youth — that is, in their smaller inner circles — the same kinds of misinterpretations and mistakes are hampering them in subsequent stages of development. In their cases, re-education by means of punishment, drilling, training, logical reasoning and persuasion, has failed. What they need is for the wanting experiences of security and encounter to be made up for them. Only in this way can sufficient courage for a more healthy expansion grow. As their offenses resulted from a serious lack of deep psychological contact, a situation has to be provided where this can be found and established.

Such a situation is group psychotherapy. The groups consist of eight inmates, a psychotherapist and two group leaders, the latter being functionaries who, in addition to attending the therapeutic sessions, join in recreational occupations and have also the task of checking the observance of rules and regulations by the inmates. They have to do this understandingly; and in the absence of the psychotherapist, first aid by means of sympathetic support in emotional disturbances has to come from them. In those cases where the group proves to be too large a circle for the restricted emotional scope of a certain inmate and for his low feeling of security, he can seek refuge in an individual conversation with either the therapist or a group leader, after which, being sufficiently relaxed and encouraged, he again faces the demands of the group. On the other hand the group provides him with insights that he can apply and with which he can experiment in the wider circle of the therapeutic community. In this he may find support in the group leader, who is a sympathetic listener to, and who occasionally joins in, the group discussions, in which that inmate wrestles for his inner discoveries.

In the same concentric way contact is made with society outside the therapeutic community. The same social worker whom he meets in that community and who deals with his family problems prepares his way towards rehabilitation. This also is done step by step from living in the community and working outside to living and working outside under supervision. In this way the psychotherapist and the social worker work in opposite directions while completing each other's tasks, the former penetrating from outward to inward relations while the latter leads the inmate towards the outer circles. In cases in which some difficulty arises in one of those outer circles the permission to work or live outside the community is suspended and the expanding inmate retires to the smaller circle of the community. It even happens that ex-offenders, who have been entirely franchised from supervision, return of their own free will and request to be re-admitted because they feel led into temptation again by certain circumstances. They return in order to renew their vision and regain their courage for a fresh start. In this way psychotherapy, re-education, and rehabilitation are blended in a dynamic structure of concentric circles. Psychotherapy in this institution is communal, and it thrives within a community with a psychotherapeutic atmosphere. The results of this method are sufficiently satisfying. While about all the inmates are repeaters — some of them with seventeen sentences or more — about half of them are satisfactorily rehabilitated, though in a number of cases after some relapses. As it is an open institution, inmates are selected from the point of view of their possible danger to the public and their degree of impulsiveness. Moreover, they have to be of about normal intelligence to enable them to understand uncovering psychotherapy, although psychologically they are seriously disturbed and inaccessible by other measures.

SECTION 18: GROUP PSYCHOTHERAPY WITH SEXUAL OFFENDERS

INTENSIVE GROUP THERAPY WITH SEXUAL OFFENDERS

by G. di Furia and H. L. Mees

We have for the past 3½ years at Western State Hospital been developing a treatment program for sexual offenders utilizing intensive group therapy and including some novel treatment and social living techniques (Mees, 1962).

Selection of patients for treatment is based on many rather arbitrary factors and a few clinical judgments. Whether or not the patient is sent to the hospital for observation for Sexual Psychopathy is a decision of the courts and may have no clinical relevance whatsoever. This is often a matter of geography and luck. Once in the hospital, however, the patient is interviewed and tested psychologically for preliminary evaluation. If he is not mentally defective, overtly psychotic, or completely resistive to treatment, he is put in the group on a trial basis. At the end of his observation period the senior administrative psychiatry staff evaluates him and recommends to the courts whether he should be treated. The clinical judgment is made of whether further treatment will help him change sufficiently to be safe at large. The desires of the patient are also taken into consideration. Typically, the patients feel they are benefitting from treatment and request a return to the hospital.

Insofar as possible, all of the sex offenders are housed on two adjoining wards, one open-door and one locked door, along with other hospital patients. Soon after their arrival at the hospital they are interviewed, started in the therapy group, given a work assignment, and given freedom to be unsupervised on the grounds as they earn trust and privileges. They attend group therapy after working hours, 5 days a week for an hour and a half. As many as 20 members may be in the group at any one time.

The table indicates the types of offenses and diagnosis of the 71 patients seen in intensive group psychotherapy between August 1959 and January 1963.

TABLE 1

OFFENSES AND DIAGNOSIS OF SEXUAL OFFENDERS

Rape	8	Personality Disorders	
Exhibitionism	9	Unstable	1
Incest	8	Passive-aggressive	29
Homosexuality	8	Compulsive	2
Indecent liberties with daughters	16	Inadequate	10
Child molesting	13	Schizoid	7
Transvestism	2	Sociopathic	9
Obscene telephoning	3	Psychoneurotic Reactions	7
Voyeurism	4	CBS - arteriosclerosis	1
	—	Adult situational reaction	3
	71	Schizophrenic reaction	2
			—
			71

The age range of these patients is 18 to 76 and the median age is 36. Of this group 14 were treated while on observation for sexual psychopathy, 38 as committed sexual psychopaths, 13 committed as mentally ill, and 6 on voluntary status. Fifty-nine

660

patients have been discharged, and 12 are receiving treatment. Basic to the therapy program is the assumption that deviant sexual behavior is a *learned phenomenon* which becomes an *habitual reaction* to stress.

Perhaps the best way to communicate the nature of the treatment program is with case history illustrations. If we consider two quite different patients, both of whom have been apparently successful in their rehabilitation, the picture may become more clear.

Our first case is Frank, a Catholic, age 36, the only child of average working class parents. His first illicit sexual experiences started when he was 16. He lived near a school, and would watch girls go by the house while masturbating in his room. He then became more bold and would place himself where he would be seen by the girls. On two occasions at this age he was arrested for indecent exposure and was released in his parents' custody and was seen twice by a psychiatrist. He participated in both solitary and heterosexual experiences from this age on. At 17, he was arrested for knocking down a girl, trying to undress her and exposing himself to her. He was sent to a boy's training school for 3 months. Shortly thereafter he went into the Navy and was arrested at the age of 20 for window peeping, receiving a $25 fine. His fifth arrest was at 23 for window peeping and he was told to see a priest regularly, which he did not do. His next arrest a short time later, for window peeping, resulted in referral to a psychiatrist whom he saw for 3 or 4 months. At 25 his seventh arrest was for indecent exposure, and he was again referred to a psychiatrist for about 3 months. He was not arrested again for 5 years, but was caught exposing himself and was again referred to a priest. At 32 he was caught for indecent exposure and threatening to harm the woman he exposed himself to. By this time he had started entering homes and masturbating in front of or on his victims while fondling or exposing them. He was sent to our hospital for 17 months before our present treatment program had been developed. He received some group psychotherapy and individual attention, but was arrested again shortly after his release. I might add that he was a man of superior intelligence who had more than 2 years of college.

On his tenth arrest he was returned to Western State Hospital for treatment and entered the new program that was developing.

He participated actively for several months and was considered a leader in the group. Then one day the therapist discovered that he had made unacceptable sexual advances toward a psychotic woman patient. In the next meeting he was asked about his sexual activities on the hospital grounds. Under pressure of the group he confessed, but since he did not know just what the therapist was referring to, he confessed to several attempted exposures and an illicit affair with a promiscuous woman as well. This put him in an uncomfortable position with the group. When his wife came to the next husband-wife group meeting, he was put under pressure to confess again. After this his wife and the group kept him under pressure, and he later said that this was the first time he could remember in his life that he could not manipulate himself out of the situation.

In this case it seems apparent that Frank had a repertory of solitary and socially unacceptable ways of receiving gratification. In the group he was not permitted the freedom to continue sexual acting out. His wife also became more active in controlling his behavior. With more direct communication she became able to provide him with various kinds of gratification, including understanding, attention, and sex, for which she had not been aware of his particular needs. We believe we have significantly changed a life-long pattern of unacceptable sexual behavior but whether or not the change will continue depends on the controls and satisfaction afforded by his social environment.

A second case is that of Phil, a 41 year old Protestant, also an only child of working class parents. Prior to an episode of incest with his 13 year old daughter, he had apparently never had any sexual relations with anyone other than his wife and denied having any experience or interest in deviant sexual behavior. His attitudes and appearance were of a sullen, angry, aloof man who showed no desire to interact with others and who frequently abused others verbally. His relationship with the group was one of mutual antagonism, and he frequently berated his wife and family when they visited. It seemed that his primary preoccupation was with hobbies and gadgets, and he was compulsively busy in solitary activities.

Phil's wife was quite faithful and submissive to him, and in the husband and wife group his attempts to dominate her became a matter of concern to the whole group. In one fit of anger he told her he never wanted to see her again, that she was not attractive to him, and that no matter what we did to him he would not change. In the regular group, several incidents between him and other aggressive group members nearly culminated in physical violence. Fortunately, the group was strong and cohesive enough to withstand these tirades and since the members were together almost continuously, the issues were resolved with significant change in the attitudes and behavior of all members concerned. Phil's attitude mellowed and he became considerate, happy, and showed affection both for his wife and other group members. Upon his release following 7½ months of hospitalization, he moved some 200 miles away, having lost his home that was only a few miles from the hospital. He voluntarily and regularly returned for monthly meetings, often driving all night over icy roads to meet in the husband and wife group. He also visited the homes of other members, some of whom he had initially treated with so much hostility. Now, after 7 months he and his wife and children no longer find him to be an unapproachable tyrant.

With Phil we also see a person who had developed patterns of solitary behavior but had not developed interactive social skills. He had, from childhood, been able to manipulate others and get his own gratification by using temper outbursts, hostility, and belligerence. In the group he was not permitted to escape social interaction. His belligerent attitudes did not pay off for him, and he found that he could get satisfaction by using more appropriate social behavior. He became accessible not only to group members, but also to his own wife and children. This was a marked contrast to his previous behavior which would make sexual advances by his daughter the way in which she could win his attention and approval.

Admittedly, these two cases do not prove success of this program, but they do demonstrate the results of a procedure which seems to be more effective than any procedures we have previously used. Our program is not static. We are constantly looking for ways to make patients more directly responsible for their own behavior and to get a greater degree of intensive interaction in a shorter period of time. The group treatment method is considered to be the only feasible type of treatment which will give almost total control over the patient and which will utilize the greatest amount of therapeutic experiences possible for the patient.

663

A RATIONALE FOR THE TREATMENT OF THE HOMOSEXUAL SYMPTOM

by CORNELIUS BEUKENKAMP

This writer views the clinical entity of homosexuality as the expression of a symptom. He has been unable to verify it as a character defect or character neurosis. Furthermore, he concurs with recent investigators that the complexity known as paranoia is not necessarily endogenous to homosexuality. Nor is homosexuality a universal causative or a mutually present property in the paranoid condition. Yet it is occasionally associated with it and sometimes can serve as its etiological basis. Moreover, I see no similarity between overt homosexual contact and homosexual thought process as it manifests itself in the form of a defense. Instead, the homosexual symptom can be a particular mode of non-being or interlaced with other expressions of the denial of personal existence.

Whatever the etiology, the homosexual symptom seems to arise, as do other symptoms, when to be instead of non-being represents a threat to the Self and its identity with the Self. Such threats convert subjects and feelings into objects and objectifications. The authentic Self, failing to become, is replaced by a narcissism that rejects the Self. Apparently another commonality with the symptom of homosexuality is the overt or latent presence of violence. This violence can be projectional or non-projectional. Frequently, it is archaic and primordial. As such, it is either externalized as homicidal or internalized as suicidal potentials. However, regardless of what twist or turn this symptom of non-being may take, the therapist who follows the course of its manifestation will become hopelessly lost in understanding the absent Self unless he can focus upon the purpose of the symptom —namely, to protect the Self by the formation of a non-self.

The schools of psychology that stress interpersonal relationships, or those that view the patient as consisting of healthy and unhealthy parts which require unravelling, run the peril of such confusion; for the patient is a whole human being. If his symptom is viewed by the therapist as a faulty mode of relating or a psychosexual retardation or fixation, such an approach will unknowingly eventuate in a maze of confusion and dualism. The therapist will find himself in a perennial dilemma in his attempt to relate to the patient, oscillating between subjective and objective reactions, thereby falling prey to the dualism the patient is suffering from, even though lacking the same clinical symptom.

Obviously, then, it is not necessary to split the patient or the therapist-patient relationship into segments. To do so will succeed only in keeping the Self and the nonself of the patient in a condition of estrangement. This estrangement is reported by the patient as feelings of separateness. The symptom is, as all symptoms are, symptomatic of sickness. Sickness is alien matter to the Being. Thus, the therapist who accepts the wholeness of the patient's Self and rejects the false identity bestowed by the symptom on the patient by the patient, has the opportunity to free the Self of the alien symptom—sickness. The viability of the therapist-patient relationship carries this task: to encourage, through experiential experience, the establishment of the patient's Self, while the process synchronously renounces the grandeur, illusions, and omnipotent fantasies.

In the writer's successful cases, such fresh experience apparently has been responsible in bringing about despair. This is not despairing despair, for as long as the patient is despairing, he is only continuing to lament his feelings about having to give up his omnipotence rather than choosing his real Self. In realistic despair, the Self is accepted and acknowledged. Facts are alive and relatable. The courage To Be and live as himself encourages the patient to exercise further courage to encounter all his daily agonies. In this special environment of intensive group psychotherapy, no one individual can sustain unrealities for any prolonged time. Here the climate places a primacy on authenticity. This is the greater asset of group experience over individual treatment. However, as most experienced and sensitive group therapists know, necessary transferential and fantasy responses are not stifled despite the setting's proclivity toward reality.

Within individual treatment, the transference and countertransference life is less easily penetrated with alive truth than in the group. The small group of eight members increases the process of Becoming authentic. The patients' effect upon one another does not dilute either the transference or the growth phenomenon, as many authorities unfortunately still contend. Rather, the strength of reality, not to be confused with the intensification of labile emotions, solidifies the inner core of the Beings in this more structured, yet not rigid, therapeutic setting. By contrast, the individual session is more likely to contain rigidity without structure. Therefore, the narcissistic climate of the one-to-one setting is less vulnerable to the permeation of personal meaning and existence.

I have never been able to free either male or female patients from the symptom of homosexuality with the exclusive use of individual sessions. In experiential group psychotherapy, with or without concurrent individual treatment, such successful clinical results have been attained. I have revised my former evaluation concerning the effectiveness of individual treatment. Formerly, I felt that the greatest depth of personal validity was attained in this setting. The weight of evidence to date has revamped this opinion. My present conviction is that the deepest therapeutic mutations occur in the experiential group. Here, the events seem capable of converting mere happenings into meaningful experiences. And most important, the closure of the gap between the non-being and the Being has been more strikingly effected in experiential group therapy than in any other group climate.

A RATIONALE FOR THE GROUP TREATMENT OF THE MALE HOMOSEXUAL SYMPTOM

by Nathan Cooper

This paper hypothesizes: (1) a homosexual's concept of mistrust toward us is inapplicable to most treatment definitions, since he has been unable to develop enough trust in his primary relationships which could be considered "mature love" (Fromm-Reichman, 1952) and thereby evolve trust, nor to engage another individual in an adequate give and take relationship; (2) the very nature of his "acting out" symptomatology is a way of survival (Ekstein and Friedman, 1957). The patient forces the therapist to relate to him, rather than relating to the therapist in the usual treatment method. This communication will illustrate how the "opening gambits" (Ekstein, 1961) are similar to the beginning phases of the treatment of a schizophrenic child. The patient is likely to press the therapist through several stages (Gomberg, 1949). First, he will present himself with the paradox of both wishing for and fearing his relationship with the therapist, or, he will use isolation, and, or, withdrawal by teasing or stimulating the therapist. The perversity of his primary processes, which are so gratifying, will cause him to use many forms of non-human identifications. Second, he will gradually permit himself to become involved in the group, and, in a conflict struggle related to his identity. This "identity" is then shuttled back and forth between his down deeply narcissistic need which he simultaneously loathes, requires, and, loves to the fleeting "identifications" with various group members and back again to the leader. As he travels through this process, he will feel he has harmed himself, the group, and the leader, and will frequently experience the need for flight. Third, at this stage he forces the therapist and group into helping him with the process of consolidating his new identifications. These include the techniques of re-education in which he develops feelings of gratification different from his primary process.

Group Composition

The group consists of three men and four women. All are schizoid personalities. The group has been functioning for three and one-half years. Kim is one of the original members. Only one other member of the group remains since the group's inception. Joe, an aircraft technician, now works with aircraft and electronic engineers, but was a longshoreman and seaman. He is the oldest, approximately 55. The youngest is Elaine, age 34. She had several psychotic attacks, multiple affairs, followed by psychosomatic symptoms, and, is now in remission. She was a former labor organizer. There is Rene who is a musician who played frequently with girls' dance bands. She assumes many male roles. Greg, age 42, the homosexual with torticollis, has been in treatment several years. He has been in group for a year and a half. He is an expert in sailing and works as a corporation mathematican. Then we have Mary, who is a shapely brunette. She was suicidal and shuttles between a variety of feelings of elation and depression, presents herself as quite phallic some sessions and maternal at others. Finally, there is Ed. He is a postman. He frequently hospitalizes himself at the Veterans' Administration when the mail is heavy. He calls the Veterans' Administration his country club. All members have been in individual therapy from one to three and one-half years.

Methods of Involving the Homosexual Patient

Although groups are usually less upset by incest feelings than by homosexuality, the homosexual, despite his protestation, is an unhappy individual who feels isolated from the main stream of society, because of this sense of isolation, seeks the company of fellow homosexuals. This is another reason for some substitute group form of treatment. Since both manifest, and, latent homosexual patients often develop paranoid feelings when the defensive function of their homosexuality fails, as is evidenced by few homosexuals remaining in treatment, carefully tailored structure and techniques are a necessity. This, of course, is applicable to

668

many schizophrenics and others in treatment. In my experience with twenty-seven homosexuals, they, in particular, apparently have to retain even greater distance with unique disguised methods to continue relationships with other persons. Because of the instinctual primary process way the homosexual functions, the therapist will find himself frequently quite thwarted. Of course this is due to our not having developed sufficient techniques for such 'acting out' patients, and, our transference feelings which stem from our middle class intellectual backgrounds. It therefore becomes necessary to develop a technique of an almost parent-like relationship with a homosexual, as though he were a small youngster. He can then reach out and establish the very beginnings of a relationship. This relationship will sometimes have a trigger-like quality, i.e. "one false move or word and I'll . . . " and the patient will withdraw from treatment. He is similar to the 'acting out' adolescent who has a need to be related to at his own level as his way of handling his anxieties, regardless of the therapist. To establish a beginning fragmentary relationship, the therapist must allow the patient to "force" him (the therapist) to relate with opening gambits similar to those used in treating delinquents.

Fearing and Wishing the Relationship

How did each of the two homosexuals wish for and fear the therapeutic relationship? Kim, age 30, was originally referred because his lobotomized mother was receiving psychiatric help. Although he was acting out through homosexual relationships, he came in essentially because of his upset related to his mother. In the initial interviews, in no way, verbally or non-verbally, did I indicate the referral was due to his homosexual acts. Greg, age 42, suffering with torticollis and in terror of his wife's pregnancy was similarly not confronted. It was necessary to follow the behavior of the homosexual peer group culture, i.e. using the approach of one homosexual to another by innuendo, making it extremely impersonal, as though names, places or details did not count. The therapist waited for the patient to present such nondescript approaches. He then would align or league himself with the patient as he revealed the circumstances under which he was encountering difficulties. Kim used distancing devices claiming detailed difficulties with his mentally sick mother who attempted to kill him, and, his business which was losing money. The second patient Greg, had trouble related to sailing his new boat and his mother-like male boss in his office. Both men joked about their difficulties, but, simultaneously maintained non-human images in these relationships. The individuals were depersonalized as they talked about them. With the therapist and the group they both shuttled between extensive teasing or stimulations to presenting many types of instinctual primary process feelings. They had a lack of capacity to relate, to trust, and instead substituted indirect forms of denial, used "homosexual peer-world language" with terms such as "cruising", "gay", and "straight."

*The Conflict Struggle with the Therapist and the
Group Over His Identity*

Mary interpreted Kim's hide and seek technique by saying he wanted to be included, receive group benefits without putting much in. Kim was aghast, glared like an accosted female, pushed his chair from the circular table, and, asserted he wanted to get going with the real problems. It was interpreted that although we understood his responses partly as his wanting closer relationships, he also gave us the feeling that he feared being hurt by direct relationships which he did not control. He felt we didn't accept him as a person. The females interpreted how he would tease men with sharp glances, and, if they returned the response, he would admonish them like a "hit and run driver," who would escape into freeway traffic. Attention was called to his gratifications of teasing and his "non human gruntings." Kim did not comprehend this non-human identity is his reality, but, not reality as it is, and, actually gets him into difficulty. In this second phase of his conflict in relation to his identity to gain the group and leaders' affection, he grudgingly intensified his need to identify with both. He submerged much of his neurotically oriented approach in order to become a part of the group. His behavior seemed different from most patients in that his instinctual sexual feelings were closer to the surface as were his trigger-like paranoid defenses. He would either flee the room, or, stare into space and disengage himself from the group. The group through the leader gave him the right to participate or not without banishment. His fears of intimacy were slowly interpreted. His omnipotent needs which denied him the authentic intimacy he wanted were similarly repeated. He was shown how he would automatically defeat what he longed for.

Consolidating New Identifications

As each tested their capacity to have closer feelings with people, they both laughed at the way they stumbled in this new world of new ways to relate to people. They indicated that each had their own ping pong game. Both members gradually obtained more gratification in their struggle toward health which replaced their previous hurtful methods of relating. Kim, although he regressed one night when he decided to leave his frigid wife, was able to share an incident of "fellatio play" in a public wash room in which he sucked a penis through a hole. The group's capacity to listen non-punitively, nor with horror, but, rather with deep concern for him as a member of the group family. The warm mothering of the female members, and, the reducing of guilt by the ex-seaman gave Kim feelings of concern for him he said he had never experienced before. This led to multiple positive transferences; by then he could really use the group for ego-support, and, also substitute the group with its members for restitution of early oral mothering. Concurrently, with both of the patients individual twice a week sessions continued.

MALE HOMOSEXUALITY: OBSERVATIONS ON ITS PSYCHOGENESIS AND ON ITS TREATMENT BY GROUP PSYCHOTHERAPY

by Samuel B. Hadden

Until the last five years, there have been relatively few communications in literature on the treatment of homosexuality. Freud's pessimistic comments might have much to do with the paucity of psychiatric and psychoanalytical literature on the subject. He stated that "The removal of genital inversion or homosexuality is, in my experience, never an easy matter. On the contrary, I have found success possible only under special favorable circumstances, and even then the success essentially consisted in being able to open to those who are restricted homosexually the way to the opposite sex which has been until then barred, thus restoring to them full bisexual function. To undertake to convert a fully developed homosexual into a heterosexual is not much more promising than to do the reverse, only that for good practical reasons the latter is never attempted." The Wolfenden report, and the report of the Group for the Advancement of Psychiatry, are utilized by organized groups of homosexuals to perpetuate the idea that homosexuals cannot be helped.

Many equivocal views are expressed, such as those of Saul and Beck, who comment that "Analysis of motivation can lessen intensity of drive." Bergler, Hadfield, Hadden and more recently Biebler are among those who believe that the treatment of the disorder offers promise.

There is no general agreement on the cause of homosexuality, but at the present time very few adhere to the hormonal and genetic theories of its determination. Treatment with hormones has about ceased. Heredity as a determining factor is less frequently supported and while conclusions reached from studies

672

of one egg twins are conflicting, work which demonstrates the absence of female sex chromatin patterns in male homosexuals supports the view that homosexuality is experientially determined. Kallman reports concordance of sexual pattern in a large number of one egg twins while Rainer and Mesnikoff and others report discordant patterns of sexual behavior in one egg twins. The latter carried out physical, biochemical and tissue studies along with psychological and psychoanalytical studies for an explanation of the divergent traits, and found no evidence that anything inherent was responsible. They feel strongly that homosexuality is determined by incidents in early life.

Freud's theory of bisexuality is less acceptable among those who investigate the problem. Monroe and Enelo reject the dubious concept of bisexuality and feel that, from their investigations, experiential interpersonal forces within the child-parent family relationships are the most important determining factors. It is my belief that homosexuality is an experientially determined neurotic pattern.

Material brought forth in homosexual groups confirms the fact that many experiences are involved in the determination of the homosexual pattern of sexual object choice. Invariably it is apparent that traumatic experiences in the oral and anal phase of development of the homosexual are probably universal. Almost every patient included in the study reveals an awareness of his being "different" from the time of his earliest recollection, and most of them were recognized by their families as being a problem by age three to five. At this early time they were incapable of making effective peer attachments and suffered from feelings of being aloof and lonely. The most significant trauma is a disturbance in the relation with the mother. The mother is, as a rule, cold and rejecting or overly-protective, cajoling and seductive. In most cases the mother had consciously or unconsciously rejected her feminine role and had, through her harshness, contemptuous manner or otherwise, castrated the father. The father reacted to the mother's role denial either by over hostile aggressive traits, which threatened her, or by passive withdrawal. The son, being unduly identified with the mother, is thereby threatened by the male parent. The struggle for supremacy between the parents makes ultimate identification a difficult one, with resultant confusion in choice of sex role. When the male parent submits to

673

the dominant mother, the son sees the father figuratively castrated and wards off a similar fate by a fear-induced over-identification with the mother.

In the cathartic phase of treatment the disturbed interparental relationship is freely discussed. There is recognition that the response of the father to the mother's rejection of her feminine role is an important experience in determining sexual adjustment. Many patients finally realize that they came to regard the masculine role as undesirable because there was no observable acceptant love relationship between the parents, and they see the male as burdened with the responsibility of support and protection of the family. To some, the masculine role became one of travail with little in the way of gratification, because of the apparent subjugation to the hypercritical, threatening, overwhelming mother. Many male homosexuals regard the father as being completely unnecessary and rejected, and because they fear a similar lot at the hands of the mother, the protective over-identification with her becomes a feature of prime importance in the constellation of etiologic factors. The dominant mother, by her consistent hypercritical attitude, interferes with the son's ability to establish peer attachments and contributes to an early dissociation from group activity. In the group, it soon becomes apparent to the members that each has developed a fear, rather than a hatred, of women, and this excludes women as chosen sexual partners.

The overly protective and seductive mother contributes to the development of a homosexual adjustment in a slightly different manner. She is anxious about the possibility of the son being hurt or becoming ill. She transmits this anxiety to him by encouraging him to give up rough play and very often to turn to the arts or to intellectual pursuits. Having avoided rough play when he joins his peer group in the play lot, he is inept and becomes self-conscious. He withdraws from his peer activities and becomes absorbed in those fostered by the mother. Many times she fulfills her own ungratified desires by having her son become a sexual object to other men. It is revealed that the son of the overly solicitous, overly protective mother becomes aware of his lack of masculine interests and endowments. He finds himself lonely and aloof from his peers, and when they begin to reveal and discuss their interest in sexual outlets with females his normal aggressive trends have been so repressed that he offers himself

674

as a sexual object to his male peers or to older men. In this sort of family constellation, the father may be very passive, or, as he observes his son turning away from masculine pursuits, he rejects him as a sissy and thus insures his regression into a homosexual pattern.

On initiating the discussion of the treatment of the homosexual in groups, the type of patients treated in such groups should be noted. We consider as homosexual only those who have repeated and consistent preference for orgastic sexual contacts with persons of the same sex, often with a renunciation or even disgust for similar experience with the opposite sex. This does not exclude those who have heterosexual capabilities but prefer homosexual outlets. The patients treated in our groups were from private practice, with most of the patients being referred by fellow psychiatrists, other physicians, and a few by lawyers.

From some of our early experiences with groups we found that when a homosexual revealed his problem to a mixed neurotic group, it had a disrupting effect. Despite my efforts to protect him, he empathically felt the rejection of the group and usually withdrew from treatment. Because of this rejection, we turned to treating homosexuals in groups made up exclusively of homosexuals—with gratifying results. The low degree of social tolerance of the homosexual is difficult to influence. In groups made up entirely of homosexuals, we have found that they have little tolerance for the obvious homosexual—"The Fairy". This type is frowned upon and vigorously rejected unless his conspicuous dress and mannerisms are quickly altered. It was surprising, on several occasions, to see how rapidly a change in appearance and behavior was brought about by group pressure on a member who made his homosexuality obvious by his mannerisms or dress.

In organizing a homosexual group, as with other groups, we have found it desirable to have the patients close together in age and intelligence. When the difference in age is too great, the transference activated between the young and old members involves a reality aspect that is difficult to work through. We have had little success with the adolescent who is actively homosexual, but we feel that a group of adolescent homosexuals can be successfully treated.

We now have such a group in the early stage of treatment. Men after forty are quite resistive to change and are prone to withdraw from treatment, but alteration of sexual pattern has been effected in those who persevere.

From several experiences we have learned that homosexuals who were treated in an exclusively homosexual group can later be integrated with psychoneurotics who are well advanced in treatment. When the homosexual ego is no longer fragile and the group has become quite mature, they can tolerate the homosexual member and help him to deal with this and other aspects of his neurosis.

Freud and others have pointed out that success in treating the homosexual is unlikely unless the individual is strongly motivated to alter his sexual pattern. We have found that a strong desire to change is not essential to success in the treatment of the homosexual in a group because the group is able to activate desire to change by breaking down the rationalization of the individual that homosexuality is really his choice and that he would not change if he could. The group attacks this assertion of members by alluding to the ostracism, loneliness, social isolation and other problems that homosexuality brings. This type of behavior activates anxiety, which makes it possible to explore its genesis. Eventually, the acceptance that their homosexuality has been experientially determined by factors beyond their control is brought about, and the members soon discard any beliefs that they are an especially gifted and unique group. They accept themselves as different only in that they are sick. They no longer denounce society for its harsh attitude toward the homosexual. Being able to recognize themselves as sick, they want to undergo change. They soon encourage each other in their efforts to change and there is obvious growth by identification with those who are progressing.

In an exclusively homosexual group the individual member is soon able to relinquish his rationalized belief that he wants to remain homosexual, and he loses his fear that he cannot he helped. He is prone to seek eagerly an understanding of the experiences which have interfered with his ability to accept the male role in life. He realizes that not only has he failed to accept male sexuality but that he is a dependent person prone to avoid responsibility for self and certainly for others. The fear of the female he recognizes as a vigorous obstruction to a masculine role. A father figure, which seems to threaten annihilation if the son accepts masculine sexuality, is another deterring experience, and the struggle between parents is quite universally recognized as the determining factor.

Defects in character and various neurotic patterns are revealed in the analyses which occur in the group. The recognition that their homosexual acts are only a part of their maladjustment activates strong motivation for change, and the reality demands of the group presses for the change of these as well as the homosexual pattern. Quite often the group angrily attacks the psychiatric attitude of hopelessness that prevails about the treatment of homosexuality and is especially hostile to "gay" groups which assure the young homosexual that he can never be changed. In the group, the homosexual pattern of behavior is constantly under condemnation and attack, but there is relatively little discussion of the homosexual activity of the members. We have never used diminished frequency of outlets or diminished intensity of drives as a gauge of improvement. Only the overall movement toward a full acceptance of masculine responsibility and the relinquishing of neurotic patterns is considered significant. The development of positive, meaningful relationships within the group enables the members to begin the reconstruction of a more mature relationship within the circle in which they function. Those who have not retreated into the isolation of gay groups find this movement toward a mature adjustment much easier. As members move toward the acceptance of the female as a potentially gratifying love object, they soon move from a consideration of physical endowment to seeking in females traits such as cheerfulness, agreeableness, acceptance, warmth and tolerance. Often the feeling toward an attractive female has been summed up by saying, "She just makes me feel like a man." Revelations of this sort are far more significant of progress than continence over a particular period of time.

We are unwilling to speak in terms of a cure of homosexuality because we regard homosexuality to be only a symptom, and its suppression without definite personality reorganization to be of little value. We have observed homosexual patients who changed from 'cheats' and 'liars' into productive and reliable citizens, still struggling with strong homosexual drives but constantly striving to move toward a heterosexual adjustment which might be some years away. Such a change might be more worthwhile than the suppression of the symptom with the activation of a pattern of forgery and financial irresponsibility. We aim at a personality reorganization rather than symptom control. The group sets the goal and realistically demands maturity of its members.

From more than ten years of experience with the treatment of homosexuals in groups, we would plead for a change in the pessimistic attitude which prevails about the treatment of homosexuality. We regard homosexuality as a symptom of a deep-seated neurosis and not as a clinical entity.

We feel that a group can motivate the majority of homosexuals to cooperate in treatment. While adolescents are more resistive, we feel they, too, can be effectively treated in groups. With 100-150 hours of treatment, we believe that the majority of homosexuals can be changed into exclusively heterosexual males. It is about time we liberated ourselves from the influence of the castrating authorities who have pronounced homosexuality as untreatable and deterred us from effective investigation and experimentation in the area.

SECTION 19: PSYCHOSOMATIC MEDICINE AND GROUP PSYCHOTHERAPY

THE TREATMENT OF ACUTE ALCOHOLIC PATIENTS WITH ADRENAL CORTEX EXTRACT INTRAVENOUSLY

by Emanuel D. Kotsos

The effects of Adrenal Cortex Extract in the alcoholic when given intravenously, as evidenced by the rapid elimination of the physical as well as the mental symptoms harassing the patient, could be called dramatic.

Both the physical and the mental symptoms are eliminated within one or two minutes following the injection, or they are reduced to a minimum. The patient, overtaken all of a sudden by an immense feeling of well-being, is prompted to call the injection miraculous. This feeling of well-being and tranquillity observed in these patients is far above any tranquillization I have witnessed in any patients under any tranquillizers or psychic energizers known to me.

While observing and treating alcoholics on their admission to the hospital it occurred to me that their mental as well as their physical symptoms had a striking resemblance to the symptoms of patients in acute panic. Consequently, I extended the above treatment to them also. The results, though not as dramatic as with the alcoholic, are definitely very favorable.

It is my hope that in employing the mechanism of Adrenal Cortex Extract injections I am contributing in some way to the efforts of our profession in helping people, and that other doctors may pursue this treatment further for the benefit of humanity.

GROUP PSYCHOTHERAPY WITH HEADACHE PATIENTS

by MAX COOPER

Several years ago the writer collaborated and reported on the use of group psychotherapy techniques with 35 patients suffering from migraine and tension headache. The following statement is a direct quotation from this report: "It would be justifiable to state that the results observed and the impressions obtained warrant the use of this type of therapy either independently of, or simultaneously with, medical or other forms of treatment. We are, thus, in essential agreement with group therapists who have described their results and experiences with patients who exhibit various types of somatic symptomatology."

In this investigation patients were seen once a week in sessions which lasted from sixty to seventy-five minutes each. The groups ranged in number of patients from five to ten, with an optimum number of seven or eight. The average number of sessions attended by each patient (who was included in the study group) was between 75-80 over a period of 18 months. Most patients were in contact with the group therapist only in the group setting, but the therapist did on occasion have individual therapeutic contact. The basic therapeutic orientation was eclectic, but with considerable use of psychoanalytic theory and method. The goals of therapy were limited, with specific emphasis on symptom relief and reduction of anxiety in general. The investigators made specific reference to their observation that most of the patients treated obtained at least symptomatic relief. In several instances distinct behavior changes were noted, *e.g.* patients who were previously unable to express overtly hostile feelings were subsequently able to do so with minimal guilt.

The writer has been consulted from time to time by several patients subsequent to the completion of the above investigation. In three such cases the patients entered into long term intensive individual psychotherapy with him. In these three patients, in addition to the traits mentioned above, there was extremely masochistic behavior in general. Patient A, for example, from early childhood was constantly pre-occupied with pleasing her parents, especially her mother, and in adult life exhibited this pattern in her relations with not only her husband and children, but to go to the other extreme, was similarly inclined in her dealings with merchants and casual acquaintances. Her mother had always indoctrinated her with the dictum "you must never show your love or anger to anyone." This patient frequently referred to the fact that she and her husband had never quarreled in over twenty years of married life. It was of considerable interest to note that this patient, as well as the other two described below, married men who were apparently extremely masochistic in personality make-up. Patient A was thus forced into a role of dominance, similar to the role her mother had assumed with her father. She had hoped to marry a man "upon whom I could lean completely". It would appear, therefore, that in this case the patient consciously sought an aggressive spouse but on an unconscious level selected one whom she could dominate. The patient soon revealed a deep-seated conflict in the area of sexuality. Here she exhibited a strong need to control her feeling and thus reduce the guilt which was related to unresolved oedipal problems and fears of homosexuality. Following the period of group psychotherapy, she became strongly motivated and recognized her need for long term intensive psychotherapy, if she was to relieve her head symptoms to an appreciable extent. Following three years of individual psychotherapy she was able to achieve sufficient freedom, not only in sex relations with her husband (who incidentally also benefitted to a lesser but significant extent in this respect), but was able to occasionally enter into mild disputes with him as well as others without developing a headache.

In the second case, the patient presented a history quite similar to that of Patient A. In the case of Patient B, the father died suddenly as the result of a heart attack when she was twelve years old. The mother was apparently a passive-dependent character type who was forced, much against her desires, into the role of dominance following the death of her husband. The patient, who was thrown into an intense reaction pattern after her father died, began to experience almost constant head pain (which at times appeared to be delusional), growing in frequency and intensity. She subsequently never married but did enter into a sexual relationship with a married man who had a family and who (with her encouragement) used this as a subterfuge for maintaining his marriage and home and enjoying what appeared to be a satisfactory sexual life, at least for himself. After group therapy, the patient recognized her masochistic pattern and entered into psychoanalysis. She was able to establish for herself the relationship between her masochism and her unresolved oedipal conflict following her father's death (for which she thought she was in some way responsible), so that she was able to enjoy more adequate relations with her family and friends, although she could never bring herself to the point of demanding that her lover divorce his wife and marry her.

Patient C spent the first eighteen years of her life in a home where the father never provided adequately for the family. The mother appeared to rationalize this fact for the benefit of the patient and her two sisters under the guise that she "loved him and could not leave him". The patient began to have head pain during early adolescence and verbal productions during psychotherapy strongly suggested oedipal problems associated with fears about homosexuality. When the father died suddenly in an automobile accident during the patient's eighteenth year, the head pains became intensified and were subsequently diagnosed "migraine". This patient married an obviously masochistic lawyer who always feared entering private practice and who has spent his life as a law secretary. To complicate the situation, the patient gave birth to a mongoloid child and began to devote her life to his care until she was able to send him to a state school for mental retardates. This event occurred shortly after she began to attend group psychotherapy sessions.

In reviewing the histories of these three individual therapy patients, as well as the patients referred to in the investigations mentioned above, it was most interesting to note the fact that in no case was there ever any attempt, or for that matter any mention, of separation or divorce, and so far as the writer can determine, there was never any evidence of extra-marital or promiscuous sexuality. In the case of Patient B, who had chosen to be a mistress rather than demand marriage from her lover, there was sufficient evidence to indicate that the patient had never had a sexual affair with another man. These observations would, of course, be consistent with the extreme pattern of masochism exhibited by headache patients in general.

It is the writer's impression in re-reading the literature and reviewing other cases from his private practice where patients exhibited somatic symptoms in association with their psychoneurosis, that the pattern of masochism is quite common. It would appear, therefore, that the somatic symptom probably represents a mechanism of defense against anxiety, and in some cases against complete disintegration of the personality structure. As a matter of fact, the writer has in certain cases utilized strictly supportive techniques in order to preclude a psychotic reaction. In such cases it was possible, after prolonged supportive methods, to undertake depth analysis and uncover the basic conflict and to free the ego of the individual sufficiently to utilize previously established defense mechanisms which had become immobilized in the face of overwhelming conflict.

The theoretical relationship between specific personality trait patterns and specific somatic syndromes has been proposed by some investigators who study symptom patterns in psychoneurosis. For example, we can still find references to the "ulcer personality" or the "colitis patient". On the basis of his personal research, as reported above, and clinical experience, the writer has not yet found a basis for subscribing to any theory which proposes a relationship between specific somatic symptoms and personality traits or patterns. One might seek to establish some relationship between the fact, for example, that headache patients as a group score above the average on tests of intelligence and the use of the head as the organ for expressing some form of neurotic conflict. This would involve the theory of organ language as a displacement mechanism for anxiety. The writer also reviewed the Rorschach protocols which he used in the above study of Rorschach patterns in headache patients. He found considerable evidence to suggest that the patient group in general made extensive use of the form aspects of the blots, which is usually interpreted as a tendency to use the intellect as a defense mechanism. It would, however, be very difficult to go beyond this point in speculating upon the above relationships in personality patterns.

Similarly, one might deduce that headache patients exhibit repressed sexual behavior in association with unresolved oedipal problems. For example, in the three cases described as A, B, and C, psychotherapy in each case did uncover extreme hatred of the mother during adolescence. Yet all three patients revealed a pattern of almost total dependency on the mother during adolescence and in two cases reacted with extreme guilt when the mother died. The third patient lost her mother after many years of marriage during which they resided under the same roof. The behavior exhibited by each could be interpreted as a reaction pattern to cover and conceal the basic hatred of the mother, which in turn might involve some association with the use of head pain as a neurotic mechanism.

SECTION 20: GROUP PSYCHOTHERAPY AND LSD

GROUP PSYCHOTHERAPY AND LYSERGIC ACID DIETHYLAMIDE

by Alberto Fontana

The potentialities of LSD 25 as a therapeutic aid in group psychoanalysis became apparent to us on the basis of our experience in individual therapy, combining the usual analytic technique with the administration of lysergic acid. To the best of our knowledge, group-analytic experimenting with lysergic acid has so far been undertaken by Lerner, Jarvik and Abramson, and by Talliaferro and Iraldi. Their reports refer explicitly to the

685

increase in communication between the experimental subjects, who showed, moreover, "improvement with regard to ego-structure". No reference is made, however, to any special psychotherapeutic technique, the authors merely pointing out that these were "social" psychotherapeutic or collective sessions. Our own conclusions—which have hitherto seen only partial publication—have encouraged us in the further study of group dynamics and clearly established the particular value of lysergic acid as a therapeutic aid in group analysis.

As we have shown in previous papers, the action of this drug helps to bring out plainly the defenses against communication put up by patients in the course of individual or group analysis. At the same time, the motivations behind these defenses are made arrestingly clear to the patients' awareness and understanding, thus enabling them to exercise a correspondingly greater insight.

The group situation is particularly suited to expose defense mechanisms in a dramatic light. Basically, the material that finds dramatic expression in time during the individual session with lysergic acid, is as it were spatially dramatized in the course of group analysis with the aid of lysergic acid. The patient subjected to individual analysis will go through varying defensive technique in the immediate situation ("here and now"), and this of regression being reached. One may observe the workings and the sequential externalization of all sorts of defenses when the patient, under the influence of lysergic acid, is terrified by the loss of ego-boundaries owing to the intensity of his avidity. At this stage, psychopathic behavior, projection, dissociation, introjection, short-lived or protracted hypochondriac spells, and ultimately even intra-uterine regression fantasies, will be observed; the latter, representing a maximum degree of defensiveness in the face of a most intense avidity leading up to a complete block both within and without the ego, resulted in the loss of all boundaries and self-control.

The capability to overcome this fear of the loss of ego boundaries makes it possible for the patient later to achieve communication with inner and outer reality without experiencing this as ego disintegration. All these mechanisms, which are dramatized in time during individual psychoanalysis, will be exposed in the course of group analysis in the same situation with combined therapy. The difference between the individual-analytic situation and the group-analytic situation lies in the fact that every member of the group characteristically seems to adopt a particular defensive technique in the immediate situation ("here and now"), and this is seen to take place both dramatically and spatially. This characteristic activity would appear to represent each member's social role prior to the emergence of group relatedness. Thus, a certain member will at a given moment lapse into psychopathic behavior, another will adopt hypochondriasis as his own role, a third will take charge of the intra-uterine regression fantasies of the group; in this way each one of them will control, in a rigid, stereotyped manner, the possibilities of communication with the self and with the group.

This we wish to emphasize especially. The dread occasioned by confrontation with the unknown—*i.e.* the group situation—causes every patient to undertake a single defensive role. This role appears to be closely associated with the habitual techniques employed by the patient in order to avoid any sort of communication that might seriously jeopardize the stability of this internalized object.

An interchange of roles is observed to occur as an intermediate stage in the process of mobilization affecting these internal objects, but the group *gestalt, vis* the group's basic fantasy, is nevertheless maintained. The sense that haunts every individual on joining the group—that of his ego disintegrating through communication with the group—is then made conscious to all the members by thorough interpretation of the fear and reluctance toward participating in the group, and by the exposure of the rigidity of the roles and of the maintenance of the group *gestalt*.

It was clear to us that through the analysis of verbalization and the resulting interpretation of avidity, we were able to transform patients who were stereotyped in their roles into individuals unafraid of being absorbed, "sucked in" and disintegrated by the group.

In this situation, previous to individuation, the group *gestalt* was shaped notably on the group's oral fantasies. Every patient will project his oral fantasies on the others, thus conceiving the group as an enormous mouth ready to devour and destroy him.

The integration of the individual with the group is characterized by the patient's overcoming this basic fantasy. The individual now comes to regard the "we" as participation without loss of individuality.

Those subjects who prove extremely avid experience the shedding of the roles as a sense of doom, as the world being at an end. Apparently this is due to the mobilization and release of archaic internal objects both within and without the ego, being sensed as disintegration of the ego. In order to avert complete destruction (since the ego is also a bodily ego), the individual has recourse to the fantasy of fusion as manifested by that of intra-uterine regression, which is the equivalent of his psychosis. The opposite possibility is represented by the internal objects, and the possibility of integration with the same. Interpretation of these fears in connection with archaic and inherited structure is conducive to an enhanced communication within the group and with the patient's self. Surprisingly, group acting-out is observed in this connection, representing an attempt to express and elaborate upon this collective experience.

No longer do the group members express that which is purely personal; rather, they seek that which is somatic, inherited and instinctual. The possibility of communicating at these archaic levels is achieved by the individual who can break through the mind-body dichotomy and commune with the primitive images generically present in his soma.

We believe that the group-analytic situation under the influence of lysergic acid favors the emergence of phenomena from the collective unconscious to a degree seldom seen in the course of individual analysis. The dominant *gestalt* is usually represented by a symbol which the group comes to adopt as a veritable totem. Thus, in a group undergoing intense regression and with a keen feeling of its own avidity, the *spider* was adopted to signify the group as voraciously absorbing every one in it, and the voracity of each one of its members as well.

The re-creation of these archaic objects brings about in some instances an omnipotent identification with the same, whereby the patients are apt to assume a Messiah-like attitude. Other patients are overwhelmed by these unconscious experiences, but they nevertheless maintain their omnipotence. Interpretation of the above situation effects the transition from magic to communication. Here each patient abandons his reluctance to admit his relatedness and

688

simultaneously accepts time and its limitations, feeling a decrease in his omnipotence, yet enriched by his relatedness. There arise existential impressions of the passage of time, the fear of death, and preoccupation with regard to the possibilities of creation or separation. At this stage the integration and maturity of the group is attained, as is the integration and maturity of every member to a different degree and on a different level. This may be compared with a musical group in which the tune and rhythm of every player fuse with those of the rest to create a collective rhythm and melody that does not interfere with the individual themes.

The foregoing is a brief account of what (up to this point) we believe to be the explanation for the phenomena observed in the psychotherapeutic group when placed under the influence of LSD 25 employed as a variant of the usual analytic technique. Our personal experience is based on seven years' work and on the study of 25 groups in progress and of almost 500 patients under treatment at the present time. The scrutiny of this material has led us to the belief that group psychotherapy, in conjunction with lysergic acid diethylamide, is a very effective method of research and treatment. A growing interest in it has been evinced by several colleagues who have begun to put it into practice.

OBSERVATIONS ON GROUP PSYCHOTHERAPY WITH PATIENTS UNDER PSYCHOLYTIC TREATMENT WITH *LSD 25*

by G. W. ARENDSEN HEIN

The LSD is administered to the patients in therapeutic doses, ranging from 40-250 gamma per os, early in the morning. They are put in separate rooms, isolated from external stimuli as much as possible. After about three hours, most of them receive an injection of methedrine or ritalin, after which a certain elucidation, structuring and interpretation of previous experiences takes place. After six to eight hours, the effect of the drug gradually disappears. Patients then get food and drinks; they can paint, write or indulge in other specific desires. Then, after 5 o'clock in the afternoon, a group-session is held. Only after it is finished are the effects of the drug terminated by administration of chloropromasine.

Normal group psychotherapy already favors emotional expression, but typical of the LSD group is a tendency to unmask oneself in a most complete form of liberating discharge. Transference phenomena toward the group therapist and other group members appear to be of less importance, because in the previous LSD experience, the images of the original persons involved, or their symbolic substitutions, had been encountered with the feeling of full actuality, thus providing the patient with the opportunity to relive specific situations in a most direct form, and diminishing considerably the inclination to transference behavior.

Another feature is, that group members take each other more seriously. Judgments tend to become more realistic and objective, which promotes a constructive atmosphere and favors strong catharsis. That does not merely mean abreaction of emotions, but also exposure of self in the group, giving oneself away to the group and by doing so, being accepted by the group. The feeling of being accepted by others, leads to a new form of self-acceptance. Usually, the quality of the affective contact is better than in the average group. Discussions are accompanied by different forms of non-verbal expressions, thus adding to their honesty and spontaneity. Anxiety over the loss of self-control is strongly diminished by an increased sense of value and trust in one's own judgment regarding the experiences. There is less inclination towards dependent reaction patterns — the patient does not worry so much about what other people think of him because he feels so much more himself. On the other hand, uncontrolled behavior by other group members is less threatening. Human contact is more direct and complete. Not only are facades, make-believe attitudes and habitual behavior-patterns eliminated; strivings for power and domination come to the fore. The fact that each member relates to deeper layers of the personal and collective unconscious entails that each meets the other on a different level and discovers what a deeper emotional contact actually means. This leads to fortification of the ego and reduces the need to fall back upon defense mechanisms.

After the period of regression that many experience during their treatment in the miraculous LSD world, it is difficult for them to span the gap to reality alone, and it is the group that provides the bridge to re-established contact with normal life. At that moment, the patient only wants to speak about his impressions. He feels that such a discussion is meaningful, and finds sufficient response only with people who have gone through the same experiences. This also enhances the feelings of solidarity and the awareness of the unique experience that they share together. As the after-effect of the drug may last for several days, and one has to take into account a reactive increase of the tendency to act out in psychopaths, close supervision after treatment is necessary. To take full advantage of the process that LSD has initiated, we can with profit hold two or three group sessions a week under normal conditions; we may observe how the process of integration proceeds, and how the whole group therapeutic procedure is intensified and gains in intensity and significance.

GROUP PSYCHOTHERAPY WITH LSD 25

by Francisco Perez Morales

Psychotherapy and LSD 25

When we started working in group psychotherapy with LSD 25, we did so along lines laid down during our experience with the same method in individual, bi-personal relationships. This approach includes the following points:

1) The effect of LSD 25 is to diminish the identity of the ego and its orientation in reality through the inhibition of the synapses of certain axodendritic circuits. The primary process then becomes more accessible with the consequent strengthening of the defenses. There thus comes about a dialectic process, which, through the therapist's activity, leads towards integration.

2) Communication is the operational factor around which the psychotherapeutic work pivots. We define as communication all modes of giving and receiving in which the subject expresses his degree of capacity to accept the object as something external to, and separate from, himself.

3) From this standpoint, we regard any and every pathological form of object relationship as modes of defense against communication.

4) The psychotherapeutic process, under the effect of LSD 25, appears at first a movement towards utter lack of communication, and then towards communication. This finds expression in the relationship the patient forms with the LSD 25, which becomes integrated with the one he forms with the psychotherapist.

5) This whole process (extreme lack of communication-com-

munication) is experienced by the patient through concrete elements: light, heat, cold, color, sound. This is what characterizes the method: the quality of the experience, which brings the patient to feel his degree of communication in a significant way, so that it ceases to be a concept and becomes a live relationship.

6) The activity of the therapist is of particular importance if the patient is to attain awareness of his extremely low degree of communication. He should feel that his therapist possesses great assurance, for his yielding to this possibility means his breaking away from his stereotypes, which, in many cases, is conceived by him as a falling into psychosis. We deem it indispensable that the physician working with this method should first have experienced it upon himself.

7) The effect of LSD 25, in sharpening perception, favors the breakdown of the symbol system (system of adaptation to reality by means of speech), thus aggravating the confusion between the world of words and actual experience. This makes possible that, parallel to the increase in his degree of communication, the patient progressively reconnects the symbols with the experiences from which they originate.

Communication and group

In accordance with the aforesaid, the aim of the group is to cure all its members through the concrete task of improving the communication of each one of them. The group is at once an instrument and an aim; the former, because it is through the group that the individual receives stimuli that further that task, and the latter, because it is the aim of every individual to attain to communication within a group situation.

We point out under 3) that the lack of communication assumes particular forms according to the patient. Thus, in a subject in whom hysterical elements predominate, the lack of communication will display itself through "as if"; in one in whom obsessional elements predominate, through ritualization and control; in the schizoid, through dissociation. Within the group, these defenses assume original forms peculiar to this situation—namely, roles.

The assumption of roles is the characteristic defense of the group situation, where we understand by the term role the behavior that expresses a partial aspect of the personality. By means of his role, the patient avoids assuming other forms of behavior that are undertaken by the other members of the group. In this way the subject finds a means of maintaining his lack of communication, for, by stereotyping himself in a role, he blocks the connection with himself and hence with objects. But at the same time, in order to be able to keep up this situation of refusing to express and act other roles, each patient needs to drive his companions into assuming their roles more and more thoroughly (and in no way departing from them). The object of this is a twofold control; on the one hand he ensures that there is present an aspect of himself which he needs to control; on the other hand he avoids the appearance of new aspects which would demand of him an additional effort at control. In this way, each member of the group comes to personify one role, which simultaneously expresses the aspect of his personality that he allows himself to show and which is one that another patient needs to hide.

Communication, group and LSD 25

The effect of the LSD 25 is to enhance the group situation and cause every situation to be experienced in a concrete and dramatic fashion. Spoken words, which, according to the degree of lack of communication, function as a symbol system independent of experience, sound empty under the effect of the drug, and the human voice seems subdued and cold. Speech is felt to be something useful through being disconnected from the primary process; for the same reason, it is senseless to listen. Aggression and fear, primitive forms of defense against communication, are lived in a univocal manner. The extreme lack of communication is felt as intense cold, colorlessness, and disregard for sound. All this is identified with immobility and death. As the patient progressively increases his ability to communicate, he starts projecting himself onto objects by means of hallucinations. He feels warmth better; color and sound come to life; and movement acquires sense and vitality. He contemplates objects with wonder, seeing them as independent entities, separate from himself.

The group situation, combined with the effect of the LSD 25, produces a dramatization of every situation, for each subject hallucinates into his companions, and merges into them; he fears them or needs them, manages them or submits—as is clearly displayed in his overt behavior. The roles are felt as monotonous automatisms; the patient comes to experience himself as an isochronous rhythm that expresses his stereotyped repetition. This comes to be felt as death and can no longer be kept up. In accordance with the role he is living, the patient sees his companions' faces change; in so far as he becomes integrated, he begins to see them as they really are. Speech is now a means of communication, because it becomes united with experience, or rather, springs from it.

Indications and counter-indications

The application of this method is useful, in general, for neuroses, characteropathies and psychosomatic illness, particularly those in which emotional blockage is intense and communication therefore at a minimum. We counter-indicate the method for certain psychopathic personalities whose need of acting out exceeds the possibility of therapeutic control. On the other hand, we may state that those psychopathic personalities, whose need of acting out may be confined within therapeutic limits, may be improved by this technique, in a measure unattainable by any other therapy, as far as our experience goes.

695

GRUPPENPSYCHOTHERAPIE IN DER PSYCHOSOMATISCHEN KLINIK

von H. Enke, A. Houben, E. Ferchland, G. Maas,
P. Rotas und G. Wittich

1. Grundlegung: Psychoanalyse und Klinik

Nachdem Viktor von Gebsattel vor 5 Jahren allein einen
Spaziers gang durch die Abteilung unternommen hatte, re-
sumierte er: "Merken Sie sich — die Therapie beginnt hier im
Hause, wenn die Ärzte das Haus verlassen!". Damit war uns mit
aller Prägnanz vor Augen gestellt, dass die Interaktionen und
Kommunikationen im Rahmen der Lebensgemeinschaft die Therapie entscheidend — positiv oder negativ — beeinflussen.

In diesem Zusammenhang ist auch an die bekannte Vermutung
von Balint zu erinnern, der es für möglich hält, "dass der
Patient nach einer . . . psychoanalytischen Behandlung *deutlich
weniger neurotisch,* aber vielleicht nicht. . . reif geworden ist;
nach einer erfolgreichen Behandlung mit Gruppenmethoden ist
der Patient nicht notwendigerweise weniger neurotisch, aber *deutlich
reifer* geworden" (S. 25).

Hiermit ist das so überaus schwerige Kapitel "Psychoanalyse
und Klinik" angeschnitten. Diese Situation ist dadurch verschärft,
dass nicht nur die Balint'sche Antonomie zwischen Psychoanalyse und "Gruppenmethode" besteht, sondern in der Klinik sogar
eine *realitätsorientierte Lebensgemeinschaft* vorgegeben ist.

Es steht fest, dass eine Psychoanalyse im klassischen Sinne nur
durchführbar wäre, wenn in der Klinik alle "nichtärztlichen" Kommunikationen ausgeschaltet, unterbunden würden. Nur dann könnte
der Arzt als Analytiker Übertragung und Widerstand in der
üblicher Weise empfangen und aufarbeiten. Aber auch eine analytische Gruppenpsychotherapie im strengen Sinne ist nicht gewähr-

leistet. Die Gruppen sind, wie gesagt, offen. Die psychosomatischen Indikationen, die sozialen und gesellschaftlichen Ereignisse des Hauses machen es dem Therapeuten unmöglich, die Rolle des neutralen Gruppenanalytikers durchzuhalten, wie das von der engeren analytischer Gruppenpsychotherapie gefordert wird (Grinberg et al., Bahia).

Es hat den Anschein, als müsse man auf die psychoanalytische Bemühung in der Klinik verzichten, wenn man die Interaktionen im Rahmen der Lebensgemeinschaft bestehen lässt. Im Falle eines solchen Verzichtes wären wir gezwungen gewesen, das psychotherapeutische Schwergewicht auf psychagogische Verfahren, auf organismische Umstimmung und auf Trainingsmethoden zu legen. Diese Beschränkung auf "aktiv-klinische" Methoden (J. H. Schultz) hätte jedoch den Indikationsbereich unterträglich eingeschränkt. Besonders jenen psychosomatisch Kranken, die einer tiefergreifenden Psychotherapie bedürfen und wegen ihrer Krankheit gleichzeitig in einer Klinik sein müssen, hätten wir nicht helfen können.

In der Tat haben wir n i c h t auf die analytische Bemühung verzichtet. Ermutigt wurden wir dazu wesentlich durch die wertvollen Arbeiten des Ehepaars Balint aus der Tavistock-Klinik. Dort geht es bekanntlich um die Frage: Was kann die Psychoanalyse dem praktischen Arzt oder — neuerdings — dem Facharzt an psychotherapeutischen Möglichkeiten und an analytischer Selbsterfahrung vermitteln? In der Durchführung dieses Programms hat die Psychoanalyse zahlreiche Veränderungen, Abweichungen von den strengen Regelhaftigkeiten erfahren, ohne dabei aufzuhören, Psychoanalyse zu sein. Grundsätzlich zeight das Balint 'sche Forschungsprogramm, dass es möglich ist, die psychoanalytische Grundkonzeption in anderen "Feldern" ärztichen Handelns fruchtbar werden zu lassen. Warum sollte es dann nicht auch im Feld der Klinik möglich sein? Auch in anderen Kliniken, in denen stationäre behandelt wird, ist man um die Einführung der Psychoanalyse in die stationäre Therapie bemüht, z.B. in Tiefenbrunn (Kuhnel u. Schwidder). (Es handelt sich, wie gesagt, nicht um die Durchführung der Psychoanalyse *trotz* stationärer Asylierung und auch nicht um die stationäre Vorbereitung einer späteren ambulanten psychoanalytischen Behandlung.)

Wir sind davon überzeugt, denn unsere Erfahrung hat es uns gelehrt, *dass in der systematischen Durcharbeitung der gruppen-*

psychotherapeutischen Möglichkeiten der Klinik der Schlüssel für
die Einführung des psychoanalytischen Grundanliegens in die kli-
nische Arbeit zu finden ist.

2. *"Arztgruppe" und "Hausgruppe"*

Es ist zu fragen, inwieweit die Determinanten der Klinik-Grup-
pensituation dem Vorhaben, die Psychoanalyse in der Klinik wirksam werden zu lassen, nicht nur hinderlich sind, sondern ihm auch
entgegenkommen und förderlich sind.

Von vornherein bietet sich die *Arztgruppe als Instanz für eine*
analytisch orientierte Arbeit an. Die hier stattfindenden Interaktionen werden vom Therapeuten registriert, sie sind als Projektion-
en, Identifikationen, als "multilaterale Übertragungen" (Reiss)
(die aber über die engere Arztgruppe hinausreichen) interpretier-
bar oder in dramatischer — auch psychodramatisch inszenierter-
weise — als Wiederholungen früherer neurotisierenden Konstellationen zu erkennen. Hier können die soziodynamische Katharsis
und das "acting out" (Moreno) als biographisch verstehbare
Veranstaltungen erkannt werden, auch dann, wenn diese Ereignisse im Feld der weiteren Hausgruppe stattfanden.

In Summa: Die Arztgruppe ist die Instanz für die Bewusstmachung, die Erkenntnis- und Erlebnisvermittlung.

Die Tendenz, der Arztgruppe die analytische Aufgabe zuzuweisen, kommt auch darin zum Ausdruck, dass der Therapeut, der
mindestens viermal wöchentlich für jeweils eine Stunde mit einer
Gruppe zusammentrifft, bestrebt ist, weitgehend passiv zu bleiben
und sich darauf beschränkt, die Interaktionen zu interpretieren,
allenfalls der Gruppe Interpretationsangebote verbal oder durch
psychodramatische Inszenierungsvorschläge zu übergeben.

Neben der Arztgruppe steht als wesentliches Interaktionsfeld die
"Hausgruppe". Rein äusserlich werden alle Patienten des Hauses
viermal in der Woche versammelt: Einmal zur Unterweisung im
autogenen Training, zweimal zur gemeinsamen Durchführung dra-
matischgestaltungstherapeutischer Verfahren und einmal zu einer
gemeinsamen Diskussion über Probleme des Hauses.

Der Betreuer der Hausgruppe ist — seit einiger Zeit — nicht einer
der Therapeuten, sondern der klinische Psychologe der Abteilung.
der im übrigen vorwiegend diagnostisch arbeitet. Die Patienten
haben im Rahmen der Hausgruppe eine Selbstverwaltung. Es sind
ein Hausvater und eine Hausmutter gewählt, ebenfalls durch Wahl

sind verschiedene "Ausschüsse" gebildet, z.B. ein "Einführungsausschuss", der Neuankömmlinge begrüsst und in die Gegebenheiten der Hauses einführt und ein "Vergnügungsausschuss", der gemeinsame Unternehmungen, wie Ausflüge, Unterhaltungsabende, Tanzabende etc. organisiert. Die Hausgruppe hat auch disziplinäre Funktion. Keiner der Therapeuten, auch nicht der Leiter der Abteilung, ist im Regelfall gezwungen, bei Verstössen gegen die Hausordnung einzugreifen.

Die Selbstregulation der disziplinären Seite durch die — vom' klinischen Psychologen betreute — Hausgruppe ermöglicht überhaupt erst eine echte *analytische Therapie in der Klinik*. Das Bestehen einer "Klinikhierarchie" (bei uns gibt es keine Visiten im üblichen Sinn) und die disziplinären Funktionen der Therapeuten in vielen Kliniken stellen ein wesentliches Hindernis für die Psychotherapie dar. Der Arzt kann nicht Analytiker und Disziplinärvorgesetzter in einem sein. — Ein weiteres Problem ist die soziodynamische Stellung der Krankenschwestern in diesem System. Wir können an dieser Stelle nicht darauf eingehen; es sei nur mitgeteilt, dass der klinische Psychologe mit den Schwestern des Hauses eine "kontrollanalytische Schwesterngruppe" gebildet hat. Der klinische Psychologe ist auch Teilnehmer bei der "kontrollanalytischen Therapeutengruppe".

Man erkennt unschwer, dass die Hausgruppe — schwerpunktmässig—keine analytische orientierte Gruppe ist: Ihre Grundtendenzen sind normativ und sozialisierend. Sie vermittelt neue Erfahrungen im sozialen Kontakt und ermöglicht den einzelnen Patienten das "Ausprobieren" neuartiger Kontaktnahmen. So ist die Hausgruppe sozusagen das Feld einer "Lebensschule"; die Hausgruppe stellt eine "L e r n g r u p p e" dar, wobei "Lernen" im weitgefassten Sinn seiner allgemeinpsychologischen Definition verstanden werden muss.

Lernen ist in der allgemeinen Psychologie definiert als die Fähigkeit des Individuums, Erfahrungen der Vergangenheit nutzbar zu machen für die erfolgreiche Bewältigung zukünftiger ähnlicher Situationen. Bekanntlich werden zwei Arten von Lernprozessen unterschieden: Erstens das Signallernen und zweitens das Lernen nach dem Gesetz des Effektes. Das Signallernen beruht auf dem bedingten Reflex. Es entsteht eine Koppelung zwischen einer Reaktion und einem Reiz. Auf dem Wege des Signallernens können sekundäre Bedürfnisse (Quasibedürfnisse) entstehen. Das Lernen nach dem Gesetz des Effektes beruht darauf, dass von einer Vielzahl von Probierhandlungen zur Befriedigung eines Bedürfnisses diejenigen am besten behalten werden, welche zum Erfolg geführt haben. Es ist an das bekannte Experiment von Miller und Dollard zu erinnern. Das Gesetz des Effektes wurde von Tolman dahingehend präzisiert, dass nicht der Erfolg als solcher die Lernleistung steigert, sondern seine Wirkung als Akzentuierer sämtlicher auf dem Wege zur Triebreduktion auftretender Reize, wobei auch evtl. Hindernisse oder Bestrafungen als erfolgsbetonte Hinweise wirken.

Es ist noch zu betonen, dass es sich an dieser Stelle n i c h t darum handelt, die von der Psychoanalyse beschriebenen tiefenseelischen Mechanismen lerntheoretisch zu erklären, wie das bekanntlich von Dollard und Miller versucht worden ist. Mowrer hat die neurotischen Phänomene auf die Interaktion zweier Lernprozesse zurückgeführt: Das Signallernen führe zur Über-Ich-Bildung, während das Ich durch Lernen nach dem Gesetz des Effektes aufgebaut würde. Gewiss liegen in solchen lerntheoretischen Modellvorstellungen produktive Ansätze für die tiefenpsychologische Forschung; wit Tolman sind allerdings die in diessen Konzeptionen enthaltenen Verallgemeinerungen und Simplifikationen durchaus zu kritisieren.

In unserem — pragmatischen — Modell zweier verschieden soziodynamisch wirkender Gruppen halten wir die Vorstellung einer *Polarität* von Analyse und Lernen jedenfalls für realitätsgerecht.

Wir können jetzt die Arztgruppe als den Pol im soziodynamischen Feld der Klinik bestimmen, von dem die analytische Arbeit ausgeht die Bewusstmachung von Fehleinstellungen, Projektionen, Reaktionsbildungen usw. — Die Erlebnisvermittlung in der Wiederholung neurotischer Konstellationen erweckt bei den Patienten in der Regel das Bedürfnis "umzulernen". Die Langzeitanalyse kann dieses "Umlernen" dem souveränen Reifungsprozess zuweisen. Die klinische Kurzzeittherapie kann das nur in sehr beschränktem Masse. In ihr kommt dem Umlernbedürfnis des Patienten die Instanz der Hausgruppe entgegen.

Die Hausgruppe ist zu bestimmen als der Pol im soziodynamischen Feld der Klinik, der eine Umlernen ermöglicht. Dies geschieht unter zwei übergreifenden Gesichtspunkten:

1. Jeder einzelne Patient soll andere Konfliktlösungen als seine bisherigen neurotischen im Gemeinschaftsleben des Hauses "ausprobieren".

700

2. Die Patienten können mit einem ausgewogenen Überich Erfahrungen machen. Die Gruppe selbst gestaltet ihr Überich: Hausordnung, Eigenverantwortlichkeit für gute Normen und Sitten. Bei auftretenden Konflikten wird in der Hausgruppe die Auseinandersetzung mit dem Überich geübt.

3. Zur Soziodynamik des bipolaren Feldes

Wir haben bewusst das Bild zweier *Pole* — *Analyse* und Lernen — gewählt. Die Pole haben für die gesamte Gruppenarbeit der Klinik gleichsam einen zwingenden Aufforderungscharakter, sie sind die Brennpunkte der beiden therapeutischen Grundtendenzen. Keiner der Pole aber hat ein umgrenztes Feld, beide Pole wirken vielmehr auf alle Gruppen und Gruppierungen der Klinik.

Es wurde schon betont, dass eine konsequente analytische Arbeit im strengen Sinn auch in der Arztgruppe nicht immer durchzuhalten ist. Es besteht immer wieder ein "Bruch der Hausgruppe". Häufig sieht sich die Arztgruppe veranlasst, über Ereignisse im Rahmen der Hausgruppe weiter zu diskutieren und Probleme und Kontroversen einer "Klärung" zuzuführen. Es ist Aufgabe des Therapeuten, die Arztgruppe so zu gestalten, dass das Schwergewicht nicht auf der "Klärung" einer Hausgruppenkonstellation, sondern vielmehr auf deren Interpretation liegt.

Umgekehrt hat die Hausgruppe bei ihren konstituierenden Versammlungen mitunter das Bedürfnis, Ereignisse analytisch zu interpretieren. Es besteht sodann ein "Bruch der Arztgruppe", der analytische Pole wirkt in die Hausgruppe hinein. Der klinische Psychologe kann der Hausgruppe nicht untersagen oder verbieten, Interpretationen vorzunehmen. Das würde ein unzulässiges Eingreifen in Selbstverwaltung und Selbstregulation sein. Er kann aber in der Hausgruppe das Bewusstsein wecken, es sei opportun, tiefergreifende Interpretationen der Arztgruppe zuzuweisen. Denn nur die Arztgruppe hat die Möglichkeit, Interpretationen von Hausereignissen von der Biographie der einzelnen Patienten her zu verstehen und zu interpretieren.

Für dieses Ineinanderstrahlen der beiden Pole könnten wir eine Fülle praktisch-kasuistischer Belege bringen. Im Rahme der hier beabsichtigten allgemeinen Übersicht möchten wir uns auf *ein* Beispiel beschränken:

Laufende *soziometrische Untersuchungen* (in Anlehnungen Moreno) haben uns gelehrt, dass die Interaktionen der Patienten zueinander einmal mehr in die Hausgruppe, einmal mehr in die Arztgruppe gehen. Man kann einen Hausgruppen/Arztgruppen-Interaktionsquotienten bilden. Bestimmte Ereignisse können recht rasch zu wesentlichen Veränderungen im Soziogramm führen.

Zwei Soziogramme, die im Abstand von 2 Wochen mit fast den gleichen Patienten des Hauses (zwischenzeitlich 2 Entlassungen) vorgenommen wurden: Im ersten Soziogramm überwiegen die Wahlen für die Hausgruppe (59 Wahlen wurden insgesamt für die Hausgruppe abgegeben, 46 Wahlen für die jeweiligen Arztgruppen), im zweiten hat sich das Verhältnis wesentlich geändert (43: 57). In einer Arztgruppe (Gruppe IV) war es zu einer dramatischen Selbsterkenntnis e i n e r Patientin gekommen, begleitet vom sofortigen Symptomverlust. Sofort stiegen die Wahlen innerhalb dieser Gruppe im Vergleich zu den Wahlen nach aussen (in die Hausgruppe) erheblich an, auch eine andere Arztgruppe nimmt, wenngleich schwächer, an dieser Bewegung teil. Man könnte sagen, dass das Ereignis in der einen Arztgruppe zur Ausrichtung mehrerer Patienten auf den analytischen Pol geführt hat.

4. Der Patient im bipolaren Feld

Wir glauben, dass die bipolare Gruppenpsychotherapie nicht nur "klinikgerecht", sondern auch "patientengerecht" ist. Der neurotische Mensch ist zwar kontaktgestört, er bringt aber in die Behandlung eine ganze Reihe mehr oder minder latenter "Bindungsvalenzen" mit. "Die Nervösen sind das Salz der Erde" (Marcel Proust). Immer aber besteht die Gefahr einer starren einseitigen Kontaktnahme, einer Kontaktnahme, die regressiv und nicht progressiv ist.

Die Tendenz zu regressiven, einseitigen, starren Kontaktnahmen konnten wir immer wieder sehen: Die Gesamtgruppe aller Patienten war früher oft in Gefahr, zum einseitigen Hort des Lustprinzips zu werden: das Wirtshaus drohte wichtiger zu werden als die Klinik. Mitunter setzten sich einseitig "normative Bindungsvalenzen" (besonders in den Zimmergruppen) durch: Es kam zu einer moralisierenden und das Individuum korsettierenden Gleichmacherei.

Eine wieder andere Tendenz zur regressive Bindung bestand im Theoretisieren und Rationalisieren; ja sogar die schöpferischen Gruppierungen haben eine regressive Entgleisungsmöglichkeit, das Aesthetisieren und Illusionieren. Es ist in diesem Zusammenhang an eine frühere Arbeit aus unserer Klinik von Clauser über "neurotische Symbiose und Sympathose" zu erinnern.

Alle diese einseitigen Bindungen haben zum Ziel, in der psychotherapeutischen Klinik ein "seelisches Schonklima" (Langen) herzustellen. Man kann sie deshalb mit Recht als regressive Kontaktformen den progressiven, dynamischen gegenüberstellen. Ihr gemeinsames Kennzeichen ist, dass der Patient in einer Schonungshaltung nur eine Bindungsvalenz gegenüber dem Partner oder der Gruppe wirksam werden lässt. Es kommt — um ein Bild zu gebrauchen, zu ruhenden "Klumpen-Bildungen". Es ist das Bestreben jeder dynamischen Gruppentherapie, gleich welcher Schule, solche Erstarrungen nicht aufkommen zu lassen. Im bipolaren Feld der kinischen Gruppenpsychotherapie wird der einzelne Patient ständig in Bewegung gehalten, immer neue Bindungsvalenzen werden ihm abgefordert. Er ist — wiederum bildlich gesprochen — dem Anker eines Elektromotors vergleichbar, der durch die wechselnden Impulse der beiden entgegengesetzten Pole (Analyse-Lernen) dauern bewegt wird.

Tatsächlich sind regressive Erstarrungen in unserer Klinik mit zunehmenden Ausbau der bipolaren Gruppenpsychotherapie immer seltener geworden.

5. Psychosomatische Probleme

Wie einleitend betont, leiden die Patienten einer im eigentlichen Sinne psychosomatischen Klinik vordergründig unter ihrer körperlichen Symptomatik. Immer ist das Körpersymptom im Erleben des Patienten und in seiner medizinischen Vorgeschichte ("Medizinische Odyssee", Clauser) das Dominante, oft beeinflusst der somatische Aspekt der Krankheit die Therapieplanung.

In der Gruppensituation der Klinik ist die Körpersymptomatik auch als kommunikatives Mittel wirksam: Mit seinem Symptom wird der Patient als Gleicher unter Gleichen in die Gruppe aufgenommen. Die Gruppe "versteht" seine Krankheit, akzeptiert ihn (im Gegensatz zur Haltung mancher ärztlicher Voruntersucher) als "wirklich Kranken", aber sie stellt auch sogleich eine Bedin-

703

gung: Der neuankommende Patient wird in die Gemeinschaft nur aufgenommen, wenn er bereit ist, das Körpersymptom auf seine neurotische Bedingunge zurückzuführen. (Das ist ubrigens wiederum ein Vorteil der 'offenen' Gruppe.)

Bevor wir im Hause die systematische Gruppenpsychotherapie pflegten, waren wir gezwungen, dem Patienten in der Einzelbehandlung ausführlich die Genese des Symptoms zu erklären ("Symptomannahme") und ihn ausdrücklich mit seinem 'Somatisierungsarrangement zu konfrontieren' ("Symptomkonfrontation") (Enke). Diese Arbeit hat uns die Gruppe weitgehend abgenommen. Das bedeutet für den einzelnen Therapeuten eine weitere Ermöglichung der analytischen Grundhaltung.

Beeinträchtigt aber wird die analytische Grundhaltung des Therapeuten durch bestimmte *psychosomatische Indikationen*. So wissen wir, dass die initiale psychotherapeutische Behandlung der *Colitis ulcerosa-Patienten* (Curtis, Enke) in einer universellen Verwöhnung, d.h. in der aktiven Ermöglichung einer Objektbeziehung, zu bestehen hat. Jede Versagung, jede Frustration kann ein Rezidiv, ein septisches Zustandsbild oder eine Blutung auslösen. Unter dem "Diktat des somatischen Aspekts der Krankheit" müssen also Colitis-ulcerosa-Patienten in jeder Weise verwöhnt und geschont werden Das hat zur Folge, dass diese Patienten nach Möglichkeit zunächst nicht in die analytisch orientierte Arztgruppe hineingenommen werden. Doch auch dies schafft ein Frustrationserlebnis. Werden sie nach einiger Zeit in die Gruppe eingeführt, so besteht die Aufgabe des Therapeuten darin, sie zunächst vor jedem konfrontativen Zugriff der Gruppenmitglieder zu schützen. Das kann die Gruppenarbeit stören, muss es aber nicht, wenn es gelingt, die Gruppe dazu zu bringen, den Colitiker zunächst als "Kind der Gruppe" aufzunehmen und zu behandeln.

Ganz andere Anforderungen stellt die *Pubertätsmagersucht* an die Gruppenpsychotherapie. Die initiale psychotherapeutische Behandlung der Pubertätsmagersucht besteht in einer scharfen, krassen Konfrontation der Patientinnen mit der Realität zur Erzwingung der Krankheitseinsicht (Clauser). Ob es sich bei dieser Methodik darum handelt, einen Organpsychotiker aus seinem "Ausder-Welt-Sein" quasi mit dem Lasso in unsere Welt zurückzuholen (Enke) oder ob es darum geht, die einzig vorhandene Triebvalenz, die sadomasochistische der pubertätsmagersüchtigen Mädchen anzusprechen (Friedemann — persönliche Mitteilung), braucht uns hier nicht zu beschäftigen. Jedenfalls muss, wenn ein magersüchtiges Mädchen in die Arztgruppe kommt, diese die analytische Linie verlassen und zu einer sadistischen Überich-Gruppe werden. Wir sind gerade dabei zu erproben, ob es nicht möglich ist, diese Funktion der Hausgruppe, die ohnehin Überich-Funktionen hat, zu übertragen.

Es kam hier darauf anzuzeigen dass sich aus den verschiedener psychosomatischen Indikationen für eine konsequente und in bestimmter Weise ausgerichtete sich eigengesetzlich entwickelnde Gruppenpsychotherapie *Komplikationen* ergeben. Die Integration der psychosomatischen Indikationen in das System der klinischen Gruppenpsychotherapie ist ein von uns noch keinsfalls bewältigtes Problem. Noch ist auch die Frage nicht entschieden, ob die Gruppenpsychotherapie bei bestimmten psychosomatischen Krankheiten, z.B. der Colitis-ulcerosa, vielleicht einfach kontraindiziert sei.

SECTION 21: INDICATIONS AND CONTRA-INDICATIONS

INDICATIONS ET CONTR'INDICATIONS A LA PSYCHOTHÉRAPIE DE GROUPE

par S. Blajan-Marcus, M. D.

Une expérience clinique de douze ans, dont six à diriger des groupes psychanalytiques, et les six derniers à mener des groupes de psychodrame moréniens, nous ont permis de dégager quelques notions concernant ce problème. Il ne semble pas que la littérature internationale, à notre connaissance, ait apporté beaucoup d'éléments clairs et précis sur les indications de la psychothérapie de groupe. Cela peut provenir des faits suivants:

La diversité (parfois inquiétante!) des méthodes employées, dans certains cas même, sous un nom commun;

La diversité des combinaisons de malades au sein même des groupes;

Et surtout, la très grande difficulté d'enfermer les symptômes dans une nosographie, une classification, et de s'entendre sur certaines définitions de base. Là aussi, une diversité parfois proche de la Tour de Babel rend très épineux tout travail scientifique sur la question.

Les classifications anciennes des grands maîtres de la psychiatrie ne s'appliquent pas aux névroses dans leurs variétés, la révolution freudienne a bouleversé et bousculé toutes les tentatives de voir la maladie mentale comme une entité statique que l'on peut classifier en l'enfermant dans des catégories.

Freud a apporté, au moins pour les névroses, une nouvelle notion, celle de *structure,* qui n'est pas figée, mais semble en rapport avec un *mode* de relation avec les objets intérieurs et avec autrui, et un type de défenses. L'hystérie, la névrose d'angoisse (ou phobique), la névrose obsessionnelle, nous aident à comprendre comment le sujet souffre et tente de s'adapter au monde de son enfance qu'il transforme dans sa vie présente.

Male et Lebovici ont cherché à enrichir cette classification, et ont buté sur les difficultés presque insurmontables.

Pourtant, même si nous ne précisons pas notre diagnostic, nous évaluons et jugeons plus ou moins clairement, parfois intuitivement, si tel ou tel malade peut bénéficier ou non de la psychothérapie de groupe.

Il nous paraît plus satisfaisant, à l'heure actuelle, d'établir des grandes catégories de malades sur le mode purement clinique et même empirique, en tenant compte du prognostic plus que du diagnostic.

D'une part, selon l'ancienneté, la profondeur et la nature des troubles, une névrose "bien compensée" pendant des années sera moins souple, moins accessible qu'une névrose traumatique ou en tous cas relativement récente; un malade peut avoir bâti, sur une névrose profonde, prégénitale, tout un système de constructions et de formations réactionnelles qui lui donnent l'apparence d'adaptation, mais qui ne tiennent pas devant un choc un peu sérieux; une psychose n'est pas une névrose en plus grave, il y a une différence de nature, et par conséquent d'approche thérapeutique et de prognostic.

D'autre part, selon les modes de communications des patients avec autrui, ce qui recoupe partiellement le paragraphe précédent. Ceci, qui est important dans une thérapie individuelle, est essentiel dans un groupe.

Le patient capable essentiellement de relation à *Un* (c'est-à-dire avec lui-même — narcissique) est évidemment handicapé dans un groupe. Cependant le prognostic sera différent s'il s'agit d'un certain type de délinquant ou d'un psychosé autique, d'un malade qui n'a jamais communiqué avec autrui, ou d'un patient qui a regressé.

Celui qui a atteint la relation à *Deux* aura des possibilités d'expressions très riches. Mais il ne prendra pas conscience de la réalité du groupe et de sa tâche, cherchera toujours à échanger, surtout à recevoir d'autrui, pour parachever son propre développement par une symbiose (ou même un parasitage très infantile) souvent paralysant pour d'autres membres du groupe qui ne savent pas refuser d'entrer dans ce véritable duel. Les relations de type sado-masochiste en "vase clos" en sont le meilleur exemple.

Enfin celui qui, par l'abord du Complexe d'Oedipe, a pu amorcer la relation à *Trois*: complémentaire de deux êtres en vue du troisième terme, fruit de cette relation, sera le plus à l'aise dans un groupe, y apportera la contribution la plus riche et la plus mûre.

Toujours sur le plan clinique et empirique, cette fois au sujet de l'interrelation groupe-malade, la question se pose aussi de savoir si l'entrée au groupe de tel malade est opportune, autant pour le malade que pour tel groupe défini auquel nous nous proposons de l'intégrer.

Il paraît utile de se poser la double question: L'entrée du malade dans un groupe donné est-elle bonne pour lui? Est-elle positive pour le groupe?

La première question se réfère non seulement à la "maladie" du sujet, et au point donné de son évolution, mais à sa fragilité (difficile à établir avec précision, mais qu'un bon thérapeute peut jauger, s'il a une expérience clinique suffisante). Il y a des groupes plus brutaux, plus traumatisants que d'autres, de même que certains patients, bien que pas très "malades" en apparence, sont en vérité très vulnérables.

Ceci, à son tour, pose un problème également difficile à résoudre, car il nous paraît se placer sur le plan de l'intersubjectivité humaine: Jusqu'où peut-on accepter qu'un malade soit "secoué", choqué, et y-a-t-il des chocs positifs et d'autres négatifs? La réponse paraît résider dans deux ordres de choses: L'attitude plus ou moins sereine ou anxieuse du thérapeute, qui conditionne en grande partie la fécondité de telle ou telle épreuve, thérapeutique ou non; La capacité plus ou moins grande de surmonter et d'utiliser les épreuves subies, pour le patient.

Certains chocs sont grandement instructifs et pour le sujet et pour son médecin, et amèneront au minimum une prise de conscience, et parfois un profond remaniement de sa structure, en lui faisant gagner un temps précieux; d'autres seront suivis de régression stérile ou de retour au statu quo ante, faute d'avoir pu supporter l'impact de l'agression. Enfin, des états confusionnels, des crises hystériques spectaculaires ou même des passages à l'acte destructifs, peuvent être à craindre devant une tension trop angoissante que le malade ne peut vivre jusqu'au bout, si son seuil de tolérance est trop bas.

La souplesse des défenses est une notion utile. Avec un thérapeute expérimenté, quelques séances individuelles en cas de doute, permettront assez vite de s'en rendre compte. Attitude plus ou moins rigide, réceptivité plus ou moins grande aux interventions ou interprétations du médecin, stéréotypie ou labilité, tout cela se voit généralement au cours même du premier entretien, en tous cas après une dizaine de séances maximum.

Le transfert du malade à l'égard de son thérapeute, surtout si ce dernier conduit aussi le groupe où il sera intégré, est capital. Il n'est pas aussi important de savoir s'il est positif ou négatif (bien qu'un transfert négatif en début d'expression soit une indication d'attendre le plein développement de celui-ci, et même son déclin), mais plutôt s'il y a prise de conscience, expression plus ou moins libre, et richesse des fantasmes et images.

Le transfert à l'égard d'un animateur s'il est différent du thérapeute individuel, les fantasmes que le malade exprimera à l'égard des membres du groupe inconnus de lui, voire même les relations affectives conscientes ou non des thérapeutes les uns vis-à-vis des autres, sont de grand intérêt, et peuvent rendre l'appartenance du patient au groupe aisée ou au contraire très ardue.

Quant à la deuxième question, celle de l'adaptabilité du groupe à un ou plusieurs nouveaux venus, elle est en rapport avec des éléments qui ne sont pas sans relations avec les points précédents: Caractère particular du groupe en tant que tel — traumatisant ou réceptif, vulnérable ou peu réactif, ceci, évidemment en connexion avec les personnes dominantes de ce dernier; Les phases du développement du groupe, de sa dynamique, ses états de tension, ses courants affectifs dominants, par exemple, ambivalence ou révolte à l'égard des animateurs, crises de "croissance" (phase dépressive en rapport avec une désillusion collective, par exemple), ou au contraire stagnation par manque de stimulus, ou crainte et fuite devant les tensions.

Tel groupe demandera à grands cris des "nouveaux" . . . et

réagira avec une forte hostilité à leur arrivée; tel autre accueillera poliment le nouveau venu, mais sera pendant plusieurs séances, incapable d'avancer.

Nous avons posé ces questions, en essayant d'être aussi claire que possible. Mais il est plus facile d'en poser que d'y répondre. Nous allons cependant essayer, en nous empressant de dire qu'il s'agit:

de propositions que nous faisons, qui n'ont rien d'impératif, car nous jugeons qu'une expérience de douze ans, même enrichie par celle de nombreux collègues de pays divers, est loin d'être suffisante;

d'éléments qui, nous l'espérons, ouvriront autant de discussions fécondes pour tous.

Pour commencer, il nous a paru que la *psychanalyse de groupe,* étant donné qu'elle fait appel exclusivement à l'expression verbale, s'adresse de façon plus étroite à des sujets:

d'intelligence au moins subnormale, sinon normale;

capables d'utiliser un langage verbal, suffisamment expressif, donc, ayant atteint le niveau du *dialogue* situation duelle ou à trois.

Il est vrai que des malades plus détériorés ou profondément atteints ont pu progresser dans des groupes purement verbaux. On peut se demander si cette amélioration est durable, et si elle ne provient pas d'une adaptation superficielle par imitation, plus que par réelle identification. L'expérience que nous en avons, nous a montré que les indications de la psychanalyse de groupe sont à peu près les mêmes que celles de la psychanalyse individuelle, qui, sous sa forme classique, est réservée aux névroses proches, en niveau, de la phase oedipienne.

Le psychodrame, qui fait participer le *corps* à l'expression verbale, convient à un éventail beaucoup plus vaste de malades. Spontanément, l'enfant, l'hystérique, l'extraverti, se servent de leur corps comme moyen de communication avec autrui. Mimique, gestes, attitudes, sont des moyens de traduire (et souvent d'en *trahir* les défenses) le message, parfois très profond du sujet. D'ailleurs le passage à l'acte aveugle, "acting-out" impulsif est aussi un message corporel, inconscient, de même que les symptômes psycho-somatiques, véritables acting-out des organes du corps dans leur signification symbolique. Le psychodrame permet de faire le trait d'union entre un corps qui généralement *subit* les émotions qui lui impriment la souffrance et l'élan, et un réseau linguistique souvent appauvri ou gauchi par la névrose. Le malade, dans le psychodrame, prend peu à peu la direction active, consciente de de l'expression corporelle, transformant en *langage* ce qui n'était qu'émoi envahissant et diffus.

Dans les groupes psychodramatiques, la richesse des moyens d'expressions permet de mélanger des catégories et des niveaux intellectuels très variés et riches, on risque bien moins le "dialogue de sourds".

Le directeur aura évidemment pour tâche de transformer ce qui se présentera d'abord comme un affrontement stérile des tendances opposées, en complémentarité féconde. Mais il aura moins à "traduire" les patients les uns aux autres, car ils se comprendront plus vite et plus profondément.

En général, il apparaît que les grands pervers, les paranoïaques rigides ou trop délirants, les schizophrènes catatoniques, les toxicomanes, c'est-à-dire finalement les malades, soit, enkystés dans une coque trop impénétrable, soit incapables de contrôler leurs actes, sont à écarter de tout groupe, tant que dureront ces deux caractéristiques. C'est moins une question de diagnostic qu'une évaluation de la dureté de la coque ou de la fragilité du contrôle. Un essai prudent avec les précautions nécessaires auprès du service hospitalier ou de la famille, en cas de réactivation des symptômes ou de "décompensation", peut, dans certains cas-limites, être tenté: "Qui ne risque rien n'a rien", et on a vu plus d'un malade, auparavant abandonné à lui-même, revivre, si l'on ose prendre des responsabilités hardies à son égard.

Parmi les contr'indications moins absolues, on trouvera, avec des symptômes variés et des diagnostics multiples, toute une catégorie de malades ayant souffert de carence affective profonde, massive ou précoce (ou les deux). Le sort de ces malades dans un groupe de névrosés ordinaires est généralement celui-ci: leurs relations avec autrui s'établissent sur un mode parasitaire, celle du nourrisson avide de lait et de tendresse ("des océans de lait" disait un malade) et s'ils sont tolérés au début et même souvent adoptés par un autre membre du groupe ou l'ensemble, ils donnent vite l'impression d'un tonneau des Danaïdes. Leurs revendications plaintives ou agressives retardent le reste du groupe qui désire progresser, et ils se font, ou rejeter, ou reléguer dans un coin où un membre du groupe plus patient leur servira de "mère" nourricière, mais sans espoir de changement notable. Car le seul vrai bénéfice, dans ce cas, est, pour le sujet en question, un milieu tolérant qui lui permet d'avoir quelques pauvres relations humaines, mais sans progrès réels possibles, s'il n'y a pas un traitement individuel en profondeur, en même temps (traitement qui a, lui-même, hélas, des chances d'échouer dans beaucoup de cas).

Le milieu tolérant, entourant un malade qui, sans cela, serait isolé, est pourtant un des éléments qui permettent, sinon la cure, du moins la réintégration sociale de certains malades réputés non-guérissables même par thérapie profonde. Par exemple, beaucoup d'homosexuels masculins, certains toxicomanes (à condition qu'ils soient volontaires et non contraints, ce qui suppose déjà un début de travail thérapeutique personnel ou médical) peuvent fortement bénéficier du soutien moral très intense du groupe. Ce dernier agit même parfois sur un *patient qui n'a pas encore pris contact avec lui!* C'est bien un travail symbolique qui s'opère, tel alcoolique cessant de boire avant son entrée dans un groupe, galvanisé qu'il est par son désir de plaire aux inconnus qui le composent, telle tabagique ne pouvant reprendre la cigarette dont elle meurt d'envie "pour ne pas décevoir" les membres d'un groupe vus à un weekend et qu'elle pourrait fort bien ne jamais revoir de sa vie. Cet engagement tacite, libre, est une sorte de "multiplication" de la force d'un moi idéal défaillant par le nombre de membres du groupe et donne à chacun son maximum de chance de briser ses chaînes compulsives.

Même chez le patient incapable d'identification vraie, l'incorporation d'une image de bon sens (le *sens commun* du groupe) de guide ou de bon parent (l'animateur) lui apportera, au moins tant qu'il viendra aux séances, un mieux-être et un plus grand sentiment de valeur.

Donc il n'y a rien d'absolu dans les contr'indications, il suffit de voir clairement la différence entre psychothérapie de *soutien* et psychothérapie *en profondeur,* réellement curative, l'un n'excluant pas l'autre d'ailleurs.

PART IV

THE INTERNATIONAL COUNCIL
OF GROUP PSYCHOTHERAPY

A. *LIST OF MEMBERS BY COUNTRIES*

ARGENTINA
Dr. *E. E. Krapf*
16 Parc Chateau Banquet
Geneva, Switzerland

Dr. *J. J. Morgan*
Buenos Aires British Hospital
Calle Pedriel 74
Buenos Aires

Dr. *Arnaldo Rascovsky*
Pueyrredon 1194, 9º, 32º
Buenos Aires

AUSTRALIA
Dr. *F. W. Graham*
56 Powlett Street
East Melbourne, Victoria

Dr. *W. C. Wheeler*
Sr. Lecturer in Education
The University of Western
    Australia
Nedlands, Western Australia

AUSTRIA
Dr. *W. Doleisch*
Karl Schweighofergasse 8
Vienna 7

Dr. *Hans Hoff*
Psychiatrisch-Neurologische Klinik
    der Universitat Wien
IX-71 Lazarettgasse Nr. 14
Vienna

Dr. *Traugott Lindner*
Betriebsberatung
Viktorgasse 9
Vienna IV

Dr. *L. Rosenmayr*
Sozialwissenschaftliche
    Forschungstelle
Universitat Wien
Karl Luegerring 1
Vienna 1

Dr. *R. Schindler*
Bennogasse 8
Vienna VIII

Dr. *S. Schindler*
Schonbrunnestr. 111
Vienna V

Dr. *H. Strotzka*
Daringergasse 16/24
Vienna 19

BELGIUM
Dr. *G. Bastin*
Conseiller-Directeur du
    Centre Psycho-Medico-Social de
    l'Etat a Huy
16 Rue Delloye-Mathieu
Huy

Dr. *Rene Dellaert*
Italielei 221
Antwerp

717

BRAZIL
Dr. W. Kemper
Rue Gustavo Sampaio 576
Rio de Janeiro

Dr. Gilberto de Macedo
Professor da Faculdade
de Medicina
Senador Mendonca 180
Maceio, Alagoas

Dr. Walderedo Ismael de Oliveira
Praia do Flamengo 118, 6A
Rio de Janeiro

Dr. A. C. Pacheco e Silva
Clinica Psiquiatrica
Faculdade de Medicina da
Universidade de Sao Paulo
Caixa Postal 8091, Sao Paulo

Dr. David Zimmermann
Av. Sen. Salgado F 204 Ap. 21
Porto Alegre

BULGARIA
Dr. Nikola Shipkovensky
54 Patriarch Euthymius
Sofia

CANADA
Dr. Miguel Prados (†)
1025 Pine Avenue West
Montreal, P.Q.

Dr. E. J. Rosen
Department of Psychiatry
University of Toronto
Toronto 5

CEYLON
Dr. W. G. Wickremesinghe
48 Buller's Lane
Colombo 7

CHILE
Dr. Ramon Ganzarain
Av. Paraguay 461 1º C
Santiago

CUBA
Dr. Jose Bustamante
Calle K Num. 309 Vedado
La Habana

Dr. F. Potts
1808 Eastern Pkwy.
Louisville, Ky.

CZECHOSLOVAKIA
Dr. F. Knobloch
University Policlinic
Karlova nam 32
Prague 2

DENMARK
Dr. C. Jorgensen
Box 163
Copenhagen K

Dr. O. Martensen-Larsen
Alcoholics Treatment Center
35 Stormgade
Copenhagen V

Dr. Paul Reiter
Kommunehospitalet
Copenhagen

Dr. G. K. Sturup
Vingarde Alle 36
Hellerup

EAST GERMANY
Dr. B. Bauer
Medizinische Poliklinik
Bachstrasse 18
Jena, Thuringen

Dr. Hans Szewczyk
Humboldt-Universitat
Schumannstrasse 20-21
Berlin N.4

718

EGYPT
  Dr. S. M. Tawadros
  Institute of Education
  Monira, Cairo

FRANCE
  Dr. Juliette Favez-Boutonier
  Faculte des Lettres
    et Science Humaines
  Université de Paris
  Paris

  Dr. Rene Diatkine
  30 Rue de Miromesnil
  Paris VIIIe

  Me. E. Kestenberg
  6 Rue Friant
  Paris XIVe

  Dr. Serge Lebovici
  3 Av. du President Wilson
  Paris XVIe

  Dr. Simone Blajan-Marcus
  4 Villa Eugene Manuel
  Paris XVIe

  Dr. Charles L. Pidoux
  96 Rue Pierre-Demours
  Paris XVIIe

  Dr. Marcel Raclot
  26 Avenue Perrichont
  Paris XVIe

  Anne Ancelin Schutzenberger
  14 Avenue Paul Appell
  Paris XIVe

  Dr. F. Tosquelles
  Medicin des Hopitaux
    Psychiatriques
  Saint Alban, Lozere

GERMANY
  Dr. H. Heiss
  Psychologisches Institut

der Universitat
Freiburg i. Br.

  Dr. E. Hohn
  Schaffhausenstrasse 27
  Tubingen

  Prof. Ernst Kretschmer
  Universitats Nerven Klinik
  Osianderstr. 22
  Tubingen/Neckar

  Dr. D. Langen
  Universitats Nerven Klinik
  Osianderstr. 22
  Tubingen/Neckar

  Dr. J. H. Schultz
  Bayern Allee 17
  Berlin-Charlottenburg 9

  Dr. Hildebrand R. Teirich
  Mozartstrasse 48
  Freiburg i. Br.

GREECE
  Dr. G. C. Lyketsos
  16A Roosevelt Street
  Athens

  Dr. Anna Potamianou, Director
  Mental Health Section
  Royal National Foundation
  58 Notara Street
  Athens

  Dr. N. C. Rassidakis
  The Public Mental Hospital
  47 Omirou Street
  Athens

HAWAII
  Miss Rosie K. Chang
  Nursing Director
  Territorial Hospital
  Kaneche

HUNGARY
   Dr. Z. Boszormenyi
   Voroshads 116
   Budapest II

INDIA
   Dr. K. R. Masani
   Silver Oaks
   Warden Road
   Bombay 26

   Dr. Pandharinath H. Prabhu
   Gujarat University
   Ahmedabad 9

IRAN
   Dr. E. Tchehrazi
   Hospital Pahlavi
   Avenue Shah Reza
   Tehran

ISRAEL
   Dr. H. Kreitler
   Tel Aviv University
   155 Herzl St.
   Tel Aviv

   Dr. J. Schossberger
   Government Work Village
   Kfar Shaul
   Jerusalem

ITALY
   Dr. Luigi Meschieri
   Lungotevere Flaminio, 22
   Rome

   Dr. Giuan Franco Tedeschi
   Viale Bruno Buozzi 109
   Rome

JAPAN
   Dr. Masaaki Kato
   National Institute of Mental Health
   Konodai Ichikawa Chiba

Taro Ogawa
12312 Fuchu
Tokyo

MALAYSIA
   Dr. T. L. Green
   Director, School of Education
   University of Singapore
   Singapore

MEXICO
   Dr. Luis Feder
   Leibnitz No. 1
   Mexico 5, D. F.

NETHERLANDS
   Dr. C. Van Emde Boas
   Stadionweg 80
   Amsterdam-Z

   Dr. E. Carp
   University of Leiden
   Leiden

   Dr. G. W. Arendsen Hein
   Klomperweg 113
   Ederveeen

   Dr. L. Hut
   Dir., Mental Health
   182 Oudegracht
   Alkmaar, North Holland

   Dr. M. L. Meijering
   W. de Zwijgerstraat 27
   Utrecht

   Dr. J. Spanjaard
   Paviljoenslaan 11
   Haarlem

   Dr. B. Stokvis (†)
   Psychosomatic Center
   University of Leiden
   Oegstgeest

Dr. *Armand Sunier*
Med. Supt.
Sinai Mental Hospital
Laan 1914, nr. 23
Amersfoort

NEW ZEALAND
Dr. *Wallace Ironside*
Prof. of Psychological Medicine
University of Otago Med. School
Great King Street
Dunedin C.1

Dr. *R. W. Medlicott*
Ashburn Hall
Dunedin

NORWAY
Dr. *Finn Askevold*
The University Hospital
Rikshospitalet
Oslo

Dr. *Kjell von Krogh*
Barnepsykiatrisk Institutt I
Munkedamsvn 84
Oslo

Mrs. *Maison Mose*
Barnepsykiatrisk Institutt I
Munkedamsvn 84
Oslo

Dr. *Bjorn Urdal*
Barnepsykiatrisk Institutt I
Munkedamsvn 84
Oslo

PERU
Dr. *B. Caravedo*
Medico-Jefe del Depto. de Higiene
Mental
Ministerio de Salud Publica y
Asistencia Social
Lima

Dr. *C. A. Seguin*
Huancavelica 470
Lima

PHILIPPINES
Dr. *Estefania Aldaba-Lim*
The Philippine Women's University
Taft Avenue
Manila

POLAND
Dr. *K. Dambrowski*
Choroby Nerwowe 1 Psychiczne
Doroslych I Dzieci
ul. Gwiandzista 81
Warsaw

PORTUGAL
Dr. *V. Fontes*
Instituto Antonio Aurelio da Costa
Ferreira
Lisbon

Dr. *Joao dos Santos*
Praca Andrade Caminha 5
Bairro de S. Miguel
Lisbon

PUERTO RICO
Dr. *R. Fernandez Marina*
Clinical Director
Puerto Rico Institute of Psychiatry,
Inc.
P.O. Box 127
Bayamon, Puerto Rico

Dr. *Luis Manuel Morales*
Box 12248
Santurce

SPAIN
Dr. *Ramon Sarro-Burbano*
Dept. of Psychiatry
University of Barcelona
Barcelona

721

Dr. J. L. Marti Tusquets
Doctor Amigant No. 15
Barcelona

Dr. C. Ruiz Ogara
Cardenal Vives y Tuto 40
Barcelona

SWEDEN
Dr. Hans Curman
Kungsholmsgatan 106
Stockholm K

Dr. Goesta Harding
Institute for Orthopsychiatry of
   the Erica Foundation
Odengatan 9
Stockholm

Dr. Sven Larsson
Barrstigen 5
Bromma

Mr. Nils Lindgren
Parkvagen 5
Handen

SWITZERLAND
Dr. Harry Feldmann
6 Cours de Rive
Geneva

Dr. A. Friedemann
Psychohygienisches Institut
Institut d'Hygiene Mentale
Biel-Bienne

Dr. Adolf Guggenbuhl Craig
Untere Zuane 1
Zurich

Jakob W. Hug
Beundenfeldstrasse 18
Bern

Dr. Heinrich Meng
Lerchenstr. 92
Basel

TAIWAN
Dr. Eng-kung Yeh
National Taiwan University
   Hospital
No. 1 Changte-Chieh Section 1
Taipei

THAILAND
Dr. Phon Sangsingkeo
Dept. of Med. Service
Ministry of Public Health
Bangkok

Dr. Prasop Ratanakorn
The Prasat Hospital for
   Neurological Disorders
Phyathai
Bangkok

TURKEY
Dr. Ihsan S. Aksel
Taksim
Cumhuriyet Cad. Stadyum
   Palas No. 3
Istanbul

Dr. M. Sion
P.O.B. 484 Beyoglu
Istanbul

UNION OF SOUTH AFRICA
Mr. R. C. Albino
Dept. of Psychology
University of Natal
King George V Avenue
Durban

Dr. L. S. Gillis
Head, Dept. of Psychiatry
Groote Schuur Hospital
Observatory
Cape Town

U.S.S.R.
Dr. D. D. Fedotov
Academy of Medical Science
Psychiatric Institute
Moscow

Dr. Aina G. Ambrumova
Inst. of Psychiatrics
Ministry of Health of the
   R.S.F.S.R.
Sokolniri Poteshnaya
Ulites, Dom. 3
Moscow

UNITED KINGDOM
Mrs. M. L. Johnson Abercrombie
14 Park Drive
London, N.W. 11, England

Dr. Joshua Bierer
140 Harley Street
London, W. 1, England

Dr. Donald Blair
St. Bernard's Hospital
Southall
Middlesex, England

Dr. H. Ezriel
Tavistock Clinic
2 Beaumont St.
London, W. 1, England

Dr. S. H. Foulkes
22 Upper Wimpole Street
London, England

Dr. Maxwell Jones
Dingleton Hospital
Melrose
Roxburghshire, Scotland

Dr. T. Main
The Cassel Hospital
Ham Common
Richmond
Surrey, England

Dr. P. B. de Mare
St. George's Hospital
Psychiatric Department
15 Knightsbridge
London, S.W. 1, England

Dr. T. P. Rees (†)
47 Chelsea Square
London, S.W. 3, England

U.S.A.
Dr. Robert S. Drews
12500 Broadstreet Blvd.
Detroit 4, Mich.

Dr. Helen Durkin
59 East 79 St.
New York, N.Y.

James M. Enneis
Director
Psychodrama Department
St. Elizabeths Hospital
Washington, D.C.

Dr. Martin Grotjahn
416 N. Bedford Drive
Beverly Hills, Calif.

Dr. Samuel B. Hadden
250 South 18th Street
Philadelphia 3, Pa.

Dr. Helen Hall Jennings
470 West End Avenue
New York 24, N.Y.

Dr. Wilfred C. Hulse (†)
382 Central Park West
New York, N.Y.

Dr. Maurice E. Linden
Dept. of Public Health
Room 530, City Hall Annex
Philadelphia, Pa.

Dr. David Mendell
The Medical Towers
Houston, Texas

Dr. Jacob L. Moreno
Moreno Institute
Beacon, N.Y.

Mrs. Zerka T. Moreno
Moreno Institute
Beacon, N.Y.

Mr. S. R. Slavson
321 East 18 Street
New York, N.Y.

Dr. Wellman J. Warner
Woodstock, Vermont

Dr. Lewis Yablonsky
San Fernando Valley
 State College
Northridge, Calif.

VENEZUELA
Dr. Pedro Reyes
Avenida Cajigal No. 32
San Bernardino
Caracas

Dr. Rafael L. Araujo
Instituto Medico Del Este
Caracas

YUGOSLAVIA
Dr. S. Betlheim
Neuroloskopsihijatrijska klinika
Rebro
Zagreb

Dr. Dimitrije Pivnicki
Allan Mem. Inst. of Psychiatry
1025 Pine Ave. West
Montreal, P.Q., Canada

Dr. Boroslav P. Stevanovic
Prof. of Psychology & Chairman of
 Psychological Department
Faculty of Philosophy
University of Belgrade
Belgrade

B. PROPOSALS AND ACTION OF THE EXECUTIVE COMMITTEE

Zürich, August 31, 1957

(1) It is proposed that the International Committee take the necessary steps to form an International Society of Group Psychotherapy.

(2) The first step is that the present International Committee will constitute the provisional Council of such a future International Society. It will immediately proceed to enlarge its membership in order to make it representative of all professional interests in all the different countries of the world.

(3) The enlarged Council will then proceed to elect its officers and executive committee by mail ballot.

(4) The Officers and the Council will then set up the appropriate machinery to perform the following three functions (in addition to others that may be needed):

(a) to prepare a constitution of the projected International Society.

(b) to define the qualifications for membership or organizations in the various countries and the qualifications for the membership of individuals.

(c) to stimulate the development of organizations concerned with group psychotherapy in the national areas throughout the world.

(5) The Council will decide the time when this preparatory work has reached the stage when the International Society of Group Psychotherapy will come into operation as an organization. At that time, the Council will set up the machinery for carrying out the provisions of the constitution as approved by the Council.

(6) All matters of not purely administrative nature must be submitted to the Council by mail and approval will require 2/3 of the votes received.

It should be noted that these proposals provide for a simple series of steps as follows:

(a) The first step is to enlarge the membership of the International Committee (now the International Council) so

725

as to make it more representative of the various professional groups, such as psychiatry, psychology, sociology, social work, and others concerned with the study or practice of Group Psychotherapy, as well as of the different national areas. No limited number of new members is set, but it is assumed that such an expansion of the membership of the Council will possibly range from 25 to 40 additional members.

(b) The second step will take place as soon as the first step has been completed. An election will be held by mail ballot to name a new Executive Committee and a new set of officers.

(c) The third step consists of setting up machinery by the Council and its newly elected officers to perform 3 tasks: (1) To write a constitution for the organization; (2) to decide upon the qualifications of membership for (a) individuals; (b) organizations in the national areas; (3) to encourage the growth of Group Therapy and its organization in the various areas of the world.

(d) The fourth and final step is for the International Council and its officers to decide upon the date that the new organization will go into operation.

These proposals were approved without a dissenting vote by the International Committee which thereupon became the International Council. They were then presented to the Congress for unlimited discussion. The result was their approval by a unanimous vote of the business session of the Congress.

(7) By action of the International Council the approval of the proposals listed above was held to carry with it the following provisions:

(a) All members of the former International Committee automatically become members of the International Council which will in turn be a part of the new International organization when it comes into existence.

(b) The Officers and Executive Committee of the former International Committee continue during the first stage of the procedure outlined above to hold office in the International Council. A new set of officers will be elected when that Council has been expanded.

726

C. COUNCIL MEETING IN MILAN, ITALY, JULY 20, 1963

The council meeting was attended by over 100 delegates. The discussion centered largely on the proposed constitution of the International Association of Group Psychotherapy. Dr. J. L. Moreno opened the discussion and pointed out that only the entire membership of the International Council can make ultimate, binding decisions by anonymous ballot.

The discussion brought out a number of valuable suggestions as to what form the constitution of the International Society should take.

Dr. S. Hadden of the U.S.A. suggested that membership in the International Society should be limited to collective membership of societies of good standing. Dr. S. H. Foulkes, United Kingdom, thought it advisable to organize the International Association according to the schools and trends which dominate the movement. Dr. J. L. Moreno, U.S.A., pointed out that the most inclusive participation of individual as well as collective membership is necessary for the progress of the movement. Dr. A. Friedemann, Switzerland, who, besides Dr. Moreno and Dr. Stokvis, was assigned to prepare the proposals for the constitution, suggested that an international lawyer should be employed to draw it up. Legal considerations differ from country to country.

There is great need for early preparation of the constitution, which should be undertaken as soon as the Proceedings of the Third International Congress have been released. The grave illness of Dr. B. Stokvis, Secretary of the Council, has unduly delayed action. Dr. Friedemann is now the Secretary pro tem. Dr. Lebovici proposed that a fee of $10 (50 francs) be self-imposed by every member of the Council to assist the treasury.

A word of thanks was given to the organizer and secretary of the Milan Congress, Dr. Enzio Spaltro, and to Dr. A. Friedemann, treasurer. The Council meeting was closed with the unanimous hope that at the meeting of the Fourth International Congress, three or four years hence, a constitution of the International Council will be formulated and presented for discussion.

D. IN MEMORIAM

T. P. REES, M.D.

The importance of Dr. Rees for the group psychotherapy movement rests in his great contribution as superintendent and hospital administrator, one of the first in the United Kingdom to introduce group psychotherapy and the open door policy in a mental hospital setting.

W. C. HULSE, M.D., 1900-1962

Dr. Hulse served on the Executive Committee since 1954, and continued on the International Council until his death. On the international scene he made a contribution of the first magnitude.

BERTHOLD STOKVIS, M.D., 1906-1963

Dr. Stokvis was the first Secretary of the International Council of Group Psychotherapy, but he had no opportunity to see the fruits of his great efforts with his own eyes. He fell gravely ill at the time of the Third International Congress of Group Psychotherapy in Milan, July 1963. Dr. A. Friedemann wrote about Dr. Stokvis as follows: "In September we received the sad news that our dear friend, Berthold Stokvis, had succumbed to a vicious disease. Up until May, 1963, we enjoyed the vigor, superior judgment and the human friendliness and ever-ready cooperation of this good man, who had been our friend for the last twenty years.

"We have many thanks to give to our great friend, now deceased. We mourn his departure and our deepest sympathy goes to his wife and children."

E. E. KRAPF, M.D.

Dr. Krapf's prominent position in the World Federation for Mental Health made him a valuable supporter of group psychotherapy on the international scene.

728

SUBJECT INDEX

A

acting-out, 65, 158, 272, 381, 501, 540, 541, 545, 551, 553, 556, 557, 558, 595, 610, 622, 624, 662, 667, 669, 698
acting-out procedures, 72
action catharsis, 73, 158
action methods, 87, 109, 121, 152, 153
action therapy, 116, 158
activistic group psychotherapy, 160
activity group therapy, 101, 143, 508, 543, 638
actor in situ, 246
adolescent groups, 532
ahistorical treatment, 39
Alcoholics Anonymous, 19, 88, 98, 157, 383, 387, 601
alcoholics, group psychotherapy of, 253, 590, 593, 601, 603
alcoholics, psychodramatic treatment of, 93, 232, 381, 382
all-identity, matrix of, 77, 232
American Group Psychotherapy Association, 89
American Society of Group Psychotherapy and Psychodrama, 70, 71, 106
analysis of psychoanalysis, 75
analytic group psychotherapy, 85, 89, 90, 91, 92, 101, 144, 145, 169, 170, 174, 179, 200, 226, 228, 287, 289, 290, 303, 375, 403, 408, 498, 508, 530, 531, 532, 540, 554, 565, 638, 680

analytic psychodrama, 102, 178
audience, role of, 369, 372
audience therapy, 369, 370, 371
autogenous training, 102, 209
auxiliary chair technique, 80, 382
auxiliary ego, 80, 237, 324, 326, 382, 528
auxiliary therapist, 177, 178, 627

B

behavior training, 158
bifocal group psychotherapy, 98, 101, 218, 402

C

catharsis, 197, 321, 331, 339
catharsis, mass, 153, 501, 516, 551
catharsis, social, 158
chance, 472
chemotherapy, 143
child guidance, 531
Christianity, 28, 42, 43
church-group therapy, 527, 528
client-centered therapy, 132
client-centered group psychotherapy, 144, 145
closed group, 261, 274
co-actional group psychotherapy, 155
co-conscious states, 78, 79, 81
co-creative group psychotherapy, 439, 440
code of ethics, 113, 114, 115
collective reflexology, 94

729

collective therapy, 94
collective unconscious states, 79, 80, 262
communication, non-verbal, 540, 545, 553, 560, 610
community therapy, 115, 116, 193
conditioned reflex, 28
conditioning reflex, 21
conjoint therapy, 102, 441, 535, 594
control group, 145
corrective therapy, 138
cosmic alienation, 159
co-therapist interaction, 446, 455
co-therapists, 391
couch, 391
co-unconscious network, 81
co-unconscious states, 78, 79, 81
couples group, 446, 531
creativity, 37, 38, 159, 236, 237, 386, 410
creativity neurosis, 160
crises and emergencies in group psychotherapy, 540, 554, 555, 556, 558, 560, 562
cultural conserve, 159

D

day center, 259
day hospital, 151
delinquents, group psychotherapy of, 421, 656
diagnostic group, 418
didactic group psychotherapy, 101, 508, 569
doctor groups, 390
double technique, 80, 155, 326, 382
drama therapy, 102
drug-induced group psychotherapy, 102
drug-induced psychodrama, 102

E

eclectic group psychotherapy, 638, 680
economic alienation, 159
educational group psychotherapy, 619, 626
electric shock therapy, 138
embryonic matrix, 77
empty chair technique, 80, 326, 382
encounter, 36, 81, 82, 83, 87, 153, 155, 302, 327, 385, 387, 491
endo-psychic reality, 169
existential group analysis, 609, 610, 611
existential group therapy, 613
existentialism, 22, 386, 605, 615, 616, 617
existential mysticism, 22
experiential group psychotherapy, 101, 508, 509, 666
experimental group, 417
experimental group psychotherapy, 130, 158

F

family conjoint therapy, 441
family dynamics, 41
family group therapy, 395, 397, 458, 506
family groups, 78, 174, 218, 236, 245, 378
family homeostasis, 445
family psychodrama, 195, 197
family structure, sociometric, 233, 234
family therapy, 31, 38, 45, 75, 101, 116, 155, 158, 162, 218, 259, 441
fantasy baby, 239
fantasy roles, 232
fantasy techniques, 93, 326

feedback, 401, 487, 488, 490, 491
fees for group psychotherapy, 324, 507, 559
field theory, 93, 95
First International Committee of Group Psychotherapy, 103
First International Congress of Group Psychotherapy, 103
free association, 75, 76, 77, 78, 79, 171, 298, 501, 544, 545, 557
free, spontaneous interaction, 77
future technique, 155, 326

G

group analysis, 22, 50, 51, 53, 69, 72, 75, 92, 102, 116, 117, 118, 170, 206, 271, 281, 419, 501, 560, 562, 570, 609, 686
group analyst, 285, 468, 564
group analytic situation, 171, 688
group association, 171
group catharsis, 73
group-centered group, 342, 419, 605, 606, 607, 608
group, closed, 261, 274
group cohesiveness, 84, 85, 260, 291, 323, 403, 544, 548, 553
group configuration, 504
group counseling, 134, 421, 508
group development, 93
group, diagnostic, 418
group discussion, 375, 376, 427, 508, 512, 538, 563, 587, 629, 630
group dynamic principles, 64
group dynamics, 22, 69, 113, 167, 168, 176, 214, 220, 227, 246, 350, 351, 352, 362, 413, 415, 418, 423, 429, 434, 494, 495, 514, 517, 536, 539, 563, 585, 614, 632, 633, 634, 686
group dynamics of sleep-deprived patients, 492
group evaluation, 552
groups, experimental, 417

group formation, 76, 91, 211, 352, 353, 416
group formation of psychiatric personnel, 350
group formation, sociometric, 573
group guidance, 508, 576
group identification, 388, 585
group image therapy, 407
group interaction, 73, 83, 89, 455, 512, 543, 544, 559, 598, 599
group interaction, guided, 101
group leader, 392, 488, 507, 560, 563, 615
group locus, 300, 501
group matrix, 72, 77, 299, 302
group methods, 61, 62, 85, 86, 87, 93, 117, 121, 152, 153, 157, 259, 342
group monopolist, 475
group mysticism, 22
group, natural, 419
group oath, 112, 113, 114, 115, 116, 196, 545
group, occupational, 501
group, open, 259, 275, 430, 704
group-oriented psychodrama, 313, 314
group participation, 170
group-play analysis, 501
group process, 78, 96, 186, 187, 188, 214, 504, 536, 545, 556, 606, 607, 614, 691
group production, 75
group psychoanalysis, 70, 75, 93, 101, 271, 273, 279, 287, 289, 290, 292, 297, 298, 333, 334, 336, 468, 533, 543, 549, 551, 685
group psychotherapist, 70, 72, 73, 75, 82, 83, 87, 89, 95, 107, 110, 111, 114, 115, 116, 117, 118, 119, 160, 170, 172, 227, 228, 229, 231, 239, 539, 540, 553, 555, 558, 560
group psychotherapists' code of ethics, 113, 114, 115

731

group psychotherapists, training of, 106, 108, 180, 263, 378, 379, 389, 390, 529, 564

group psychotherapy, 17, 18, 19, 21, 22, 27, 28, 29, 30, 31, 32, 35, 39, 61, 62, 63, 64, 65, 66, 67, 68, 69, 70, 71, 72, 73, 75, 80, 81, 82, 83, 84, 85, 87, 89, 90, 91, 92, 93, 94, 95, 96, 97, 98, 99, 100, 101, 102, 103, 107, 108, 109, 110, 111, 112, 113, 115, 117, 118, 119, 120, 129, 130, 144, 145, 146, 152, 153, 158, 159, 160, 161, 162, 169, 170, 173, 178, 180, 181, 182, 188, 195, 210, 213, 214, 215, 216, 227, 228, 229, 234, 246, 250, 252, 258, 265, 284, 296, 300, 319, 328, 332, 351, 352, 353, 354, 375, 377, 378, 379, 390, 407, 410, 413, 415, 416, 417, 436, 465, 466, 467, 468, 474, 475, 479, 487, 488, 489, 490, 491, 500, 504, 505, 539, 540, 543, 544, 555, 558, 559, 565, 566, 567, 568, 577, 587, 590, 594, 603, 609, 632, 633, 638, 639, 642, 644, 656, 657, 682, 689, 696, 697, 698, 702, 703, 704, 705

group psychotherapy, activistic method, 90

group psychotherapy, activistic trend, 160

group psychotherapy, analytic method, 85, 89, 90, 91, 92, 101, 144, 145, 169, 170, 174, 179, 200, 226, 228, 287, 289, 290, 303, 375, 530, 531, 532, 540, 554, 565, 638, 680

group psychotherapy, analytic trend, 85, 101, 160, 265, 299, 304

group psychotherapy of alcoholics, 253, 590, 593, 601, 603

Group Psychotherapy Association, 89

group psychotherapy, bifocal, 98, 101, 218, 402

group psychotherapy for church groups, 527, 528

group psychotherapy, class method, 61, 68, 71, 72, 90, 508

group psychotherapy with college students, 619

group psychotherapy, client-centered, 114, 145

group psychotherapy, co-creative, 439, 440

group psychotherapy, conference method, 109

group psychotherapy for couples, 446

group psychotherapy, crises and emergencies in, 540, 554, 555, 556, 558, 560, 562

group psychotherapy with delinquents, 421, 656

group psychotherapy, didactic, 101, 375, 508, 569, 638

group psychotherapy, drug induced, 102

group psychotherapy, dynamic, 508, 509

group psychotherapy, eclectic, 638, 680

group psychotherapy, educational, 619, 626

group psychotherapy, existential, 92, 93

group psychotherapy, experiential, 101, 508, 666

group psychotherapy, experimental, 158

group psychotherapy with families, 395, 397, 506

group psychotherapy, fees for, 324, 559

group psychotherapy with headache patients, 680

group psychotherapy with homosexuals 664, 667

group psychotherapy, indirect, 484

group psychotherapy in situ, 156

group psychotherapy, inspirational, 638

group psychotherapy, institutional, 101

group psychotherapy, intensive, 101, 375, 665

group psychotherapy, interactional method, 71, 73, 90, 91, 155, 543

group psychotherapy, interactional trend, 84, 85, 101, 160

Group Psychotherapy Journal, 64, 103

group psychotherapy, leaderless, 101

group psychotherapy, lecture-centered method, 70, 71, 508

group psychotherapy with LSD, 685, 690, 692

group psychotherapy with married couples, 259, 531

group psychotherapy with married alcoholic couples, 593, 594

group psychotherapy in mental hospitals, 389

group psychotherapy with mentally ill offenders, 637

Group Psychotherapy Movement, 15, 27, 28, 64, 70, 73, 82, 88, 94, 100, 101, 102, 106, 116, 120, 121, 156, 160, 165

group psychotherapy, non-directive, 101, 131, 196, 228, 638

group psychotherapy with offenders, 644, 646

group psychotherapy and pantomime, 328, 329, 330, 331

group psychotherapy with parents of psychotic children, 457

group psychotherapy with parents without partners, 458

group psychotherapy, placebo effect in, 465, 466, 468, 469, 470

group psychotherapy, playback method, 109

group psychotherapy in private practice, 102

group psychotherapy of psychosis, 93

group psychotherapy, psychosomatic, 198

group psychotherapy, round table, 101, 134

group psychotherapy with schizophrenics, 143, 144, 394, 395, 398

group psychotherapy, silent, 102

group psychotherapy, sociometric, 30

group psychotherapy with students, 511, 512, 513

group psychotherapy, for study of affect, 497

group psychotherapy, theoretic, 159

group psychotherapy training, 378, 379, 389

group psychotherapy, tutorial, 102

group psychotherapy with unmarried mothers, 531

group psychotherapy, violent, 101

group remedial reading, 102, 142

group research, 543

group sensitivity training, 487, 488, 490, 491

group sharing, 544

group stability, 405

group structure, 78, 85, 92, 176, 201, 213, 404, 503, 594

group supervision, 529, 576

group therapist, 64, 107, 172, 259, 377, 468, 489, 505, 513, 543, 555, 611, 612, 640, 680, 690

group therapy, 17, 18, 28, 31, 33, 34, 35, 49, 50, 51, 61, 63, 64, 71, 72, 75, 82, 85, 87, 90, 102,

LSD group treatment, 101

M

magic shop technique, 326, 382
marriage counseling, 456
married couples, group therapy of, 259, 531
mass catharsis, 53
mass media, 162, 163, 164, 258
mass psychodrama, 162
mass psychiatry, 152, 153, 162, 163
mass psychosis, 460
mass psychotherapy, 111, 162
mass psychotherapy, religious, 42
mass treatment, 63, 163
maternal deprivation, 189, 190
matrimonial therapy, 38
matrix of all-identity, 77, 232
mental hospitals, group psychotherapy in, 389
microsociology, 21
milieu therapy, 116, 376, 379, 413, 458
miniature society, 586
mirror technique, 80, 155, 382
motor phenomena, 279
multilateral resistance, 271
music and rhythm therapy, 101
mutual mental contagion, 459, 461, 462

N

natural groupings, 75, 78, 419
night hospital, 151
non-directive group psychotherapy, 101, 132, 196, 228
non-verbal communication, 540, 545, 553, 554, 560, 610
normosis, 154
normotic, 154

O

observation group, 535, 536
occupational group, 501

occupational group therapy, 97, 99, 138, 637
offenders, group psychotherapy of, 644, 646
open community, 158
open door, 151
open group, 259, 275, 430, 704
organic isolation, 232

P

pantomime, 328, 329, 330, 331
parent groups, 406, 530, 532
parental group guidance, 287
parents without partners, group psychotherapy of, 458
patient as therapist, 191
patient clubs, 271, 286
patient government, 89
patient groups, 91, 403, 404
patient interaction, 191
patient-therapist relationship, 468, 650, 665
personnel training, 91
pharmacological therapy, 138
phyloanalysis, 51, 52, 69, 102, 159
phyloanalytic alienation, 159
phyloanalytic studies, 64
phylobiology, 53
phylopathology, 53
placebo effects in group psychotherapy, 465, 466
protagonist, 239, 324, 325, 382, 527
psychiatric revolution, first, 151
psychiatric revolution, second, 151
psychiatric revolution, third, 152
psychoanalysis, 19, 22, 28, 30, 91, 95, 96, 97, 107, 108, 117, 169, 171, 173, 196, 225, 259, 262, 270, 275, 391, 414, 475, 482, 501, 515, 566, 609, 673, 682, 686, 697, 700
psychoanalyst, 78, 92, 107, 117, 174, 335, 419, 538

public session (psychodrama), 164, 324, 326, 327, 382

739

Buber, M., 82
Buchner, A., 200
Buddha, 154
Burdon, S., 540, 543
Burrow, T., 29, 35, 50, 53, 54, 61, 69, 70, 71, 72, 85, 102, 159
Burt, C., 578
Bustamante, J., 99
Buxbaum, H., 100

C

Cadman, W. H., 134
Calderon, 340
Camus, A., 616, 617
Caravedo, B., 99
Carson, S., 490
Carstairs, G. M., 620
Cerletti, A., 153
Chapin, F. S., 106
Chappell, E., 71
Charcot, 152, 247
Chertok, L., 96
Chesterfield, Lord, 632
Clampitt, R. R., 141
Clauser, A., 703, 704
Clemens, G. H., 92
Comte, A., 211, 245
Cooley, C., 163, 211
Corsini, R., 15, 30, 34, 63, 66, 68, 71, 92, 101
Cotrell, L., 106
Cowden, R. C., 144
Cummings, E., 194
Cummings, J., 194
Curran, F., 71
Curtis, 704

D

Daniels, M., 138
Dederick, C., 101
Delay, J., 96, 153
Descartes, R., 166

Dewey, J., 106, 212
Diatkine, R., 175
Di Giovanni, P., 143
Dillon, L. O., 390
Doll, E., 71
Dollard, J., 700
Dostoyevski, F., 340
Dreikurs, R., 71, 92, 113
Drews, R., 92, 102
Durkheim, E., 211, 212

E

Ehrenwald, J., 463
Ekstein, 667
Elefthery, D., 93
Ends, E. J., 144
Engels, F., 28
Enke, H., 704
Enneis, J., 71, 92, 102
Epicurus, 256
Eysenck, H. J., 186
Ezriel, H., 71, 95, 101

F

Fantel, E., 92
Favez-Boutonier, J., 96, 105
Feder, L., 99
Fedotov, D. D., 99
Feifel, H., 135
Ferenczi, S., 56
Festinger, L., 214
Fine, L., 93, 377, 379
Fischer, B., 142
Fitzpatrick, G. A., 94
Fleming, L., 131
Foulkes, S. H., 71, 95, 96, 101, 102, 104, 201, 277, 299, 301, 477, 540
Francus, J. B., 142
Frank, J., 92, 469
Franklin, G. H., 137
Freed, E. X., 138
French, 377

744

745

746

COMPREHENSIVE BIBLIOGRAPHIES
OF GROUP PSYCHOTHERAPY:

R. J. Corsini — 1908-1956
Bernard J. Lubin — 1956-1964
Both bibliographies contained in the Group Psychotherapy Journal and
Monographs published by Beacon House, Beacon, N. Y., 1956, and
1964.